Integrator:

$$V_{\text{OUT}} = -\frac{1}{CR} \int_0^t V_{\text{IN}}(t)\, dt \qquad (2.13)$$

Differentiator:

$$V_{\text{OUT}} = RC \frac{dV_{\text{IN}}}{dt} \qquad (2.14)$$

Frequency Response:

$$f_{\text{max}} = \frac{\text{GBW}}{A_{V_{\text{cl}}}} \qquad (3.09)$$

Bias Current:

$$I_{\text{B}} = \frac{I_{\text{B}^+} + I_{\text{B}^-}}{2} \qquad (3.01)$$

$$f_{10\%} = 0.484 f_{\text{c}} \qquad (3.14)$$

$$f_{\text{c,total}} = f_{\text{c,individual}} \sqrt{2^{1/n} - 1} \qquad (3.20)$$

$$V_{\text{error}} = I_{\text{B}}(R_{\text{f}} \| R_{\text{i}}) \qquad (3.02)$$

$$R_{\text{comp}} = R_{\text{f}} \| R_{\text{g}} - R_{\text{Thevenin, source}} \qquad (3.03)$$

$$f_{\text{c}} = \frac{\text{GBW}}{A_V \sqrt{2^{i/n} - 1}} \qquad \text{(from 3.09 and 3.20)}$$

$$t_{\text{rise, unity-gain}} = \frac{0.35}{\text{GBW}} \qquad (3.22)$$

Tee Feedback:

$$V_{\text{output offset}} = R_{\text{mismatch}} I_{\text{B}} A_V \qquad (3.04)$$

$$t_{\text{rise.SR}} = \frac{\Delta v}{\text{SR}} \qquad (3.23)$$

$$R_{\text{t}_1} = R_{\text{t}_2} = R_{\text{t}} \qquad (3.05)$$

$$f_{\text{max.SR}} = \frac{\text{SR}}{2\pi V_{\text{P}}} \qquad (3.24)$$

$$R_{\text{s}} = \frac{R_{\text{t}}^2}{R_{\text{i}} A_V + 2R_{\text{t}}} \qquad (3.06)$$

$$C_{\text{IN}} = \frac{10}{2\pi f_{\text{low}} R_{\text{IN}}} \qquad (3.37)$$

$$R_{\text{ground}} = R_{\text{t}} + (R_{\text{t}} \| R_{\text{s}}) \qquad (3.07)$$

$$C_{\text{OUT}} = \frac{10}{2\pi f_{\text{low}} R_{\text{load}}} \qquad (3.38)$$

$$R_{\text{f}} = \frac{R_{\text{t}}^2 - 2R_{\text{s}} R_{\text{t}}}{R_{\text{s}}} \qquad (3.08)$$

$$C_{\text{g}} = \frac{10}{2\pi f_{\text{low}} R_{\text{g}}} \qquad (3.39)$$

OP AMPS AND LINEAR INTEGRATED CIRCUITS

Richard A. Honeycutt

DAVIDSON COUNTY COMMUNITY COLLEGE
LEXINGTON, NORTH CAROLINA

 **DELMAR PUBLISHERS INC.**®

NOTICE TO THE READER

Delma Staff

Assistant Managing Editor: Gerry East
Production Editor: Christopher Chien
Production Coordinator: Linda Helfrich
Design Coordinator: Susan Mathews

Cover artwork reproduced courtesy of Analog Devices, Inc., Norwood, Massachusetts

For information, address Delmar Publishers Inc.
2 Computer Drive, West, Box 15-015
Albany, New York 12212-5015

Printed in the United States of America
Published simultaneously in Canada
by Nelson Canada,
A Division of International Thomson Limited

10 9 8 7 6 5 4 3 2 1

Library of Congress Cataloging-in-Publication Data

Honeycutt, Richard A.
    Op amps and linear integrated circuits.

    Includes index
    1. Linear integrated circuits.   2. Operational
amplifiers.   I. Title.
TK7871.58.06H64   1988   621.381'73   88-11801
ISBN 0-8273-2695-5
ISBN 0-8273-2696-3 (Instructors guide)

Contents

chapter seven   **Active Filters**

chapter eight   **Signal Generation and Shaping**

chapter nine   **Specialized Analog Functions**

Preface

PURPOSE OF THE BOOK

The introduction of the integrated circuit (IC) has revolutionized both the practice and the teaching of electronics. In the past, block-diagram approaches to circuitry were usually relegated to survey courses; now one can often buy a "block" in the form of an IC and simply insert it into the circuit. In the past, the study of feedback was an integral part of amplifier design. The analysis of a feedback loop was inseparable from the analysis of the circuit in which it was contained. Now, the unique characteristics of linear ICs usually make feedback analysis independent of the circuit around which the loop is connected.

This change in the field of electronics has spawned many new books. The first of these books were directed toward updating the training of practicing engineers. Often these books went into great detail concerning the design and construction of the ICs themselves. Later, textbooks began to be introduced. For good or ill, many of these books included the same material as the earlier ones. For the future engineer who would be designing ICs, this material was valuable, but for the other, more numerous, readership, this material was superfluous and unnecessarily burdensome.

This book was written to provide students, technicians, and engineers a practical understanding of linear integrated circuits. These three groups share five common needs. These are:

1. To understand basically how linear ICs work. Black boxes have an unnecessary aura of mystery.
2. To know the most common circuit configurations in which ICs will be used.
3. To understand manufacturers' specification sheets, and thereby to have access to reliable application data and the most current information on new devices.
4. To be able to simply design—from one's understanding and without memorizing a great number of formulae—most of the commonly-needed circuits that use ICs.
5. To be able to troubleshoot existing circuits that incorporate ICs.

This book attempts to fulfill these needs. It does it without much derivation of formulae and with no math beyond algebra, except for the unavoidable calculus involved in the discussion of differentiators and integrators. The approach throughout is basically intuitive. Theoretical material is given in sufficient depth to provide a firm foundation for understanding the principles involved. However, the emphasis is on information that is useful, and therefore easy to learn and retain. Because of the inclusion of specific sections on design and troubleshooting, the book will be useful long after a specific course of study is completed. It will also be helpful as a memory-jogger to the practicing technician or engineer.

PREREQUISITES

In order to gain the most benefit from this book, the reader should have a good understanding of high-school algebra and trigonometry. No calculus background is required. The reader should also be familiar with electric circuit analysis, including the application of Norton's and Thevenin's theorems. Finally, a familiarity with bipolar transistor and FET small-signal amplifiers is assumed. Readers who lack some of these prerequisites will still find the book useful, but may have to refer to appropriate reference books in order to fully understand some sections.

MAJOR FEATURES

- *Objectives:* Each chapter begins with objectives to help the student focus on the essential ideas to be gained from the chapter.
- *Examples:* The text includes numerous worked-out examples to illustrate all important design methods and many of the theoretical concepts.
- *Design Notes:* Most chapters include a *Design Notes* section that summarizes the approach to designing the specific circuits with which the chapter deals.
- *Summary:* Each chapter concludes with a summary of the important ideas presented in the chapter.
- *Problems:* At the end of each chapter, there is a set of problems designed to give the student practical experience and reinforce his understanding.
- *Laboratory Experiments:* After each chapter, there is a set of laboratory experiments to give the opportunity to see important concepts at work.
- *Appendices:* Four appendices are included in this book. Appendix A is the most extensive, and includes data sheets from representative linear ICs of all the types discussed in the text. Appendix B summarizes the techniques of calculating with decibel notation. Appendix C contains a wealth of application information on current-differencing amplifiers. Appendix D presents answers to the even-numbered problems presented in the text.

APPLICATIONS

The integrated circuits used as examples in this textbook have been chosen after consultation with the marketing department of a major IC manufacturer. With few exceptions, the specific units chosen are the most popular ICs of their type at the time of writing. It may surprise some readers to see such "old" devices as the 709 op amp and the 723 voltage regulator included in a modern text. However, according to current sales figures, these devices are still important in both replacement use and new designs. Several of the data sheets included in Appendix A are of the "long-form" type rather than the "short-form" variety more commonly included in text-books. These complete data sheets include much valuable application information, design techniques, and circuits specific to the particular IC. This helps to familiarize the student with one of the important working resources of the professional engineer, as well as making available a sampling of that resource for use in the student's own projects. It is the hope of the author that after finishing this book, the reader will feel comfortable designing, using, and troubleshooting the vast majority of linear IC circuits.

COURSE PLAN

This book contains sufficient material for a full two-quarter or one-semester course on linear integrated circuits. If the text must be adapted to a shorter time frame, specific chapters can be omitted, depending upon the particular needs as perceived by the instructor. In any case, Chapters 1 through 4 are fundamental, and should be covered thoroughly. Chapters 6 and 7 also present material that is very important for the technician or engineer in today's work environment. With these basics covered, the remaining chapters can be used in any combination. It is recommended that the sequence of chapters not be modified, as each chapter is written with the assumption that earlier material has been assimilated.

INSTRUCTOR'S GUIDE

An instructor's guide is available as a companion to this text. It includes suggested lecture outlines, test objectives, and solutions to the problems.

A PERSONAL NOTE TO THE STUDENT, FROM THE AUTHOR

In any endeavor, there are certain techniques that make one's use of time more efficient and productive. The study of electronics is no exception. In order to make the most of the time you spend studying this book, I offer the following suggestions.

1. Read the text thoroughly, and with a notebook and pencil at hand. Our schools go to a great deal of effort to teach people how to read fiction. Unfortunately, the difference between reading fiction and reading technical material is seldom discussed. Fiction is approached with a view toward appreciation of the overall story line. It is usually read rapidly and with a great deal of emotional involvement on the part of the reader. Technical material must be read more slowly and with more attention to detail. Important sections should be marked in the text. One of my college professors once said, "A textbook is never truly yours until it is illuminated with your own notes." Some concepts will need to be reworded in your own fashion and written in your notebook, since learning is a highly individualized process. Rather than identifying with the exhilaration and despair of a fictional hero, you can ex-

perience for yourself the excitement of new discovery as you add to your own tree of knowledge in your chosen field.

2. Be very sure that you understand each example in the text. Work the examples out for yourself with the book closed, if necessary.

3. Do not approach this book as a series of facts that people have discovered and that you now have to memorize. This approach may have gotten you good grades in some history courses in the past, but it will not succeed in your study of electronics. Worse, it robs the study of the joy of understanding that should properly accompany your efforts. Instead, make sure that you understand the *why* behind every fact and equation. A student who knows where an equation came from has little need to memorize it. Spend a little time at the end of each section asking how the concepts of that section could be applied to some application of particular interest to you. Go beyond the examples and applications described in the book.

4. Use the objectives at the beginning of each chapter to set up mental file drawers in which to store the knowledge presented in the chapter. Knowing what a chapter is going to cover is a significant part of being ready to learn.

5. Use the summaries at the end of each chapter, not as a list of everything you need to know from that chapter, but as a checklist of important topics under which your knowledge from that chapter should be organized. Make absolutely sure that you understand the material in each chapter before going to the next. The study of electronics is cumulative in the sense that tomorrow's learning must be built upon today's understanding.

6. The *Design Notes* sections included in most chapters summarize design techniques. After you have mastered the material in the chapter, and for years to come, these sections will serve as a refresher on details of specific designs. Attempting to use the *Design Notes* sections as a substitute for learning the background material in the body of the chapter almost guarantees frustration. These sections are your quick-reference handbook to details of the design process.

7. Work all the practice problems at the end of each chapter. In my teaching experience, the most successful students have always been those who took the time to work through all the problems, even if their instructor only assigned some of them. Besides, these problems are chosen to simulate actual situations that you will encounter on the job. Since you have chosen electronics, you should find solving electronics problems stimulating.

8. If you do not have facilities at home for building and testing your own circuits, you should arrange immediately to get them. Design and/or build some projects. Successful engineers and technicians invariably have a hobby interest in electronics that motivates their professional interest. One of my best students of AC circuits routinely took problems home and implemented their solutions on his computer. I still use a drawing he gave me that was generated from a computer summation of the first five component frequencies of a square wave. Another of my best students had taught himself to redesign guitar amplifiers before ever enrolling in an electronics program. These students will be very successful—and, more importantly, very happy—in their careers. If you immerse yourself in the challenge of working with electronics, you will experience the thrill of discovery, of making the science and art of electronics your own. Success will follow.

ACKNOWLEDGMENTS

The author gratefully acknowledges the valuable assistance rendered by the following people during the preparation of this book:

Mr. Kevin Shaw, technical assistance
Mrs. Edith Honeycutt, general miracle-work
Alyson, April, and Erin, all kinds of stuff

Manuscript reviewers:
Leelan C. Blackmon, Wallace Community College
Robert Coughlin, Wentworth Institute of Technology, Boston, Massachusetts
Frank Gergelyi, Metropolitan Technical Institute
Ronald W. Hartley, DeVry Technical Institute, Columbus, Ohio
Walter Kester, Analog Devices, Greensboro, North Carolina
Clay Laster, San Antonio College
Albert E. Pistilli, Hudson Valley Community College
Art Seidman
William Sheehan, State University of New York at Alfred
Gerhardt Steinke, Milwaukee Area Technical College
James Stewart, DeVry Institute of Technology, New Jersey
Harry S. Waller, San Antonio College

Thanks are also due to the following companies for permission to reprint materials:
Analog Devices, Inc.
AT&T Technologies, Inc.
Exar Integrated Systems
Fairchild Semiconductor, Inc.
Motorola Semiconductors, Inc.
National Semiconductor, Inc.
Panasonic Industrial Company, Inc.
Raytheon Semiconductor, Inc.
Signetics, Inc.
Sprague Electric Co., Inc.
Teledyne-Philbrick Co.
Texas Instruments, Inc.
Thermalloy, Inc.

chapter one

Building Blocks of the Linear Integrated Circuit

OBJECTIVES

Upon completing this chapter, you will be able to:

- Give a brief account of the historical development of the linear integrated circuit.
- Describe the difference between linear and digital integrated circuits.
- Describe the operation of each of the three major building-block circuits that make up most linear integrated circuits.
- Discuss the variations that are possible in the design of the building-block circuits, and the effect of these variations upon the performance of the complete integrated circuit.

INTRODUCTION

Interesting, isn't it? Lee De Forest invented the vacuum triode in 1907, and an enormous electronics industry was spawned. Shockley, Brattain, and Bardeen invented the transistor in 1947, and we were told that Mr. De Forest's venerable baby was on its way out. The first reasonably priced linear integrated circuits (ICs) appeared in the late 1960s, and the death of the discrete transistor was announced. Yet here we are a couple of decades later with very large numbers of vacuum tubes still being sold (and a small amount of new tube-based equipment still being designed!), discrete transistor circuitry still being essential to our technology, *and* an ever-increasing number of ICs appearing to simplify the technician's life. So what's the moral of this little story? Don't believe everything you read in the newspaper (or in textbooks, for that matter!).

What has really occurred in electronics since 1907 is the continual *addition* of new technology. It is possible that transistors may someday completely replace vacuum tubes. But it is not conceivable that ICs will *ever* replace transistors, because of the flexibility of discrete parts in building one-of-a-kind circuits. Nevertheless, ICs do offer convenience, cost savings, reduced size, easier design, and, in some cases, improved performance when compared to discrete circuitry. For these reasons, an understanding of ICs is essential for any competent electronics engineer or technician.

1

For study purposes, ICs are customarily separated into two groups: digital and linear. *A **linear circuit** is one whose output signal bears a linear relationship to its input signal.* For example, the output of an amplifier is just its input multiplied by a constant gain. Multiplication by a constant is a linear function. A summing circuit's output is just the sum of its inputs. Addition is a linear function. The input and output signals of a linear circuit can have *any* value, within certain limits; they form a bounded continuum. Another name for linear circuits is *analog* circuits, because the signals with which they deal are analogous to some quantity in nature. For example, the electrical wave that corresponds to a sound wave (its analog) is processed in an analog circuit. The same is true for an electrical analog of video information, an electrical analog of the pH of a chemical solution, and an electrical analog of the temperature in a fiberglass oven. As an engineer friend of mine once truly said, "Mother Nature is analog!"

A **digital circuit** *is one whose output signal can have only certain specific values, corresponding to the digits of a number system.* Most often, the number system is binary, so there are only two possible values of input and output, corresponding to the digits 0 and 1. The output signal thus bears a logical/mathematical relationship to the input, not usually a linear one.

Number systems are a result of our attempts to quantify natural events. Most of those events being analog, they must be artificially assigned numerical values, or *digitized,* before they can be analyzed mathematically. This gives rise to a "half-breed" class of ICs that are part linear and part digital. These include primarily those circuits that interface between computing circuits and the outside world—analog-to-digital converters and digital-to-analog converters.

This book is primarily concerned with the first class of ICs, the linear ones. The first linear ICs were plug-in amplifiers made with vacuum tubes. (See Fig. 1–1A, page 7). Although not exactly today's idea of an IC, these were complete circuits that were integrated into a single package. With the introduction of transistors, ICs took the form of plug-in circuit boards full of parts (Fig. 1–1B, page 8). It occurred to some engineers that most of the "acreage" required for a circuit board was used up by spacing between components and by the individual cases of the components themselves. Hence, the *hybrid* IC (Fig. 1–1C, page 8, and 1–1D, page 9) was developed. This device is a small slab of ceramic onto which resistors have been built and other components have been mounted. Finally came the last step (so far, that is!), the monolithic IC. This is a complete circuit fabricated from a single tiny piece of silicon (Fig. 1–1E, page 10). When engineers today speak of ICs, they are talking about hybrids or monolithics. Plug-in circuit boards are now called *modules.*

DIFFERENTIAL AMPLIFIERS

Basic Circuit

Most linear ICs are constructed largely of a versatile building-block circuit called the differential amplifier. Understanding the way diff amps (as they are often called) operate is important to understanding the operation of the ICs that use them. Figure

FOUR STEPS IN MONOLITHIC IC PRODUCTION

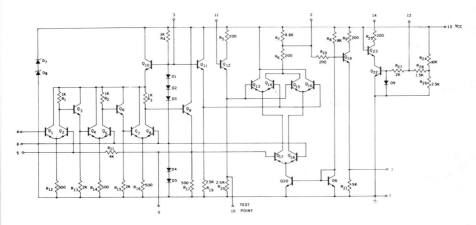

Schematic diagram of the IC, showing the components and interconnections to be formed on the silicon wafer. Numbered circles represent terminals of the finished IC. (Photos courtesy of Sprague Electric Co.)

(continued)

(continued from page 3)

Sidebar

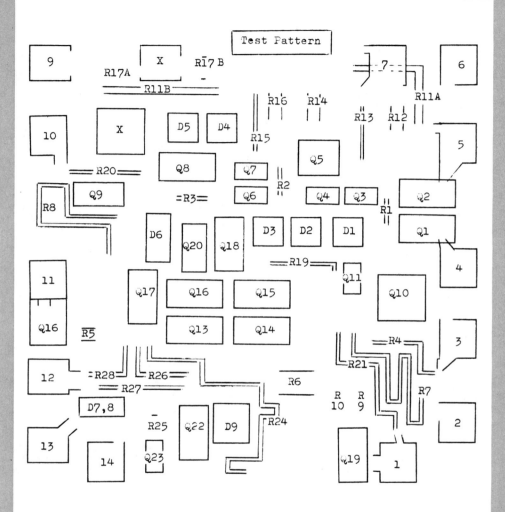

Test Pattern

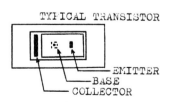

TYPICAL TRANSISTOR

EMITTER
BASE
COLLECTOR

Parts layout, showing which component will be formed where on the silicon wafer.

(continued from page 4)

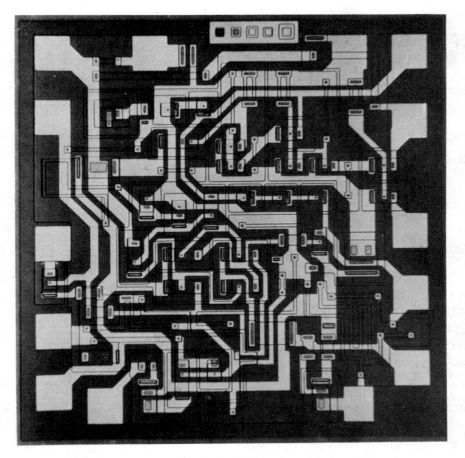

Photograph of the die, or circuit, that has been formed on the silicon wafer.

6 Chapter One

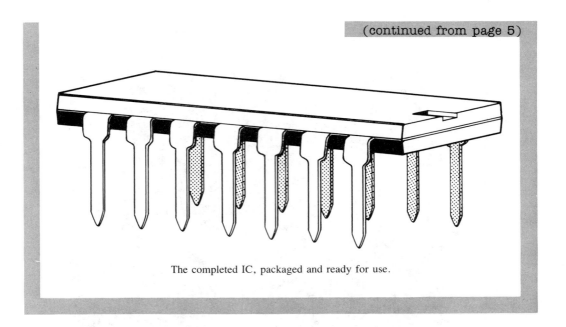

(continued from page 5)

The completed IC, packaged and ready for use.

1–2 (page 11) shows the circuit of a diff amp. In operation, the current source provides the current for both transistors. Since the source current is constant and the transistors must share it, if one transistor draws more current the other must draw less, and vice versa.

There are four modes of operation of a diff amp, as shown in Fig. 1–3 (page 11). Part A of the figure shows the *single-ended-input/single-ended-output* mode. (The reason for this name will become apparent as we go on.) The input is applied to the base of Q_1, which acts as a common-emitter stage. If this input is a positive voltage, it will make the collector voltage of Q_1 become less positive, because of the phase inversion provided by the common-emitter circuit. However, it does this by causing Q_1 to draw more current, thus leaving less for Q_2. Therefore, the collector voltage of Q_2 becomes more positive. In other words, when the base of Q_1 goes positive, the emitter follows the base (at a distance of 0.6 V) and goes more positive also. Since the base of Q_2 is grounded, Q_2 acts as a common-base amplifier, and the voltage change that appears on Q_2's emitter also appears, amplified, on Q_2's collector, with no phase inversion. Thus an inverted, amplified output can be taken from the collector of Q_1, or a noninverted, amplified output can be taken from the collector of Q_2. In the circuit in the figure, the output is taken from Q_1's collector, making an inverting amplifier. The gain of this amplifier is approximately

$$A_V = \frac{R_{C_1}}{2r_{e'}}$$

where A_V is the voltage gain ($V_{\text{OUT}}/V_{\text{IN}}$), R_{C_1} is the collector resistor of Q_1, and $r_{e'}$ is the equivalent AC emitter resistance of the transistor.

FIGURE 1–1: Five Stages of Integrated Circuit Development

FIGURE 1–1A: Vacuum-Tube "Integrated Circuit"; This device was used widely during the 1950s and 1960s. *(Courtesy of Teledyne-Philbrick, Inc.)*

In this configuration, the diff amp may look like a very complicated way of doing the job of a single-stage common-base or common-emitter amplifier, but there are two significant differences. First, since Q_1 and Q_2 are physically close together, any temperature changes that might lead to DC instability are shared by both transistors. Thus, if Q_1 tries to hog current because of a temperature increase, so does Q_2. But since the total of both transistors' currents is set by the current source, neither transistor is able to *get* more current, and the operating point remains stable in spite of temperature changes. This makes the diff amp very useful for DC amplifier circuits, especially if matched transistors are used, so that their temperature characteristics are identical.

FIGURE 1–1B: Plug-In Circuit Board; A miniaturization concept developed during the 1960s and still in use today. *(Courtesy of Analog Devices, Inc.)*

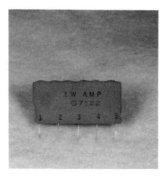

FIGURE 1–1C: Early Ceramic-Dipped Hybrid IC; A one-watt audio power-amplifier IC manufactured in the early 1970s. *(Courtesy of Sprague Electric Co.)*

FIGURE 1–1D: Modern Hybrid Integrated Circuit; Leadless components mounted on a ceramic substrate are presently used to build circuits that cannot yet be fabricated in monolithic form. *(Courtesy of Analog Devices, Inc.)*

The second difference between the diff amp and a common-base or common-emitter amplifier is that the diff amp has much lower distortion. In a normal common-emitter amplifier, the variation in $r_{e'}$ with emitter current causes the gain of a transistor amplifier to vary with signal level. This causes distortion of the output waveform. In a diff amp, though, the signal impedance to ground seen from the emitter is the sum of the $r_{e'}$ of both transistors. This is true because current sources have an infinite internal impedance, so the signal path to ground from the Q_1 emitter is through $r_{e'}$ of Q_1, through $r_{e'}$ of Q_2 to the base of Q_2, and so to ground. And since any decrease in emitter current of one transistor is matched by a similar *increase* in the emitter current of the other, the variations in $r_{e'}$ are canceled out. Thus the diff amp is very linear.

Notice that the output point in Fig. 1–3A was chosen arbitrarily. We could have just as easily chosen to take the output from the collector of Q_2. In fact, we could have taken the output *between* Q_1's collector and Q_2's collector, so that neither of the output connections would be grounded. This option is shown in Fig. 1–3B. This connection is said to have a *balanced* output because the impedance from either output lead to ground is the same; that is, the two impedances are balanced. It follows that single-ended outputs are *unbalanced*. An advantage of the balanced-output mode is that twice the voltage gain is available from the same circuit. The reason is that any increase in voltage on collector 1 is matched by a decrease in voltage on collector

FIGURE 1–1E: Monolithic Integrated Circuit; Two monolithic IC chips mounted in dual-inline packages. These completed ICs are resting on a silicon wafer containing approximately 1400 of the circuit chips. *(Courtesy of Analog Devices, Inc.)*

2, resulting in a doubling of the voltage dropped across the load. We'll talk about another advantage shortly.

Figure 1–3C shows the balanced-input, single-ended output connection of the diff amp. Let's assume a gain of 10 and consider how this circuit works in four cases:

1. *Input* 1, +0.1 V; *input* 2, −0.1 V: Input 1 by itself would cause collector 1 to go 0.1 V × 10 = 1 V negative and collector 2 to go 1 V positive. Input 2

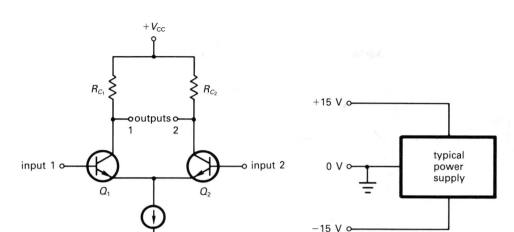

FIGURE 1–2: Circuit of the Differential Amplifier

would cause the same results. So the combined effect is that collector 1 goes 2 V negative and collector 2 goes 2 V positive.

2. *Input* 1, +0.1 V; *input* 2, +0.1 V: Input 1 by itself would cause collector 1 to go 1 V negative and collector 2 to go 1 V positive. Input 2 would cause collector 1 to go 1 V positive and collector 2 to go 1 V negative, so the two effects cancel out and no output appears.

3. *Input* 1, −0.1 V; *input* 2, +0.1 V: The inputs are reversed from case 1, so

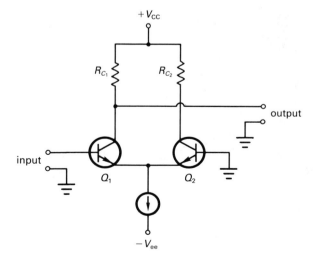

FIGURE 1–3A: Single-Ended Input/Single-Ended Output

FIGURE 1–3: Operating Modes of Diff Amps

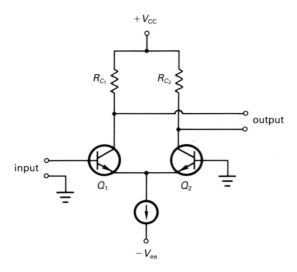

FIGURE 1–3B: Single-Ended Input/Balanced Output

the output is reversed also; collector 1 goes 2 V positive and collector 2 goes 2 V negative.
4. *Input* 1, -0.1 V; *input* 2, -0.1 V: Case 4 produces no output for the same reason that case 2 produced no output.

Now you can see the reason for the name *differential amplifier:* It is a circuit that amplifies the *difference* between the two input voltages.

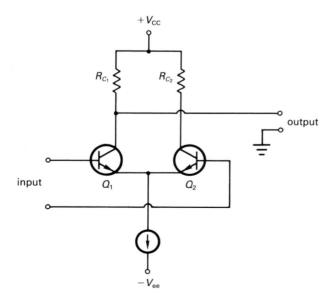

FIGURE 1–3C: Balanced Input/Single-Ended Output

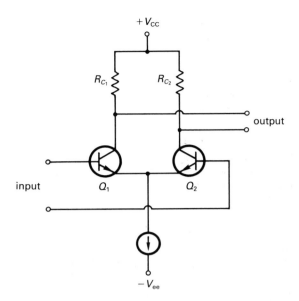

FIGURE 1–3D: Balanced Input/Balanced Output

Figure 1–3D still amplifies the difference between the two input voltages but has a balanced output like the circuit of part B.

A great advantage of the balanced mode of operation has to do with interference. Imagine that you are sending a signal from hither to yon through a region fraught with electromagnetic interference from electrical power cables, motors, and other normal industrial beasts. Being a good engineer, you shield the signal leads. However, it is not economically feasible to *magnetically* shield the leads because that would require iron pipe—normal thinwall conduit would not do. Therefore, some noise voltages are magnetically induced into your signal leads, and over at the far end these noise voltages cannot be separated from your signal. However, if you could arrange for the noise voltages to be induced equally in both signal leads so that they appear in phase and with equal impedances to ground (thus producing identical currents in both leads), then you could feed the far-end signal to a diff amp and the noise would be ignored. The reason is that equal-voltage, in-phase signals would provide no difference to amplify, so the output signal from the diff amp would not contain any noise voltage. For this reason, virtually all long-distance signal transmission by wire uses balanced circuits, whether they be signals from a microphone to an amplifier, telephone signals, or industrial-process sensor signals. Arranging to have equal, in-phase voltages induced in both signal leads requires only that both leads be isolated from ground and physically arranged in an identical fashion with respect to the shield. In other words, you use a cable having two conductors within the shield, and you do not ground either conductor. By the way, the shorter name for equal-voltage, in-phase signals is *common-mode* signals. Signals appearing in different phases and/or voltages on the two signal leads are called *normal-mode* signals. *Differential-mode* signals is still another name for normal-mode signals.

Linear ICs almost always use some form of balanced-input diff amp for their input stages. Usually the outputs are unbalanced, and special circuits are used when balanced outputs are needed. (This is covered in Chapter 2.) Therefore, a thorough understanding of the operation of the balanced-input diff amp is important for understanding linear IC operation.

Variations

Several variations on the basic diff amp are possible. The first one that was used was the Darlington input stage, as shown in Fig. 1–4. This circuit differs from the common diff amp only in that each transistor is a Darlington. In a Darlington connection, the input transistor's emitter current is just the base current of the second transistor. This results in a very high input impedance—approximately $2\beta^2 r_{e'}$. In practical terms, this means that the input impedance of a Darlington diff amp can be a hundred or so times higher than that of the normal garden-variety diff amp. For even higher input impedances, another Darlington stage can be added.

Another variation of the diff amp that is sometimes used is the FET-input diff amp, as shown in Fig. 1–5. The FET used can be either a junction or an MOS type. The obvious advantage is high input impedance, even higher than that of the Darlington input diff amp.

All versions of the diff amp that we have considered have had some form of constant-current source supplying the emitter current to the transistors. We have not discussed just what this current source might consist of. In a discrete diff amp, the current source might vary from something as simple as a large resistor to a rather

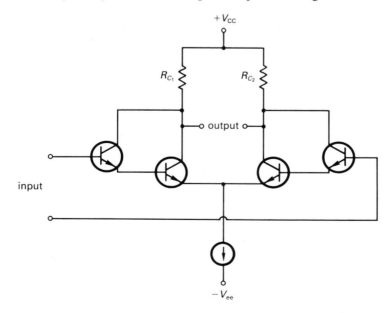

FIGURE 1–4: Darlington-Input Diff Amp

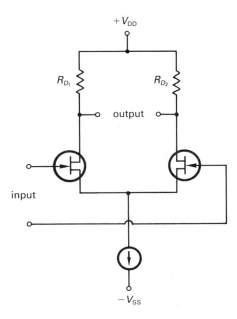

FIGURE 1–5: FET Diff Amp

involved transistor current source. Just using a large resistor works reasonably well in some cases because it approximates the infinite internal impedance of an ideal current source. However, if we consider a diff amp using ±15-V supplies (a very common choice) and we use, say, a 1-MΩ resistor, we can easily compute the maximum and minimum currents possible. If the transistors' bases were biased at +13 V, the emitters would be at roughly +12 VDC. The voltage drop across the 1-MΩ resistor would be about 27.4 V. Ohm's law tells us that 27.4 V/1 MΩ = 27.4 μA would flow. With both transistors' bases biased at −13 V, there would be about 1.4 V across the 1-MΩ resistor, so 1.4 V/1 MΩ = 1.4 μA would flow. Thus we see that using a resistor for a current source will not provide a very constant current for large swings in common-mode input voltage. Using a constant-current diode is a possibility, and this works very well in discrete circuits where diodes having the desired current rating are available. But constant-current devices are a bit tricky to integrate into ICs, so a transistor current source is usually used. Such a current source can be made as shown in Fig. 1–6. As you can see, it is simply a common-emitter DC amplifier using a very stiff universal-bias circuit. Thus the collector current is very stable. Recall from our earlier discussion that this stable constant current is very important to the proper operation of a diff amp. A diff amp whose total current can vary will not ignore common-mode signals very well.

It was mentioned earlier that the gain of an unbalanced-output diff amp is:

$$A_V = \frac{R_C}{2r_{e'}} \tag{1.01}$$

Dr. William Shockley showed that $r_{e'}$ is inversely proportional to emitter current and

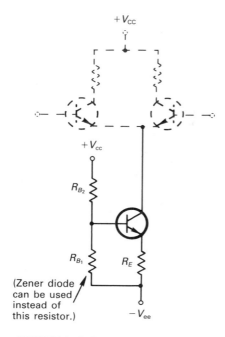

FIGURE 1-6: Transistor Current Source

is between 20 mV/I_E and 50 mV/I_E, where I_E is the emitter current. A common approximation is

$$r_{e'} = \frac{25 \text{ mV}}{I_E} \qquad (1.02)$$

Substituting, we have

$$A_V = \frac{R_C}{2(25 \text{ mV}/I_E)}$$

$$= \frac{R_C I_E}{50 \text{ mV}} \qquad (1.03)$$

Sometimes it is desirable to have an amplifier whose gain is electronically variable. As you can see, if we could control the current ($I_{E_1} + I_{E_2}$) fed to a diff amp, we could vary the gain. Using a transistor current source, we can do it. If we simply apply a control voltage to the base of the current-source transistor, we can control the gain via that voltage. This is yet another advantage of diff amps; they provide an easy way to linearly control the gain of an amplifier. The industry jargon for an amplifier that permits such control is *programmable-gain amplifier*.

As with any other type of amplifier circuit, sometimes more gain is required of a diff amp than one stage can provide. In such a case, diff-amp stages can be cascaded as shown in Fig. 1-7. Notice that the first stage is a balanced-input/balanced-output stage, and the second stage is a balanced-input/unbalanced-output stage. The total gain, of course, is the product of the stage gains. (Naturally, the effect of the input resistance of stage 2 upon the net collector load of stage 1 must be calculated in computing the gain of stage 1.) You may have noticed that there is no collector resistor for Q_4. Since a collector resistor would not contribute to the gain in the unbalanced-output mode, it can be omitted with no ill effects.

One other thing should be noticed about Fig. 1–7: the quiescent DC output voltage is not zero. This is obviously a problem if the circuit is to be used as a DC amplifier. It is also a problem for AC amplifiers because the output voltage can only swing 5 V positive, although it can swing 25 V negative. This means that each time we cascade another stage, our maximum symmetrical output voltage swing is decreased. In order to prevent this, we can use *level translator* stages. Figure 1–8 shows such a circuit. Notice that it is nothing more than an emitter follower with a tapped emitter resistor. However, it returns the output to 0 V DC while retaining virtually all of the gain of our circuit.

OUTPUT STAGES

The diff amp is primarily a voltage amplifier; that is, while it provides current gain, it is not capable of providing large output currents. Therefore, circuits using diff amps as input stages usually have some sort of high-current power-amplifier output stage. The most common output stages are either complementary or quasi-

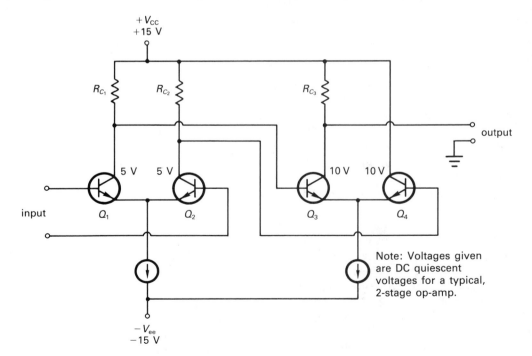

FIGURE 1–7: Cascaded Diff-Amp Stages

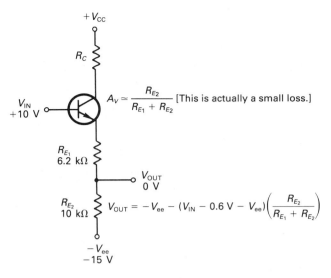

FIGURE 1–8: Level-Translator Circuit

complementary designs. Both of these circuits are shown in Fig. 1–9. The complementary stage uses two stacked emitter followers. The top one is NPN, and the bottom one is PNP. These emitter followers are biased so that either one or the other is conducting at any given time. Thus a positive input voltage to the stage results in an approximately equal positive output voltage, caused by conduction of current through the NPN transistor and the load resistance. Likewise, a negative input voltage results in a negative output voltage because of conduction by the PNP transistor. With zero signal voltage, both transistors are biased very slightly into conduction. This prevents the output wave from having a glitch as it crosses the zero-voltage line. The quiescent bias is regulated by diodes or a bias-regulator transistor, so that variations in temperature do not cause thermal runaway.

The quasi-complementary circuit works similarly. However, since both output transistors are NPN, the one that handles negative voltages must be made to respond to a negative bias; that is, its input signal must be inverted. This is accomplished by a PNP transistor direct coupled in a complementary-compound configuration. The result is that the compound thinks it is a PNP transistor. Thus the same biasing circuit can be used.

With either type of output stage, short circuits present a great danger, because the emitter resistor controls the current in an emitter follower. (Remember, the emitter voltage follows the base voltage minus a 0.6-V drop. Therefore, the emitter current equals the base voltage minus 0.6 V divided by the emitter resistor.) Since the load *is* the emitter resistor, a shorted load means that the transistor will try to deliver infinite current until it melts. There is a way to protect output stages against the effects of short circuits. This involves using transistors to short out the base drive to the output transistors whenever too much current is drawn. The current in the output transistors is sensed by small resistors (R_P) in series with the emitters. The circuit is shown in Fig. 1–10. For example, let us assume that each R_P has a value

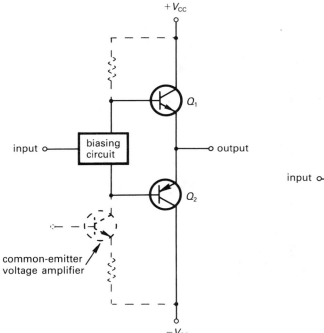

FIGURE 1–9A: Complementary Output Stage

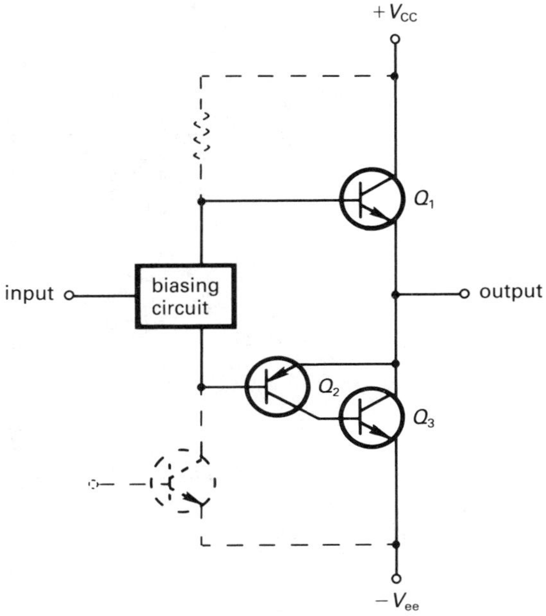

FIGURE 1–9B: Quasi-Complementary Output Stage

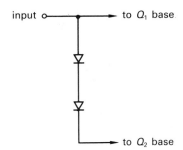

FIGURE 1–9C: Diode Biasing Circuit

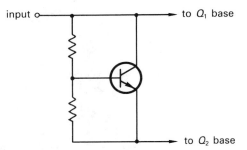

FIGURE 1–9D: Transistor Biasing Circuit

FIGURE 1–9: Output Stages

of 27 Ω. Then whenever more than 0.6 V is dropped across either 27-Ω resistor, the corresponding protection transistor turns on, removing base drive to the output transistor. In this case, maximum output current would be limited to 0.6 V/27 Ω = 22 mA. Of course, depending upon the heat-dissipation capability of the output transistors, they might still overheat if called upon to deliver a sustained output of 22 mA. But they are protected against catastrophic failure from a shorted output.

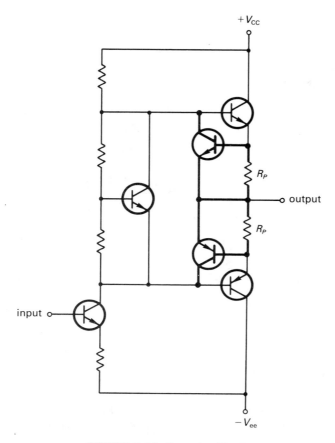

FIGURE 1–10: Protection Circuit

FEEDBACK CONCEPTS

Positive and Negative Feedback

The use of linear integrated circuits (LICs) is intimately involved with the use of feedback. In fact, it is almost fair to say that the study of LIC applications is a study of feedback networks. Therefore, we will spend some time discussing the basic principles of feedback.

In the early years after Lee De Forest invented the triode vacuum tube (the Audion), engineers attempting to use the device had frequent problems with oscillation in their amplifier designs. In other words, their amplifier circuits whistled and howled. It was soon discovered that this problem was caused by *positive feedback:* Some of the output signal was being fed back in phase into the input of the amplifier. In 1927, H. S. Black of Bell Telephone Laboratories invented a way of using feedback to *control* tendencies toward oscillation. He applied a phase-inverted portion

H. S. Black, who invented negative feedback in 1927 while working for Bell Telephone Laboratories. (Courtesy of AT&T.)

of the output signal to the input of the amplifier. In addition to eliminating the troublesome oscillations, this *negative feedback* had other benefits: It reduced distortion and increased the frequency range of the amplifier.

The type of feedback that is most often used in linear circuit design is negative feedback. We will study positive feedback in more detail in Chapter 8, when we discuss waveform generators.

Types of Negative Feedback

For any amplifier circuit, we can derive a feedback signal that is proportional to either the output current or the output voltage. In addition, we can add the feedback signal to the input signal by connecting the feedback network either in series or in parallel (shunt) with the input signal source. This leads to four types of negative-feedback connections, as illustrated in Fig. 1–11:

1. Voltage-series
2. Voltage-shunt
3. Current-series
4. Current-shunt

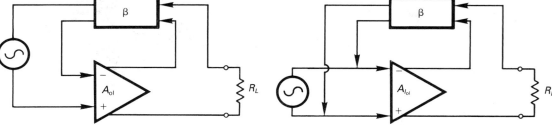

Note: Arrows represent signal-flow direction.

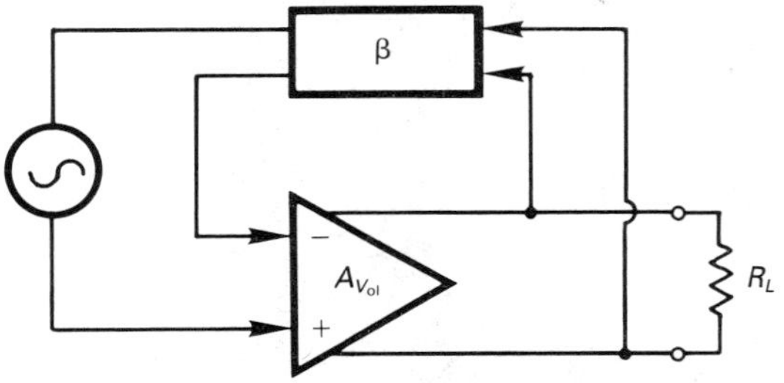

FIGURE 1–11A: Voltage-Series Feedback

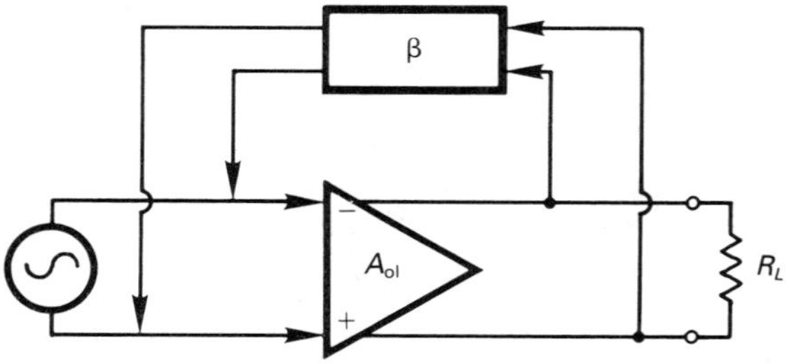

FIGURE 1–11B: Voltage-Shunt Feedback

FIGURE 1–11C: Current-Series Feedback

FIGURE 1–11D: Current-Shunt Feedback

FIGURE 1–11: The Four Negative-Feedback Connections

In order for the feedback signal to be able to be fed in series with the input signal source, that source must have a low internal (Thevenin) impedance. Therefore, the series-feedback connections imply voltage sources for the input signals. Likewise, since a low-impedance signal source would tend to short out a feedback signal applied in parallel, the shunt-feedback connections imply a signal source with a high internal impedance, which means a current source.

Because negative feedback tends to stabilize the quantity to which it is made proportional, voltage-feedback circuits act as constant-voltage sources, whereas current-feedback circuits act as constant-current sources. If we put this information together, we have what is called the *controlled-source* method of classifying amplifiers; that is, the nomenclature we have used to identify types of negative-feedback connections has its counterpart in a sort of "what-controls-what" system. Table 1–A summarizes this comparison.

TABLE 1–A Feedback *vs* Controlled-Source Terminology: A Comparison

FEEDBACK CONNECTION	INPUT SOURCE	OUTPUT TYPE	CONTROLLED-SOURCE NAME
voltage-series	voltage	voltage source	voltage-controlled voltage source
voltage-shunt	current	voltage source	current-controlled voltage source
current-series	voltage	current source	voltage-controlled current source
current-shunt	current	current source	current-controlled current source

Next we will examine the operation of each of these circuits.

Voltage-Series Feedback. By far the most common amplifier circuit in which LICs are used is the voltage-series feedback circuit. Referring to Fig. 1–12, you will notice a number of symbols. The amplifier's gain without feedback is indicated as $A_{V_{ol}}$, for *open-loop voltage gain*. (The words *open-loop* indicate that the feedback loop is not closed; therefore, there is no feedback when $A_{V_{ol}}$ is measured.) The portion of the output that is fed back is given by β (a lowercase Greek beta). Thus the feedback voltage V_f is βV_{OUT}. The source voltage is V_s, and the total voltage applied to the input of the amplifier is V_i; R_i and R_o are the input and output resistances of the amplifier; and R_L is the load resistance.

With no feedback, $V_s = V_i$, so the gain is simply $A_{V_{ol}}$, the open-loop gain of the amplifier itself:

$$A_{V_{ol}} = \frac{V_{OUT}}{V_s} = \frac{V_{OUT}}{V_i} \qquad (1.04)$$

Once we connect the feedback loop, the input signal to the amplifier becomes

$$V_i = V_s - V_f \qquad (1.05)$$

Notice that we have assumed that the feedback signal is out of phase with the signal source, as indicated by the minus sign in front of V_f. Let us calculate V_{OUT}:

$$V_{OUT} = A_{V_{ol}}V_i = A_{V_{ol}}(V_s - V_f) = A_{V_{ol}}(V_s - \beta V_{OUT})$$

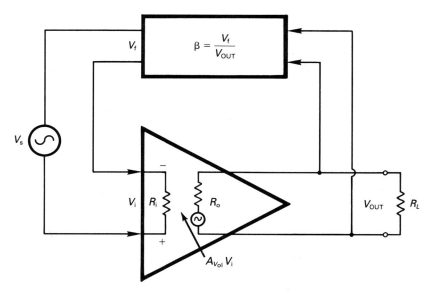

FIGURE 1–12: Voltage-Series Feedback

Solving this last expression for V_{OUT}, we have

$$V_{\text{OUT}} = A_{V_{\text{ol}}}V_{\text{s}} - A_{V_{\text{ol}}}\beta V_{\text{OUT}}$$

$$V_{\text{OUT}}(1 + A_{V_{\text{ol}}}\beta) = A_{V_{\text{ol}}}V_{\text{s}}$$

$$V_{\text{OUT}} = \frac{A_{V_{\text{ol}}}V_{\text{s}}}{1 + A_{V_{\text{ol}}}\beta} \tag{1.06}$$

Now the voltage gain with feedback (the *closed-loop* gain) can be found as follows:

$$A_{V_{\text{cl}}} = \frac{V_{\text{OUT}}}{V_{\text{s}}} = \frac{A_{V_{\text{ol}}}V_{\text{s}}}{V_{\text{s}}(1 + A_{V_{\text{ol}}}\beta)}$$

where $A_{V_{\text{ol}}}$ is the closed loop gain.

$$= \frac{A_{V_{\text{ol}}}}{1 + A_{V_{\text{ol}}}\beta} \tag{1.07}$$

The input and output impedances of an amplifier using voltage-series feedback are affected by the presence of the feedback. Thus they are not identical to the impedances without feedback, R_{i} and R_{o}. In order to determine the input impedance with feedback, let us first find the input current I_{s}. This is just the same as the current in R_{i}:

$$I_{\text{s}} = \frac{V_{\text{i}}}{R_{\text{i}}} = \frac{V_{\text{s}} - V_{\text{f}}}{R_{\text{i}}} = \frac{V_{\text{s}} - \beta V_{\text{OUT}}}{R_{\text{i}}} \tag{1.08}$$

Since by definition V_{OUT} is just $A_{V_{\text{ol}}}V_{\text{s}}$, we may write

$$I_{\text{s}} = \frac{V_{\text{s}} - \beta A_{V_{\text{ol}}}V_{\text{s}}}{R_{\text{i}}} = \frac{V_{\text{s}}(1 - \beta A_{V_{\text{ol}}})}{R_{\text{i}}} \tag{1.09}$$

Substituting equation 1.07 for $A_{V_{ol}}$ in equation 1.09 gives

$$I_s = \frac{V_s[1 - A_{V_{ol}}\beta/(1 + A_{V_{ol}}\beta)]}{R_i} \tag{1.10}$$

This can be algebraically simplified to yield

$$I_s = \frac{V_s}{R_i(1 + A_{V_{ol}}\beta)} \tag{1.11}$$

Now to find the input impedance, we simply divide:

$$Z_{IN} = \frac{V_s}{I_s} = \frac{V_s}{V_s/R_i(1 + A_{V_{ol}}\beta)}$$

or

$$Z_{IN} = R_i(1 + A_{V_{ol}}\beta) \tag{1.12}$$

Thus we see that the input impedance of an amplifier using voltage-series feedback is increased by a factor of $1 + A_{V_{ol}}\beta$ compared to that of the amplifier without feedback.

The output impedance is also affected by feedback. Let us see how. The output impedance of any device is the same as its Thevenin impedance. The Thevenin impedance is the open-circuit output voltage divided by the short-circuit current:

$$Z_{OUT} = \frac{V_{oc}}{I_{sc}} \tag{1.13}$$

The open-circuit output voltage is just

$$V_{oc} = V_{OUT} = \frac{V_s A_{V_{ol}}}{1 + \beta A_{V_{ol}}} \tag{1.14}$$

Now when the output is shorted, $V_{OUT} = 0$, so $V_f = \beta V_{OUT} = 0$. Thus

$$V_{sc} = A_{V_{ol}}V_s$$

and

$$I_{sc} = \frac{A_{V_{ol}}V_s}{R_o}$$

Then

$$Z_{OUT} = \frac{V_s A_{V_{ol}}/(1 + \beta A_{V_{ol}})}{V_s A_{V_{ol}}/R_o} = \frac{R_o}{1 + \beta A_{V_{ol}}} \tag{1.15}$$

In summary, then, the gain and output impedance of a voltage-series feedback amplifier are decreased by the factor $1 + \beta A_{V_{ol}}$, and the input impedance is increased by that same factor. Since a high input impedance and a low output impedance are an attractive combination, the voltage-series feedback connection is one of the most popular ones.

Voltage-Shunt Feedback. As has already been mentioned, the voltage-shunt feedback amplifier is sometimes called a current-controlled voltage source. Since the input quantity is a current, and the output quantity is a voltage, the gain is expressed as a *transresistance:*

$$A_{ol} = \frac{V_{OUT}}{I_i} \qquad (1.16)$$

(The prefix *trans* means that the voltage in the numerator and the current in the denominator are measured at different places in the circuit. The terms in this and the following equations are as defined in Fig. 1–13.) The closed-loop gain can be derived as follows:

$$A_{cl} = \frac{V_{OUT}}{I_s} = \frac{A_{ol}I_i}{I_i + I_f}$$

$$= \frac{A_{ol}I_i}{I_i + \beta V_{OUT}} = \frac{A_{ol}I_i}{I_i + \beta A_{ol}I_i}$$

$$= \frac{A_{ol}}{1 + \beta A_{ol}} \qquad (1.17)$$

This is just the same result that we obtained for the voltage-series circuit. Often when this circuit is used, there is an input resistor placed in series with a voltage source that provides the signal input. This converts the circuit to another form of voltage-controlled voltage source. Then the gain can be stated in the form of a voltage gain, as with the voltage-series circuit. This variation will be discussed under the heading "Inverting Amplifiers" in Chapter 2.

The effect of voltage-shunt feedback upon input impedance is different from the effect of voltage-series feedback. Let us calculate the input impedance. Since

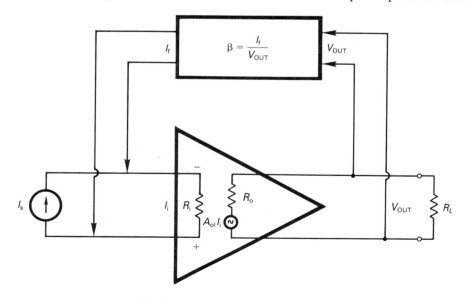

FIGURE 1–13: Voltage-Shunt Feedback

the signal source and the output of the feedback network are connected as branches of a parallel circuit, the voltage across the two is the same:

$$V_i = V_s = V_f$$

The input current is the sum of I_i and I_f, and

$$Z_{IN} = \frac{V_i}{I_s} = \frac{V_i}{I_i + I_f} = \frac{V_i}{I_i + \beta V_{OUT}}$$

Since $V_i/I_i = R_i$ and $V_{OUT}/I_i = A_{ol}$, if we divide both numerator and denominator by I_i we have

$$Z_{IN} = \frac{V_i/I_i}{I_i/I_i + \beta V_{OUT}/I_i} = \frac{R_i}{1 + \beta A_{ol}} \qquad (1.18)$$

Notice that the input impedance of this connection is decreased by the feedback. In fact, if the open-loop gain of the amplifier is quite high, the input impedance approaches zero ohms.

The output section of this circuit is much like the output section of the voltage-series circuit, and the same equation (equation 1.15) for output impedance applies.

The voltage-shunt feedback circuit can be used as a current-to-voltage converter, as discussed in Chapter 9.

Current-Series Feedback. The current-series feedback circuit is a voltage-controlled current source. Therefore, its gain must be stated as a *transconductance:*

$$A_{ol} = \frac{I_{OUT}}{V_i}$$

The derivation of the gain and input-impedance equations will be left as student exercises. The results are the same as for the voltage-series circuit. The output impedance can be determined as follows. If we short the signal source, then

$$V_s = 0 \qquad \text{and} \qquad V_i = V_f = V_{OUT} \qquad (1.19)$$

(The terms are defined in Fig. 1–14.) We can then connect a voltage source V to the output of our circuit, and the resulting current will be determined only by the output impedance, including the effects of the feedback, since there is no input to the circuit. The output current that will result can be determined from the superposition principle. It is the sum of the currents from the voltage across R_o and from feedback:

$$I_{OUT} = \frac{V}{R_o} + A_{ol}V_i$$

According to equation 1.19, we can rewrite this as

$$I_{OUT} = \frac{V}{R_o} + A_{ol}\beta I_{OUT}$$

Solving for V, we have

$$V = R_o(1 + \beta A_{ol})I_{OUT}$$

This means that

$$Z_{OUT} = \frac{V}{I_{OUT}} = \frac{R_o(1 + \beta A_{ol})I_{OUT}}{I_{OUT}}$$

$$= R_o(1 + \beta A_{ol}) \tag{1.20}$$

The combination of a high input impedance and a high output impedance is characteristic of a transconductance amplifier, as this circuit is sometimes called. It will be investigated more fully in Chapter 9.

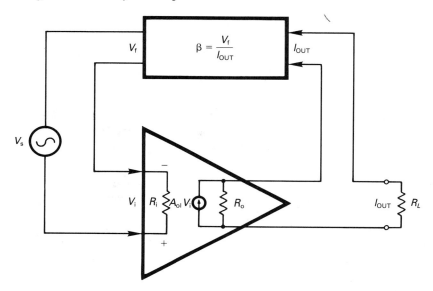

FIGURE 1–14: Current-Series Feedback

Current-Shunt Feedback. The current-shunt feedback amplifier is a current-controlled current source or, in other words, a current amplifier. The derivations of the gain and impedance equations are left as student exercises. The results are

$$A_{I_{cl}} = \frac{A_{I_{ol}}}{1 + \beta A_{I_{ol}}} \tag{1.21}$$

$$Z_{IN} = \frac{R_i}{1 + \beta A_{I_{ol}}} \tag{1.22}$$

$$Z_{OUT} = R_o(1 + \beta A_{I_{ol}}) \tag{1.23}$$

In summary, any amplifier having voltage feedback acts as a controlled voltage source, and has an output impedance that is reduced by the feedback. This makes the amplifier into a more perfect voltage source. Any amplifier having current feedback acts as a controlled current source, and its output impedance is increased by the feedback. This makes it act as a more perfect current source.

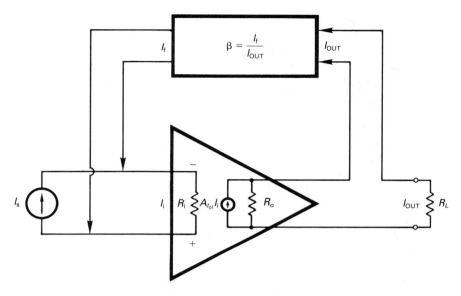

FIGURE 1–15: Current-Shunt Feedback

Series feedback causes the amplifier to have a higher input impedance, which is desirable if the input is fed by a voltage source. Shunt feedback causes the amplifier to have a lower input impedance, which is desirable if the input is fed by a current source.

All varieties of negative feedback reduce the gain by the same factor $(1 + \beta A_{ol})$. These effects are summarized in Table 1–B.

Other Effects of Negative Feedback

Aside from reducing gain and changing impedances, negative feedback has three other important effects: (1) it improves gain stability; (2) it reduces distortion; and (3) it increases bandwidth. Gain stability is a measure of the extent to which the

TABLE 1–B Equations for Feedback Amplifiers

TYPE	A_{cl}	Z_{IN}	Z_{OUT}
Voltage-Series	$\dfrac{A_{Vol}}{1 + A_{Vol}\beta}$	$R_i(1 + A_{Vol}\beta)$	$\dfrac{R_o}{1 + A_{Vol}\beta}$
Voltage-Shunt	$\dfrac{A_{ol}}{1 + A_{ol}\beta}$	$\dfrac{R_i}{1 + A_{ol}\beta}$	$\dfrac{R_o}{1 + A_{Vol}\beta}$
Current-Series	$\dfrac{A_{ol}}{1 + A_{ol}\beta}$	$R_i(1 + A_{ol}\beta)$	$R_o(1 + A_{ol}\beta)$
Current-Shunt	$\dfrac{A_{Iol}}{1 + A_{Iol}\beta}$	$\dfrac{R_i}{1 + A_{Iol}\beta}$	$R_o(1 + A_{Iol}\beta)$

gain of a circuit remains at the design value in spite of temperature- and age-induced variations in components. Negative feedback makes the gain of a circuit more dependent upon the values of the passive components in the feedback (β) network, and less dependent upon the active devices (transistors, ICs, etc.). Since passive devices are usually much more stable than active ones, the net effect is a great improvement in the gain stability as a result of the addition of negative feedback.

Strictly, the term *distortion* refers to any difference, other than amplitude, between the input and output signals of a circuit. There are two general kinds of distortion: nonlinear distortion and frequency distortion. *Nonlinear distortion* results whenever the output voltage of a circuit is not strictly proportional to the input voltage. The result is a change in the waveform of any signal. *Frequency distortion* refers to the inability of a circuit to equally handle all frequencies that are in the input signal. Thus the output signal contains proportionally more or less of some frequencies than others. In common usage, *distortion* is taken to mean only nonlinear distortion. However, it is a fact that both kinds of distortion are reduced by the addition of negative feedback. As shown in Fig. 1–16A and B, if you plot the input voltage versus the output voltage of an amplifier without feedback, the graph will exhibit some curving at the extremes. This results in nonlinear distortion in the output. The distortion level increases with the output voltage. When negative feedback is added, the graph becomes essentially a straight line in between the clipping points. The distortion is low until clipping occurs. Figures 1–16C and D show two clipped waveforms. The one in Fig. 1–16C is from a circuit having no negative feedback and shows distortion even before the clipping occurs. The waveform in Fig. 1–16D

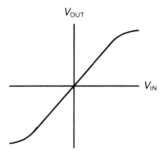

FIGURE 1–16A: No Feedback

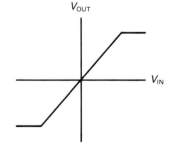

FIGURE 1–16B: With Feedback

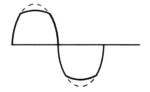

FIGURE 1–16C: No Feedback

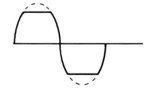

FIGURE 1–16D: With Feedback

FIGURE 1–16: The Effect of Feedback Upon Distortion

is from a circuit using negative feedback and is an accurate sine wave except where it is actually clipped. Distortion will be discussed more fully in Chapter 5.

Negative feedback increases bandwidth. In amplifier design, there is often a tradeoff between gain and bandwidth. Negative feedback follows this same pattern: When negative feedback is added, bandwidth is increased at the expense of gain.

SUMMARY

Linear ICs produce outputs that are linearly related to their inputs. They are also called analog ICs.

Digital ICs produce outputs that can have only certain discrete values.

Hybrid ICs are made up of discrete parts mounted on a ceramic slab.

Monolithic ICs are constructed entirely of etched and processed silicon.

The differential amplifier is an important building-block circuit used in linear ICs.

Diff amps have two inputs and two outputs. They can be connected as:

- Unbalanced-in/unbalanced-out
- Balanced-in/unbalanced-out
- Unbalanced-in/balanced-out
- Balanced-in/balanced-out

Diff amps amplify the difference between the two input voltages.

Balanced circuits help to reduce noise and interference problems.

Diff amps can be made with Darlington or FET input stages for higher input impedance.

Diff amps can use several different kinds of current sources. The most common is the transistor current source, which can be modified to give a programmable-gain amplifier.

Diff amps can be cascaded to provide more gain.

To correct for the shift in DC level that occurs when diff amps are cascaded, level translators are used.

Power-amplifying output stages are used in linear ICs. These are usually complementary or quasi-complementary stages. Some output stages incorporate short-circuit protection in the form of automatic current limiting.

There are two types of feedback: negative and positive. Positive feedback tends to cause oscillations. Negative feedback can improve amplifier performance in several ways. However, it also decreases gain.

Voltage-series feedback increases input impedance and reduces output impedance. A circuit using this type of feedback is a true voltage amplifier and is sometimes called a voltage-controlled voltage source.

Voltage-shunt feedback decreases input and output impedances. A circuit using this type of feedback can be called a current-controlled voltage source. Its gain is a transresistance.

Current-series feedback increases input and output impedances. A circuit using this type of feedback is a voltage-controlled current source. Since its gain is a transconductance, it can also be called a transconductance amplifier.

Current-shunt feedback decreases input impedance and increases output impedance. A circuit using this type of feedback can be called a current-controlled current
source. It is a true current amplifier, and its gain is a current gain.

Negative feedback decreases distortion, increases bandwidth, and improves gain
stability.

REVIEW QUESTIONS

1. How is a linear circuit different from a digital one? Give two examples of
applications for which linear circuits would be used and two for which digital
ones would be preferred.
2. How does a hybrid IC differ from a monolithic IC?
3. What output would you expect from a diff amp if you fed:
(a) a signal from a signal generator to both inputs?
(b) a DC signal into one input and a sine wave into the other?
(c) a sine wave into one input and a square wave of the same phase, frequency, and average voltage into the other?
(d) a signal from a signal generator to both inputs, *and* a 20-kHz sine wave
to one input at the same time.
4. Discuss two advantages that a diff amp has when compared to a common-
emitter amplifier.
5. What is the advantage of a Darlington-input diff amp compared to the normal
variety?
6. What advantage does an FET diff amp have, when compared to the normal
variety? Compared to a Darlington-input diff amp?
7. Draw a circuit that could be used to multiply two voltage levels; that is, the
output is the product of the two inputs. No component values need be given.
8. Design a level translator to reduce the DC voltage level of a signal from 10
V to 0 V. Give all component values. Assume ±15 V supplies.
9. Draw a complementary output stage with a protection circuit included. Calculate the proper value for the protection resistors for a maximum output current of 100 mA.
10. (Optional—more challenging.) Design an amplifier circuit using two differential stages, a level translator, and a complementary output stage with 20-
mA current limiting. Use a ±15 V supply and make the gain of each diff
amp stage 100. Include all component values.
11. Derive the equations for the gain and input impedance of the current-series
feedback amplifier.
12. Derive the equations for the gain, input impedance, and output impedance of
the current-shunt feedback amplifier.
13. Calculate the percent change in closed-loop gain that would result if the open-
loop gain of a feedback amplifier decreased 20% from its nominal value. Let
$\beta = 0.1$ in each case. $A_{V_{ol}}$ is nominally (a) 100, (b) 10,000, (c) 10^6. What is
the effect of the open-loop gain upon gain stability?

14. Calculate the input impedance of the following feedback amplifiers for which $A_{ol} = 1000$, $\beta = 0.1$, and $R_i = 10 \text{ k}\Omega$:
    (a) voltage-series
    (b) voltage-shunt
    (c) current-series
    (d) current-shunt
15. Repeat question 13 for (a) $A_{ol} = 10,000$ and $\beta = 0.1$, and (b) $A_{ol} = 10,000$ and $\beta = 0.01$. What is the effect on Z_{IN} of increasing the product βA_{ol}?
16. Calculate the output impedances of each type of feedback amplifier in question 14. The value of R_o is $100 \ \Omega$.
17. Repeat question 13, using $\beta = 0.01$. Compare your results to those obtained when β was 0.1. What happens to gain stability as $\beta A_{V_{ol}}$ decreases?

Laboratory Experiment—IC Building Blocks

Objective:

To use discrete components to build and understand an amplifier circuit similar to those used in linear ICs.

Materials:

5 NPN transistors, 2N2222 or equivalent
1 PNP transistor, MPSA56 or equivalent
3 15-kΩ resistors
2 150-kΩ resistors
1 1-kΩ resistor
1 270-kΩ resistor
2 100-kΩ resistors
1 3.3-kΩ resistor
1 470-Ω resistor
2 1N914 or equivalent diodes
3 50-kΩ potentiometers
1 1-MΩ potentiometer

Procedure:

1. Build the circuit shown in Fig. 1–17A.
2. Adjust the 50-kΩ potentiometer to obtain 0 V DC at the output.
3. Feed a 30-mV, 1-kHz sine wave to the inputs, and measure the resulting signal voltage at points A _____, B _____, and C _____.
4. Insert a 1-MΩ potentiometer in series with the signal generator. Adjust it for 0 Ω resistance and measure the output signal voltage from the amplifier. _____ Now adjust the 1-MΩ pot until the output voltage drops to half this value. Take out the 1-MΩ pot without disturbing its setting, and measure it. _____ This is the input resistance of your amplifier.
5. Feed the 30-mV signal to the amplifier again and measure the no-load output voltage. _____ Now connect a 470-Ω resistor as an output load and measure the voltage across it. _____
6. Disconnect the signal generator and the load resistor. Using a 50-kΩ pot connected to the positive power supply as the positive signal source and another 50-kΩ pot connected to the negative power supply as the negative signal source (Fig. 1–17B), measure the output for the following conditions:
   (a) +30 mV to − input, 0 V to + input _____
   (b) −30 mV to − input, 0 V to + input _____
   (c) +30 mV to + input, 0 V to − input _____

(continued)

(continued from page 34)

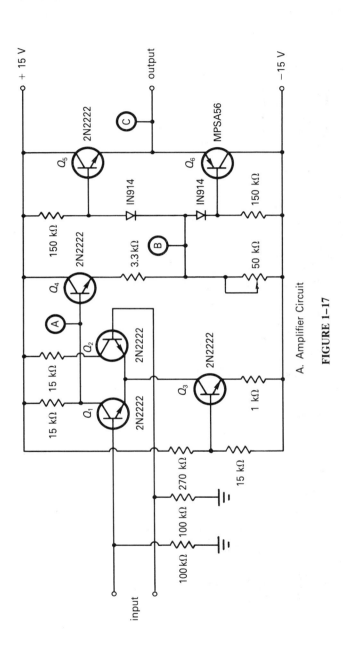

A. Amplifier Circuit

FIGURE 1–17

(continued from page 35)

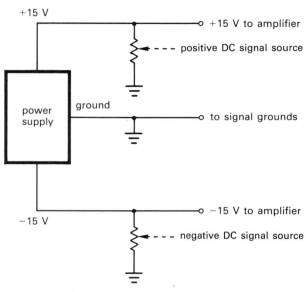

B. DC Signal Sources

FIGURE 1–17

(d) -30 mV to $+$ input, 0 V to $-$ input _____
(e) $+30$ mV to $-$ input, 30 mV to $+$ input _____
(f) -30 mV to $-$ input, $+30$ mV to $+$ input _____
(g) -30 mV to $-$ input, -30 mV to $+$ input _____
(h) $+30$ mV to $-$ input, -30 mV to $+$ input _____

Analysis:

1. Calculate the gain of each stage and the total gain of the amplifier, based upon your measurements in step 3.
2. Calculate the output (Thevenin) resistance of your amplifier, based upon your measurements in step 5.
3. Discuss the operation of your circuit, including common-mode rejection, based upon your measurements in step 6. Common-mode rejection is specified in terms of the *common-mode rejection ratio* (CMRR):

$$\text{CMRR} = \frac{V_{\text{OUT}} \text{ caused by common-mode input signal}}{V_{\text{IN,common mode}}}$$

4. Discuss the operation of each stage and how it contributes to the working of the total circuit.

Laboratory Experiment

chapter two

Ideal Operational Amplifiers

OBJECTIVES

Upon completing this chapter, you will be able to:

- Describe the characteristics of the ideal operational amplifier (*op amp*).
- Design and analyze the following circuits using op amps, assuming ideal characteristics: comparators, analog-to-digital "flash" converters, inverting and non-inverting amplifiers, instrumentation amplifiers, integrators, and differentiators.

CHARACTERISTICS OF IDEAL OP AMPS

Well, here we are already talking about operational amplifiers, abbreviating that name to op amps, and we still have not told you just what the things are. Let's correct that problem right away. Back during World War II, the military had great need of analog computers for fire-control systems for big guns and missiles. Dr. C. A. Lovell of Bell Telephone Laboratories introduced the concept of a general-purpose amplifier circuit whose characteristics could be controlled by the external feedback components connected to it. Such circuits would be used in analog computers to perform the mathematical *operations* of addition, subtraction, multiplication, and division, as well as more complex operations. Thus they were called *operational amplifiers* (*op amps*). Of course, these early op amps used vacuum tubes, but still they provided a greatly simplified way to design and construct complex circuits. In 1948, George A. Philbrick built the first commercially marketed single-tube op amp.

The characteristics necessary to make an amplifier circuit perform entirely under the control of its feedback components are easy to understand, even if they were not so simple to achieve. The first is *infinite voltage gain*. Of course, truly infinite gain is a logical impossibility, since it would imply an infinite output voltage resulting from an infinitesimal input voltage. What we really mean by infinite in this case is that the gain is so great that in the design equations it can be treated as if it were infinite. This greatly simplifies the process of designing with op amps. Naturally, when we close the feedback loop around the op amp, the resulting gain will have some well-defined, finite value. So the characteristic that applies to the op amp itself is better described as infinite *open-loop* voltage gain. Recall that *open-loop* means having no external feedback applied.

The second requirement is that of *infinite input impedance*. This also is really not possible, but if the impedance is very, very high, then the amount of current drawn by the op amp's input will be small enough to be ignored. This simplifies design requirements and makes the basic op amp a voltage-controlled device, like a vacuum tube or an FET, rather than a current-controlled device like a transistor. It is possible to make the op amp behave as a current-controlled device, but that is done through the addition of external components.

The third characteristic of an ideal op amp is *zero output impedance*. You will recognize this as one of the characteristics of an ideal voltage source. A zero-output-impedance device produces an output voltage that is independent of the load to which it is connected. Obviously this is desirable, because fluctuations of the output voltage with changes in loading would represent a gain that depended upon loading. Naturally, there aren't any zero-impedance devices, but if the load impedance is kept within certain prescribed limits, we can get away with pretending that $Z_{OUT} = 0$.

The fourth characteristic of an ideal op amp is that *the output voltage is zero when the input voltage is zero*. Although this sounds pretty obvious and simple, perhaps a bit of explaining is needed. First of all, op amps are usually DC amplifiers, meaning that zero output voltage also means 0 V DC, not simply zero AC signal voltage. This fact makes this characteristic more meaningful as well as more difficult to achieve. DC amplifiers tend to drift with temperature, and they require carefully selected components to avoid having their operating points shift. A DC output voltage that is present when the input voltage is zero is called an *offset voltage*. So this fourth characteristic is often stated as "zero offset voltage." The meaning of zero input voltage also requires some explaining. Almost all op amps use the differential-input/single-ended-output configuration. The net input voltage to such a circuit is $V_{IN\ a} - V_{IN\ b}$, where the *a* and *b* inputs are as shown in Fig. 2–1. Since an op amp typically has a diff amp as its input stage, it amplifies the difference between the two input voltages. Thus a zero input simply means that the voltages at the two inputs are equal, not that they are necessarily both zero.

The fifth characteristic of an ideal op amp is *infinite bandwidth*. Since we've already said that op amps respond to DC inputs, we know that response including 0 Hz is a practical necessity. However, the other end of *infinite* means that there are no high-frequency limitations. Obviously this is a characteristic in which real op amps fall short of the ideal.

The sixth characteristic for the ideal op amp is *infinite common-mode rejection* (CMRR). Recall from Chapter 1 that common-mode signals are signals that appear with equal voltage, frequency, and phase on both inputs at the same time. Such input voltages have no difference to amplify and should produce no output voltage. If they indeed produce no output voltage, the op amp is said to have infinite common-mode rejection. This sounds a lot like characteristic 4. But as mentioned above, characteristic 4 is usually taken to mean zero offset voltage, whereas characteristic 6 means zero output voltage when the individual input voltages are not zero but their difference is zero. Since output offset voltage and poor common-mode rejection are caused by different things within the op amp itself, they are usually specified separately. Thus, even though characteristics 4 and 6 are closely related, they are not identical.

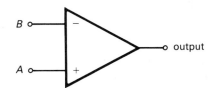

FIGURE 2–1A: Schematic Symbol

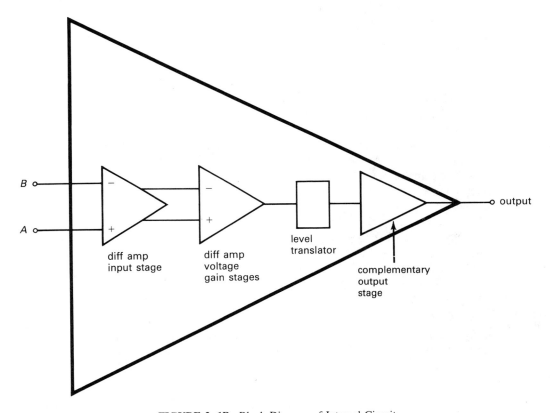

FIGURE 2–1B: Block Diagram of Internal Circuit

FIGURE 2–1: Basic Op Amp

The final characteristic of the ideal op amp is *infinite slew rate*. Slew rate is the rate at which the value of instantaneous output voltage of an op amp can change. It is specified in volts per microsecond. Obviously this characteristic is related to bandwidth, since higher-frequency signals require the output voltage to change more rapidly. However, a 10 V_{P-P} sine wave will also require the output voltage to change more rapidly than a 1 V_{P-P} sine wave of the same frequency. In Chapter 3, we will discuss why slew-rate limitations exist. For now, just remember that infinite band-width only means that at some signal level the op amp has equal gain at all frequencies, whereas infinite slew rate means that at *any* signal level the op amp has equal output voltages available at all frequencies.

We have not said anything about some characteristics that you may consider very important in an amplifier, such as noise, distortion, maximum input and output voltages, and maximum output current or power. These characteristics do make a difference in the designer's choice of one op amp over another, but they are not part of the specifications required for an ideal op amp.

Some of these ideal characteristics are more nearly attainable than others. Table 2–A lists characteristics of several real op amps. Notice that some of the op amps are identified by three-digit numbers, which are the generic numbers for these particular op amps. When you get an op amp, this number will have prefixes and possibly suffixes added to it to make up the complete manufacturer's number. For example, a 741 op amp can be bought as a μA741, μA741A, μA741ADM, μA741C, μA741CA, μA741CT, μA741CV, μA741EC, or μA741TC, all of which are 741 op amps made by Fairchild or Signetics. The different suffixes indicate different packages, operating temperature ranges, and so on. The meaning of each suffix can be determined from the appropriate manufacturer's data sheets. Or you can get any of the LM741 series (National Semiconductor), the MC1741 series (Motorola), the SN52741 series (Texas Instruments), or perhaps some others that I have inadvertently omitted. Any op amp in these series is still a 741 op amp and shares the same basic characteristics indicated in Table 2–A. By the way, complete manufacturers' specification sheets for a 741 op amp are included in Appendix A of this book.

As you can see, some of the op amps in the table come quite close to having some of the ideal characteristics. In particular, open-loop gain and input impedance are both normally quite high. Also, common-mode rejections of 100 dB or better, though not infinite, are certainly quite good. (100 dB = a voltage ratio of 100,000:1.) The other characteristics are less nearly ideal but can be assumed to be ideal if certain requirements are adhered to:

1. Make sure that the load resistance connected to the op amp is at least 1 kΩ.
2. Make sure that the bandwidth that you require is not over 20 kHz.

TABLE 2–A Typical Op Amp Characteristics

CHARACTERISTIC	OP AMP TYPE					UNITS
	709	**741**	**301**	**LF147**	**LF411A**	
A_{Zol}	4.5×10^4	2×10^5	1.6×10^5	10^5	2×10^5	None
Z_{IN}	4×10^5	6×10^6	2×10^6	10^{12}	10^{12}	Ohms (Ω)
Z_{OUT}	150	75	75	30	30	Ohms (Ω)
A_{offset}	1.0	1.0	2.0	1.0	0.3	mV
Bandwidth	1.2×10^6	1.5×10^6	10^6	4×10^6	4×10^6	Hz
CMRR	90	90	90	100	100	dB
Slew Rate	0.25	0.5	10	13	10	V/μs
Notes				FET Input	Low-Offset, FET Input	

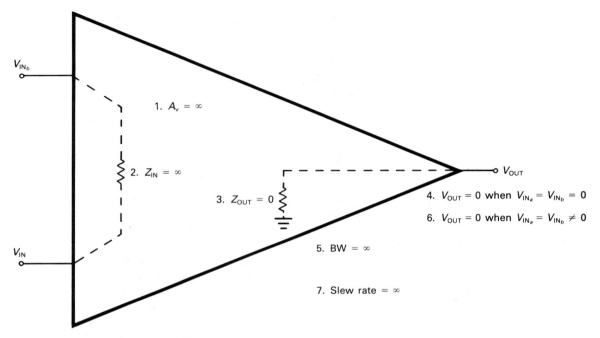

FIGURE 2–2: Summary of Ideal Op-Amp Characteristics

3. Capacitor-couple multiple stages.
4. Do not require full output-voltage swing at frequencies above 1 kHz.
5. Make sure that the common-mode rejection of the op amp you use is great enough for your needs. (This is discussed more fully in the section on Instrumentation Amplifiers (page 67.)
6. Do not try to design amplifiers in which output offset voltage is critical until you study Chapter 3.

Even with these limitations, there are quite a few circuits you can design by using real op amps and assuming that they have ideal characteristics. Next we'll see how.

BASIC CIRCUITS USING IDEAL OP AMPS

Comparators

You've already noticed from the heading that you can build a comparator using an op amp. But you may be wondering just what a comparator is. *A **comparator** is a device whose output state indicates which of its two input voltages is greater*. Thus it is an analog-input, digital-output device. Figure 2–3 illustrates a comparator made from a 741 op amp. It is simply the op amp with power-supply connections added. The output voltage is

$$V_{\text{OUT}} = (V_{\text{IN}\,a} - V_{\text{IN}\,b})A_{V_{\text{ol}}} \qquad (2.01)$$

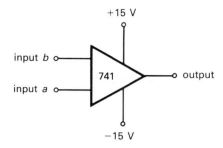

FIGURE 2–3: Op-Amp Comparator Circuit

where $A_{V_{ol}}$ = the open-loop voltage gain of the op amp, and $V_{IN\,a}$ and $V_{IN\,b}$ are the voltages from inputs a and b, respectively, to ground. If $V_{IN\,a}$ is greater than $V_{IN\,b}$, the term in parentheses in the equation is positive, and an ideal op amp will give an output of infinitely great positive voltage. If $V_{IN\,b}$ is greater than $V_{IN\,a}$, the term in parentheses is negative, and an ideal op amp will give an output of infinitely great negative voltage. Actually, the output is limited by the supply voltage and the internal circuitry of the op amp to about 1 V less than the power supply, which is a value called V_{SAT}, the saturation voltage. Thus for a typical ±15-V op-amp power supply, $V_{SAT+} = 14$ V and $V_{SAT-} = -14$ V. For an op amp that has a unipolar power supply of, say, 30 V, V_{SAT+} would be about $+29$ V and V_{SAT-} would be about $+1$ V. Thus the comparator shown in Fig. 2–3 has two possible output states:

- $V_{OUT} = V_{SAT+}$ means that $V_{IN\,a}$ is greater than $V_{IN\,b}$.
- $V_{OUT} = V_{SAT-}$ means that $V_{IN\,b}$ is greater than $V_{IN\,a}$.

Figures 2–4 through 2–8 show several possible variations of comparator circuits. Figure 2–4 shows a couple of diodes and resistors added to the input of a standard comparator circuit. These components provide protection for the input circuitry of the op amp. Whenever the differential input voltage to an op amp exceeds the breakdown voltage of two base-emitter junctions in series, one or both of the input differential transistors will break down. Depending upon the amount of current that results, the IC may or may not be damaged. Since a comparator needs only a very small differential input voltage (remember A_V is very high), the use of clamping diodes to limit the differential input voltage to about ±0.6 V will not affect the operation of the circuit. The resistors have two purposes: They limit current to the diode, and they prevent loading of the circuit that feeds the comparator. Therefore, their value depends upon the output characteristics of the circuit feeding the comparator. The diodes are usually 1N914's or similar signal diodes.

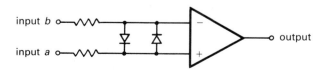

FIGURE 2–4: Comparator with Input Protection

Often a comparator is needed to indicate whether a signal is greater than or less than zero. One example of an application for such a comparator is in the *AC zero-voltage switch.* A zero-voltage switch opens or closes only when the instantaneous value of the AC line voltage is zero. In this way, large switching transients are avoided when inductive loads are switched. A comparator used to operate such an electronic switch is called a *zero-crossing detector.* Figure 2–5A shows the circuit of such a comparator. In fact, it is only a normal comparator with one input grounded. In the more general case, the fixed input could have a certain DC voltage applied, allowing comparison of the other input voltage to any chosen DC level. Such comparators are shown in Figs. 2–5B and C. By the way, comparators with two active inputs are called *differential comparators;* comparators having one input grounded or connected to a fixed reference voltage are called *single-ended* comparators.

Sometimes the signal applied to a comparator contains a substantial amount of noise. If the comparator could be made so that the output state changed only when $V_{IN\,a}$ was greater than $V_{IN\,b}$ *by a certain amount,* or vice versa, then much of the noise would be ignored. For example, if a comparator had an *upper threshold point* of 2 V and a *lower threshold point of* −2 V, then when the output was in the high state, it would remain in that state until $V_{IN\,a} - V_{IN\,b}$ equaled −2 V. In other words, short −3-V noise spikes added to a differential input voltage of 2 V would still only reach an instantaneous input voltage of −1 V, and the comparator would not switch. Such a characteristic is called *hysteresis.* In general, hysteresis can be defined as

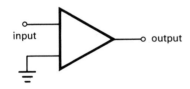

FIGURE 2–5A: Zero-Crossing Detector

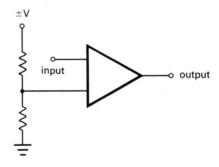

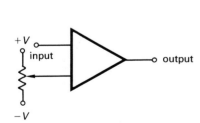

FIGURE 2–5B: Comparator with Variable
Reference Voltage

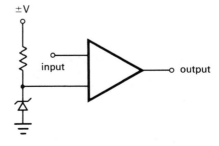

FIGURE 2–5C: Comparators with Fixed
Reference Voltages

FIGURE 2–5: Single-Ended Comparators

any characteristic in which the output depends not only on the input but also on the preceding output state. In other words, a device with hysteresis has a sort of memory.

Figure 2–6 shows a comparator with hysteresis. Its operation is fairly easy to understand. A portion of the output is fed back to the input through R_2. Since there is no phase inversion (output is fed to the noninverting (+) input), we have positive feedback. Now if power is applied to the circuit and, say, a 5 V signal is applied to input b, then the output will change to V_{SAT-}. Even with no signal applied to input a, there will be a voltage there resulting from the feedback. This voltage will be

$$V_{IN\,a} = V_{SAT-}\left(\frac{R_1}{R_1 + R_2}\right) \tag{2.02}$$

For this circuit, the voltage would be

$$V_{IN\,a} = (-14\ V)\left(\frac{1\ k\Omega}{1\ k\Omega + 10\ k\Omega}\right) = -1.3\ V$$

Even if we remove the signal from input b, this voltage will remain. Now a signal applied at input b will have to be more negative than -1.3 V in order to cause the output to change state. A similar situation would occur if a negative voltage were first applied to input b. The resulting voltage at input a would then be $+1.3$ V, and a $V_{IN\,b}$ greater than $+1.3$ V would be required in order to switch the output states again. If input a were not grounded, but instead a signal voltage were applied to input a, both the upper and the lower threshold points would be shifted by the amount of that voltage. Thus, in general, the threshold voltages are

$$V_{threshold} = \pm V_{signal\,a} + V_{SAT}\left(\frac{R_1}{R_2}\right) \tag{2.03}$$

With this comparator, then, noise signals less than $2(1.3\ V)$ or $2.6\ V_{P-P}$ will not cause the comparator to change state. Such comparators are often used in digital circuits as input stages for devices used in electrically noisy environments. You may have heard of them under their other name, *Schmitt triggers*.

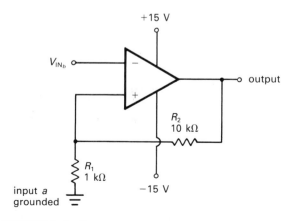

FIGURE 2–6: Comparator with Hysteresis (Schmitt Trigger)

The comparator shown in Fig. 2–6 provides a low output (V_{SAT-}) if its most recent *b* input is greater than +1.3 V. It provides a high output (V_{SAT+}) if its most recent input is more negative than −1.3 V. But it tells you nothing about signal voltages within the ±1.3 V range. This is what it was designed to do. However, sometimes a circuit is needed that indicates whether an input signal is within a certain range. For example, a certain manufacturing process might work correctly only if the temperature were between +20° and +40°C. A temperature sensor could be used to provide an output voltage proportional to temperature. Then a circuit would be needed to indicate whether that voltage were within the proper range. Such a circuit is shown in Fig. 2–7A. It is called a *window comparator* because it indicates whether the input voltage is inside the "window" formed by the upper and lower threshold voltages. As you can see, it is really two comparators with their outputs fed through diodes. If V_{IN} is greater than the upper threshold voltage, the top comparator's output will go high (V_{SAT+}). The lower comparator will go low (V_{SAT-}), but its output does not affect V_{OUT} because of diode D_2. If V_{IN} is more negative than the lower threshold voltage, the lower comparator will go high and the upper one will go low. This time, the output of the lower comparator is V_{OUT} because the output of the upper one is blocked by D_1. If V_{IN} is within the window, both comparators' outputs will be negative and the diodes will block them, so $V_{OUT} = 0$ V. In our example, V_{OUT} could be used to trigger an alarm circuit to indicate when the temperature is not in the correct range.

Figure 2–7B shows a practical window comparator circuit designed for upper and lower threshold voltages of +5 V and −3 V, respectively. The upper and lower threshold voltages are provided by voltage dividers fed by the positive and negative power supplies. The output state (either V_{SAT+} or 0 V) is indicated by the LED, whose current is limited to a safe value by a resistor. The LED will light if V_{IN} is outside the window extending from −3 to +5 V.

We must consider several things when designing op-amp comparator circuits. The first is the range of input voltages. If no op amp can be found whose maximum differential input voltage (given on the specification sheet) is greater than the maximum difference between the input signals being compared, input protection should be used, as discussed earlier. Second, if the difference between input voltages can be quite small, typically less than a volt, op amps having small offset voltages must be used. Third, if the output from the comparator is to be used to drive logic circuitry, V_{OUT} will need to be clamped to the proper voltage range for the logic family being used. Figure 2–8 shows an example of a comparator designed for output voltages of approximately 0 V or +4.5 V to work with TTL circuits. The 1N914 diode is biased at +0.6 V, keeping the output at or above 0 V. The Zener limits the positive output to +4.5 V. Fourth, if the comparator must change output states rapidly, the op amp must have sufficient slew rate. For example, an op amp with a slew rate of 1 V/μs would require 28 μs to change from V_{SAT+} to V_{SAT-} or vice versa, assuming a ±15 V supply.

For critical applications, there are ICs specifically designed for use as comparators. A specification sheet for an LM1414 comparator is given in Appendix A.

In many applications, the output of a comparator is used directly to drive an LED. Less frequently, it drives a relay to switch some device that draws a high

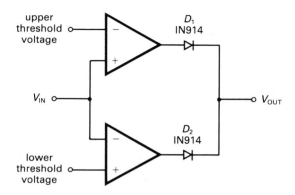

FIGURE 2–7A: Basic Circuit

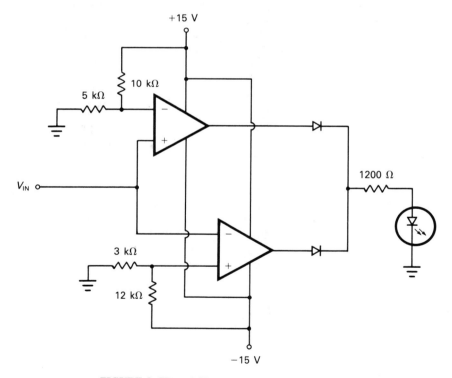

FIGURE 2–7B: −3-V to +5-V Window Comparator

FIGURE 2–7: Window Comparators

current or which must be electrically isolated from the comparator. In both of these applications, the maximum output-current capability of the comparator must be taken into account. Typical IC op amps have maximum output currents ranging from 4 to 20 mA, although there are high-current devices available that handle much larger currents. The brightness of an LED depends upon its current. Most LEDs require

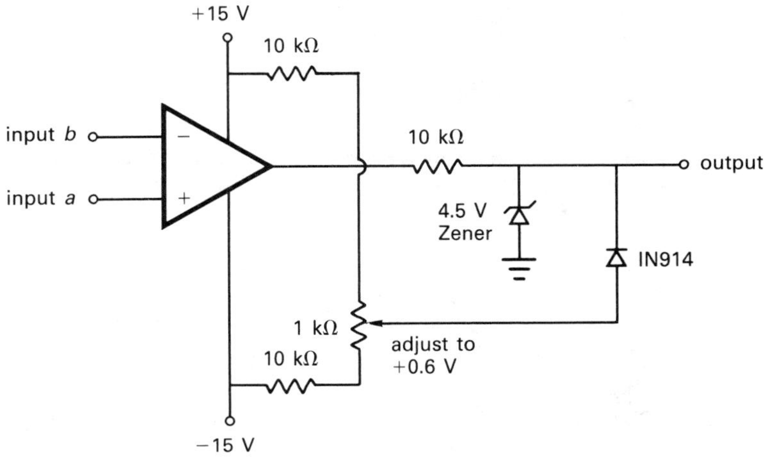

FIGURE 2–8: Comparator with TTL-Compatible Output

about 10 mA in order to be easily visible in normal room light. Maximum current for an LED varies from about 10 mA for a miniature unit to 50 mA for a large one. Therefore, when an LED is used with a comparator, a series resistor must be used to limit its current to a value that is safe for both the LED and the op amp.

EXAMPLE

Problem

Design a comparator to drive an LED with a current of 10 mA.

Solution

(See Fig. 2–7.) The maximum output voltage of the comparator is V_{SAT+}, which is about 14 V. Most LEDs require a forward bias of about 1.7 V. Therefore, the value of the current-limiting resistor is

$$R_{CL} = \frac{14 \text{ V} - 1.7 \text{ V}}{10 \text{ mA}} = 1230 \text{ } \Omega$$

We would use a 1200-Ω resistor.

Using an op amp to drive a relay is a more complex design problem and will be dealt with in Chapter 4.

ADVANCE IN HYBRID IC MANUFACTURE

Traditionally, hybrid ICs have been made from slabs of ceramic with conductors and resistors deposited on them by thick-film vacuum deposition. Then discrete capacitors and semiconductors were soldered onto them. It has been impractical to incorporate capacitors in the thick-film man-

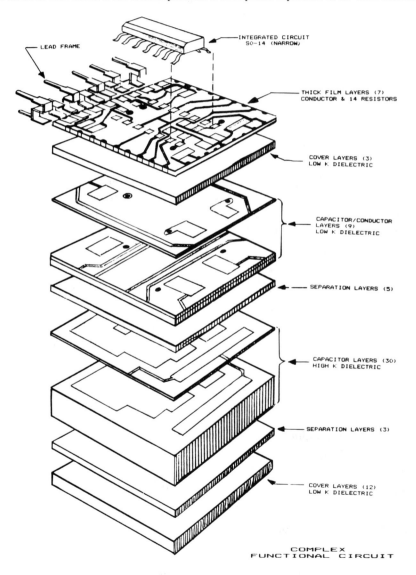

Sidebar

(continued)

(continued from page 48)

(continued from page 48)

ufacturing process. However, in recent years, multilayer ceramic capacitors have been manufactured as individual components using a process very similar to that used in making hybrid ICs. In 1986, Sprague developed a process for combining multilayer ceramic capacitors with the manufacture of hybrid ICs. Dubbed the "Multilythic®" process, this system incorporates a number of ceramic layers of differing dielectric constant, each with its own conductor pattern, as shown at left. The drawings below and on page 50 show an audio amplifier circuit and screens from which the various ceramic layers are fabricated. (Courtesy of Sprague Electric Co.)

The drawings below and on page 50 show an audio amplifier circuit

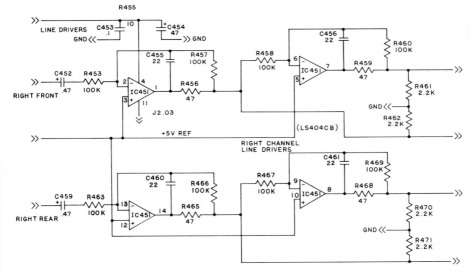

Dwg. No. A-14,302

(continued from page 49)

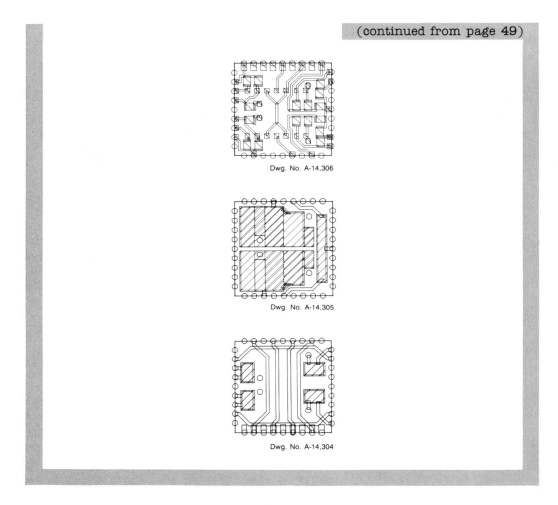

Dwg. No. A-14,306

Dwg. No. A-14,305

Dwg. No. A-14,304

Analog-to-Digital Flash Converters

The step from a window comparator to an analog-to-digital (A/D) converter is a small one. A window comparator is a device that indicates whether the input signal is within a certain voltage "window." An A/D converter indicates which of several possible windows the input signal falls within. Figure 2–9 shows an A/D converter made of five stacked window comparators. It operates as follows. The input voltage is applied simultaneously to all the op amps' inverting inputs. Each op amp acts as a simple comparator and decides whether the input voltage is greater than its reference voltage. The reference voltage is 1 V for op amp A_1, 2 V for A_2, and so on. For example, an input voltage of 3.8 V to this circuit would make the signal at the inverting input greater than the reference signal for amplifiers A_1, A_2, and A_3, but the reference signal would be larger for A_4 and A_5. Therefore the lower three LEDs would be lighted, indicating 3 V. Thus by counting the number of LEDs that are lighted, we can determine the input voltage with a resolution of 1 V. In a practical

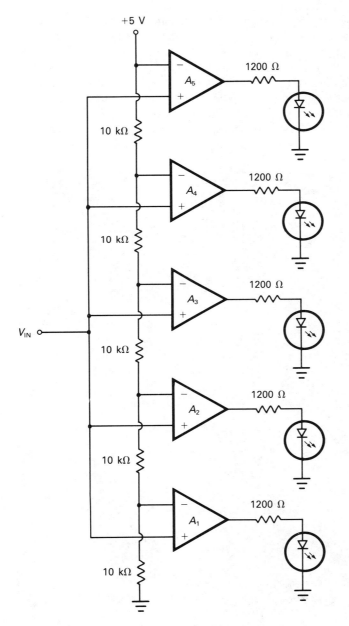

FIGURE 2–9: Five-State Flash Converter

circuit, the output of this type of A/D converter would be applied to a binary adder, producing a binary number equal to the input voltage value. This binary value can then be converted to BCD and displayed on an LED array or manipulated in any other way necessary. A/D and D/A converters are discussed in more detail in Chapter 9.

Because the conversion of analog values to digital numbers by this type of circuit is so fast (limited only by the slew rate of the op amps), this circuit is called a *flash converter*. The advantage of the great speed of a flash converter is offset by the large number of op amps required to build a practical one. A flash converter that would convert voltages within a 100:1 range with one-digit resolution would require 100 op amps. (In other words, in order to make a digital voltmeter that would measure voltages in the range of 1 to 100 V, in 1-V increments, you would need 100 op amps.) Nevertheless, the speed of flash converters makes them the only choice for some high-speed applications. Figure 2–10 shows a commercially produced high-

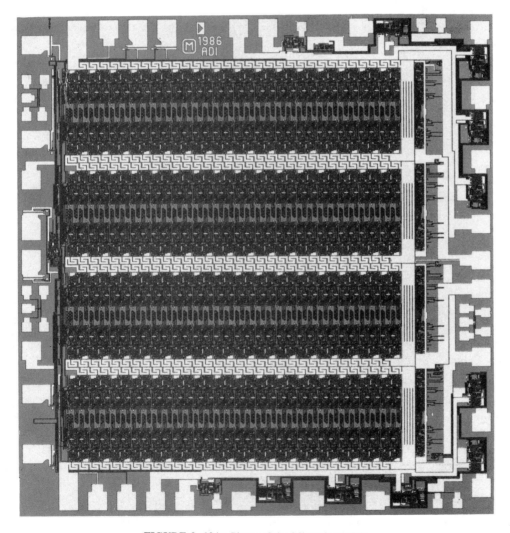

FIGURE 2–10A: Photo of the Microcircuit Die

FIGURE 2–10: High-Speed Flash Converter *(Photo Courtesy of Analog Devices, Inc.)*

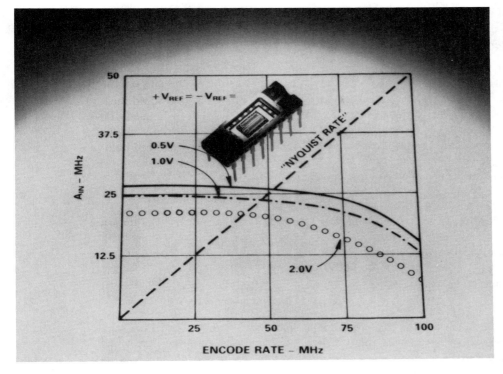

FIGURE 2–10B: The AD9000 6-bit, 75-MHz Flash Converter and its Specifications

speed flash converter mounted in a 16-pin dual-in-line package. This particular circuit will convert a voltage level to a digital value in 2 ns.

Inverting Amplifier

Probably the most obvious application of an op amp is an amplifier! However, some external circuitry is needed to make an op amp into a usable amplifier, so we discussed comparators first, since a comparator can be made of an op amp by itself. Now that you're comfortable with op-amp operation, we can move on to amplifier circuits. All practical amplifier circuits using op amps involve feedback. As mentioned in Chapter 1, there are two kinds of feedback: positive and negative. When a portion of the output signal of an amplifier is fed back to the input in phase with the original input signal, you have positive feedback. If the portion of the output that is fed back is out of phase with the original input signal, you have negative feedback. Positive feedback is used primarily in waveform-generating circuits. Negative feedback is the variety most commonly used in amplifiers.

Negative feedback is used to:

1. Set the gain of an amplifier
2. Control frequency response

3. Control the voltage transfer characteristic
4. Make the circuit's performance independent of individual component characteristics

The first two uses are self-explanatory, but the last two probably require a bit of explanation. The voltage transfer characteristic is the relation of input voltage to output voltage for a circuit. It can be expressed by an equation or by a graph. Figure 2–11 shows several voltage transfer characteristics. Graph A is the voltage transfer characteristic of a voltage divider. The output voltage is a fraction of the input. Graph B is the transfer characteristic of an amplifier. The output voltage is a multiple of the input voltage. Both of these are *linear transfer characteristics:* the output voltage is a linear function of the input voltage. They can be expressed by the equation

$$V_{OUT} = kV_{IN}$$

For the voltage divider, the attenuation k is a number less than unity. For the amplifier, k is the gain and is a number greater than unity. Graph C is the transfer characteristic of a limiting amplifier, which has one gain for input voltages below the threshold and a lower gain (often unity) for input voltages above the threshold. This is a *piecewise-linear transfer characteristic*. It can be expressed by the equation

$$V_{OUT} = mV_{IN},$$

where m = one value for small input voltages and another value for larger input voltages. Graph D is the transfer characteristic of a compression amplifier, which has a gain that decreases smoothly as the input voltage increases. Graph E is the

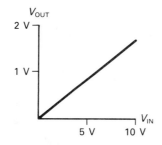

FIGURE 2–11A: Voltage Divider

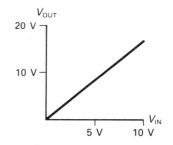

FIGURE 2–11B: Amplifier

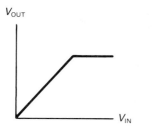

FIGURE 2–11C: Limiting Amplifier

FIGURE 2–11D: Compression Amplifier

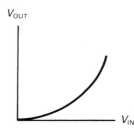

FIGURE 2–11E: Expander

FIGURE 2–11: Voltage Transfer Characteristics for Several Types of Circuits

transfer characteristic of an expander, which has a gain that increases smoothly as the input increases. Graphs D and E are *nonlinear transfer characteristics*. They can be expressed by the equation

$$V_{\text{OUT}} = gV_{\text{IN}},$$

where g is a function of V_{IN}. Feedback can be used to create piecewise-linear and nonlinear transfer characteristics, as will be discussed in Chapter 9.

When an engineer designs a circuit, he or she wants it to work when built from standard parts. For example, if a 2N2222 transistor is specified, the circuit must work correctly with *any* 2N2222; the person building the circuit should not have to carefully select a 2N2222 whose gain is exactly right. Likewise, when a circuit uses an op amp, variations among the gains of different op amps should not change the way the circuit works. By using feedback to control the gain, we can prevent differences among various op amps (of the same type number) from seriously affecting the performance of the completed circuit. In other words, the circuit performance can be made largely independent of the individual components' characteristics.

There are two basic kinds of op-amp amplifier circuits: the inverting amplifier and the noninverting amplifier. These names are used because the output of the inverting amplifier is 180° out of phase with its input—it is *inverted* compared to the input—whereas the noninverting amplifier's output is not inverted. Each type of amplifier has advantages for certain applications, so we will discuss both. We will start with inverting amplifiers. Figure 2–12 shows the circuit for an op amp used as an inverting amplifier. This amplifier's feedback connection is of the voltage-shunt type discussed in Chapter 1. Therefore the equations for voltage gain, input impedance, and output impedance are as follows:

$$A_{\text{cl}} = \frac{A_{\text{ol}}}{1 + \beta A_{\text{ol}}} \tag{1.17}$$

$$Z_{\text{I}} = \frac{R_{\text{i}}}{1 + \beta A_{\text{ol}}} \tag{1.18}$$

$$Z_{\text{OUT}} = \frac{R_{\text{o}}}{1 + \beta A_{\text{ol}}} \tag{from 1.15}$$

The input resistor R_{i} in the inverting amplifier has two purposes: it acts as a part of the feedback network, and it converts the input voltage into a current. (Remember that the voltage-shunt feedback amplifier is a current-controlled voltage source.)

The operation of the inverting amplifier can be easily understood. First, any voltage applied at the input will produce a voltage of the opposite polarity at the output. This opposite-polarity voltage will be fed back to the input, and if the gain of the op amp is infinite it will cancel out all but an infinitesimal part of the input voltage. Another way of saying this is that an op amp with negative feedback varies its output voltage as required to keep its inputs at equal voltages. Since the noninverting input is grounded (zero volts), the inverting input will also be kept at zero volts by the portion of the output voltage that is fed through the feedback loop. Now any point whose input current can be varied but whose voltage always remains zero

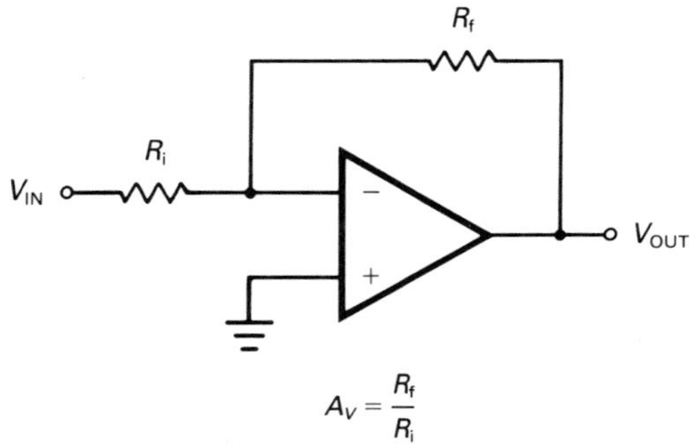

$$A_v = \frac{R_f}{R_i}$$

FIGURE 2–12: Inverting Amplifier Circuit

must have zero impedance to ground. Therefore, the inverting input of the op amp connected as in Fig. 2–12 is called a *zero-impedance point* or a *virtual ground*. We can verify this mathematically by evaluating equation 1.18 with A_{ol} set equal to infinity:

$$Z_{IN} = \frac{R_{in}}{1 + \beta \cdot \infty} = 0 \ \Omega$$

Notice carefully that this is the input impedance at the *inverting input to the op amp*, not at the point marked V_{IN} in Fig. 2–12.

Second, you must remember that the output impedance of the op amp is assumed to be 0 Ω. This means that the output is an ideal voltage source, from the point of view of the input. Also, the Thevenin impedance of the signal source is strictly included in the value of R_i (more on this later), so from the point of view of the output the signal source is an ideal voltage source. Since, as shown by equation 1.15, voltage-shunt feedback reduces output impedance by the factor $1/(1 + \beta A_{ol})$, any small output impedance presented by the op amp itself is reduced to an even smaller value.

Third, according to the superposition principle, at any given point the net voltage to ground resulting from two voltage sources is the sum of voltages that would result from each source considered independently, with the other source replaced by its internal resistance. This gives us the equivalent circuit of Fig. 2–13A for V_{ii}, the voltage produced at the op-amp input by the signal source. Mathematically, then,

$$V_{ii} = \frac{V_{IN}R_f}{R_i + R_f} \tag{2.04}$$

Figure 2–13B shows the equivalent circuit for figuring V_{io}, the voltage produced at the op-amp inverting input by the op amp output voltage.

$$V_{io} = \frac{V_{OUT}R_i}{R_i + R_f} \tag{2.05}$$

Since the output voltage is 180° out of phase with the input voltage, if the magnitudes of V_{ii} and V_{io} are equal they will cancel each other, and the net voltage at the inverting input will be zero. (Specifically, the voltage *difference* is zero between the inverting and noninverting inputs. With the noninverting input grounded, this means zero volt-age-to-ground at the inverting input.)

$$\frac{V_{IN}R_f}{R_i + R_f} = \frac{V_{OUT}R_i}{R_i + R_f} \tag{2.06}$$

Solving for the gain, which is just V_{OUT}/V_{IN}, we have

$$A_V = \frac{V_{OUT}}{V_{IN}} = \frac{R_f}{R_i} \tag{2.07}$$

From Chapter 1, recall that β for the voltage-shunt feedback amplifier is I_f/V_{OUT}. Therefore, if we consider β_V, a corresponding voltage-feedback ratio, it would be

$$\beta_V = \frac{V_f}{V_{OUT}} = \frac{I_fR_i}{V_{OUT}}$$

Now, as you may have noticed, V_f is just the same quantity we have been calling V_{io}, so from equation 2.05 we have

$$V_{io} = V_f = \beta_V V_{OUT} = \frac{V_{OUT}R_i}{R_f + R_i}$$

Canceling V_{OUT}, we have

$$\beta_V = \frac{R_i}{R_f + R_i} \tag{2.08}$$

It was mentioned earlier that the value of R_i must include the Thevenin imped-ance of the signal source. In practice, this is often overlooked, since the resistor called R_i is usually much larger than the Thevenin impedance of the source. In cases where this is not true, or where the Thevenin impedance of the source varies with frequency, its value will have to be taken into account in the gain equation.

There are some applications in which gain is not needed but signal inversion is. For these applications, an inverting amplifier can be used, with R_f set equal to R_i. Then the gain is unity. Such a circuit is called an *inverting voltage follower*.

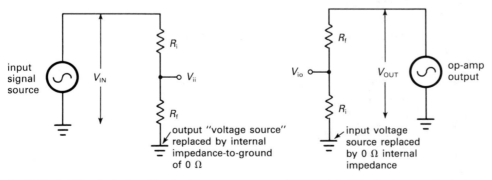

FIGURE 2–13A: Equivalent Circuit of Inverting Amplifier from Input Side

FIGURE 2–13B: Equivalent Circuit from Output Side

FIGURE 2–13: Equivalent Circuits of Op-Amp Inverting Amplifier

Since the inverting input is a virtual ground, the input impedance of the inverting amplifier circuit is just the resistor R_i. As you know, the input impedance of an amplifier is important for determining several things; among them are the types of signal sources it will work with and the sizes of coupling capacitors for a specified low-frequency cutoff. With transistor circuits this calculation involved β, $r_{e'}$, the emitter resistor, and the bias resistors. For the inverting op-amp circuit, as you have seen, the situation is much simpler. In fact, we usually begin the design of an inverting amplifier by setting R_i equal to the desired input impedance. Then R_f is calculated for the correct gain.

The selection of an op amp for the inverting amplifier will be discussed more fully in Chapter 3. However, there are a few points that you need to be aware of now, so that the circuits you design will work with any op amp. First, although most op amps have output impedances from 10 to 100 Ω, they are not able to drive loads of anywhere near that low an impedance, because of the limited output-current capabilities of most op amps. Typically an op amp can supply about 10 to 15 mA of peak output current. Since the peak output voltage is V_{SAT} (typically 14 V or so), this means that the lowest load impedance that can safely be driven is 14 V/10 mA = 1400 Ω. If a lower load resistance is connected, the op amp will have a distorted output because of internal current limiting; if the op amp does not have internal current limiting, it may overheat and be destroyed.

Second, the high-frequency response of an op-amp circuit depends upon several things, which will be discussed more fully in Chapter 3. For now, if you keep A_V no greater than 100 for each stage and don't expect your upper-frequency cutoff to extend beyond 10 kHz, you'll not be disappointed.

Third, because of the extremely high open-loop gain of an op amp, you must be very careful with circuit layout: keep connecting leads short, make good connections, and keep input and output leads separated. The penalty for poor layout is that your carefully designed amplifier may become a high-frequency oscillator instead. The high open-loop gain also requires that the power supply be firmly kept at AC ground (no signal voltages on the power-supply leads). The electrolytic capacitors used for power-supply filters do not work well at frequencies above 1 kHz. Also the small inductances and resistances in the leads themselves can cause problems. The solution to these ills is decoupling capacitors from positive supply to ground and from negative supply to ground. These capacitors should be located on the circuit board or breadboard itself. They should be polyester or ceramic capacitors with a value between 0.1 and 1 μF.

Fourth, for two reasons that will be discussed in Chapter 3, you should not plan on using an R_i greater than 10 kΩ.

EXAMPLE

Problem

Design an inverting amplifier with an input impedance of 2.5 kΩ and a gain of 80.

Solution

Since $Z_{IN} = 2.5$ kΩ, we will choose the next larger standard 5% resistor value for R_i. This makes $R_i = 2.7$ kΩ. If we solve equation 2.07 for R_f, we have

$$R_f = A_V R_i$$
$$= (80)(2.7 \text{ k}\Omega) = 216 \text{ k}\Omega$$

The nearest standard value is 220 kΩ, which will give us a gain of 81.48, which is pretty close to the design value. If a more exact result is required, we can use precision resistors.

Inverting Summer

The above heading is not the title of some avant-garde beach novel. Perhaps the full name, *inverting summing amplifier*, would be clearer. At any rate, a summing amplifier, or summer, is just an amplifier that adds several different analog signals linearly. A familiar example is an audio mixer, with which a sound technician blends the signals from several different microphones before they are fed to a recorder in a studio or to a power amplifier for a concert. This linear addition is not the same as the nonlinear mixing that occurs in a superheterodyne radio receiver, even though both processes are sometimes called *mixing*. Nonlinear mixing is really amplitude modulation, and it produces additional frequencies that were not in the original signals. What we're talking about here is the linear process, in which the output signal is the linear addition of the two input signals. Figure 2–14 shows a block diagram of a linear summing circuit.

One important characteristic of any linear summing circuit is the isolation between inputs. This refers to the extent to which the signal denoted as V_1 in Fig. 2–14 is prevented from bleeding back into the V_2 input line, and vice versa. Isolation is often expressed in dB. The signal that bleeds from one input to another is called *crosstalk*.

EXAMPLE

Problem

A summing amplifier has input isolation of −68 dB. If V_{IN_1} and V_{IN_2} each equal 2 V, what is the signal voltage or crosstalk from input 1 that leaks into input 2?

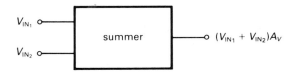

FIGURE 2–14: Block Diagram of a Linear Summing Circuit

Solution

Recall that dB is a logarithmic representation of a ratio:

$$\text{ratio in dB} = 10 \log_{10}(\text{power ratio}) = 20 \log_{10}(\text{voltage ratio}).$$

Therefore, first, change -68 dB to a ratio:

$$\text{voltage ratio} = \text{antilog}_{10}\left(\frac{-68 \text{ dB}}{20}\right) = \text{antilog}_{10}(-3.4) = 0.004$$

Second, multiply the input voltage by the ratio: (2 V)(0.004) = 0.8 mV.

If you need a review of dB calculations, refer to Appendix B.

Figure 2–15 shows an op amp connected as an inverting summer. Its output is given mathematically as

$$V_{\text{OUT}} = -(V_{\text{IN}_1}A_{V_1} + V_{\text{IN}_2}A_{V_2}) \qquad (2.09)$$

Notice from the equation that each signal may have a different voltage gain. That occurs because the gain from input 1 is R_f/R_{i_1} and the gain from input 2 is R_f/R_{i_2}. We can make a very simple audio mixer in this way by simply using potentiometers for the R_i's. Figure 2–16 shows an example. The 10-kΩ resistors in series with the potentiometers prevent the input impedance from falling too low, and they also set a maximum value on the gain from any input.

The circuit in Fig. 2–16 has four inputs. There is no practical limit to the number of signals that may be summed in an inverting summer. And since each signal creates an independent term in the equation for V_{OUT}, there is no interaction between individual signal gains. The isolation between inputs is theoretically infinite, since the inverting input of the op amp (the *summing point*) is a virtual ground. Another way this is often stated is that the inverting summer has a *summing-point impedance* of zero. You've probably studied enough electronics to know that quantities of zero and infinity are only approximations, and that is true in this case also. But nevertheless the summing-point impedance of an inverting summer is very low, and therefore the input isolation is very good.

Another application for summing circuits is amplifying and setting the DC level of measurement circuits. For example, if a temperature sensor is used to provide a

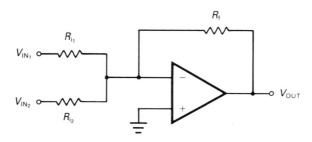

FIGURE 2–15: Op Amp Inverting Summer

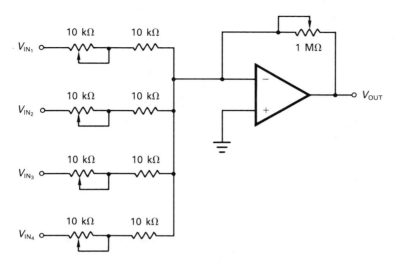

FIGURE 2–16: Simple Audio Mixer

voltage output proportional to temperature, that output may need to be converted to a specific number of millivolts per degree, and the DC level might have to be changed. The conversion to the correct number of millivolts per degree is an amplification function, and the addition of the DC level is an *offsetting* function. Both functions can be performed by a single summing circuit.

EXAMPLE

Problem

Design an inverting summer for use in a temperature-sensing system to provide an output of 10 mV/°F. The temperature sensor to be used provides an output voltage of 300 μV/°C and has an offset voltage of 1.3 V at 0°C. The recommended minimum load impedance into which the sensor should work is 2 kΩ.

Solution

1. $1°F = \frac{5}{9}(°C)$. Therefore, $10\ mV/°F = \frac{9}{5}(10\ mV)/°C = 18\ mV/°C$. The gain is therefore

$$\frac{V_{OUT}}{V_{IN}} = \frac{18\ mV/°C}{0.30\ mV/°C} \simeq 60$$

2. Since R_{IN} must be no less than 2 kΩ, we will let $R_{i_1} = 2.2\ kΩ$, which is the nearest higher standard 5% value.

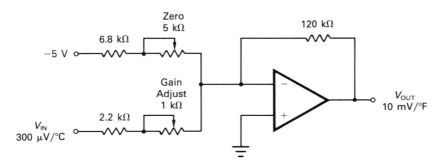

FIGURE 2–17: Summing Circuit for Temperature Sensor

3. R_f must then be $R_{i_2}A_V = (2.2 \text{ k}\Omega)(60) = 132 \text{ k}\Omega$. We could use a precision resistor, but our design work will be much easier, and the resulting circuit more versatile, if we use a 120-kΩ resistor and add a 1-kΩ trimmer potentiometer in series with R_{i_1}. This would probably be a practical necessity anyway, since measurement circuits usually need to be quite accurate, and the sensor itself may vary somewhat from the specified output value. Therefore adding this *calibrating potentiometer* will make things better all around.

4. Our remaining task is to provide offsetting for the output. When the sensor is at 0°C, it will put out 1.3 V. This means that without offsetting, the summer's output would be $(1.3 \text{ V})(60) = 78$ V when the sensor is at 0°C, if it could. (Of course, the output would be limited to $V_{\text{SAT+}}$.) We have two possible ways of canceling out this offset voltage. The first is to use the same value of resistor for R_{i_2} as we used for R_{i_1} and apply a -1.3-V reference to input 2 of the summer. It makes much more sense to use a readily available voltage for our reference and adjust the gain accordingly by proper choice of R_{i_2}. Since -5 V is easily generated by a Zener diode and a resistor, we will choose -5 V as the reference voltage. (The voltage must be negative in order to cancel out a positive offset voltage.) We want to generate a theoretical output voltage of -78 V, so the necessary gain is -78 V$/-5$ V $= 15.6$. Since $R_f = 120$ kΩ, this calls for $R_{i_2} = 120 \text{ k}\Omega/15.6 = 7.7$ kΩ. We will use a 6.8-kΩ resistor and a 5-kΩ *zeroing potentiometer*. The complete circuit is shown in Fig. 2–17. As an exercise, calculate the output voltages for -30°C, $+20$°C, and $+70$°C.

Noninverting Amplifier

Figure 2–18 shows the circuit of a noninverting amplifier. The gain of this circuit can be derived as follows. The portion of the output that is fed back to the inverting input is

$$V_{i-} = \frac{V_{\text{OUT}}R_g}{R_f + R_g}$$

according to the voltage-divider rule. Since $V_{\text{OUT}} = A_V V_{\text{IN}}$ (the voltage gain multiplied by the voltage at the noninverting input), we can write

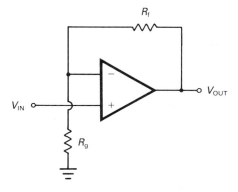

FIGURE 2–18: Noninverting Amplifier Circuit

$$V_{i-} = \frac{A_V V_{IN} R_g}{R_f + R_g}$$

By the same reasoning that we used to derive the gain of the inverting amplifier, $V_{i-} = V_{IN}$, except for an infinitesimal difference. Thus, for all practical purposes,

$$V_{IN} = \frac{A_V V_{IN} R_g}{R_f + R_g}$$

Canceling V_{IN} and solving for A_V, we get

$$A_V = \frac{R_f + R_g}{R_g} = \frac{R_f}{R_g} + 1 \qquad (2.10)$$

This amplifier uses voltage-series feedback, so by comparing equation 2.10 with equation 1.07 and allowing $A_{V_{ol}}$ to approach infinity, we can find β:

$$A_{V_{cl}} = \frac{A_{V_{ol}}}{1 + \beta A_{V_{ol}}} \qquad (1.07)$$

As $A_{V_{ol}}$ approaches infinity,

$$A_{V_{cl}} = \frac{1}{\beta} = \left(\frac{R_f}{R_g} + 1 \right)^{-1} = \left(\frac{R_f + R_g}{R_g} \right)^{-1}$$

Thus,

$$\beta = \frac{R_f + R_g}{R_g} \qquad (2.11)$$

At first glance, you might expect that the input impedance of a noninverting op-amp circuit would just be the input resistance of the op amp itself. Actually, this is not the case. Theoretically the input impedance is greater than the op-amp input resistance by a factor of $A_{V_{ol}}/(1 + A_{V_{ol}}\beta)$. For an op amp whose input resistance is 500 kΩ and whose $A_{V_{ol}}$ is 300,000 (fairly typical values), the calculated input impedance of a circuit in which $A_V = 1000$ (that is, $\beta = 0.001$) would be 0.5 GΩ! The measured value would not be that high; after all, 1.5 GΩ is pretty good insulation! Typically the op amp in a circuit might have a measured Z_{IN} of 10 MΩ or so. Usually, when input impedances are this high, their exact value is of no great importance, so it is usually good enough to say that the input impedance of a noninverting amplifier is always greater than the specified input resistance of the op amp itself, and that the input impedance rises as the closed-loop gain is reduced. For reasons that we'll see in Chapter 3, there are limitations to the maximum useful input impedance of a real-world op-amp circuit.

Many times, an electronic circuit that has no voltage gain but that converts impedances is required. One example is an amplifier for use with a piezoelectric transducer. A *piezoelectric* device is one that works because some materials flex when an electric field is applied across them, or produce a voltage difference if flexed. A *transducer* is a device that changes energy from one form to another. Thus, a microphone is a transducer; so is a loudspeaker. A crystal microphone is one type of piezoelectric transducer: it changes acoustical energy to electrical energy. All piezoelectric materials are insulators, and therefore their internal impedances (Thevenin impedances) are very high. If a source with a high internal impedance is connected to a low-impedance amplifier, much of the voltage is lost across the internal impedance. With piezoelectric transducers, the internal impedance not only is high, but it varies inversely with frequency. So if you connect one of these devices to a low-input-impedance amplifier, the signal reaching the amplifier will be small and the low frequencies will be weak. Typically, an amplifier with an input impedance of at least a megohm is needed. A noninverting op-amp circuit works well in this application. If no gain is needed, a noninverting voltage follower can be used. This is just a noninverting amplifier with R_f set equal to 0 Ω. The gain of such a circuit is unity. Figure 2–19 shows a noninverting voltage follower. The resistor from the noninverting input to ground is needed to provide a path for bias current from the input transistors of the op amp. (Chapter 3 will cover bias-current effects in much more detail.) The input impedance of the noninverting voltage follower is theoretically infinite, but the need for the bias resistor makes the input impedance essentially equal to the value of that resistor. The impedance-changing effect (high Z_{IN}, low Z_{OUT}) combined with unity voltage gain allows this circuit to function effectively as a *buffer amplifier*, which isolates a circuit from the effects of a load.

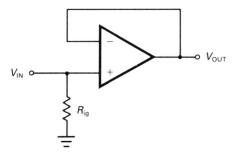

FIGURE 2–19: Noninverting Voltage Follower

Noninverting Summer

The noninverting summer does pretty much the same thing that the inverting summer does: It provides an output that is the linear sum of its input voltages, perhaps with some gain thrown in. The circuit of a noninverting summer is shown in Fig. 2–20. Although this circuit is occasionally used, it possesses two distinct disadvantages compared to the inverting summer. The first is that the gain equation is more complex and does not easily allow the gains from each input to be adjusted independently. We can derive the gain by assuming that each source has its Thevenin resistance included in the value of its associated input resistance (R_1 or R_2). Then the voltage appearing at the noninverting input of the op amp from V_{IN_1} is (by the voltage-divider rule)

$$V_{i_1} = V_{IN_1} \frac{R_2}{R_1 + R_2}$$

Likewise, the voltage at the noninverting input from V_{IN_2} is

$$V_{i_2} = V_{IN_2} \frac{R_1}{R_1 + R_2}$$

These voltages are multiplied by the gain, $1 + (R_f/R_g)$, to give

$$V_{OUT} = -\left(1 + \frac{R_f}{R_g}\right)\left(\frac{V_{IN_1}R_2}{R_1 + R_2} + \frac{V_{IN_2}R_1}{R_1 + R_2}\right) \tag{2.12}$$

The second disadvantage of the noninverting summer is the lack of input isolation. Since the summing-point impedance of the noninverting summer is not zero, the isolation is not very high; consequently, crosstalk is a problem.

Since each source typically has a low internal resistance, the input resistance of the noninverting summer is just

$$R_{IN} = R_1 + R_2$$

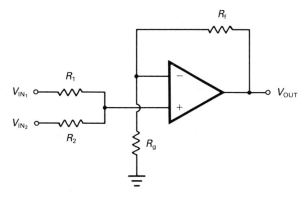

FIGURE 2–20: Noninverting Summer

So we see that we don't even have the high input impedance of a noninverting amplifier as an advantage to offset the disadvantages of this circuit.

EXAMPLE

Problem

Design a noninverting summer to mix signals from two dynamic microphones. The gain from each input to the output is to be 100. Each microphone has an internal resistance of 75 Ω. The input resistance of the summer is to be 2 kΩ. After completing the design, calculate the isolation of your circuit in dB.

Solution

1. The gain from each input is just the voltage-division ratio multiplied by the overall gain of the amplifier:

$$A_{V_1} = \left(1 + \frac{R_f}{R_g}\right)\left(\frac{R_2}{R_1 + R_2}\right)$$

$$A_{V_2} = \left(1 + \frac{R_f}{R_g}\right)\left(\frac{R_1}{R_1 + R_2}\right)$$

Since both gains are to be the same, we will make $R_1 = R_2$. In order to make the input resistance 2 kΩ, we will choose $R_1 = R_2 = 1$ kΩ.

2. The gain from each input is

$$A_{V_1} = \left(1 + \frac{R_f}{R_g}\right)\left(\frac{1 \text{ k}\Omega}{2 \text{ k}\Omega}\right) = \frac{1}{2}\left(1 + \frac{R_f}{R_g}\right)$$

Thus $1 + (R_f/R_g)$ must equal 200. For all practical purposes, we can ignore the 1 and say that $R_f/R_g = 200$. We arbitrarily choose $R_g = 470$ Ω. (Actually, it's not so arbitrary, as you'll see in Chapter 3.) This makes $R_f = (470 \ \Omega)(200) = 94$ kΩ. The closest standard 10% value is 100 kΩ. The design is now complete.

3. The crosstalk at input 2 from a signal at input 1 will be the voltage at the noninverting input of the op amp multiplied by the voltage-divider ratio $R_{\text{Thevenin 1}}/(R_{\text{Thevenin 1}} + R_1)$. For our design, this ratio works out to 75 $\Omega/(75 \ \Omega + 1$ k$\Omega) = 0.07$. Since this is a voltage ratio,

$$\text{Isolation in dB} = 20 \log_{10}(0.07) = -23 \text{ dB}$$

This is not really very good isolation. The completed design is shown in Fig. 2–21.

There are some applications in which a noninverting summing circuit is needed and in which isolation doesn't matter but parts count is critical. For these circuits, a noninverting summer would be the first choice, in spite of the greater design dif-

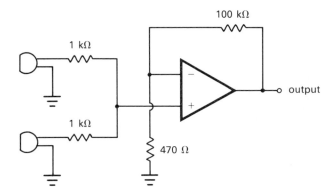

FIGURE 2–21: Two-Input Microphone Mixer

ficulty. However, for the many cases in which inversion doesn't matter, the inverting summer, with its superior isolation, is almost universally preferred. In fact, even when the inversion is a problem, an inverting summer is often used anyway, followed by an inverting voltage-follower stage.

Balanced or Differential Operation—The Instrumentation Amplifier

Recall from Chapter 1 that the output voltage of an op amp depends upon the difference between the input voltages at the noninverting(+) and inverting(−) inputs. If the op amp is used in the balanced-input mode, this feature can be used to minimize the effects of induced noise voltages. The reason for this is that the noise voltages are induced in phase and with equal magnitudes on both of the signal conductors. Therefore, there is no difference between the noise signals on the two conductors, so no noise is amplified. Applying this concept to a practical circuit requires several things. First, the op amp must have a very good common-mode rejection ratio. Since we are assuming the op amp to be ideal, this condition is met. Second, the signal conductors must be susceptible to equal induction. This means that they must be physically located in identical relationships to the source of interference, which usually implies that a twisted pair of wires is used. It also means that if one of the signal wires is shielded, the other must also be shielded. Third, the conductors and the input circuit of the amplifier must have equal complex impedances in series and from each input to ground, to avoid common-to-normal-mode conversion. This last condition requires some explanation. Consider the circuit shown in Fig. 2–22A. The signal conductors have four impedance components:

1. R_{series} is the series resistance of the conductors themselves.
2. L_{series} is the small but measurable inductance of the conductors. It is usually of concern only at high frequencies or when the wire run is very long.
3. R_{shunt} is the leakage resistance through the insulation of the wires to the cable shield, which is almost always grounded. This resistance is quite large, so its

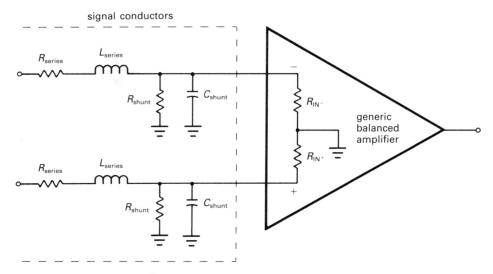

signal conductors

FIGURE 2–22A: Individual Components

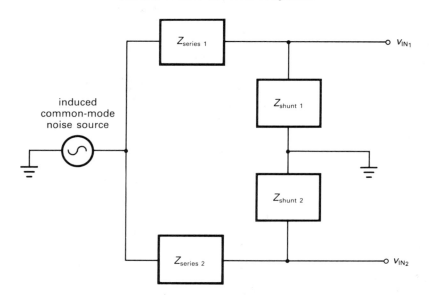

FIGURE 2–22B: Lumped Equivalent Circuit

FIGURE 2–22: Equivalent Input Circuit of a Balanced Amplifier

effect is small when modern cables are used. (Many cables in the past used "pulp" or paper insulation, whose insulation resistance was not so high, especially when moisture seeped in between the conductors and the shield. For these cables, some of which are still in use, R_{shunt} cannot always be ignored.)

4. C_{shunt} is the capacitance between the conductors and the cable shield. This capacitance can be considerable, ranging from about 10 pF/ft upward.

In addition to the series and shunt impedances of the signal conductors, the amplifier input impedance forms another shunt impedance. (Since Z_{IN} is primarily resistive, it is shown in the figure as the resistance R_{IN}.) Figure 2–22B shows the result of lumping together these complex impedances. The voltage v_{IN_1} equals the noise voltage v_n multiplied by the voltage divider ratio:

$$v_{IN_1} = v_n \left(\frac{Z_{\text{shunt } 1}}{Z_{\text{series } 1} + Z_{\text{shunt } 1}} \right)$$

Likewise,

$$v_{IN_2} = v_n \left(\frac{Z_{\text{shunt } 2}}{Z_{\text{series } 2} + Z_{\text{shunt } 2}} \right)$$

As you can see from the equations, unless $Z_{\text{shunt } 1} = Z_{\text{shunt } 2}$ and $Z_{\text{series } 1} = Z_{\text{series } 2}$, v_{IN_1} will not equal v_{IN_2}, and some noise will be amplified. Only if the respective shunt and series impedances are equal on both sides of the signal path will the common-mode noise be completely canceled out. Any imbalance will cause some of the common-mode noise to be converted to normal-mode noise, which will be amplified along with the signal.

The impedance components having to do with the cable itself are not generally under our control. Cable engineers take care to design their cables so that both series and shunt balance are generally quite good. However, the input impedances of the two amplifier inputs are our concern. You can see now that we can't just use an inverting amplifier as a balanced amplifier simply by ungrounding the noninverting input and applying a signal there. There are two solutions, though. The first is shown in Fig. 2–23. In order to make the input resistance-to-ground equal for the common-mode signal, we make R_{i_1} equal to R_{i_2} and R_f equal to R_g. Now if you're thinking carefully about this, you may object that this will not result in equal resistances to ground because the inverting input is a virtual ground, making the input resistance there equal to R_{i_1}, whereas the input resistance of the noninverting input is very high, so that the input resistance there would be equal to $R_{i_2} + R_g$. However, it is feedback that makes the inverting input act as a virtual ground; the signal from that input is fed back out of phase to cancel the input voltage at that input. Since ideally no output voltage corresponding to the common-mode signal will appear, there is no out-of-phase feedback to the inverting input; so for common-mode signals, the inverting input and the noninverting input have essentially equal resistances to ground, namely, the R_{IN} of the op amp. Therefore, the input resistance to common-mode signals is just $R_{i_1} + R_f$ for the inverting input or $R_{i_2} + R_g$ for the noninverting input. If these resistors are carefully matched, common-mode rejection will be good. Assuming that the (ideal) op amp has very high common-mode rejection, the use of 1% resistors will result in a minimum CMRR of 100, which is 40 dB. Using 0.1% resistors will improve the minimum CMRR to 60 dB. Figure 2–24 shows a circuit that uses a trimmer potentiometer to improve the balance still further. Using this technique to adjust for optimum balance, we can obtain CMRRs of 100 dB or better.

With respect to normal-mode signals, the balanced amplifier behaves very much like an inverting amplifier. The gain is still R_f/R_i, R_i in this case being R_{i_1}. The input resistance is the sum of the two input resistors, which is just $2R_{i_1}$.

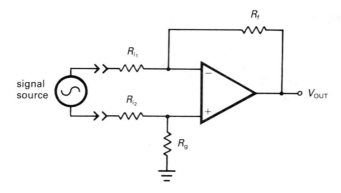

FIGURE 2–23: Balanced Amplifier

Many applications that require balanced amplifiers also require very low-noise amplification. Some op amps are specifically designed to produce a minimum of noise. Unfortunately, the very processes that reduce noise can also give a poor CMRR. In order to use such low-noise op amps and still have good balance, we can use the circuit of Fig. 2–25. It consists of two noninverting voltage followers with their outputs feeding a balanced amplifier such as we have just studied. Since the noise in a multistage amplifier is almost entirely controlled by the noise in its first stage, the use of low-noise op amps for A_1 and A_2 results in a low-noise circuit, even though the last stage uses a high-CMRR op amp rather than a low-noise one. This amplifier is most often used in test and measuring instruments and is therefore called an *instrumentation amplifier*. Since A_1 and A_2 are operated as voltage followers, they add no voltage gain, so the gain is still R_f/R_{i_1}, as in the previous case. The input resistance, however, is almost infinite, due to the use of the noninverting configuration for the follower stages. Also as before, matching of the resistor pairs controls the CMRR.

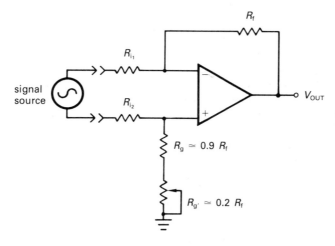

FIGURE 2–24: Balanced Amplifier with Pot for CMRR Adjustment

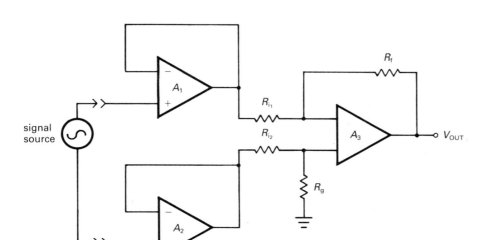

FIGURE 2–25: Instrumentation Amplifier

The ultimate in balanced amplifiers, from both noise and CMRR standpoints, is the transformer-balanced amplifier shown in Fig. 2–26. The addition of an input transformer renders the CMRR of the op amp unimportant, and the balance of a well-designed transformer is excellent. In addition, by connecting the transformer as a step-up unit, it gives some "free" voltage gain. (Impedances at the input of low-noise circuits are usually designed to be much higher than the source impedance, so a noninverting amplifier with $R_{IN} = 1$ MΩ or so can be used; add a $10:1$ step-up transformer, and you still have an input impedance of 1 M$\Omega/10^2 = 10$ kΩ. This is still higher than many sources, and you have 20 dB of noiseless voltage gain!) Chapter 3 will discuss low-noise-amplifier design in more detail.

In addition to balanced-input amplifiers, some applications require balanced-output amplifiers. One example is a line driver or *line amplifier,* which is used by

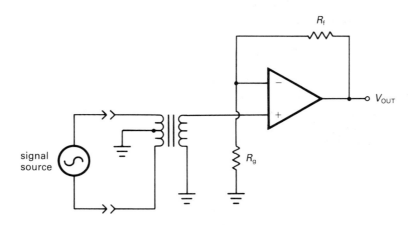

FIGURE 2–26: Transformer-Balanced Amplifier

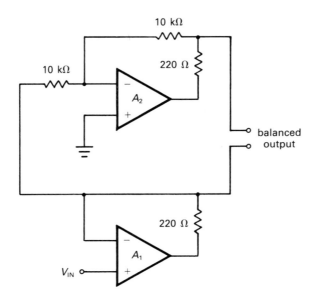

FIGURE 2–27: Balanced-Output Amplifier

radio stations to transmit audio signals over telephone lines. The telephone lines themselves are balanced, and a balanced-input amplifier must be used at the receive end of the line, but a balanced transmit amplifier is also necessary. Figure 2–27 shows the circuit of such an amplifier. Amplifier A_1 is essentially a noninverting voltage follower, and A_2 is an inverting follower. The 220-Ω resistors help keep the amplifiers stable in spite of the highly reactive load presented by long lines.

Integrators

If you have studied calculus, you know that integration is a process for summing many small slices of something. For example, the equation $Y = 2X$ specifies a particular value that Y will take for each given value of X. If this value of Y is visualized as a line extending vertically upward from the X axis and terminating at Y (in the same way as your eye would move if you were plotting the graph of $Y = 2X$), then you can qualitatively appreciate that if we added all such lines together between, say, $X = 0$ and $X = 10$, we would have the *area* under the $Y = 2X$ graph. (By *under* we mean between the graph line and the X axis, and bounded on the ends by the $X = 0$ and $X = 10$ lines.) Adding all such lines together—an infinite number of them, since they are of infinitesimal width!—is the mathematical process of *integration*. An example of a similar process in electronics comes to mind immediately. The charge on a capacitor is

$$Q = CV$$

However, if the voltage across the capacitor is not constant, then each value of voltage, applied for a certain period of time, would contribute to the final total value of Q. By integrating the equation

$$\frac{dQ}{dt} = C\,\frac{dV}{dt}$$

we will obtain the total value of Q. In this equation, dQ/dt is the small change or increment in Q that occurs in the small period of time dt during which period the change in voltage is dV. In mathematical terms, we write

$$Q = C \int_0^t \frac{dV}{dt}\,dt = C \int_0^t dV$$

where V is the instantaneous voltage.

This equation says that the total charge is the integral of the instantaneous voltage values from zero time until some time t. Alternatively, we can say that the final voltage on the capacitor is the integral of all the small changes in charge, divided by the capacitance:

$$V = \frac{1}{C} \int_0^t i\,dt$$

We indicated the "small changes in charge" as the instantaneous current, because that's just what current is.

Since this section is headed "Integrators," you have probably deduced that there is an op-amp circuit that provides the integration function; not surprisingly, it includes a capacitor. Figure 2–28 shows such a circuit. When the circuit is initially powered up, there will be no charge on the capacitor. Both inputs and the output will be zero. If a small positive DC input voltage is now applied, the output will be driven negative. But how far negative? For an input resistance R, there is an input current equal to V_{IN}/R. Since the op amp is assumed to have an infinite input impedance, no current can flow into its input. Therefore, the input current must flow into the capacitor. (We're talking about conventional current. A more precise statement would say that electrons are being removed from the capacitor plate that is connected to the inverting input.) Conventional current flowing into a capacitor will build a charge on the capacitor, causing the plate that is connected to the inverting input to tend to develop an increasingly positive voltage in accordance with the equation

$$V_C = \frac{i_{in}t}{C}$$

where t is the amount of time that the input current flows.

In order for the output to keep the voltage at the inverting input zero (it's a virtual ground), the op-amp output has to produce a negative voltage equal to the positive voltage resulting from the charging capacitor. In other words, if the capacitor has developed a voltage of 5 V at a certain instant in time, then only by making the terminal connected to the output 5 V negative can we ensure that the terminal connected to the input remains at 0 V. The output voltage of the integrator circuit is therefore

$$V_{OUT} = \frac{(V_{IN}/R)t}{C}$$

Theoretically, the output ramp voltage will continue increasing linearly as long as the constant input voltage is maintained. We know, however, that this is impossible and that the output voltage will be limited by V_{SAT+} or V_{SAT-}, depending upon the polarity of the input voltage. More generally, the input voltage does not have to remain constant; it can vary, so we must say

$$V_{OUT} = -\frac{1}{CR} \int_0^t V_{IN}(t) \, dt, \tag{2.13}$$

where $V_{IN}(t)$ is the input voltage expressed as a function of time.

Figure 2–29 shows an integrator with several different inputs and their corresponding outputs. For DC and square-wave inputs, the slope of the output wave is the negative of the input amplitude. This slope determines the amplitude of the triangle wave that results from a square-wave input, because the peak of the triangle is reached when the polarity of the square wave reverses direction. The sine-wave input produces a cosine-wave output. (A cosine wave is just a sine wave phase-shifted by 90°.) The amplitude of the sine wave depends upon the values of R and C, as discussed next. In general, a DC component is also introduced by the integrator. In calculus terms, this DC component represents the constant of integration.

It is interesting to notice that the op amp is not really providing the integrating function here; the capacitor is doing that. In fact, a series resistor followed by a shunt capacitor will also provide an integrating function. What the op amp is doing is making the integration more perfect by charging the capacitor with a constant current when the input is a constant voltage. It is this fact that causes the output voltage to take the form of a linear ramp rather than an exponential function, as it would if the capacitor were charged from a constant voltage. The comparison with a series resistor and a shunt capacitor raises an interesting question, since you have probably been introduced to this circuit as an *RC* low-pass filter. The question is, what is the frequency response of the op-amp integrator circuit? Since it is almost an inverting amplifier, we can calculate the response using the same method as for

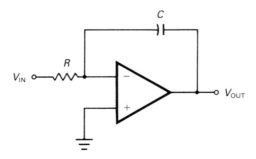

FIGURE 2–28: Op-Amp Integrator Circuit

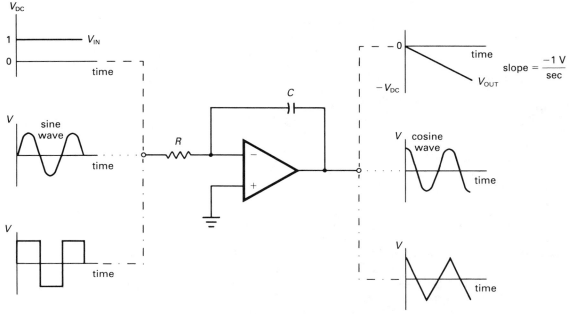

FIGURE 2–29: Op-Amp Integrator Inputs and Outputs

the inverting amplifier. For the inverting amplifier

$$A_V = \frac{R_f}{R} \qquad \text{(from 2.07, using R in place of R}_i)$$

Since the capacitor takes the place of the feedback resistor, its reactance $1/j\omega C$ will take the place of R_f in the gain equation:

$$A_V = \frac{1/j\omega C}{R} = \frac{1}{j\omega CR} \qquad \text{where } \omega = 2\pi f$$

The gain is therefore inversely proportional to frequency, making the integrator a low-pass filter, just as its passive RC counterpart is. This gain equation reveals a practical problem with our integrator circuit: It has infinite gain at zero frequency (DC). If all op amps were perfect, this would not present a problem. However, in the real world, there are slight offset currents at the inputs that produce small voltages as they flow to ground through R. With infinite gain, even a minuscule DC input voltage will produce an "infinite" output—really, V_{SAT+} or V_{SAT-}. In order to prevent the op amp from "locking up" in this fashion, a practical integrator circuit will include a feedback resistor to limit the low-frequency gain to some reasonable value, as shown in Fig. 2–30. This circuit is sometimes called an *AC integrator* because it will not maintain a steady (DC) output voltage if its DC input is removed, due to the capacitor discharging through R_f. Typically, the value of R_f is about 10 R. The gain of such an integrator equals R_f/R at low frequencies. Near the frequency at which $X_C = R_f$, the gain is 3 dB less than (0.707 times) the maximum value, and at higher frequencies the AC integrator behaves pretty much as an ideal integrator.

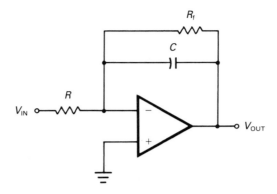

FIGURE 2–30: Practical Integrator Circuit

Comparing the op-amp integrator with the passive RC circuit raises another question. Passive RC circuits have a time constant that affects their operation. In integrator terms, we might consider this to be the time of integration; that is, the t in the limits of integration. In other words, it represents the period of time over which the input voltage is summed. This means that for the input waveform to be accurately integrated, the time constant RC must be shorter than the period of the input wave. Otherwise, the positive and negative excursions of the input wave will cancel out.

EXAMPLE

Problem

Design an integrator to convert a square wave to a triangle wave. The square-wave frequency can range from 100 Hz to 10 kHz.

Solution

The time constant of the integrator must be less than the period of the highest input frequency, so we will choose

$$RC = 0.5\left(\frac{1}{10 \text{ kHz}}\right) = 0.05 \text{ ms}$$

If we choose R as 1 kΩ, C must then equal $(0.05 \cdot 10^{-3} \text{ s})/1 \text{ k}\Omega = 0.05 \text{ }\mu\text{F}$. We then let $R_f = 10R = 10 \text{ k}\Omega$, and the design is complete.

Differentiators

Differentiation is a mathematical process for finding the rate at which a function changes. For example, if you differentiate an equation that gives the position of a falling object as a function of time, the result will be an expression that gives the velocity of the object. Velocity is just the rate at which the position changes. In a sense, differentiation is the opposite of integration. From the point of view of a graph, an equation that gives the area under a graphed line can be differentiated to give the equation for the line itself. That new equation can then be differentiated to give the expression for the slope at a specific point on the line.

An example of a circuit whose response includes differentiation is the simple RC high-pass filter in Fig. 2–31. The voltage across the resistor is

$$V_{OUT} = i_C R,$$

where i_C is the instantaneous charging current flowing into or out of the capacitor. The value of i_C is

$$i_C = C \frac{dV_{IN}}{dt},$$

where dV_{IN}/dt is the time rate of change of the input voltage. The *time rate of change* of the input voltage is also called the *derivative of V_{IN} with respect to time*. It represents pretty much the same thing as the expression $\Delta V_{IN}/\Delta t$. Thus

$$V_{OUT} = RC \frac{dV_{IN}}{dt} \qquad (2.14)$$

In qualitative terms, all this equation says is that the output voltage is directly proportional to the rate at which the input voltage changes. Since DC voltages do not change, a DC input produces no output, except when it is first applied. (The initial change from *no voltage* to *some voltage* does produce an output.) Low-frequency AC changes more slowly than high-frequency AC, so there is less output voltage for, say, a 1-V, 100-Hz input than there would be for a 1-V, 1000-Hz input.

Now, you're probably asking, where do op amps fit into all this? Well, just as the op amp makes an integrator more ideal, so does it make a differentiator more ideal. Figure 2–32 shows an op-amp differentiator. Its operation can be understood as follows. Since the input of an ideal op amp draws no current, the charging current that flows into the capacitor from the output side of the circuit must all come from the output of the op amp. This current equals $C(dV_{IN}/dt)$, as we have shown. The voltage drop across R when it carries this amount of current is

$$V_R = iR = RC \frac{dV_{IN}}{dt}$$

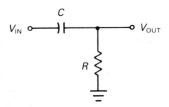

FIGURE 2–31: *RC* Passive Differentiator

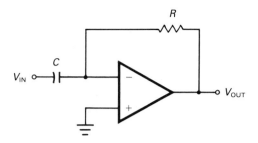

FIGURE 2–32: Op-Amp Differentiator

Since the inverting input of an op amp with negative feedback is a virtual ground, V_R must be supplied by the output of the op amp. Thus we have the same equation for the output voltage of the op-amp differentiator that we obtained for the passive RC differentiator:

$$V_{OUT} = RC \frac{dV_{IN}}{dt} \qquad (2.14)$$

Figure 2–33 shows an op-amp differentiator circuit with several inputs and their corresponding outputs. The first input shown is a sine wave, and the corresponding output is an inverted cosine wave. The amplitude of the cosine wave depends upon the values of R and C, as discussed later. The square-wave input produces a series of alternating positive and negative spikes at the output. This can be understood easily if you remember that the differentiator's output at any instant corresponds to the rate of change of the input voltage at that instant. The square wave has a very large positive rate of change as the voltage increases from zero to V_{max}, followed by a zero rate of change while the voltage is maintained at V_{max}. This produces a negative spike followed by zero output voltage. Then when the polarity reverses, there is a very large negative rate of change, producing a positive output spike, again followed by zero rate of change, yielding zero V_{OUT}. The triangle-wave input has a constant positive rate of change as the voltage increases from zero to V_{max}, then a constant negative rate of change as the voltage decreases. Consequently, the output is a constant negative voltage, then a constant positive voltage (i.e., a square wave).

Just as we noticed a resemblance between an op-amp integrator and a low-pass filter, we also notice that the op-amp differentiator is a high-pass filter. Its gain equation is given by the feedback resistance divided by the capacitive reactance:

$$A_V = \frac{R}{1/j\omega C} = j\omega RC$$

This pure high-pass characteristic introduces a problem opposite from the one encountered with the integrator. The gain of the integrator approached infinity at low frequencies and had to be limited by an additional feedback resistor. The gain of a differentiator, on the other hand, approaches infinity at high frequencies. This makes the op amp susceptible to oscillation due to stray feedback paths, some of which may have the necessary phase shift to make the feedback positive. We solve this

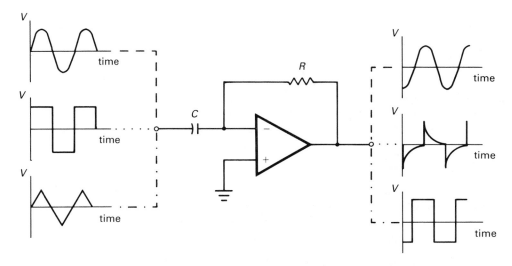

FIGURE 2–33: Op-Amp Differentiator Inputs and Outputs

problem by deliberately limiting the high-frequency gain by inserting a resistor in series with the capacitor. The maximum high-frequency gain is

$$A_V = \frac{R}{R_i}$$

The circuit is shown in Fig. 2–34.

A differentiator has a time constant, RC, just as an integrator does. For a differentiator to be effective, its time constant must be small compared to the period of the input wave.

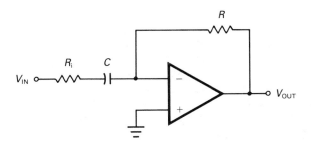

FIGURE 2–34: Practical Differentiator

DESIGN NOTES

Beginning with this chapter, most chapters will include a section called "Design Notes." This section is a condensed summary of the circuits, equations, and design methods and hints discussed in the chapter. It is not a quickie substitute for learning the material in the earlier parts of the chapter, but is a convenient guide for the student or practicing engineer or technician who understands the theory of the device to be designed and just needs a handy reference to the nuts and bolts of the design process. If you have any questions about a design that are not answered in this section, you should review the related text material in the earlier portion of the chapter.

You should know that

1. The design notes for this chapter cover only the material discussed in this chapter. The circuits will work if designed as shown. However, for an optimum design of the circuits presented here, refer to the Chapter 3 design notes.
2. All the circuits described in these pages assume the use of compensated op amps. (Compensated and uncompensated op amps will be discussed in Chapter 3. For now, just make sure the data sheet for the op amp you use says it is compensated.)

Circuits and Configurations

Comparators. The choice of an op amp for use as a comparator involves the following considerations:

1. *Resolution* (minimum difference between input voltages that the comparator must respond to accurately). If resolution smaller than 0.1 V is required, an op amp with particularly low offset voltages should be chosen. Offset voltages are discussed in detail in Chapter 3.
2. *Speed*. The response time, rise time, fall time, and slew rate are discussed in Chapter 3. In general, these must be considered in the choice of an op amp if the comparator will be required to switch at a rate greater than 10 kHz.
3. *Output current*. Must be sufficient to handle the load.

Figure 2–35 shows a comparator with input protection and output limiting. The values of the input resistors depend upon the load resistance required by the circuit or device driving the comparator. They may be made as large as 100 kΩ without ill effects. The input resistors and protection diodes can be

(continued)

(continued from page 80)

omitted in applications in which the maximum positive and negative input voltages do not exceed the supply voltages, *and* the maximum difference between the input voltages can never exceed the maximum differential input voltage given on the op-amp spec sheet (usually at least 10 V). The output limiting circuit shown provides the correct logic level voltages for interfacing the comparator with TTL logic circuits: $V_{high} = 5$ V, $V_{low} = 0$ V. We can have other values of V_{high} by choosing the appropriate Zener diode. This circuit can also be used as a zero-crossing detector if one input is grounded.

Figure 2–36 shows a comparator with bidirectional output limiting set at ±9.6 V. Again, different Zener values may be chosen for any desired positive and negative voltage values.

Figure 2–37 shows a Schmitt trigger. To design such a circuit, you need to know the desired upper and lower threshold voltages V_{ut} and V_{lt}. If the threshold voltages have the same absolute value, input *a* should be grounded. If not, calculate the required voltage to be applied at input *a*:

$$V_a = \frac{V_{ut} - V_{lt}}{2} \tag{2.15}$$

The numerator of the fraction is the algebraic difference between the threshold voltages, so the polarity sign of the voltages must be retained in the calculation. We can derive the proper voltage from the power supply, using a voltage divider. The resistors can be chosen as follows:

$$R_1 = 1 \text{ k}\Omega$$

$$R_2 = \frac{(1 \text{ k}\Omega)(V_{SAT+} - V_{ut} - V_a)}{V_{ut} - V_a} \tag{2.16}$$

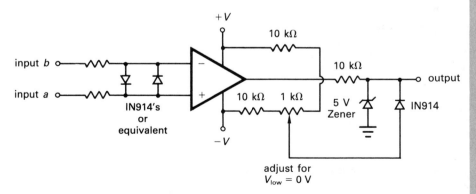

FIGURE 2–35: Comparator with Input Protection and Output Limiting

82 Chapter Two

(continued from page 81)

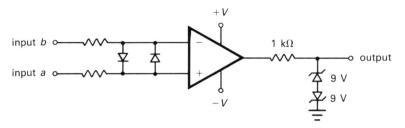

FIGURE 2–36: Comparator with Bidirectional Output Limiting

Figure 2–38 shows a flash converter. The voltage divider can most easily be designed as follows:

1. Design for 100-μA divider current so that the total resistance in the divider is $(V_{supply+} - V_{supply-})/100$ μA.
2. The value in kilohms of each resistor is just the voltage drop across that resistor multiplied by 10. For 1-V steps, 10-kΩ resistors would be used; for 0.2-V steps, 2-kΩ resistors, and so on.

The LED current-limiting resistors are not needed if the op amp is current limited. If it is not,

$$R_{lim} = \frac{V_{SAT+} - 1.7 \text{ V}}{I_{LED}}$$

The LED current I_{LED} is typically about 20 mA.

Inverting Amplifier. The choice of an op amp for use as an amplifier involves many considerations that will be discussed in Chapter 3. Applications in which just any old op amp may be used are those that meet the following conditions:

1. Noise is not a critical factor.
2. Maximum frequency to be handled is not over 20 kHz.

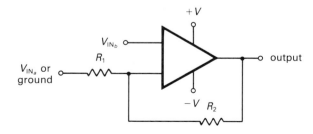

FIGURE 2–37: Schmitt Trigger

(continued from page 82)

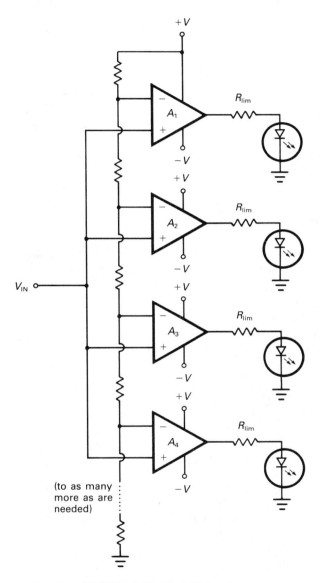

FIGURE 2–38: Flash Converter

Design
Notes

(continued from page 83)

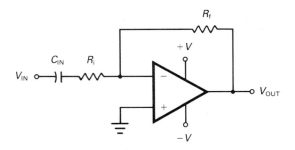

FIGURE 2–39: Inverting Amplifier

3. Maximum frequency to be handled at full output voltage is not over 10 kHz.
4. A_V is not over 100 per stage.
5. The load does not require more than 10-mA output current.
6. The required input resistance is not over 100 kΩ.

Figure 2–39 shows an inverting amplifier. It is designed by making R_i equal to the required input resistance of the circuit, then multiplying R_i by the required voltage gain to obtain the value of R_f. The input capacitor C_{IN} is needed for AC applications. At the lowest frequency of interest, C_{IN} should have a reactance equaling no more than one-tenth of R_i.

For an inverting voltage follower, make R_f equal to R_i.

Inverting Summer. The considerations involved in choosing an op amp for use in an inverting summer are the same as those discussed in the section on the inverting amplifier. Figure 2–40 shows an inverting summer. The design proceeds as follows:

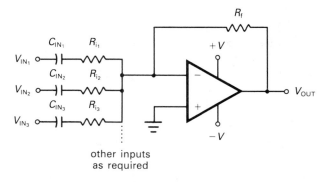

other inputs
as required

FIGURE 2–40: Inverting Summer

Design
Notes

(continued from page 84)

1. If the inputs all require the same gain, choose the input resistors to be equal to the required input resistance. If different gains and/or input resistances are required, make R_f equal to the highest required input resistance multiplied by the highest required gain. Then choose each input resistor by dividing R_f by the desired gain from that input.
2. If the circuit is to be used for AC only, use input capacitors chosen so that the reactance of each at the lowest frequency of interest is no more than one-tenth of the corresponding input resistor value.
3. If offsetting is required, divide the required shift in DC output level by the most convenient reference voltage to obtain the required gain from the offsetting input. Then choose the input resistor for the offsetting input as was done for the other inputs. For example, if the output voltage needs to be scaled by -3.3 VDC and a 5-V reference source is available, the gain required from the offsetting input is -3.3 V/5 V $= -0.66$. (The minus sign signifies the inversion provided by this circuit.) This is a fractional gain because the required output is smaller than the input. The input resistor for the offsetting input must then be $R_f/0.66$. The reference source can be one of the power supply leads, or it can be obtained by using a voltage divider, perhaps with Zener stabilization, fed by the power supply.

Noninverting Amplifier. The conditions under which op-amp choice is not critical for use in a noninverting amplifier are the same as those listed earlier for an inverting amplifier. The circuit is shown in Fig. 2–41. The input resistance is equal to or greater than the input resistance of the op amp stated in its spec sheet. The components are chosen as follows:

1. Let $R_g = 1$ kΩ.
2. $R_f = 1$ kΩ multiplied by $(A_V - 1)$. (For a noninverting voltage follower, this makes $R_f = 0$ Ω.)
3. Assume that the input resistance of the circuit is at least 1 MΩ; then choose C so that its reactance is no more than 100 kΩ (one-tenth of the input resistance) when calculated at the lowest frequency of interest.

Noninverting Summer. The op amp for use in a noninverting summer is chosen just as is the one for an inverting amplifier, as mentioned earlier. The circuit of the noninverting summer is shown in Fig. 2–42. Design of such a circuit for applications requiring different gains from each input is quite involved and seldom used. For applications requiring the same gain from each input, proceed as follows:

1. Choose all input resistors to be equal to the highest required input resistance. (The actual input resistance from input n is equal to the input re-

(continued from page 85)

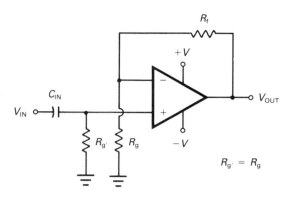

FIGURE 2–41: Noninverting Amplifier

sistor for input n plus the parallel combination of all the other input resistors.)

2. $R_f = (R_i) (A_{V \text{ required}})$ (number of inputs).

Balanced Amplifier—Single-Op-Amp Type. The choice of an op amp for use in a single-op-amp balanced amplifier involves the same considerations mentioned earlier in connection with the inverting amplifier, plus a high CMRR. The circuit is shown in Fig. 2–43. Resistor and capacitor values are chosen as follows:

1. $R_1 = R_2 = $ half the required (differential) input resistance.
2. $R_f = R_g = R_1$ multiplied by the required voltage gain. R_g can be made

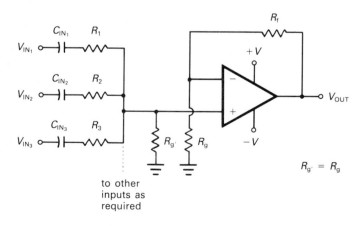

FIGURE 2–42: Noninverting Summer

Design Notes

(continued from page 86)

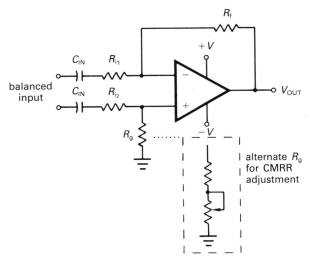

FIGURE 2–43: Single-Op-Amp Balanced Amplifier

up of a fixed resistor slightly smaller than the calculated value in series with a pot large enough to make the maximum adjusted value slightly larger than the calculated value. The pot is then adjusted for maximum CMRR by connecting both inputs to the "hot" lead of a signal generator, grounding the "ground" lead, and adjusting for minimum output.

3. The input capacitors are chosen so that their reactance at the lowest frequency of interest is no more than one-tenth of the corresponding R_i.

Balanced Amplifier—Instrumentation Type. The input amplifiers for the instrumentation-type balanced amplifier are operated as voltage followers and should use low-noise op amps. The output amplifier should be a high-CMRR op amp; it is designed by the procedure described for the single-op-amp balanced amplifier. The circuit is shown in Fig. 2–44.

Balanced Amplifiers—Transformer-Type. As Fig. 2–45 shows, the transformer-type balanced amplifier is simply a noninverting amplifier fed by a transformer. The op amp used should be of the low-noise variety. The design proceeds as follows:

1. Choose a transformer whose primary-to-secondary impedance ratio is given by

$$\frac{Z_{pri}}{Z_{sec}} = \frac{Z_{IN \text{ required}}}{25 \text{ k}\Omega}$$

Design
Notes

(continued from page 87)

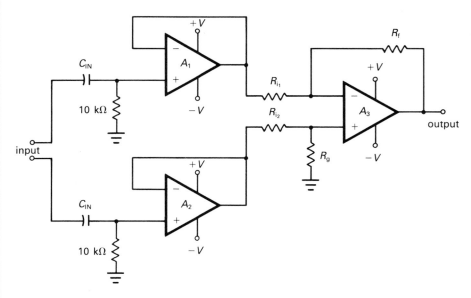

FIGURE 2–44: Instrumentation Amplifier

The figure of 25 kΩ is a typical value chosen for good noise performance. A more exact treatment of the selection of this resistance will be given in Chapter 3. Since the actual input impedance of the circuit is probably well above 1 MΩ, this guarantees a sufficiently high input impedance at the transformer primary.

2. The "free" gain provided by the transformer (since Z_{pri} is essentially always lower than Z_{sec}, making it a step-up transformer) is the square root

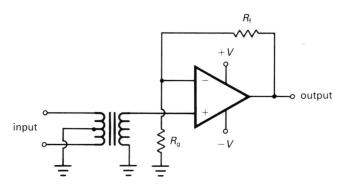

FIGURE 2–45: Transformer-Balanced Amplifier

Design Notes

(continued from page 88)

of the ratio Z_{sec}/Z_{pri}. Divide the total required voltage gain by this amount. The result is $A_{V\,amplifier}$, the gain that the amplifier will have to provide.

3. Make R_g equal to the transformer's secondary DC resistance (not impedance). Then multiply this value by $A_{V\,amplifier}$ to determine R_f.

Balanced-Output Amplifier. Balanced-output amplifiers are most commonly used to drive 600-Ω lines, although other impedances are occasionally encountered. In order to feed a sine wave with maximum swing (V_{SAT+} to V_{SAT-}), we need a peak current of $V_{SAT+}/600\ \Omega$. Assuming the usual ±15-V supplies, this value comes out to 23.3 mA. Many op amps will not produce this amount of output current safely, if at all. Therefore, the first criterion in choosing an op amp for this circuit is that the maximum output current be sufficient. The circuit is shown in Fig. 2–46. Each of the two output resistors R_o is chosen to be half the impedance of the line being driven. For good balance, these resistors should have a $\pm1\%$ or closer tolerance.

Integrators. The choice of an op amp for use as an integrator can be crucial, especially if the integration time constant is long. This is true because the input bias current of the op amp acts as an error source, changing the charge on the capacitor. For this reason, low-bias-current op amps, such as FET-input types,

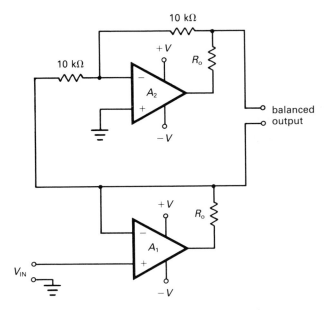

FIGURE 2–46: Balanced-Output Amplifier

(continued from page 89)

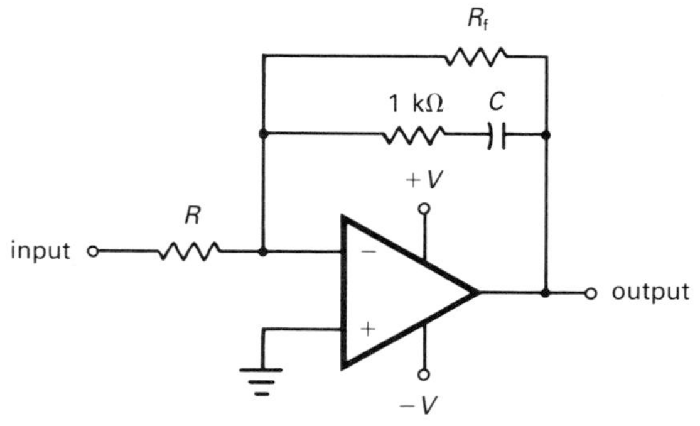

FIGURE 2–47: Integrator

should be used. The circuit of an op-amp integrator is shown in Fig. 2–47. It includes two components that require further discussion. First is the shunt resistor R_f across the capacitor. This resistor is essential because of DC drift problems. For very long integration times (RC very large), this resistor must be very large also. The second component requiring discussion is the 1-kΩ resistor in series with the capacitor. This limits the discharge rate of the capacitor and should be used if C is greater than 0.1 μF, in order to protect the input stage of the op amp from possible damage. The values of the other components are chosen as follows:

1. The time constant RC must be less than the period of the highest frequency, so choose $RC = 0.5(1/f_{high})$.
2. Make R as small as possible while still keeping it above the minimum required input resistance for your design. A commonly used value is 1 kΩ.
3. $C = $ (time constant)$/R$.
4. R_f, if used, is normally about $10R$, although if greater low-frequency gain is required, at the expense of some DC stability, values up to $100R$ can be used.

Differentiators. Op amps for use in differentiators do not need to have any special characteristics beyond those mentioned in the section on inverting amplifiers. The circuit for an op-amp differentiator is given in Fig. 2–48. The values of R and C are chosen so that the product RC (differentiator time constant) is small compared to the period of the highest frequency of interest. Then R_i is chosen so that $R_i = 1/2\pi f_a C$. In this equation, f_a is the frequency at which the gain of the differentiator circuit is to stop increasing with frequency.

(continued from page 90)

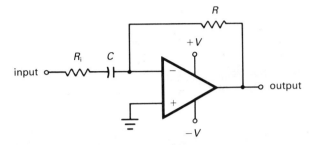

FIGURE 2–48: Differentiator

This should be well above the maximum frequency of operation, but less than the op amp's stated unity-gain frequency (given on a spec sheet).

Breadboarding Guidelines

As you would expect, any device that has (ideally) an infinite gain requires some special care in breadboarding circuits. If you follow the major precautions given here, your breadboarded circuits should work as they are designed to.

1. Avoid long lead wires. The stray capacitive coupling that these introduce can cause oscillation and/or hum pickup.
2. Make sure all ground connections are secure.
3. If possible, use a current-limited power supply. Set the current limit at about 20 mA per op amp. This can prevent errors from turning into disasters.
4. Make doubly sure that your power-supply polarities are correct. Nothing destroys an op amp faster than connecting it to a reversed-polarity supply. In fact, using diodes in series with the supply leads to block the application of reversed supply current is not a bad idea.
5. Use a nonelectrolytic decoupling capacitor connected from the op amp's positive supply terminal to ground, and another from the negative supply terminal to ground. These capacitors should be between 0.1 and 1 μF. This cancels the bad effects of the lead resistance and inductance from your power supply to your breadboard and compensates for some possible weaknesses in the power supply itself. If your supply is not well filtered, add 100-μF capacitors in parallel with the smaller ones. Remember to make sure that their polarity is correct.
6. Apply power and verify that all is well with the DC levels in your circuit before applying any signal.

Design Notes

(continued from page 91)

7. Never feed any input of an op amp with a signal whose peak voltage exceeds the power-supply voltage. This can damage the op amp by forward-biasing "parasitic junctions" within the semiconductor structure, thus causing excessive current to flow.
8. Whenever two or more op amps are used in cascade in an AC amplifier, use capacitor coupling rather than direct coupling. This prevents the buildup of DC errors from stage to stage.

SUMMARY

The characteristics of an ideal op amp are:

- Infinite voltage gain
- Infinite input impedance
- Zero output impedance
- Zero offset voltage
- Infinite bandwidth
- Infinite common-mode rejection
- Infinite slew rate

Real op amps can be assumed to be ideal as long as:

- Load resistance is at least 1 kΩ
- Bandwidth of 20 kHz is adequate
- Capacitor coupling is used between cascaded stages
- Full output voltage swing is not needed at frequencies over 1 kHz
- Common-mode rejection and offset voltage are not critical

Comparators provide an output of either V_{SAT-} or V_{SAT+}, depending upon whether the signal at the inverting($-$) or noninverting($+$) input is greater. A comparator with one input grounded is called a *zero-crossing detector*. A comparator with one input connected to a reference voltage source is called a *single-ended* comparator. A comparator that requires a different voltage to switch from the low state to the high state than for the opposite direction is called a *Schmitt trigger*. A comparator that indicates whether the input voltage is within a certain range is called a *window comparator*. For some applications, comparators need input protection and/or clamping of the output voltage.

A stack of window comparators can be used as an A/D converter known as a *flash converter*.

Feedback is used to:

- Set the gain of an amplifier
- Control frequency response
- Control the voltage transfer characteristic
- Make a circuit's performance independent of individual component characteristics

Transfer characteristics can be linear, piecewise linear, or nonlinear. An amplifier has a linear transfer characteristic.

Through proper use of feedback, an op amp can be connected as an inverting amplifier with a gain of R_f/R_i.

Alternatively, it can be connected as a noninverting amplifier with a gain of $1 + R_f/R_g$.

An amplifier with unity voltage gain is called a *voltage follower*.

An amplifier circuit with multiple inputs is called a *summer*. Summers can be made in inverting or noninverting configurations. Sometimes, a summer requires offsetting, which is a shifting of the DC level of the output through the use of a DC voltage to one of the summing inputs.

A single op amp can be used to build a balanced-input amplifier. Better noise performance can be obtained through the use of the instrumentation-amplifier circuit, which uses three op amps.

A balanced-output circuit can also be built using two op amps.

An integrator gives an output corresponding to the input voltage summed over a certain period of time. That period of time is called the time constant of the integrator.

A differentiator gives an output corresponding to the rate of change of the input voltage.

REVIEW QUESTIONS

1. Describe (don't just *list*) the characteristics of an ideal op amp.
2. Compare the specifications in Table 2–A with those for an ideal op amp. Select the op amp that is most nearly ideal in terms of:
   (a) gain (b) Z_{IN} (c) Z_{OUT}
   (d) V_{offset} (e) bandwidth (f) CMRR
   (g) slew rate
3. For the comparator in Fig. 2–3, assume input *b* is a 16-V_{P-P} 1-kHz triangle wave. For the following values of input *A*, draw the output waveforms:
   (a) -2 V (b) $+2$ V (c) $+5$ V.
4. Design a comparator to indicate whether its input voltage is greater than 4 V, and to have output voltages of ±5 V. Include input protection, and design for an input resistance of 5 kΩ.
5. Suppose R_1 and R_2 in Fig. 2–6 were 2.2 kΩ and 12 kΩ, respectively, and the supply voltage is ±15 V.

    (a) What are the positive and negative threshold voltages?

    (b) What is the maximum peak-to-peak noise voltage that this circuit would ignore?

6. Design a flash converter for use in an automotive dashboard voltmeter. It should respond to voltages from 8 to 15 V and should have a 0.5-V resolution.

7. An op-amp inverting amplifier is designed to be fed by a transducer with a Thevenin voltage of 35 mV and a Thevenin resistance of 640 Ω. R_f is 10 kΩ and R_i is 1 kΩ. Find the output voltage of the amplifier:

    (a) by determining the actual output voltage of the transducer and multiplying by the gain of the amplifier, ignoring $R_{Thevenin}$ of the transducer in the gain equation;

    (b) by determining the gain of the amplifier including the Thevenin resistance of the transducer, and multiplying by the Thevenin voltage of the transducer.

8. A certain industrial operation has a process in which one chemical is stored in a main and a reserve vat. There is a liquid-level sensor in each vat, producing an output of 10 mV/gal of liquid. When the sensors reach zero, there is a residue of 10 gal in each vat. Design an inverting summer to drive a meter that will indicate the total stock of the chemical on hand, including the residue. The meter movement requires 5 V for full-scale deflection, which is to indicate 110 gal.

9. Figure 2–49 shows a circuit for an audio microphone mixer using op amps. Assuming a ±15-V power supply, calculate:

    (a) the gain of each balanced input amplifier

    (b) the maximum output voltage of the summing stage, assuming all inputs are driven in phase

    (c) the output impedance of the balanced output stage

    (d) the maximum input voltage that can be applied to any one input without causing clipping at the output of the input amplifier stage

    (e) the minimum input voltage that can be applied to one input that will produce an output of 1 mW into a 600-Ω load

10. In Fig. 2–30, suppose $R_f = 10$ kΩ, $C = 0.05$ μF, and $R = 1$ kΩ.

    (a) Calculate the gain for 10 Hz, 100 Hz, 1 kHz, and 10 kHz.

    (b) Plot the frequency response of the circuit.

11. Assume that a perfect op amp is used in an integrator circuit and that no R_f is used. Compare the output voltage resulting from a 10-ms application of a 0.1-V input to that resulting from a 20-ms application of a 0.05-V input.

12. Design a differentiator to change square waves into positive spikes. Include a component to clip off negative spikes. The maximum frequency of operation is 10 MHz.

13. Calculate and plot the frequency response of the differentiator in Fig. 2–34, using the same component values and frequencies used for problem 10.

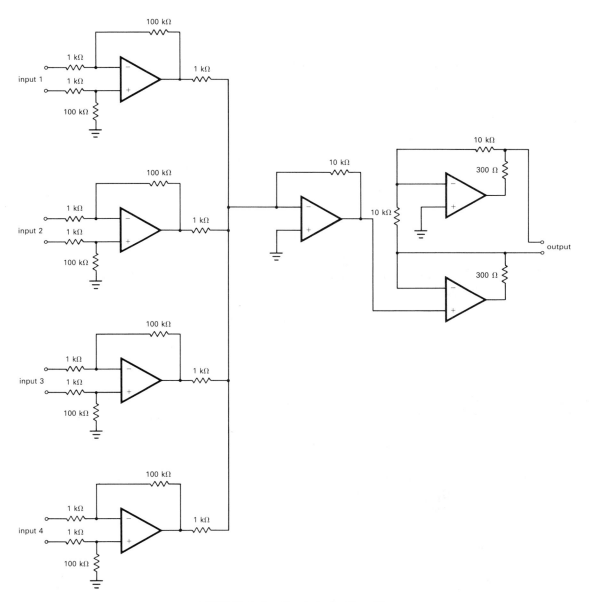

FIGURE 2–49: Circuit for Problem 19

LABORATORY EXPERIMENT—INVERTING SUMMER

Objective:

To examine the design and operating characteristics of an op-amp inverting summer.

Materials:

1 741 op amp
Miscellaneous resistors

Procedure

1. Design a two-input inverting summer circuit. The gain from each input should be 10, and each input resistance should be at least 1 kΩ.
2. Build your circuit.
3. Apply the following input voltages to your circuit and measure the outputs:

Input 1	Input 2	Output	Input 1	Input 2	Output
0	0	_____	0.2	0.2	_____
0.2	0	_____	0	0.4	_____
0.4	0	_____	0.2	0.4	_____
0	0.2	_____	0.4	0.4	_____
0.2	0.2	_____			

4. Now apply a 1-$V_{P\text{-}P}$, 1-kHz sine wave to input 1 and a 1-$V_{P\text{-}P}$, 10-kHz sine wave to input 2. Sketch the resulting output waveform as viewed on an oscilloscope.
5. With the two AC signals still applied, try to see a signal at the inverting input of the op amp itself.

Analysis

1. Calculate the expected output voltages for each of the nine combinations of DC inputs you applied in step 3. Then calculate the average deviation between the calculated and measured values as follows:

$$\text{Average deviation} = \frac{\text{Sum of all deviations without regard to sign}}{\text{Number of measurements}}$$

Now calculate the average percent deviation by dividing the average de-

(continued)

(continued from page 96)

viation by the average output voltage. A small average percent deviation indicates careful lab work.

2. Describe the general principle that explains the oscilloscope trace you obtained in step 4. What frequency components would you expect to find in the output? Would these components be different if a nonlinear mixing circuit had been used?

3. Describe what happened when you tried to observe the input signal to the op-amp's inverting input. Did you see 1-V sine waves? Explain.

LABORATORY EXPERIMENT—INTEGRATOR

Objective:

To examine the frequency response of an AC integrator circuit and to see what it does to various input waves.

Materials:

1 741 op amp
1 10-kΩ resistor
1 1-kΩ resistor
1 0.05-μF capacitor

Procedure

1. Build the integrator circuit that was designed in the example on page 76.
2. Using a constant 0.1-V_{P-P} sine-wave input voltage, measure and plot the output voltage versus frequency from 10 Hz to 100 kHz.
3. Apply the following inputs to the integrator and sketch the resulting output waveforms:
   100-Hz square wave   1-kHz square wave   10-kHz square wave
   100-kHz square wave   1-kHz sine wave

Analysis:

1. Compare the actual measured frequency response of your integrator circuit to the ideal response described in the text.
2. Compare the actual output waveforms to the ideal ones in Fig. 2–29. When differences exist, explain why.

Laboratory
Experiment

chapter three
Real Operational Amplifiers

OBJECTIVES

Upon completing this chapter, you will be able to:

- Design an op-amp circuit for minimum output offset voltage.
- Predict the frequency response of an op-amp circuit.
- Predict the maximum sine-wave output voltage available from an op-amp circuit.
- Design lead or lag compensation networks for uncompensated op amps.
- Determine the necessary slew rate for an op amp used in a particular application.
- Design op-amp circuits to avoid slewing-induced distortion.
- Select an appropriate op amp for a particular low-noise application.
- Design an op-amp circuit for optimum noise performance.

DEVIATIONS FROM THE IDEAL

In Chapter 2, we examined many basic circuits that can be built with ideal op amps. In the process, it was necessary to insert several conditions about the type of application that could be served when we didn't know the actual characteristics of the op amp being used. For instance, limitations were set on the frequency response that could be expected from the finished circuit. In this chapter, we discuss the reasons for those limitations and the design methods used to greatly extend the limits of performance.

Recall that the characteristics of an ideal op amp include

- Infinite voltage gain
- Infinite input impedance
- Zero output impedance
- Zero offset voltage
- Infinite bandwidth
- Infinite CMRR
- Infinite slew rate

Let us examine these characteristics once more. Infinite voltage gain is assumed because that simplifies the feedback equations used to predict the gain of an amplifier. Most op amps have an open-loop gain of at least 100,000. Even compared to a stage gain of 1000 (10 times the greatest gain permitted by the design guidelines in Chapter 2), this open-loop gain is large enough that our assumption of infinite gain is generally valid.

Infinite input impedance is assumed so that we can assume zero input current in our equations. Although the actual input current of an op amp is quite small, it is not always zero. This can lead to DC output errors from offset-voltage effects. We will examine this topic further in the section on offset compensation.

Assuming zero output impedance allows us to say, for example, that if $R_f = R_g$ and $R_{i_1} = R_{i_2}$ in a balanced amplifier such as the one in Fig. 2–23, then the input of a balanced amplifier has matched series and shunt impedances to ground. A non-zero output impedance would have to be figured into the calculations for accurate results, because looking from the input, Z_{OUT} is in series with R_f. Output impedances of op amps are not zero. However, feedback normally reduces the output impedance, and in any case the error introduced by nonzero output impedance is usually less than that resulting from resistor tolerances. In virtually all cases of op-amp circuit design, assuming a zero output impedance results in acceptably small errors.

No op amp has zero offset voltage. This fact must be accounted for in designs. If we fail to do so, our circuits will not perform well for DC applications, and perhaps not even for AC applications, since offset voltages in improperly designed circuits can be quite large. This topic will be discussed in detail.

No op amp has infinite bandwidth. For circuits that operate at frequencies above the low-kilohertz range, op-amp selection and circuit design must take bandwidth limitations into account. We will examine the effects of bandwidth limitations in the section on frequency response later in this chapter.

The effects of an op amp's CMRR have been discussed in connection with balanced amplifiers. For many applications, they are not important. For balanced-input applications, the CMRR matters a great deal. The slew rate of an op amp determines the maximum frequency at which the op amp can deliver maximum sine-wave output voltage. For large output signals, it can easily present a greater frequency-response limitation than the op amp's bandwidth. Slew-rate calculations will be introduced in the section on frequency-response limitations.

BIAS-CURRENT AND OFFSET COMPENSATION

Bias-Current Effects

Figure 3–1 shows the input circuit for a typical op amp of each of three families: bipolar, JFET, and MOSFET. They are all differential amplifiers. The essential difference for our purposes is in the way the three devices operate. The bipolar amplifier requires an input current to bias the transistors. This *bias current* is not needed by the JFET, whose gate is isolated by a reverse-biased junction; or the MOSFET, whose gate is insulated by a layer of metal oxide. (The arrows on the figure show the conventional-current direction of I_{bias}.) Since bipolar-transistor op amps are by far the most numerous of the three classes, we will discuss them in the paragraphs

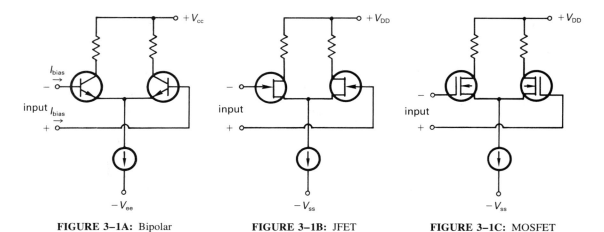

FIGURE 3–1A: Bipolar   **FIGURE 3–1B:** JFET   **FIGURE 3–1C:** MOSFET

FIGURE 3–1: Input Circuits of Various Types of Op Amps

that follow. Just remember that FET-input op amps of either variety are free from bias-current effects. (JFETs do have a very small leakage current, and MOSFETS require a leakage path from gate to ground to prevent buildup of static charges. However, the paths from gate to ground for JFET and MOSFET op amps can have extremely high resistance.)

If the input transistors in an op amp were perfectly matched, identical bias currents would flow in each input. Actually, there is usually a difference between the bias current in the inverting input and the bias current in the noninverting input. The spec sheet for an op amp gives a typical value for the average of the two bias currents:

$$I_B = \frac{I_{B^+} + I_{B^-}}{2} \qquad (3.01)$$

For a 741 op amp, this value is typically about 500 nA. The difference between I_{B^+} and I_{B^-} is called the *input offset current* I_{os}. Usually I_{os} is no more than 25% of I_B.

The effect of I_B flowing in the input circuit produces voltages at the input of the op amp. With an inverting amplifier, if the noninverting input is grounded, the bias current has a zero-ohm path to ground and produces no voltage at that input. The path to ground from the inverting input consists of R_f in parallel with the series combination of R_i and the Thevenin resistance of the source. This is because the assumed zero output impedance of the op amp results in no voltage drop from the output to ground due to any current impressed upon it. Thus an error voltage is generated at the inverting input:

$$V_{error} = I_B(R_f \| R_i) \qquad (3.02)$$

This error voltage is a part of the *input offset voltage*. In the above equation, the Thevenin resistance of the source is included in R_i. This error voltage will be amplified, and will show up as a much larger error voltage at the output of the amplifier. Figure 3–2A shows a way of neutralizing this effect. A resistor R_{comp} is inserted

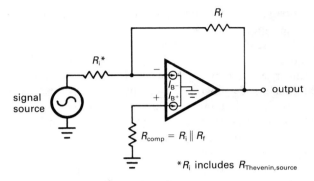

FIGURE 3–2A: Inverting Amplifier

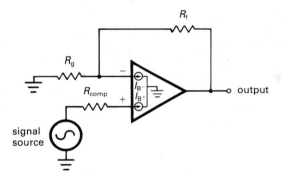

FIGURE 3–2B: Noninverting Amplifier

FIGURE 3–2: Bias-Current Compensation

between the noninverting input and ground. The value of R_{comp} is equal to $R_i \| R_f$. Thus, if the input bias currents were equal, there would be equal voltages created by them at the inverting and noninverting inputs, so they would produce no effect in the output. There is another contributor to input offset voltage: the mismatch between the base-to-emitter turn-on voltages of the op amp's input transistors. So even with perfect bias-current compensation, input offset voltage may still not be zero.

For an inverting summer, all the input resistors appear in parallel between the inverting input and ground; this combination is also in parallel with R_f. Thus the R_{comp} should be equal to the parallel combination of all these resistors.

Figure 3–2B shows the bias-current compensation method for a noninverting amplifier. Using the same reasoning as for the inverting amplifier, we find that the resistance to ground from the inverting input is $R_f \| R_g$. The resistance from the noninverting input to ground must be equal to this value if bias-current errors are to be avoided. This calls for a compensation resistor whose value is:

$$R_{comp} = R_f \| R_g - R_{\text{Thevenin,source}} \tag{3.03}$$

For a noninverting summer, a single compensation resistor between the summing point and the op-amp input is enough. This resistor should be equal to $R_f \| R_g$ minus the parallel combination of all the input resistors.

So far, we have assumed that the op amps were DC coupled at the inputs and outputs. Several new considerations arise if capacitor coupling is used. First, if the output is capacitor coupled, compensation may not be necessary. If R_i in an inverting amplifier is no more than 10 kΩ, the error voltage generated by a 500-nA bias current is $(500 \cdot 10^{-9} \text{ A})(10 \cdot 10^3 \text{ }\Omega) = 5$ mV. With a gain of 100, this will produce a quiescent output voltage of only 0.5 V. Usually such a small DC error voltage is of no consequence in a capacitor-coupled amplifier. The same holds true for a noninverting amplifier, provided that $R_f \| R_g$ is not too great. As you can see, the question of compensation depends upon the bias current of the op amp, the parallel resistance from the inverting input to ground, and the gain of the amplifier.

For capacitor-coupled inputs, however, the situation changes. Let us examine the inverting amplifier first. If the input is capacitor coupled, there is no DC path through R_i to ground. Thus if an R_{comp} is used, it must be made equal to R_f. A capacitor-coupled noninverting amplifier presents a new problem. The capacitor coupling does not change the resistance at the inverting input, but it does open the bias-current path from the noninverting input to ground. This infinite resistance will cause even a minute bias current to produce an enormous error voltage and usually will make the op amp "lock up" by forcing the output voltage to V_{SAT^-}. The solution is to provide a bias-current path by adding an external resistor from the noninverting input to ground. Ideally, the resistor should have the same value as R_{comp} would have if the input were DC coupled. This may introduce another problem. One advantage of the noninverting configuration is its very high input impedance. Now we find that we must sacrifice this advantage in order to use capacitor coupling at the input. If high input impedance is essential, a compromise must be made. Making R_{comp} larger than the ideal value will result in a DC error voltage at the output but will raise the input impedance, which can be considered essentially equal to R_{comp}. The normal design approach is to make R_{comp} high enough that the input impedance is as great as required and then to calculate the output error voltage. If this voltage is unacceptably large, R_f and R_g can be increased by the same factor to bring the error voltage back down.

EXAMPLE

Problem

Design a noninverting amplifier with an input impedance of at least 250 kΩ, to be capacitor coupled at input and output. The gain is to be 100. An output voltage of 10 V_{P-P} is required. Use a 741 op amp.

Solution

1. Since the input impedance must be at least 250 kΩ, we will make R_{comp} = 270 kΩ.

2. In order to equalize the resistances from each input to ground, we would have to make R_g about 270 kΩ and R_f = (100)(270 kΩ) = 27 MΩ. Resistances this high can cause noise problems, as we will see later, not to mention the fact that resistors over 22 MΩ are not commonly available. Therefore, let's see what kind of compromise we can make, reducing R_f and R_g while still keeping offset effects tolerable.

3. A 10-V_{P-P} output voltage corresponds to an output swing of ± 5 V_{peak} above and below the quiescent output voltage. The quiescent output voltage is just the output offset voltage. Since we are planning to make R_g smaller than R_{comp}, there will be more input offset voltage at the noninverting input. NPN transistors are used in op amps, so the electron current will flow *from* the input, making the offset voltage at the noninverting input negative. This will produce a negative quiescent output voltage. If we use ± 15-V supplies, V_{SAT^-} is about -14 V. Allowing an extra volt safety margin, we can let the signal swing to -13 V. Subtracting 5 V_{peak} from this value, we get a quiescent voltage of -8 V. This is then our maximum allowable output offset voltage. An 8-V output offset voltage divided by a gain of 100 gives an 80-mV input offset voltage. As mentioned earlier in the chapter, I_B for a 741 is typically 500 nA. We can find the maximum allowable mismatch in resistances from each input to ground:

$$R_{mismatch} = \frac{80 \text{ mV}}{500 \text{ nA}} = 160 \text{ k}\Omega$$

This means that we can use 270 kΩ − 160 kΩ = 110 kΩ for R_g. Since 120 kΩ is a standard 10% tolerance value, we will choose that value. This choice makes R_f = (120 kΩ)(100) = 12 MΩ, which is an available value.

4. Now let's recheck our design.

$$A_V = \frac{R_f}{R_g} = \frac{12 \text{ M}\Omega}{120 \text{ k}\Omega} = 100$$

$$V_{output \ offset} = I_B \, R_{mismatch} \, A_V = (-500 \text{ nA})(270 \text{ k}\Omega - 120 \text{ k}\Omega)(100)$$
$$= -7.5 \text{ V}$$

$$\text{Maximum output } V_{P-P} = 2(V_{quiescent} - V_{SAT^-})$$
$$= 2(-7.5 - (-14 \text{ V})) = 13 \text{ V}_{P-P}$$

So all specifications are met, and the design is complete. The completed circuit is shown in Fig. 3–3.

This example illustrates the importance of keeping resistances low if output offset voltages are to be minimized, and the difficulty of doing so when high input impedances are required. Another aspect of this same problem is the necessity of carefully matching large resistors for minimum offset voltage. Figure 3–4A shows an inverting amplifier with Z_{IN} = 100 kΩ. The theoretically correct value for R_{comp} is 100 k$\Omega \| 10$ MΩ = 99 kΩ. Since this is not a standard value, a 100-kΩ resistor is

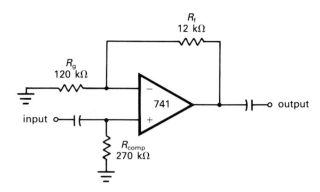

FIGURE 3–3: High-Input-Impedance Noninverting Amplifier with Partial Bias-Current Compensation

used. With $I_B = 500$ nA, the output offset voltage will be

$$V_{\text{output offset}} = R_{\text{mismatch}} I_B A_V \qquad (3.04)$$
$$= (1 \text{ k}\Omega)(500 \text{ nA})(100)$$
$$= 0.05 \text{ V}$$

Not bad. However, if both R_f and R_g are 10% below rated value (that is, only barely in tolerance) and R_{comp} is 10% above rated value, the total R_{mismatch} becomes 20.9 kΩ. Now the output offset voltage increases to 1.045 V, which is too great for some applications. Although it is highly unlikely that such a combination of resistor values would occur, circuit performance cannot be left to the chance selection of exact values. Closer-tolerance resistors are more costly, and hand-matching is even more so. It should be obvious that the same $\pm10\%$ mismatch would cause far fewer problems if the resistors were smaller in the first place. Yet, the value of R_i is usually set by input-impedance requirements. As shown in Fig. 3–4B, there is an answer to this problem. Normally, we have assumed that the resistance to ground of an inverting amplifier was controlled by the necessary value of R_i, since R_f is much larger. If we can make R_f include a low-resistance path to ground while not changing the gain, we can reduce total resistance from the inputs to ground while retaining a large R_i.

The feedback network R_f and R_i is really just a voltage divider to apply a certain fraction of the output voltage to the inverting input. The "tee" feedback circuit shown in Fig. 3–4B uses two cascaded dividers: one made of R_{t_1} and R_s, and the other of R_{t_2} and R_i. The path to ground for bias currents from the inverting input is now

$$R_i \| (R_{t_2} + (R_{t_1} \| R_s))$$

The values are chosen as follows:

$$R_{t_1} = R_{t_2} = R_t \qquad (3.05)$$

Choose R_t much less than $R_i A_V$.

$$R_s = \frac{R_t^2}{R_i A_V + 2R_t} \qquad (3.06)$$

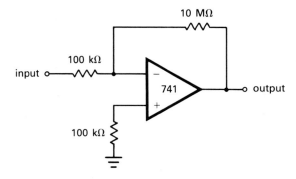

FIGURE 3–4A: Example Showing the Problem

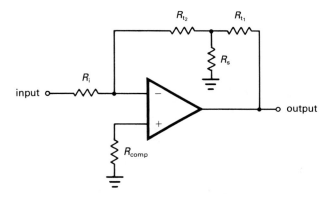

FIGURE 3–4B: Tee Circuit to Replace R_f

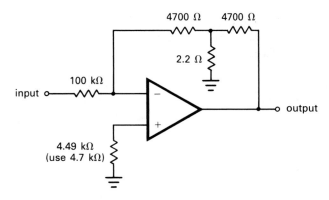

FIGURE 3–4C: Design for Smaller R_{comp}

FIGURE 3–4: Inverting Amplifier with Tee Feedback Circuit

106 Chapter Three

The resistance from the inverting input through the feedback network to ground is then

$$R_{ground} = R_t + (R_t \| R_s) \tag{3.07}$$

The equivalent R_f is

$$R_f = \frac{R_t^2 - 2R_sR_t}{R_s} \tag{3.08}$$

EXAMPLE

Problem

Design a tee feedback circuit to reduce the resistance from each input to ground in Fig. 3–4A to 10 kΩ or less.

Solution

1. Select R_t to be some convenient value about half the required R_{ground}. We will use 4700 Ω.
2. Solve for R_s:

$$R_s = \frac{R_t^2}{R_iA_V + 2R_t} = \frac{(4700\ \Omega)^2}{100\ k\Omega \times 100 + 2 \times 4700\ \Omega} = 2.2\ \Omega \tag{3.06}$$

3. The resistance to ground through the feedback network is now 4700 Ω + (4700 Ω ‖ 2.2 Ω) = 4702 Ω. The value of R_{comp} becomes 100 kΩ ‖ 4702 Ω = 4.49 kΩ. The completed circuit is shown in Fig. 3–4C.

The tee feedback circuit can also be used to help with the problem generated by noninverting amplifiers with high input-impedance requirements. On page 102 we presented a design example showing a compromise method of attaining a 250-kΩ input resistance in a noninverting amplifier with a gain of 100. We ended up with an output offset voltage of −7.5 V. Figure 3–5 shows the application of the tee feedback circuit to this problem. The values are chosen as shown in the following example.

EXAMPLE

Problem

Design a noninverting amplifier with a gain of 100, an input impedance of at least 250 kΩ, and optimum bias compensation. Use no resistors larger than 10 MΩ.

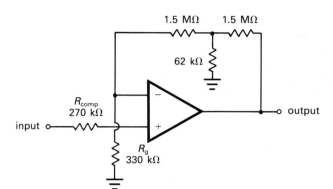

FIGURE 3–5A: High-Input-Impedance Noninverting Amplifier Using Tee Feedback Network

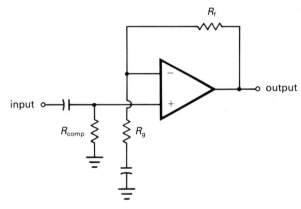

FIGURE 3–5B: Capacitor-Isolated-R_g Circuit

FIGURE 3–5: Compensation for High-Input-Impedance Noninverting Amplifiers

Solution

1. As before, we will use a 270-kΩ resistor for R_{comp}. This ensures a sufficiently high input impedance.
2. If we use a 330-kΩ resistor for R_g, the bias compensation will be nearly right, since the parallel resistance of the feedback network will make the total resistance from the inverting input to ground slightly less than R_g. Now 330 kΩ is about 20% higher than 270 kΩ, so the required resistance in parallel with 330 kΩ to achieve a total resistance of 270 kΩ is about 5(330 kΩ). We therefore make $R_t = 5\,R_g$. This calls for $R_t = 1.65$ MΩ. Using the standard $\pm10\%$ value of 1.5 MΩ, we can solve for R_s:

$$R_s = \frac{R_t^2}{R_g A_V + 2R_t} = \frac{(1.5\ \text{M}\Omega)^2}{330\ \text{k}\Omega \times 100 + 2 \times 1.5\ \text{M}\Omega} \quad \text{(from 3.06)}$$

$$= 62.5\ \text{k}\Omega$$

(This equation makes the approximation $A_V \simeq R_f/R_g$, which is pretty close for a gain of 100.)

This value is between the standard $\pm 10\%$ values 56 kΩ and 68 kΩ, so we will use the standard $\pm 5\%$ value 62 kΩ.

3. Now we check our design. First, the equivalent R_f is

$$R_f = \frac{R_t^2 - 2R_s R_t}{R_s} = \frac{(1.5\ \text{M}\Omega)^2 - 2 \times 62\ \text{k}\Omega \times 1.5\ \text{M}\Omega}{62\ \text{k}\Omega} \qquad (3.08)$$

$$= 33.3\ \text{M}\Omega$$

This gives a gain of

$$A_V = 1 + \frac{R_f}{R_g} = 1 + \frac{33.3\ \text{M}\Omega}{330\ \text{k}\Omega} = 101.9$$

which is quite acceptable. The resistance from the inverting input through the feedback network to ground is

$$R_{\text{ground}} = R_t + (R_t \| R_s) = 1.5\ \text{M}\Omega + (1.5\ \text{M}\Omega \| 62\ \text{k}\Omega) = 1.56\ \text{M}\Omega \qquad (3.07)$$

This value, paralleled with R_g, gives the ideal value for R_{comp}:

$$R_{\text{comp}} = 1.56\ \text{M}\Omega \| 330\ \text{k}\Omega = 272\ \text{k}\Omega$$

We are using a 270 kΩ resistor for R_{comp}, which happens to be the closest standard $\pm 10\%$ value. This gives us an R_{mismatch} of 272 kΩ $-$ 270 kΩ = 2 kΩ. The output offset voltage will then be about

$$V_{\text{output offset}} = I_B R_{\text{mismatch}} A_V = (500\ \text{nA})(2\ \text{k}\Omega)(100) = 0.1\ \text{V} \qquad (3.04)$$

This is much better than our previous design. If still lower $V_{\text{output offset}}$ is needed, we could add a 12-kΩ resistor in series with R_{comp} for theoretically perfect compensation.

Another approach we can use to make the input impedance of a noninverting amplifier high while retaining proper compensation is to capacitor-isolate R_g. This makes $R_{\text{comp}} = R_f$. The capacitor is chosen so that its reactance at the lowest frequency of interest is no more than one-tenth of R_g. Figure 3–5B shows the circuit. This approach is applicable to AC amplifiers only.

Offset-Current Effects

So far, we have ignored the input offset current. All our efforts have been directed toward eliminating the effects of the bias currents that flow in both inputs. As mentioned earlier, though, there is usually some mismatch between the bias currents of the two inputs of an op amp. This is caused by the impossibility of making identical input transistors. The resulting offset current may be around 25% of the bias current. This means that even if the resistances from each input to ground are equal, there will still be an input offset voltage caused by the offset current. Unfortunately, this problem is not so easy to deal with as the bias-current problem.

There are two reasons for this. The first is that the offset current itself is unpredictable; not only do we not know its amount, but we don't even know which input will have the greater current. The second reason is that offset current varies greatly with temperature.

For capacitor-coupled amplifiers, if appropriate compensation resistors are used so that bias-current effects are not a problem, then offset current is usually not a problem either. But for DC-coupled amplifiers, offset-current effects sometimes have to be dealt with. Figure 3–6 shows 10 different ways of canceling offset-current effects by use of *offset nulling* arrangements. The first five can be used with any op amp. Each of the last five is suitable for certain specific op amps that have offset nulling pins designed for that specific arrangement. Figure 3–6A is used for an inverting amplifier, and works by applying a voltage to the noninverting input; this voltage is adjusted to bring the quiescent DC output voltage to zero. The circuit of Fig. 3–6B works by applying a compensating voltage to the inverting input of a

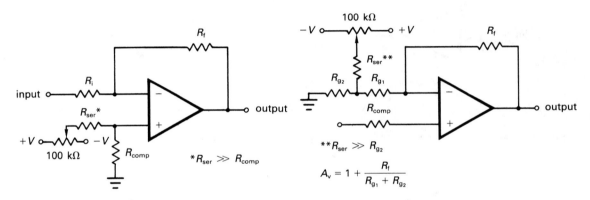

FIGURE 3–6A: General-Purpose—Inverting

FIGURE 3–6B: General-Purpose—Noninverting

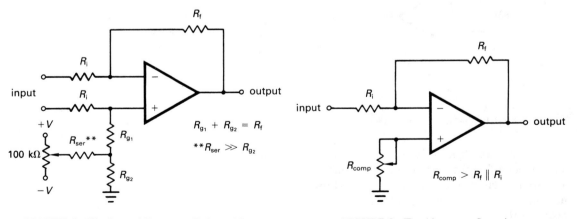

FIGURE 3–6C: General-Purpose—Balanced Input

FIGURE 3–6D: Alternate—Inverting

FIGURE 3–6: Offset Nulling Methods

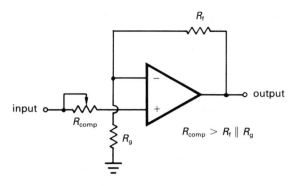

FIGURE 3–6E: Alternate—Noninverting

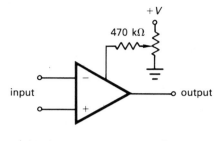

FIGURE 3–6F: 709-Type (1537, 4709)

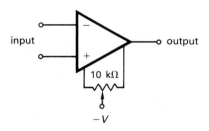

FIGURE 3–6G: 741-Type (1558, 4558, 746, 747, 4250)

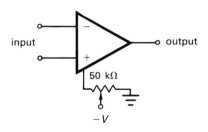

FIGURE 3–6H: 101-Type (301, 748)

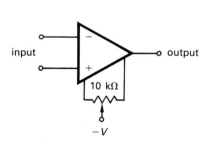

FIGURE 3–6I: 1536-Type (8007, 531)

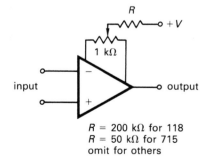

FIGURE 3–6J: 725-Type (110, 2620, 118, 715)

noninverting amplifier. Using an R_g made of two parts avoids having the nulling adjustment affect the gain. Figure 3–6C uses the same approach for a balanced-input amplifier. Figures 3–6D and E work by allowing the value of R_{comp} itself to be varied in order to null the offset voltage in an inverting and a noninverting amplifier, respectively.

The circuit in Figure 3–6F is used for the 709 op amp as well as certain others of the same design family. Figure 3–6G is for the 741 and similar op amps. Figure

3–6H is for the 101 op amp and its relatives; Fig. 3–6I is for the 1536-type, and Fig. 3–6J is for the 725-type. It is not necessary to memorize these specific nulling arrangements; they are only shown to illustrate the common nulling methods. Each op amp that has separate pins for offset nulling will have the appropriate nulling arrangement shown on its data sheet. Remember, though, even if an absolutely perfect nulling adjustment is made, so that the quiescent DC output voltage is zero, the adjustment is only valid for the temperature at which it was made. When the chip temperature varies, an output offset voltage will reappear. For this reason, low-offset, low-drift op amps such as the LF411 are used in applications where offset voltages are especially critical, as in DC measuring circuits. The spec sheet for an LF411 is shown in Appendix A.

FREQUENCY RESPONSE

Open-Loop Frequency Response

Figure 3–7 shows the gain-vs.-frequency characteristic for a typical uncompensated op amp. The shape of the $A_{V_{ol}}$ curve is determined by two things. The first is the Miller capacitances within the op amp itself. Recall that there are interelectrode capacitances within any transistor. Especially important is the collector-to-base capacitance, because its effective value is multiplied by the stage gain (Miller effect). The high-frequency response of a single stage is therefore like that of a single-stage *RC* low-pass filter, which has a rolloff slope of −20 dB/decade. The frequency at which the gain has dropped 3 dB from its maximum value is called the *critical frequency* (f_c). Two stages cascaded, each having a slope of −20 dB/decade, will

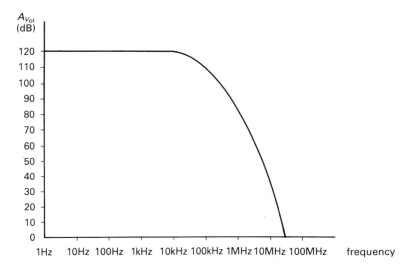

FIGURE 3–7: $A_{V_{ol}}$ versus Frequency for an Uncompensated Op Amp

produce a net slope of -40 dB/decade, beginning about the critical frequency of the stage having the higher f_c. Three stages will produce a slope of -60 dB/decade. An op amp built with no special attention to frequency response will have a high gain, and therefore a low f_c, in the input diff-amp stage; a moderate gain, and therefore a higher f_c, in the second diff-amp stage; and little voltage gain, with an even higher f_c in the level-shifter/output stage. The effects of these three rolloffs are shown in the curve of Fig. 3–8A. Also shown is the phase response of such an op amp.

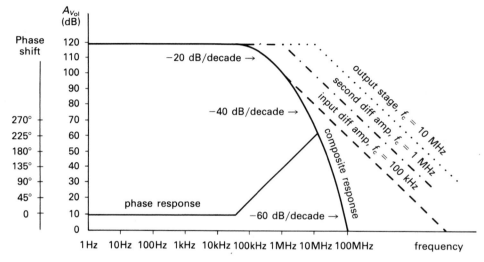

FIGURE 3–8A: Uncompensated

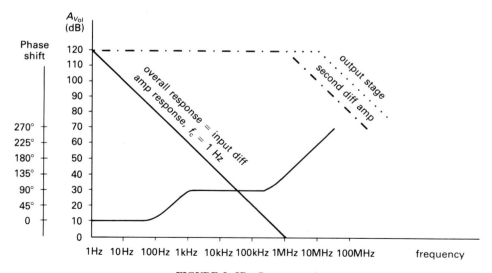

FIGURE 3–8B: Compensated

FIGURE 3–8: Gain and Phase Response of Uncompensated and Compensated Op Amps

Notice that each rolloff contributes to the total phase shift produced by the amplifier. What this means is that a 10-Hz input signal will produce an amplified, in-phase 10-Hz output signal. But a 3-MHz input signal will produce an amplified, 180° out-of-phase output signal. If this signal is fed back into the inverting input through what is supposed to be a negative-feedback network, the circuit will oscillate. This happens because the total phase shift around the loop is 360°: 180° from frequency-response effects in the amplifier, and 180° from the use of the inverting input. In other words, the feedback becomes positive at a frequency of 3 MHz.

The solution to this problem of AC instability is shown in Fig. 3–8B. If the critical frequency of one stage (or of the whole op amp) is changed through use of an internal capacitive feedback network, the second and third critical frequencies are made to occur at frequencies above that at which the gain has dropped to 0 dB—the *unity-gain frequency*. (0 dB is a numerical gain of unity.) This means that the rolloff slope is a constant −20 dB/decade up to just below the unity-gain frequency, and the maximum phase shift is limited to about 135°. This technique is referred to as *frequency compensation*. Op amps that incorporate the necessary frequency-compensation components internally are called *internally compensated op amps*. Devices that require these components to be added externally are called *uncompensated op amps*. Internally compensated op amps are much easier to design with and require fewer components in the final circuit, thus making for a cheaper design. However, as you can see from Fig. 3–8B, compensation reduces the maximum gain available at frequencies between the new critical frequency and the unity-gain frequency. Therefore, there are some applications for which the greater design flexibility of uncompensated op amps is required.

Figure 3–9 shows the frequency-response curve of an RC4136 compensated op amp. Two points on the curve are marked. Point A is the critical frequency. Since an op amp has a flat response down to DC (0 Hz), the critical frequency is numer-

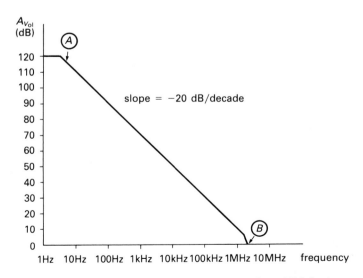

FIGURE 3–9: Open-Loop Gain versus Frequency for a 4136 Op Amp

ically equal to the *3-dB open-loop bandwidth*. Point B is the unity-gain frequency. It is numerically equal to the *unity-gain bandwidth*.

Above the critical frequency the slope of the curve is −20 dB/decade. This means that the voltage gain is reduced by a factor of 100 each time the frequency is increased by a factor of 100. In other words, the product of the gain and the bandwidth is a constant for all frequencies above the critical frequency. For the characteristic shown in the figure, the gain is 90 dB at a frequency of 100 Hz. This represents a numerical gain of 31,623. The product of the gain and the frequency is (100 Hz)(31,623) = 3.16 MHz. If the frequency is increased to 10 kHz, the gain drops to 50 dB—smaller by a factor of 100, and the product is still 3.16 MHz. You have probably noticed that 3.16 MHz is also the unity-gain bandwidth for this op amp. Therefore, another name that is often used for the unity-gain bandwidth is the *gain-bandwidth product* (GBW).

Closed-Loop Frequency Response

The closed-loop gain of any amplifier at any given frequency can never be greater than the open-loop gain at that frequency. Therefore, if the amplifier whose characteristic is shown in Fig. 3–9 is used in a circuit that is to have uniform frequency response up to 100 kHz, its maximum possible closed-loop gain will be 30 dB, or a factor of 31.62. This is illustrated in Fig. 3–10. This, then, is the first frequency limitation of an op-amp circuit. Stated another way, the maximum frequency to which an op amp will respond with uniform gain is given by

$$f_{max} = \frac{GBW}{A_{V_{cl}}} \tag{3.09}$$

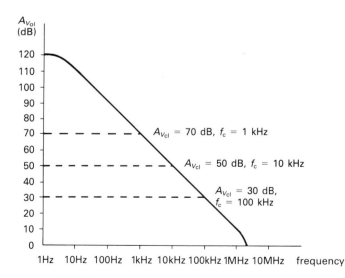

FIGURE 3–10: Closed-Loop Gain versus Frequency

Also notice that the ultimate high-frequency rolloff slope of a compensated op amp is always defined by the $A_{V_{ol}}$ curve to be -20 dB/decade.

It is possible to find out more about the frequency response of an op-amp amplifier circuit than just the critical frequency. We can find the frequency at which the gain is any desired fraction of the midband gain. Since the response is a low-pass, -20 dB/decade curve, it corresponds to that of a simple RC low-pass filter, as shown in Fig. 3–11. The equation for the output voltage of this circuit is obtained from the voltage-divider rule:

$$V_{\text{out}} = \frac{V_{\text{in}}X_C}{\sqrt{R^2 + X_C^2}} \qquad (3.10)$$

The "gain" of this circuit, $V_{\text{out}}/V_{\text{in}}$, is just

$$A_V = \frac{X_C}{\sqrt{R^2 + X_C^2}} \qquad (3.11)$$

This can be rewritten as

$$A_V^2 = \frac{1/\omega^2C^2}{R^2 + 1/\omega^2C^2} \qquad (3.12)$$

where $\omega = 2\pi f$. Let's solve this equation for ω.

$$\omega = \left(\frac{\sqrt{1 - A_V^2}}{A_V}\right)\frac{1}{RC}$$

The gain of the simple RC low-pass filter at the critical frequency is $1/\sqrt{2}$. Inserting

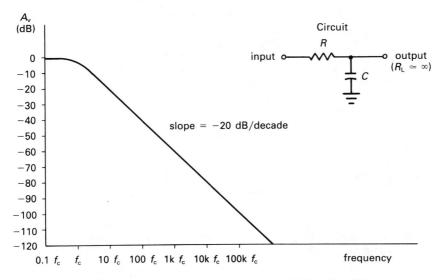

FIGURE 3–11: Gain versus Frequency for an RC Low-Pass Filter

this value for A_v, we find that the critical frequency is

$$\omega_c = \frac{1}{RC} \quad \text{or} \quad f_c = \frac{1}{2\pi RC} \tag{3.13}$$

If we wish to find the frequency at which the gain is 10% lower than its midband value, we would insert 0.9 for A_V. Then $f_{10\%}$ is

$$f_{10\%} = \left(\frac{\sqrt{1 - 0.9^2}}{0.9}\right) \frac{1}{RC} \tag{3.14}$$

$$= 0.484 \frac{1}{2\pi RC}$$

$$= 0.484 f_c$$

For gains at frequencies above the critical frequency, we use the same procedure:

For the frequency at which $A_V = 0.5$, $\quad f_{50\%} = 1.73 f_c$ (3.15)

For the frequency at which $A_V = 0.25$, $\quad f_{75\%} = 3.87 f_c$ (3.16)

For the frequency at which $A_V = 0.125$, $\quad f_{87.5\%} = 7.93 f_c$ (3.17)

For the frequency at which $A_V = 0.0625$, $\quad f_{93.75\%} = 15.97 f_c$ (3.18)

If we round off the frequencies, we see that each doubling in frequency above roughly $4f_c$ gives an approximate halving of gain. This is referred to as a frequency-response slope of -6 dB/octave. The word *octave* means a doubling or halving of frequency. As you can see from the figure, this is just the same as the -20 dB/decade slope we have been discussing.

We can use these same calculations for an op amp if the value we use for A_V is not the actual value of the gain of the amplifier, but a relative gain compared to the midband gain. This relative gain is referred to as a *normalized* gain:

$$A_{V \text{ normalized}} = \frac{A_{V \text{ actual}}}{A_{V \text{ midband}}} \tag{3.19}$$

Thus if the midband gain of an amplifier is 100 and $A_{V \text{ actual}}$ is 10% less than the midband gain, then

$$A_{V \text{ normalized}} = \frac{100 - 10\% \text{ of } 100}{100} = \frac{90}{100} = 0.9$$

This is just what we used in calculating $f_{10\%}$ before.

Now we have seen the effect of the GBW in limiting the combined maximum gain and critical frequency of an amplifier. But the question arises, what does one do if more gain is needed than can be provided by a certain op amp with the necessary high-frequency cutoff? The obvious answer is to find an op amp with a higher GBW. An alternative answer is to cascade stages. Two stages, each having the same f_c, will have a total gain at f_c that is 6 dB lower than the midband gain. Thus their combined f_c will be a bit over one-half of each individual f_c. However, since the gains of two cascaded stages multiply, the total effective product of gain and bandwidth for the two cascaded stages is greater than for either stage alone. For example, if an amplifier is needed that has a gain of 100 and an f_c of at least 50 kHz, we find immediately that a single 741 stage will not do. Since the GBW of a 741 is 1 MHz, the maximum gain available at 50 kHz is

$$A_{V \text{ max}} = \frac{\text{GBW}}{f_c} = \frac{1 \text{ MHz}}{50 \text{ kHz}} = 20 \qquad \text{(from 3.09)}$$

However, if we cascade two stages, we only need a stage gain of 10. This gives us an f_c of 100 kHz for each stage. The total gain will be $10^2 = 100$, and the total f_c will be somewhat above 50 kHz.

It is possible to accurately predict the total f_c resulting from cascading n identical amplifier stages, using the equation

$$f_{c,\text{total}} = f_{c,\text{individual}} \sqrt{2^{1/n} - 1} \qquad (3.20)$$

where n is the number of stages. For two stages, this gives $f_{c,\text{total}} = 0.64 f_{c,\text{individual}}$. Thus for our example above, $f_{c,\text{total}} = 64$ kHz. The ultimate rolloff slope of an amplifier consisting of cascaded stages is just the number of stages multiplied by -20 dB/decade.

In terms of improving frequency response, the advantage of cascading stages decreases as more stages are added. In general, the point of diminishing returns is reached at four stages.

Pulse Response

Many applications using op amps involve rectangular or pulse waveforms. For these waveforms, it is not enough that the amplifier respond to the highest fundamental frequency; the rise time of the output wave must also be fast enough that the wave still looks like a rectangular pulse. The rise time of a rectangular wave is defined as the time required for it to change from 10% to 90% of its amplitude, as shown in Fig. 3–12. This time can be predicted from the equations for the exponential response of an *RC* low-pass filter to a step waveform. The result is that

$$t_{\text{rise}} = \frac{0.35}{\text{BW}} \qquad (3.21)$$

Thus for any amplifier circuit, if the actual closed-loop bandwidth (BW) is inserted into the above equation, the resulting rise time can be found. The *unity-gain rise*

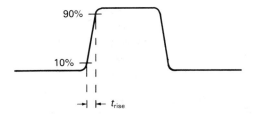

FIGURE 3–12: Rise Time

time can be found from

$$t_{\text{rise,unity-gain}} = \frac{0.35}{\text{GBW}} \tag{3.22}$$

For a 741, this value is 0.35 µs.

Some manufacturers do not list the GBW on the data sheets for their op amps; they list t_{rise} instead. In this case, the GBW can be calculated from

$$\text{GBW} = \frac{0.35}{t_{\text{rise,unity-gain}}} \quad \text{(from 3.22)}$$

The above equations are valid only for small output pulses—in general, those less than 1 $V_{P\text{-}P}$. The rise time of larger pulses will be limited by the slew rate of the op amp.

Slew-Rate Effects

Besides the GBW, the slew rate is the other limiting factor in the frequency response of an op-amp circuit. Recall that the slew rate is the fastest rate at which output voltage can change. It is specified in volts per microsecond. The slew rates of several popular op amps are given in Table 3–A. For high-frequency voltages greater than 1 $V_{P\text{-}P}$, slew rate is often a more significant factor than GBW. The slew rate of the 741 op amp is 0.5 V/µs. This means that a square pulse can have a rise time no less than 1 µs for each half volt between its 10% and 90% points. For example, let us calculate the fastest rise time that the slew rate (SR) will permit for square waves of several different amplitudes.

1:amplitude 1 V

$$v_{10\%} = 0.1 \text{ V}, \qquad v_{90\%} = 0.9 \text{ V}$$
$$\Delta v = 0.9 \text{ V} - 0.1 \text{ V} = 0.8 \text{ V}$$
$$t_{\text{rise,SR}} = \frac{\Delta v}{\text{SR}} = \frac{0.8 \text{ V}}{0.5 \text{ V/µs}} = 1.6 \text{ µs} \tag{3.23}$$

TABLE 3–A Slew Rate and GBW of Several Popular Op Amps

TYPE #	SLEW RATE (V/µs)	GBW (MHz)
301	1.4 to 12.6*	1 to 10*
LM318	50	15
709	0.3 to 20*	0.5 to 80*
741	0.5	1.5
RC4136	2	3
SE5534	13	10
TL080	13	3
LF411	10	3

Depends upon compensation network

2:amplitude 5 V

$$v_{10\%} = 0.5 \text{ V}, \qquad v_{90\%} = 4.5 \text{ V}$$

$$\Delta v = 4 \text{ V}$$

$$t_{\text{rise,SR}} = 8 \text{ μs}$$

3:amplitude 20 V

$$v_{10\%} = 2 \text{ V}, \qquad v_{90\%} = 18 \text{ V}$$

$$\Delta v = 16 \text{ V}$$

$$t_{\text{rise,SR}} = 32 \text{ μs}$$

If we now compare the slew-rate-limited rise time with the 0.35-μs unity-gain rise time for a 741, we see that the slew rate limits the rise time in each case.

If the 741 were used in an amplifier with a gain of 100, the closed-loop bandwidth would then become $\text{GBW}/A_{V_{\text{cl}}} = 1 \text{ MHz}/100 = 10 \text{ kHz}$. The GBW-limited rise time would then be

$$t_{\text{rise}} = \frac{0.35}{f_c} = 35 \text{ μs} \qquad \text{(from 3.21)}$$

Under these conditions, the slew rate is *not* the limiting factor in the rise time, even for a 20-V output. This illustration should indicate the need for calculating both the GBW-limited rise time and the slew-rate-limited rise time when you are designing op-amp circuits to handle rectangular waveforms.

Even for sine waves, the slew rate of an op amp can limit the frequency response. The maximum rate at which the voltage of a sine wave changes is given by

$$\text{maximum } \frac{\Delta v}{\Delta t} = 2\pi f V_{\text{P}}$$

This means that the maximum combination of output frequency and voltage of an op amp are limited by the slew rate (SR) to

$$f_{\text{max,SR}} = \frac{\text{SR}}{2\pi V_{\text{P}}} \qquad (3.24)$$

Let us examine the slew-rate limitations of a 741 op amp for sine-wave outputs of several amplitudes:

1: 1 V peak

$$f_{\text{max,SR}} = \frac{0.5 \text{ V/μs}}{(2\pi)(1 \text{ V})} = 0.08 \text{ MHz}$$

2: 5 V peak

$$f_{\text{max,SR}} = \frac{0.5 \text{ V/μs}}{(2\pi)(5 \text{ V})} = 0.016 \text{ MHz}$$

3: 20 V peak

$$f_{\text{max,SR}} = \frac{0.5 \text{ V}/\mu\text{s}}{(2\pi)(20 \text{ V})} = 0.004 \text{ MHz}$$

If we compare these frequencies to the critical frequencies for several different gains, we find that

$$A_{V_{\text{cl}}} = 10, \qquad f_c = 100 \text{ kHz}$$

$$A_{V_{\text{cl}}} = 100, \qquad f_c = 10 \text{ kHz}$$

$$A_{V_{\text{cl}}} = 1000, \qquad f_c = 1 \text{ kHz}$$

Thus we find that for a gain of 10, even a 1-V peak output is limited by the slew rate to a maximum of 80 kHz. For a gain of 100, a 5-V output is possible up to above f_c; but the 20-V output is slew-rate limited to frequencies below 4 kHz. For a gain of 1000, f_c is so low that it is the limiting factor for all three output voltages.

So just as you must consider both GBW and slew-rate limitations when you design an op-amp circuit to handle rectangular waves, so must you consider both of them for circuits designed to handle sine waves. Some manufacturers include a graph entitled *full-power response* on the data sheets for their op amps. This is a graph of maximum possible sine-wave output voltage plotted versus frequency. It makes it easy to determine the slew-rate limitations on sine-wave output.

Amplifiers are subject to a peculiar and hard-to-measure form of waveform distortion that is associated with the slew rate. This *slewing-induced distortion* (SID) results from the inability for capacitances associated with the feedback circuit to charge instantaneously. The effect of this finite charging time is that if an input having a steep wavefront (such as a square wave) is applied to an op amp, the circuit will act as though it had no negative feedback for the first few microseconds, while the feedback capacitances are charging. This causes an overshoot in the output, as shown in Fig. 3–13. The too-large output signal then produces too much feedback, which causes an undershoot. The process is repeated until the ringing gradually dies out. In addition to causing misshapen rectangular pulses, this phenomenon can cause an annoying edgy sound in audio systems. SID can be avoided if the maximum frequency that an amplifier is required to handle is no more than $\frac{1}{5} f_{\text{max,SR}}$.

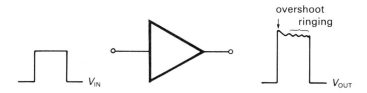

FIGURE 3–13: Effect of Slewing-Induced Distortion

EXAMPLE

Problem

Design an amplifier with a gain of 500 and an f_c at least 20 kHz. The amplifier must be capable of a 10-V_{P-P} output, and SID must be minimized.

Solution

1. This application combines a fairly high f_c with a large output swing, so we will begin by determining the necessary slew rate:

$$\text{minimum slew rate} = 2\pi f_c V_P \qquad \text{(from 3.24)}$$

$$= (2\pi)(20 \text{ kHz})(5 \text{ V}) = 0.63 \text{ V}/\mu s$$

In order to avoid SID, we will use an op amp having a slew rate at least 5 times this great. Table 3–A shows that the LF411 has a slew rate of 10 V/μs, which is great enough.

2. A gain of 500 is greater than the guideline limit of 100 per stage given in Chapter 2. A quick calculation will show why this is so:

$$f_c = \frac{\text{GBW}}{A_{V_{cl}}} = \frac{1 \text{ MHz}}{500} = 2 \text{ kHz} \qquad \text{(from 3.09)}$$

If we use two stages, each stage will need to have a gain of $\sqrt{500} = 22.4$. This will give an f_c for each stage of

$$f_{c,\text{individual}} = \frac{1 \text{ MHz}}{22.4} = 44.6 \text{ kHz}$$

The overall critical frequency is then

$$f_{c,\text{total}} = f_{c,\text{individual}} \sqrt{2^{1/n} - 1} = 44.6 \text{ kHz} \sqrt{2^{1/2} - 1}$$

$$= 28.7 \text{ kHz} \qquad \text{(from 3.20)}$$

This response is good enough.

Settling Time

We have already discussed the rise time of op amps, which is the time required for a small output pulse to rise from 10% to 90% of its peak amplitude. We have just discussed slew rate, which is a measure of how quickly an op amp's output voltage can change. The *settling time* of an op amp takes into account these and other phenomena and gives the time required for the output voltage of an op amp to rise to within 0.01% of its final value when executing a 10-V step function. Figure 3–14 illustrates the meaning of settling time. When the op-amp output is forced to change abruptly from 0 to 10 V, the initial change is limited by slew rate. As the

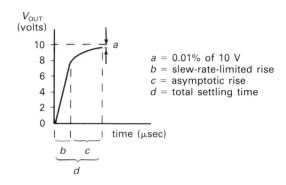

FIGURE 3–14: Settling Time

output voltage approaches the final value, however, it does not suddenly stop rising and assume that value. Instead, it approaches the final value asymptotically. The time required to come within 0.01% of the final value is the settling time of the op amp. The LF356 is an example of an amplifier having a relatively fast settling time. It requires 1.5 μs for the output voltage to arrive within 0.01% of the final value when executing a 10-V step.

Using Uncompensated Op Amps

The built-in compensation in an internally compensated op amp makes design with that type of op amp quite convenient. However, the price of that convenience is reduced design flexibility. The use of uncompensated op amps permits a degree of optimization that can result in greater bandwidth or greater slew rate or both. In order to use an uncompensated op amp, though, you must design an external compensation network. Manufacturers' spec sheets for op amps often give a great deal of help in the choice of compensation networks, but if you understand the theory behind the information they give, you can better use this information, and you can also get by when no spec-sheet info is available.

The underlying principle of good compensation is that of avoiding a 180° phase shift due to the internal capacitances of the op amp. Recall that the phase change from a single RC low-pass filter is −45° at f_c, increasing to −90° as a maximum. Two RC low-pass filters cascaded will produce twice as much phase shift. Thus at very high frequencies, it is possible for the total phase shift to equal almost 180°. If three RC low-pass filters are cascaded, the frequency doesn't even have to be very high before a 180° phase shift is encountered.

The problem with 180° phase shift is that there is already a 180° phase shift in the negative feedback loop. Whenever an amplifier has a total phase shift of 360° at any frequency, and a closed-loop gain of unity or more, it will oscillate at that frequency. So if internal RC networks add enough additional phase lag to total 180°, the criteria for oscillation will be met. The additional phase shift added by feedback networks contributes to the total. Oscillators don't amplify well at all. Therefore, the problem of good compensation is best viewed as a problem of making sure that there is not a 180° phase shift at any frequency below the unity-gain frequency.

The common low-pass RC filter to which we have compared an op amp is often called a *lag* network because it introduces phase lag. It is the equivalent circuit for the frequency-dependent elements inside the op amp itself. There are several stages in an op amp, each having its own critical frequency. If any two or more of those critical frequencies are below the unity-gain frequency, there can be a total phase shift of 180° in the op amp. The usual method of dealing with this problem in an uncompensated op amp is to use frequency-dependent negative feedback to bring the unity-gain frequency down below the critical frequencies of the individual stages. This is just what is done internally in compensated op amps. Now the peculiar thing is that accidental oscillation is more of a problem in low-gain op-amp circuits than in high-gain circuits. The reason is that when there is 180° phase shift in the amplifier, the "negative" feedback loop becomes a positive feedback loop. A low closed-loop gain implies that there is not much attenuation of the output signal before it reaches the inverting input. In other words, there is a large feedback signal. A high-gain amplifier has a smaller feedback signal. Naturally, a large positive feedback signal is more likely to cause oscillation than is a small one. For this reason, compensation of an op amp is more crucial for low gains than for high gains. Internally compensated op amps are usually compensated to be stable at any gain, including unity. Less compensation would have to be used if the amplifier were to be used at a higher gain; this would mean a higher GBW.

There are three general methods that are used to assess an amplifier's stability against oscillation. The first is to simply compare the amplifier's gain and phase shift at various frequencies. The gain that is important, however, is not the signal gain but the *loop gain* $\beta A_{V_{ol}}$. This is the gain of the feedback loop itself. For example, if an amplifier has an $A_{V_{ol}}$ of 10^6 and an $A_{V_{cl}}$ of 100, then

$$A_{V_{cl}} = \frac{1}{\beta} \quad \text{and} \quad \beta = \frac{1}{A_{V_{cl}}} = 0.01 \tag{2.10}$$

The loop gain is then

$$\beta A_{V_{ol}} = 0.01 \cdot 10^6 = 10^4$$

At the frequency at which there is a large phase shift in an amplifier, the open-loop gain is much smaller than at lower frequencies. As long as $A_{V_{ol}}$ is small enough so that $\beta A_{V_{ol}}$ is less than unity at the frequency at which the amplifier and feedback network together produce 360° phase shift, the amplifier will be stable and will not oscillate. This simply means that at the frequency at which "negative" feedback becomes positive feedback, the loop gain must be so small that no amplification occurs.

There are two measures of stability associated with this analysis. The *gain margin* is the number of dB less than unity that the loop gain is at the frequency at which the loop phase shift is 360°. For example, if at that frequency $\beta A_{V_{ol}} = 0.5$, then the gain margin would be

$$M_G = 20 \log(0.5) = -6 \text{ dB}$$

Gain margin, then, expresses the amount that the $A_{V_{ol}}$ can rise under the influence of temperature before oscillation will occur.

Phase margin is the difference between the loop phase shift of the amplifier at the unity-gain frequency and 360°. Thus an amplifier having a resistive feedback network (180° phase shift) and an internal phase shift of 150° at the unity-gain frequency would have a phase margin of

$$M_P = 360° - (180° + 150°) = 30°$$

The second method of assessing stability uses what is called a *Nyquist plot*. This is simply a phasor plot of the loop gain and phase shift of the amplifier at a number of frequencies. Figure 3–15 shows two Nyquist plots with the various points identified as to the loop gain and phase shift. The *Nyquist criterion* states that if the Nyquist plot encircles the -1 point, the amplifier is unstable and will oscillate. If it does not encircle -1, the amplifier is stable.

The third method uses the fact that frequency response and phase response are interrelated. The general criterion can be stated as follows:

The closed-loop gain-vs.-frequency curve must intersect the open-loop response of the op amp with a net slope of less than −40 dB/decade if the op amp is to be stable.

Figure 3–16 shows the same open-loop frequency-response curve that was shown in Fig. 3–8A. Added to the curve are several closed-loop gain curves. The gain shown as A_{V_1} intersects the open-loop gain curve when $A_{V_{cl}}$ has zero slope and $A_{V_{ol}}$ has a slope of -20 dB/decade. Thus the net slope is -20 dB/decade, and the amplifier is stable with no additional compensation. This is an unusual situation in that the closed-loop gain is 110 dB, which amounts to 316,000. This large a gain is almost never practical! Closed-loop gain curve A_{V_2} also intersects $A_{V_{ol}}$ when $A_{V_{ol}}$ has a slope of -20 dB/decade, but at that point A_{V_2} has a slope of $+20$ dB/decade. Thus the *net* slope at the point of intersection is -40 dB/decade. This amplifier is unstable, because the shape of the closed-loop gain curve implies a single RC high-pass filter, which can add an additional phase shift to that already contributed by the op amp. Curve A_{V_3} has a slope of zero at the point of intersection, but it intersects the open-loop gain curve where its slope is -40 dB/decade. So this amplifier is also unstable. Curve A_{V_4} has a slope of -40 dB/decade where it intersects the $A_{V_{ol}}$ curve, so even though the slope of the $A_{V_{ol}}$ curve at that point is -60 dB/decade, the net slope is only -20 dB/decade; so the amplifier is stable.

The examples in Fig. 3–16 illustrate two ways in which stability can be ensured: using a very high closed-loop gain (impractical), and modifying the feedback network to provide reduced closed-loop high-frequency response. Compensation networks connected to the "comp." pins of an uncompensated op amp provide a third method. They allow the insertion of RC elements to shape the gain of a single stage of the op amp to modify the closed-loop response curve as desired.

Figure 3–17 shows four methods of compensation that can be applied to uncompensated op amps. (Each amplifier shown in the figure is a balanced amplifier, because this is the most general kind of amplifier circuit. However, the compensation networks shown can be used with any kind of amplifier circuit.) The first and simplest is single-capacitor compensation. The capacitor forms a local feedback loop

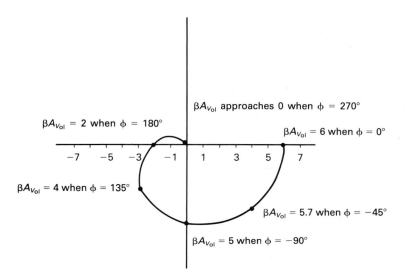

$\beta A_{V_{ol}}$ approaches 0 when $\phi = 270°$

$\beta A_{V_{ol}} = 2$ when $\phi = 180°$

$\beta A_{V_{ol}} = 6$ when $\phi = 0°$

−7   −5   −3   −1   1   3   5   7

$\beta A_{V_{ol}} = 4$ when $\phi = 135°$

$\beta A_{V_{ol}} = 5.7$ when $\phi = -45°$

$\beta A_{V_{ol}} = 5$ when $\phi = -90°$

FIGURE 3–15A: Unstable Amplifier

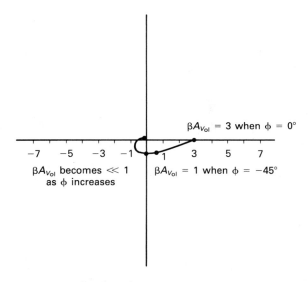

$\beta A_{V_{ol}} = 3$ when $\phi = 0°$

−7   −5   −3   −1   1   3   5   7

$\beta A_{V_{ol}}$ becomes ≪ 1 as ϕ increases

$\beta A_{V_{ol}} = 1$ when $\phi = -45°$

FIGURE 3–15B: Stable Amplifier

FIGURE 3–15: Nyquist Plots

around an internal voltage-gain stage in the op amp. The effect of this capacitor is shown in the open-loop and large-signal frequency-response graphs. Notice that the gain curve for the 3-pF compensation capacitor is a straight line only for gains above 20 dB. For lower gains, the rolloff slope increases, so the larger compensation capacitor must be used. The correct compensation capacitor can be determined from

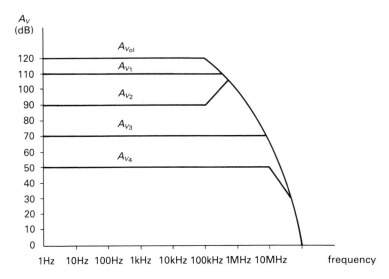

FIGURE 3–16: Closed-Loop Gain and Stability

the equation

$$C_{comp} = \frac{R_i(30\text{ pF})}{R_i + R_f}$$

(3.25)

Two-capacitor compensation incorporates a two-section *RC* filter that applies negative feedback around a voltage-gain stage and the output stage of the op amp. The critical frequencies of the two stages are different, giving a −40 dB/decade slope at lower frequencies and changing to a −20 dB/decade slope at higher frequencies. This results in the "swaybacked" open-loop characteristic shown in the figure, which still has a GBW of 1 MHz, just as the 30-pF single-capacitor network did. But it has far less detrimental effects upon the large-signal response than did the single-capacitor compensation. The values of the capacitors are chosen as follows:

$$C_1 = \frac{R_i(30\text{ pF})}{R_i + R_f}$$

(3.26)

$$C_2 = 10C_1$$

(3.27)

The reason that both the single-capacitor and the two-capacitor compensation networks affect the large-signal frequency response is that they both decrease the slew rate. This happens because time is required to charge the effective capacitances to ground. Another method of reducing high-frequency phase-shift problems is to simply isolate the stages causing those problems and shunt the high-frequency signals around them. This method *feeds* the high-frequency signals *forward* inside the amplifier, around the offending stages, and so it is called *feedforward* compensation. Another name that is sometimes used for this type of compensation is *lead* compensation, since the circuit that results is a high-pass filter, which introduces a phase lead. The circuit is shown as the third circuit in Fig. 3–17. The 150-pF capacitor is

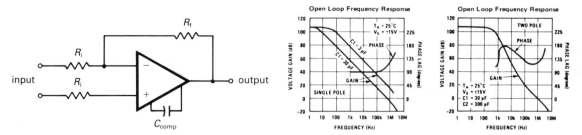

FIGURE 3–17A: Single-Capacitor Compensation *(Reprinted with permission of National Semiconductor Corp.)*

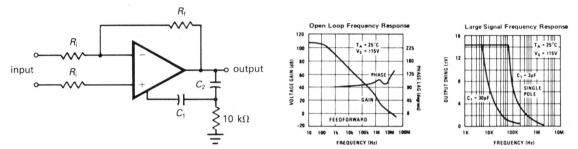

FIGURE 3–17B: Two-Capacitor Compensation *(Reprinted with permission of National Semiconductor Corp.)*

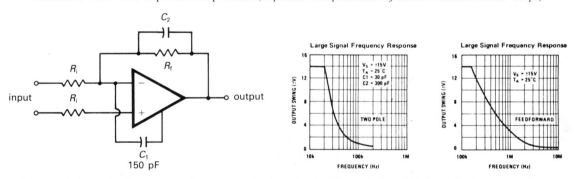

FIGURE 3–17C: Feedforward (Lead) Compensation *(Reprinted with permission of National Semiconductor Corp.)*

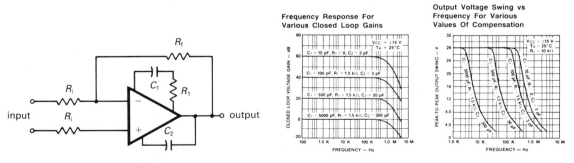

FIGURE 3–17D: Compensation for 709 Family *(Copyright Fairchild Semiconductor Corporation. Used by permission.)*

FIGURE 3–17: Frequency-Compensation Networks

the one that supplies the feedforward effect by passing the input signal around the input stage of the op amp, which is the stage having the lowest critical frequency. Capacitor C_2 is a part of a lag network that introduces a -20 dB/decade slope in the gain of the unbypassed stages of the op amp. Its critical frequency is about 3 MHz. As you can see, the resulting GBW has been increased to 10 MHz, and the large-signal frequency response has also been drastically improved. The value of C_2 is

$$C_2 = \frac{1}{(2\pi R_f)(3 \text{ MHz})} \tag{3.28}$$

The fourth compensation circuit in Fig. 3–17 is used with the 709 op amp and its relatives. The combination of C_1 and R_1 provide a lag network around the second stage of the op amp's circuitry, and C_2 provides a similar function for the output stage. The recommended compensation components for four different gains are shown in the figure, along with the resulting closed-loop and large-signal frequency-response curves.

The selection of an appropriate frequency-compensation scheme depends upon the specific op amp used. Therefore, the data sheet for the op amp you intend to use should be consulted before you try to design a compensation network.

NOISE

Many applications of op amps involve very small input signals. When these are DC signals, good compensation against the effects of bias currents and offset voltages is essential. But when the signals are AC, there are other types of error signals generated within the circuit that must be minimized. *Noise* may be defined as any undesired signal. Such a definition would include harmonics and other spurious frequencies generated within the op-amp circuit. For our purposes, we will only include the random noise created in the circuit without respect to any input signal.

Any amplifier is susceptible to different types of noise. All of them may be roughly classed as either *external noise* or *internal noise*. External noise is noise induced either electrostatically (by capacitor action) or electromagnetically (by transformer action) from external sources. These external sources include lightning, motor-vehicle ignition systems, power-line related radiation (hum), electric equipment radiation (brush noise), and sunspot, cosmic, and space noise. We can effectively reduce external noise by placing the low-signal-level conductors and circuitry within a grounded conductive enclosure. This is the purpose of shielding in cables, such as those used for oscilloscope probes.

Internal noise is generated within the circuit itself. It includes noise from several causes. The first is the discrete nature of electron flow. Since electrons are discrete charge carriers, each time an electron moves it creates a tiny noise pulse. More to the point, each time an electron bumps into another particle it releases some energy, part of which is electrical energy of random frequency content. Since bumping into other particles is partially a result of resistance and partially a result of the thermal agitation of the electrons, both temperature and resistance contribute to this type of noise. This noise, called *Johnson noise* in honor of J. B. Johnson, who described it in 1928, contains equal amounts of energy at all frequencies. Therefore, by comparison with white light, which contains equal amounts of light at all light frequencies, it is said to be *white noise*. Also, since Johnson noise is generated by a random process, we can only predict the *probable* voltage or current level of the noise at any given time; the exact level is unpredictable. The statistical prediction of noise level indicates that the likelihood that a certain noise level will exist under certain conditions decreases as the level is increased or decreased from the most likely level. This rather confusing statement is clarified by Fig. 3–18. The graph shows what is called a *Gaussian distribution* of noise levels. So we can say that Johnson noise is white, which tells us something about its frequency, and we can say that it is Gaussian, which tells us something about its probable amplitude. Again, Johnson noise is a property of all conductors. The equation for the most probable amplitude of the Johnson noise in a conductor is

$$v_n^2 = 4kTR\Delta f \text{ Volts}^2$$

where k = Boltzman's constant = $1.38 \cdot 10^{-23}$ J/°K

T = temperature in °K

R = resistance in ohms

Δf = bandwidth over which the measurement is made, in hertz

This equation clearly shows the effect of temperature and resistance upon noise level. It can be simplified by lumping all the constants and most-common variables together:

$$v_n = (4 \text{ nV}/\sqrt{\text{Hz}})(\sqrt{R/1 \text{ k}\Omega})(\sqrt{\Delta f}) \qquad (3.29)$$

This equation is valid for a temperature of 298 °K (25°C). To use it, simply plug in the value of R to be used and multiply by the square root of the bandwidth for the total voltage. (However, see page 134 for a discussion of the noise bandwidth.)

Another type of internal noise results from an electric current crossing a potential barrier, which occurs in any electronic device. This noise was dubbed *shot noise* long ago, because it sounds like lead shot hitting a tin roof. Shot noise acts as a

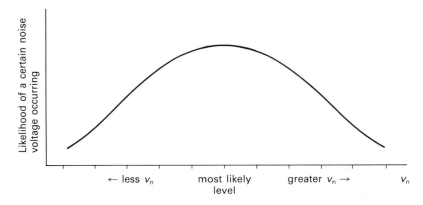

FIGURE 3–18: Gaussian Distribution

current source rather than a voltage source, and its most probable value is

$$i_s^2 = 2qI_{DC}\Delta f$$

where q is the charge in coulombs of a single electron. Shot noise is a white noise, and it also has a Gaussian distribution of levels.

The third kind of noise that occurs in op amps is popcorn noise, named for its sound. Popcorn noise is difficult to predict, but careful processing of semiconductors at the manufacturing stage reduces it. In addition, op amps producing excessive popcorn noise are usually rejected by quality-control testing at the manufacturer's plant.

The last kind of semiconductor noise is $1/f$ noise, sometimes called *flicker noise*. It is caused by imperfections in the semiconductor material. This kind of noise also acts as a current source, and, as can be seen from the next equation, its level is inversely proportional to frequency, hence its name.

$$i_f^2 = k\frac{I_{DC}a}{f}$$

where a is a constant depending upon the semiconductor material itself and k is Boltzman's constant. We see that $1/f$ noise is not a white noise, because it is prevalent at low frequencies only. However, it is Gaussian in its amplitude distribution. The $1/f$ noise of a semiconductor becomes insignificant above a certain frequency, called the *noise corner frequency*. This frequency can be controlled to some extent by manufacturing processes, and it is a manufacturer's goal to make it as low as possible. Thus the range of frequencies over which $1/f$ noise is of concern is minimized.

The important things to notice about all this information on noise are the following:

1. The total power associated with Johnson, shot, and $1/f$ noise depends upon the bandwidth of the circuit.
2. The value of the Johnson-noise-voltage source also depends upon temperature.
3. Greater resistance also results in greater Johnson noise.
4. The DC current—in this case, the bias current of the op-amp input stage—directly affects the value of the shot and $1/f$ noise sources.

It is certainly not worth your time to try to memorize the equations for the various types of noise, but understanding the brief introduction that has just been given will be a help in the study we will now make of how to minimize noise in an amplifier circuit.

Figure 3–19 shows an op-amp amplifier circuit with its internal noise sources. The noise sources are identified as follows:

- $v_{n_{s-}}$—the Johnson noise produced by the resistor R_i, including the Thevenin resistance of the signal source. (In a noninverting amplifier, this would be the noise produced by R_g.)
- $v_{n_{s+}}$—the Johnson noise produced by the resistor R_{comp}. (In a balanced or noninverting amplifier, this would be the resistance of the input or compensating resistor and of the signal source.)
- $i_{n_{i+}}$ and $i_{n_{i-}}$—the shot noise, popcorn noise, and $1/f$ noise resulting from bias-current flow in the input transistors.
- v_{n_a}—the difference signal resulting from comparing the Johnson noise in the

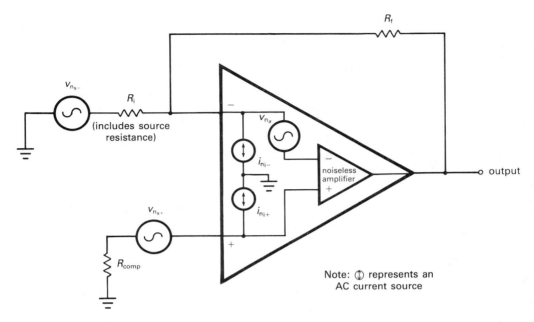

FIGURE 3–19: Op-Amp Noise Sources

inverting input to the Johnson noise in the noninverting input. This noise arises because of conduction in the equivalent base resistance of the input transistors ($r_{b'}$). Since it is random in nature, it does not in general cancel out, even though it appears at both inputs. The difference therefore acts as a differential signal source.

Since the op amp amplifies the difference between input *voltages*, the noise currents must be turned into noise voltages before they are amplified. This occurs when they flow through the resistances from each input to ground. The total equivalent input noise results from the addition of all these noise sources' values in an rms fashion:

$$v_{\text{noise,in}} = \sqrt{v_{n_a}^2 + (i_{n_{i+}}R_{\text{comp}})^2 + [i_{n_{i-}}(R_i \| R_f)]^2 + v_{n_{s-}}^2 + v_{n_{s+}}^2} \qquad (3.30)$$

In general, the schemes for minimizing noise work to reduce or eliminate the effects of one or more of these equivalent noise generators.

The most obvious way to reduce noise is to use an op amp specifically designed to have low noise. Typical specifications for noise current and voltage for standard and low-noise op amps are given in Table 3–B. Notice that there is a 4:1 difference in noise-voltage specifications between the 741 and the LM381. However, this may or may not make much difference in a specific application. If the Johnson noise for a 10-kΩ resistor is calculated for a temperature of 25°C (298 °K), we find that this resistor by itself contributes a noise voltage of 12.7 nV/$\sqrt{\text{Hz}}$. If the resistance to ground from the inputs must be this high, an LM381 will perform somewhat better than a 741, but no better than a 4136. This is another way of saying that an input-to-ground resistance of 10 kΩ causes the $v_{n_{s+}}$ and $v_{n_{s-}}$ sources to become dominant, so that the contribution of v_{n_a} is negligible.

This brings us to the next noise-reduction step, which is to keep the resistance from the op-amp inputs to ground as low as possible. In addition to reducing the values of the v_{n_s} sources, this prevents the noise currents from being turned into noise voltages, thereby reducing their contribution to the total noise. The noise current of most bipolar op amps is about 0.5 pA/$\sqrt{\text{Hz}}$. (The TL075 is an FET-input op amp. Notice that although its noise voltage is nothing to write home about, its noise current is lower than that of the others by a factor of 50.) This current becomes a noise voltage of 5 nV/$\sqrt{\text{Hz}}$ when the resistance to ground is 10 kΩ. Thus for resistances to ground less than 10 kΩ, the use of a low-noise op amp is helpful, because v_{n_a} is the dominant noise source. For resistances of 10 kΩ or so, the Johnson noise is likely to be dominant, unless a particularly noisy op amp is used. However, Johnson noise in nV/$\sqrt{\text{Hz}}$ increases with the square root of resistance, whereas voltage resulting from the i_{n_i} sources increases directly with resistance. Therefore, for resistances to ground much above 10 kΩ, the noise-current sources begin to dominate, and an FET-input op amp would become first choice, in spite of its higher noise voltage.

In the resistance-to-ground range in which Johnson noise is the most important noise source, there is another variable that can help in noise reduction. It is often assumed that temperature is a variable over which a circuit designer has no control. However, this is not always true. In circuits containing components that dissipate a lot of power, such as power-supply components, locating op amps as far as possible from these heat sources will reduce their temperature. In some cases, this reduction can have a significant effect upon noise performance. A not-to-be-ignored side benefit of this practice is the reduction of external noise induced into the op amp from the usually noisy power-supply components.

You probably noticed that all of the values of the noise sources were expressed in terms of nV/$\sqrt{\text{Hz}}$ or pA/$\sqrt{\text{Hz}}$. This implies what we said earlier—that the total rms equivalent input noise depends upon the bandwidth to which the op-amp circuit responds. There are two dimensions to the bandwidth problem. The first deals with applications for which the noise outside a certain frequency range is of no importance. Op amps used in many audio systems are examples of such applications. The ear does not respond to noise outside the range of 20 Hz to 20 kHz. Therefore, even though a given circuit may have a bandwidth of, say, 50 kHz, the noise between DC and 20 Hz and that between 20 and 50 kHz would not be important. This assumes that the noise is a very small part of the total signal voltage, which it normally would be in an audio application. The result of all this is that for applications in which the noise outside a certain frequency range is unimportant, the usable bandwidth is all that need be considered in noise calculations. Thus in our hypothetical example,

TABLE 3–B

TYPE	NOISE CURRENT (pA/$\sqrt{\text{Hz}}$)	NOISE VOLTAGE (nV/$\sqrt{\text{Hz}}$)	f_{corner} (kHz)
741 (standard)	0.54	20	10
4136 (low noise)	0.5	8	1
LM381 (low noise)	0.3	5	1
TL075 (low noise)	0.01	18	0.4

if the equivalent input noise from the v_{n_a} source (op-amp internal noise) is 12 nV/$\sqrt{\text{Hz}}$, the total source noise ($\sqrt{v_{n_{s-}}^2 + v_{n_s}^2}$) is 4 nV/$\sqrt{\text{Hz}}$, the total noise current is 0.5 pA/$\sqrt{\text{Hz}}$, and the resistance from each input to ground is 1 kΩ, we would calculate the total equivalent input noise as follows:

1. Input noise from noise-current sources:

$$v_{n_i} = i_n R \qquad (3.31)$$
$$= (0.5 \text{ pA}/\sqrt{\text{Hz}})(1 \text{ k}\Omega) = 0.5 \text{ nV}/\sqrt{\text{Hz}}$$

where R is the resistance from the current source to ground.

2. Total noise voltage per $\sqrt{\text{Hz}}$: Since the v_{n_a} noise is over 3 times the next largest noise source, it will be dominant and we can ignore the other sources, to a good approximation.

3. Total equivalent input noise:

$$v_{n,\text{total}} = v_n \sqrt{BW_n} \qquad (3.32)$$

Since we are approximating v_n as v_{n_a}, this gives

$$v_{n,\text{total}} = v_{n_a}\sqrt{BW_n} = (12 \text{ nV}/\sqrt{\text{Hz}})\sqrt{20 \text{ kHz}} = 1.7 \text{ } \mu V$$

If we had used the 50-kHz bandwidth of the amplifier for BW in the equation, the result would have been 2.7 μV. In fact, this is the amount of noise that would be measured by a wideband AC voltmeter, but much of it is not important to our application.

The second dimension to the bandwidth problem deals with applications in which *any* noise produced by the amplifier is of concern. An example of this type of situation would be a measurement system. If the output of an op amp were fed to a D'Arsonval meter, which is typically accurate up to the low megahertz range, any noise that the op amp is capable of producing would add to the meter indication. In this case, the bandwidth by which the noise sources are multiplied would be the *noise bandwidth* of the amplifier. This requires a bit more explanation. Figure 3–20 shows a frequency-response curve for an amplifier. For this amplifier, f_c is about 100 kHz. This means that if we calculated the equivalent input noise for this

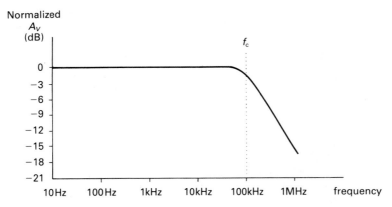

FIGURE 3–20: Frequency Response of a Typical Amplifier

J. B. Johnson, who discovered that all conductors produce a predictable amount of white noise. His 1928 experiments at Bell Telephone Laboratories led to this noise being labeled as "Johnson Noise." (Courtesy of AT&T.)

amplifier, our first inclination would be to use 100 kHz as the bandwidth. However, the gain above 100 kHz is not zero, so there is some energy present in the amplifier's output from frequencies above 100 kHz. Using a certain bandwidth in the noise calculations implies that the noise voltage and current are constant (per $\sqrt{\text{Hz}}$) below the upper end of the band and zero beyond the limits of the band. As we have just observed, this is not so. Therefore, we must use an *equivalent noise bandwidth* that will extend just far enough beyond the actual f_c so that the results of our noise calculations come out right. Sometimes this equivalent upper critical frequency is thought of as a "brick wall" to frequencies above it. We can derive this equivalent bandwidth just by multiplying the actual bandwidth by a correction factor. The value of the correction factor depends upon the rolloff slope of the amplifier, as shown in Table 3–C. Notice that as the slope becomes steeper (more nearly like a brick wall), the correction factor becomes smaller. Thus for our 100-kHz-bandwidth amplifier, the noise bandwidth would be 157 kHz. For an equivalent input noise voltage of 12 nV/$\sqrt{\text{Hz}}$, this gives a total equivalent input noise of (12 nV/$\sqrt{\text{Hz}}$)$\sqrt{157 \text{ kHz}}$ = 4.75 mV. If we had used the uncorrected bandwidth of 100 kHz, our answer would have been 3.8 mV, which is 20% low.

So far, except for identifying $1/f$ noise, we have limited our discussion to white noise. In many applications, the lower end of the frequency response includes a significant part of the range in which $1/f$ noise predominates. As you remember, $1/f$ noise begins to predominate over other internal noise sources at a certain frequency called f_{corner}, and increases linearly as frequency decreases. In including the effects of $1/f$ noise in our calculations, we find that we have three cases:

1. The lower critical frequency of the amplifier is at least twice the noise corner frequency. In capacitor-coupled circuits, this is sometimes true. In this case, the total equivalent input noise is just

$$v_{\text{n,total}} = v_n \sqrt{\text{BW}_n} \qquad (3.32)$$

    where v_n is the total noise voltage per $\sqrt{\text{Hz}}$.

2. The passband of the amplifier is entirely below f_{corner}. This could be true for many DC and VLF AC measurement circuits. The total equivalent input noise for such an amplifier is

$$v_{\text{n,total}} = v_n \sqrt{f_{\text{corner}} \ln\left(\frac{f_{\text{high}}}{f_{\text{low}}}\right)} \qquad (3.33)$$

    where f_{high} and f_{low} are the upper and lower critical frequencies of the amplifier.

TABLE 3–C Noise-Bandwidth Correction Factors

ROLLOFF SLOPE (dB/decade)	CORRECTION FACTOR
20	1.57
40	1.22
60	1.16
80	1.13

3. The passband of the amplifier includes, but is not limited to, the $1/f$ noise region. This means that f_{corner} is within the passband as is the most common case. In this case

$$v_{n,total} = v_n \sqrt{BW_n + f_{corner} \ln\left(\frac{f_{corner}}{f_{low}}\right)} \qquad (3.34)$$

So much for calculating the value of the equivalent input noise. Next we will look at ways to minimize the amount by which the op amp amplifies the equivalent input noise. At first glance, it would seem that all we need to do is to multiply the equivalent input noise by the gain of the amplifier to get the output noise. This is true if the amplifier is noninverting. If the amplifier is inverting, its gain is R_f/R_i, not $1 + R_f/R_i$, as for a noninverting amplifier. The difference between these two situations from a noise standpoint is that the input signal of a noninverting amplifier is applied *at the op-amp input*, whereas the input signal of an inverting amplifier is applied remote from the op-amp input (separated by the resistor R_i). As a result, the noise signal in an inverting amplifier is amplified by a gain that is greater by 1 than the signal gain. For amplifiers with large gains, this fact has no practical importance. However, for voltage followers, it means that the inverting version will have twice as much noise in the output as the noninverting version, for the same output signal voltage.

For summing amplifiers, the situation is even worse. Since the noise is always applied at the op-amp input, we obtain the noise gain by dividing the feedback resistance by the total resistance from the inverting input to ground. In other words,

$$A_{V_{noise}} = 1 + \frac{R_f}{R_{i_1} \| R_{i_2} \| \dots \| R_{i_N}} \qquad (3.35)$$

where R_{i_N} is the input resistor for source N.

All of this brings us to the concept of *signal-to-noise (S/N) ratio*. This value, usually expressed in dB, is the ratio of the signal voltage to the noise voltage at the same point in a circuit.

$$(S/N)_{dB} = 20 \log_{10}\left(\frac{V_{signal}}{V_{noise}}\right) \qquad (3.36)$$

Thus we can say that if we build inverting and noninverting voltage followers using the same type of op amp, the inverting follower will have a 6-dB lower S/N ratio than will the noninverting one. And if the voltage follower is a summing circuit, that S/N ratio becomes worse with the introduction of each additional input.

It can be shown that if the gain of the first stage of a multistage amplifier is at least 10, the S/N ratio of the entire amplifier is essentially determined by the first stage. In other words, the noise contribution of subsequent stages is unimportant. This, then, provides the solution to the noisiness of summing amplifiers. If several signals are to be summed, but a high S/N ratio is necessary, each signal should be preamplified by a low-noise stage with a gain of at least 10 before the signals are applied to the summing stage.

EXAMPLE

Problem

Design a low-noise microphone mixer. The completed unit is to have four balanced inputs, each having an impedance of 1 kΩ. The mixer is to be capable of a maximum output of 8 V_{rms}. At maximum gain, a 0.5-mV signal at any input must be capable of providing an output of 1 V. The S/N ratio at the output is to be at least 60 dB when the unit is operating at maximum gain with all inputs fed by 150 Ω microphones. The maximum input level before clipping must be at least 100 mV_{rms}. The frequency response is to be flat within 3 dB from 10 Hz to 20 kHz.

Solution

1. We will use the circuit shown in Fig. 3–21A for the input stages. The necessary gain is $V_{out}/V_{in} = 1$ V/0.5 mV $= 2000$.
2. We will choose a low-noise op amp. The LM381 looks like an obvious choice, based upon the noise data given on page 132. This unit has a noise voltage of 5 nV/$\sqrt{Hz}$ and a noise current of 0.3 pA/$\sqrt{Hz}$. However, as you can see from the complete data sheet in Appendix A, no CMRR is specified for this op amp. (This happens because a design tradeoff was made in designing the IC in order to have lower noise.) Therefore, we must choose between a more complex circuit (the instrumentation amplifier from Chapter 2) and a slightly noisier op amp. For simplicity, we will try the latter choice. We will use a 4136 op amp. This unit has a noise voltage of 8 nV/$\sqrt{Hz}$, a noise current of 0.5 pA/$\sqrt{Hz}$, and a GBW of 3 MHz, as we can see from the complete data sheet in Appendix A. The 4136 is internally compensated.
3. We will try a gain of 100 for the input stages. A quick check shows that the bandwidth of these stages will be 5 MHz/100 $= 50,000$, which is quite high enough. With the maximum input, this will produce an output voltage of (100 mV)(100) $= 30$ V_{rms}. The slew rate required for a 10-V_{rms} output at 20 kHz is

$$\text{SR} = 2\pi f_c V_P = (2\pi)(20 \text{ kHz})(10 \text{ } V_{rms})\sqrt{2} = 1.8 \text{ V } \mu s \qquad \text{(from 3.24)}$$

The 4136 has a slew rate of 1.7 V/μs, which is almost adequate for a sine-wave output, but it will produce some SID, since the available slew rate is not 5 times the minimum required. In order to avoid SID, we need to cut the required slew rate by about a factor of 5, which means cutting the gain by a factor of 5. We will use a gain of 20.
4. In order to have a 1-kΩ balanced input, we will use two 500 Ω, 0.1% metal-film resistors for the R_i's. This gives us a differential input resistance of 1 kΩ. We can calculate the input noise generated by the resistance of the microphones and the R_i resistors using equation 3.29:

$$v_{n_s} = \left(4 \text{ nV}/\sqrt{\text{Hz}}\right)\left(\sqrt{\frac{R}{1 \text{ k}\Omega}}\right)(\sqrt{\Delta f}) \qquad (3.29)$$

$$v_{n_s}/\sqrt{\text{Hz}} = \left(4 \text{ nV}/\sqrt{\text{Hz}}\right)\left(\sqrt{\frac{1150 \text{ }\Omega}{1 \text{ k}\Omega}}\right)$$

$$= 4.3 \text{ nV}/\sqrt{\text{Hz}}$$

This is the total v_{n_s}, the differential input noise voltage produced by the source and input resistors. The gain of 20 means that

$$R_f = R_g = A_V R_i = (500 \text{ }\Omega)20 = 10 \text{ k}\Omega$$

To avoid having noise-current-related problems, we will change R_f to a tee circuit. We will design for an input-to-ground resistance of 500 Ω. First we choose R_t equal to about 500 Ω. We will use the standard value 470 Ω. Then

$$R_s = \frac{R_t^2}{R_i A_V + 2R_t} = \frac{470 \text{ }\Omega^2}{500 \text{ }\Omega \cdot 20 + 2 \cdot 470 \text{ }\Omega}$$

$$= 20.2 \text{ }\Omega$$

We will use 22 Ω resistors for R_s. Now we make R_g equal to the resistance to ground from the inverting input, which we have just designed to be about 500 Ω. Using a 500 Ω trimpot will allow adjustment for the best CMRR.

5. The noise-voltage contribution from the noise-current sources ($i_{n_{i+}}$ and $i_{n_{i-}}$) is just the noise current of the op amp multiplied by the resistance from each input to ground. Thus,

$$v_{n_{i+}} = i_{n_{i+}} R_g = (0.5 \text{ pA}/\sqrt{\text{Hz}})(500 \text{ }\Omega) = 0.25 \text{ nV}/\sqrt{\text{Hz}} \qquad \text{(from 3.31)}$$

The noise from $i_{n_{i-}}$ is the same. Neither of these sources is significant when compared to the other sources.

6. Since the noise occurring outside the 10-Hz–20-kHz band is not important, we will use 20 kHz as our noise bandwidth. The op amp's internal noise is 8 nV/$\sqrt{\text{Hz}}$. We can find the total equivalent noise resulting from this source, including 1/f noise, as shown on page 135. Since only part of our amplifier's passband includes the 1/f range, we use the case 3 equation:

$$v_{n_a,\text{total}} = v_{n_a}\sqrt{\text{BW}_n + f_{\text{corner}} \ln\left(\frac{f_{\text{corner}}}{f_{\text{low}}}\right)}$$

$$= (8 \text{ nV}/\sqrt{\text{Hz}})\sqrt{20 \text{ kHz} + (1 \text{ kHz}) \ln\left(\frac{1 \text{ kHz}}{10 \text{ Hz}}\right)} = 1.3 \text{ }\mu\text{V} \qquad (3.34)$$

We did not include the v_{n_s} sources in this calculation because they are Johnson noise, which is white. In other words, they have no 1/f component. The total noise from the v_{n_s} sources becomes

$$v_{n_s,\text{total}} = v_{n_s}\sqrt{BW_n} = (4.3 \text{ nV}/\sqrt{\text{Hz}})\sqrt{20 \text{ kHz}} = 0.6 \text{ }\mu\text{V} \qquad (3.32)$$

Adding these two sources in an rms fashion, we obtain the total equivalent input noise:

$$v_{n,\text{total}} = \sqrt{v_{n_s}^2 + v_{n_a}^2} = \sqrt{(1.3 \text{ }\mu\text{V})^2 + (0.6 \text{ }\mu\text{V})^2} = 1.4 \text{ }\mu\text{V} \qquad (\text{from } 3.30)$$

In the above equation, we have omitted the noise-current terms, which were insignificant, and have used a single V_{n_s} term that represents the total differential input Johnson noise.

7. The noise gain of this amplifier is greater by 1 than the signal gain, as discussed earlier. Thus the output noise voltage from this stage is

$$v_{n,\text{out}} = v_{\text{in,total}} A_{V_n} = (1.3 \text{ }\mu\text{V})(21) = 27 \text{ }\mu\text{V}$$

8. The summing stage can supply the remaining gain, which is $2000/20 = 100$. In order to provide 8 V_{rms} at a maximum frequency of 30 kHz, we will use a high-slew-rate amplifier, the LM318. The data sheet for this op amp (in Appendix A) shows a slew rate of $50 \text{ V}/\mu\text{s}$. 8 V_{rms} is 11.3_{V_P}, so we only need a slew rate of

$$SR = 2\pi f_{\text{max}} V_P = 2.12 \text{ V}/\mu\text{s} \qquad (\text{from } 3.24)$$

The GBW of the 318 is 15 MHz, giving us a bandwidth of 150 kHz at a gain of 100.

9. We will apply the inputs through 1-kΩ pots from the input-stage outputs, to provide gain adjustment. (Although we could use pots as the R_i's for the summer, this would cause loading of the outputs of the input amplifiers, since the input resistance could fall too low.) We will choose a 1-kΩ resistor for each R_i. This makes $R_f = 100$ kΩ. The circuit is shown in Fig. 3–21B.

10. The equivalent resistance from the inverting input to ground is made up of four parallel combinations. Each of these combinations is a 1-kΩ resistor and a 1-kΩ pot. Thus the maximum value of each combination is 2 kΩ, and the minimum is 1 kΩ. The total resistance to ground from the inverting input must therefore fall between 250 Ω and 500 Ω. This resistance is small enough that we can probably omit R_{comp}. The data sheet for the LM318 shows a maximum bias current of 250 nA. This will give an output offset voltage of

$$v_{\text{output offset}} = I_B R_{\text{mismatch}} A_V \qquad (3.04)$$
$$= (250 \text{ nA})(500 \text{ }\Omega)(100) = 12.5 \text{ mV}$$

No bias-current compensation is needed.

11. Just as a check, we'll calculate the output noise voltage from the summer resulting from that stage alone, then compare this value to the output noise voltage resulting from the noise fed into the summer from stage 1. In this way, we'll test the validity of our assumption about stage 2's noise contribution not being important. Since the noninverting input is grounded, its V_{n_s} and i_{n_i} contributions are zero. The i_{n_i} specification for the 318 is the same as that for the 4136, so since the circuit is similar, we will ignore the con-

tribution from $i_{n_{i+}}$ on the same grounds as discussed in step 5. The remaining input noise sources are $v_{n_{s+}}$ and v_{n_a}:

$$v_{n_{s+}} = (4 \text{ nV}/\sqrt{\text{Hz}})\sqrt{500 \ \Omega/1 \text{ k}\Omega} = 2.8 \text{ nV}\sqrt{\text{Hz}} \qquad (3.29)$$

This is negligible. From the spec sheet, v_{n_a} is 11 nV/$\sqrt{\text{Hz}}$, and f_{corner} is 1 kHz. Thus

$$v_{n_s,\text{total}} = (11 \text{ nV}/\sqrt{\text{Hz}})\sqrt{20 \text{ kHz} + f(1\text{kHz}) \ln\left(\frac{1 \text{ kHz}}{10 \text{ Hz}}\right)} = 1.7 \ \mu\text{V} \qquad (3.34)$$

The worst-case noise gain from the summer will be when the resistance from the inputs to ground is minimum, which is 250 Ω. This will give

$$A_{V_n} = \frac{100 \text{ k}\Omega}{250 \ \Omega} = 400$$

Thus the output noise from the summer by itself would be $(1.7 \ \mu\text{V})(400) = 680 \ \mu\text{V}$. The output noise from the summer resulting from the noise fed into it from the four input stages is the rms combination of the four input stages' output noises, multiplied by the signal gain:

$$v_{n,\text{out } 2} = \sqrt{4}(29 \ \mu\text{V})(100) = 5.8 \text{ mV}$$

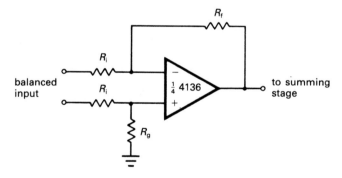

FIGURE 3–21A: Input Stage

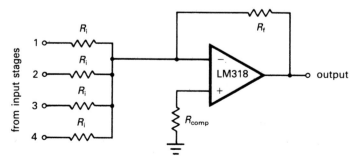

FIGURE 3–21B: Summing Stage

FIGURE 3–21: Audio Mixer Design Example

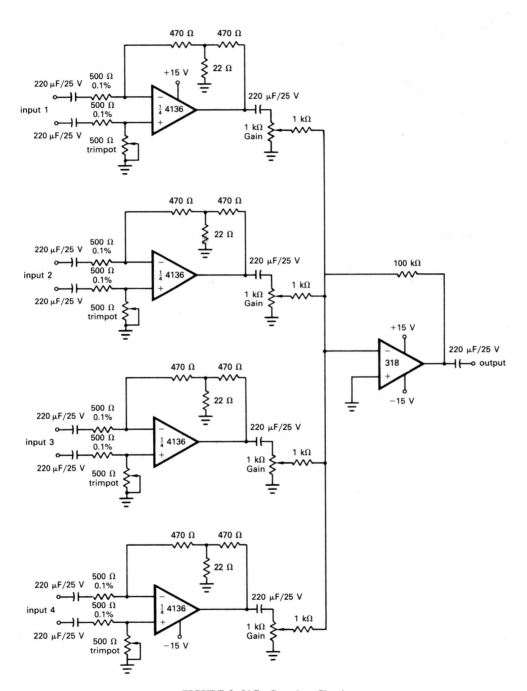

FIGURE 3–21C: Complete Circuit

The signal gain rather than the noise gain was used here because the noise fed from a preceding stage is indistinguishable from the signal coming from that earlier stage. Noise gain is used only for noise generated within the stage being considered. We see that the noise at the output of the summing stage is predominantly noise that was generated in the input stage, as we expected.

12. Now we can calculate the overall S/N ratio. We have already calculated the output noise voltage, which is about 5.8 mV. The maximum output signal is usually used in calculating S/N ratio, and this is 8 V. Therefore, the S/N ratio is 8 V/5.8 mV = 1379. We convert this to dB by taking the $\log_{10}$ of the numerical S/N ratio and multiplying by 20:

$$(S/N)_{dB} = 20 \log_{10}(1379) = 63 \text{ dB} \qquad (\text{from } 3.36)$$

This is well within specifications.

13. The input coupling capacitors are chosen so that their reactance at 10 Hz is less than one-tenth of the input resistance. This resistance is 1 kΩ, so

$$C_{input} = \frac{1}{(2\pi)(10 \text{ Hz})(100 \text{ }\Omega)} = 159 \text{ }\mu\text{F}$$

We will use 220 μF, which is the next larger standard value. The coupling capacitor from the input stage to the summing stage is the same value, since the input resistance of the summing stage is also 1 kΩ. The output should never feed a load lower than 1 kΩ, so we will also use the same value for the output capacitor.

14. In order to have an output of 8 V_{rms} (11.3 V_P), we must have at least a 14-V bipolar supply. We will use 15 V. The completed design is shown in Fig. 3–21C.

DESIGN NOTES

A number of simplified circuit design methods were presented in the Chapter 2 design notes. These methods assumed ideal op amps. In Chapter 3, we have discussed ways of taking into account several of the shortcomings that real op amps have, namely bias- and offset-current effects, frequency-response effects, and noise. The design equations for working with these topics will be given again here. The Chapter 4 design notes will present a generalized design procedure for op-amp amplifier circuits.

Bias Compensation

Bias compensation involves making the DC resistance seen from the inverting input to ground equal to the DC resistance from the noninverting input to ground. This means:

Inverting amplifier: R_{comp} connected between noninverting (+) input and ground; $R_{comp} = R_f \| R_i$ if input is not capacitor coupled; $R_{comp} = R_f$ if input is capacitor coupled (Fig. 3–22).

Noninverting amplifier: R_{comp} connected in series with input if input is not capacitor coupled; from noninverting (+) input to ground for capacitor-coupled inputs. $R_{comp} = R_f \| R_g$ (Fig. 3–23).

Balanced amplifier: The balancing process also achieves bias compensation.

Inverting summer: R_{comp} connected between noninverting (+) input and ground; $R_{comp} = R_f \|$ (all R_i's) if inputs are not capacitor-coupled; $R_{comp} = R_f$ if inputs are capacitor coupled (Fig. 3–24).

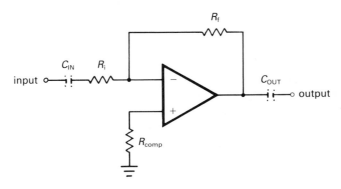

FIGURE 3–22: Bias-Current Compensation for the Inverting Amplifier

(continued)

(continued from page 143)

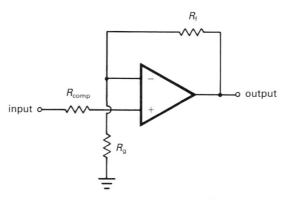

FIGURE 3–23A: Direct Coupled

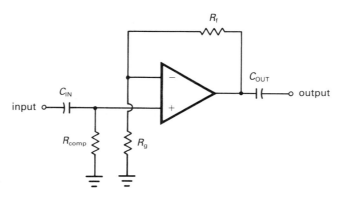

FIGURE 3–23B: Capacitor Coupled

FIGURE 3–23: Bias-Current Compensation for the Noninverting Amplifier

Noninverting summer: For capacitor-coupled inputs, R_{comp} is connected between noninverting (+) input and ground, and is equal to $R_f \| R_g$. For inputs that are not capacitor coupled, choose R_g equal to the parallel combination of the R_i's, then choose R_f accordingly (Fig. 3–25).

There are two special circuits that are useful when high input impedances are required, but low resistances from the inputs to ground are needed for proper bias-compensation and offset reasons:

Tee feedback circuit: Choose $R_{t_1} = R_{t_2} = R_t$ much smaller than R_i. Then make $R_s = R_t^2/(R_1 A_V + 2R_t)$ (Fig. 3–26).

Design Notes

(continued from page 144)

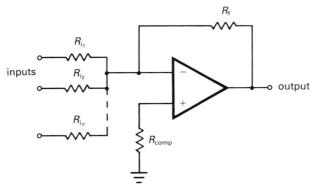

FIGURE 3–24: Bias-Current Compensation for Inverting Summer

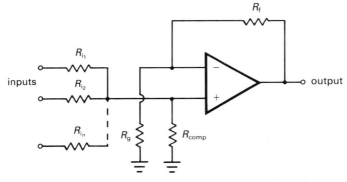

FIGURE 3–25: Bias-Current Compensation for Noninverting Summer

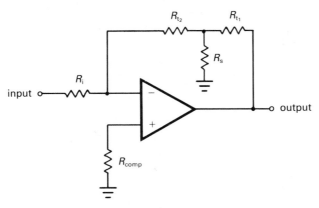

FIGURE 3–26: Tee Feedback Circuit (can be used with noninverting amplifier or summer also)

Design
Notes

(continued from page 145)

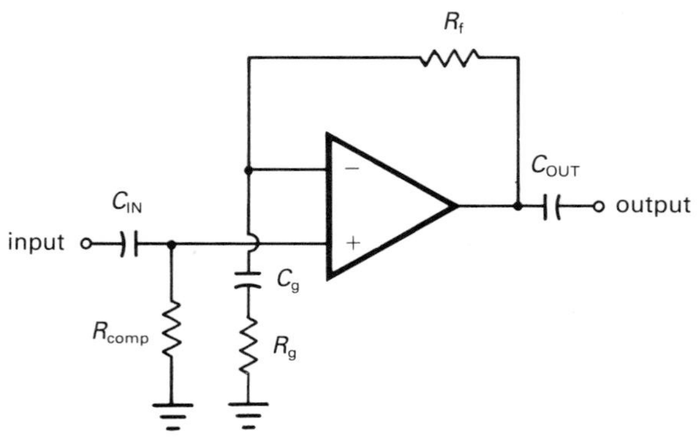

FIGURE 3–27: Isolated R_g Circuit

Isolated R_g circuit: R_{comp} connected between noninverting $(+)$ input and ground; $R_{comp} = R_f$ (Fig. 3–27).

Frequency Response

$$f_c = \frac{\text{GBW}}{A_V \sqrt{2^{1/n} - 1}} \qquad \text{(from 3.09 and 3.20)}$$

where $n =$ the number of stages.

$$f_{10\%} = 0.484 f_c \tag{3.14}$$

To determine f_{low}, choose C_{IN}, C_{OUT}, and C_g (for the isolated R_g circuit) as follows:

$$C_{IN} = \frac{10}{2\pi f_{low} R_{IN}} \tag{3.37}$$

$$C_{OUT} = \frac{10}{2\pi f_{low} R_{load}} \tag{3.38}$$

$$C_g = \frac{10}{2\pi f_{low} R_g} \tag{3.39}$$

The rise time of an output pulse is given by the greater of

Design Notes

(continued from page 146)

$$(1) \ t_{rise} = \frac{0.35}{BW} \qquad \text{(from 3.22)}$$

or

$$(2) \ t_{rise} = \frac{0.8V_{out}}{SR} \qquad \text{(from 3.23)}$$

The maximum output frequency that an op amp can deliver at a given V_P is

$$f_{max,SR} = \frac{SR}{2\pi V_P}$$

For negligible SID, this should be at least 5 times the maximum frequency needed.

In designing frequency-compensating networks for uncompensated op amps, remember that lag compensation reduces the slew rate, but lead compensation does not. Use the manufacturer's data sheets for guidance.

Noise

Noise can be reduced by the use of

1. Low-noise op amps.
2. Minimum resistance from each input to ground. Omit R_{comp} if allowable from an offset-voltage standpoint.
3. All techniques to keep the op amp cool.

The noise voltage from the various noise sources includes

Johnson noise from resistors:

$$v_{n_s} = (4 \ nV/\sqrt{Hz})\sqrt{\frac{R}{1 \ k\Omega}} \qquad (3.29)$$

assuming a temperature of 25° C. Calculate this value for each input, then sum the two values in an rms fashion:

$$v_n = \sqrt{v_{n_{s-}}^2 + v_{n_{s+}}^2} \qquad (3.30)$$

Op-amp noise-current noise:

$$v_{n_i} = i_{n_{i+}} (R \text{ to ground}) \qquad (3.31)$$

Calculate the value for each input, then sum in an rms fashion.

Design Notes

(continued from page 147)

Noise BW conversion factor: Multiply the actual bandwidth by 1.57 for a -20 dB/decade rolloff slope; 1.22 for -40 dB/decade; 1.16 for -60 dB/decade; 1.13 for -80 dB/decade.

Total white noise: Multiply v_{n_s} by the square root of the noise bandwidth.

Op-amp-generated noise: Use the v_n specification given in the op-amp data sheet. Sum this in an rms fashion with v_{n_i} to get v_{n_t} (or ignore one if the other clearly dominates), then

1. If f_{low} is at least twice f_{corner},

$$v_{n,total} = v_{n_t} \sqrt{BW_n} \qquad (3.32)$$

2. If f_{high} is less than f_{corner},

$$v_{n,total} = v_{n_t} \sqrt{f_{corner} \ln \left(\frac{f_{high}}{f_{low}} \right)} \qquad (3.33)$$

3. If f_{corner} is between f_{high} and f_{low},

$$v_{n,total} = v_{n_t} \sqrt{BW_n + f_{corner} \ln \left(\frac{f_{corner}}{f_{low}} \right)} \qquad (3.34)$$

In any design, if v_{n_i} is the dominant noise source, try an FET-input op amp in order to reduce i_n.

Finally, find $v_{n,equiv}$ by rms-summing $v_{n,total}$ and the total white noise.

$$v_{n,out} = v_{n,equiv} A_{V_n}$$

SUMMARY

Op amps require small currents to bias the inputs. These currents produce voltage differences at the op-amp inputs unless the resistance from each input to ground is equal.

Compensation techniques for equalizing the voltages from each input to ground depend upon the circuit being used.

Even when the resistances are equal, the difference between the bias currents (called the offset current) produces a voltage difference between inputs. This difference can be adjusted out by nulling methods, but the adjustment is valid only for a specific temperature.

The frequency response of an op-amp amplifier depends upon the open-loop response of the op amp itself, given on the data sheet as the gain-bandwidth product or GBW, and the closed-loop gain of the circuit.

With a given op amp, greater frequency response can be achieved by splitting the gain up into two or three stages.

The small-signal rise time of an output pulse can be predicted by dividing the constant 0.35 by the bandwidth of the amplifier.

The slew rate of an op amp defines the relationship between maximum output voltage and frequency. It also establishes the rise time for large pulses.

Uncompensated op amps require external compensation networks in order to operate at gains less than $A_{V_{ol}}$ without oscillating. The design of these networks is discussed in the op amps' data sheets.

Noise in op-amp circuits comes from three causes: Johnson noise in the external resistors, internal op-amp noise-voltage sources, and internal op-amp noise-current sources.

Noise can be minimized by proper selection of the op amp, use of low-resistance circuits, and minimizing the temperature at which the circuit operates. In some cases, the noise reduction available by limiting bandwidth is significant.

REVIEW QUESTIONS

1. List the characteristics in a real op amp that cannot be assumed to be ideal. Discuss their effect upon circuit performance.
2. Suppose a certain op amp has I_{B+} = 530 nA and I_{B-} = 470 nA.
   (a) What is the bias current?
   (b) What is the offset current?
3. In what way does an FET-input op amp differ from a bipolar one, in terms of bias current?
4. Design both an inverting and a noninverting amplifier to the following specifications: $R_{IN} \geq$ 100 kΩ, A_V = 100, $V_{\text{output offset}}$ = 0 V. Use a 741 op amp.
5. Design an inverting summer with four inputs, each having a 5-kΩ input resistance and a gain of 50. Provide bias-current compensation. Use a 741 op amp.
6. Design a capacitor-coupled amplifier using a 741, and having a 1-MΩ input resistance, a gain of 100, and an output offset voltage of 1.5 V or less. Try the design using (a) the standard circuit, (b) tee feedback, and (c) the isolated-R_g circuit. Comment on the relative merits of each design.
7. If a 741 circuit has an output offset voltage of 3.2 V and a gain of 80, what is the minimum resistance-to-ground mismatch, assuming the op amp to be within its specifications?
8. Design an op-amp amplifier that has a gain of 100 $\pm$ 10% from 20 Hz to 50 kHz. Use capacitor coupling. Do the design using (a) 741's, and (b) any op amp chosen from the data sheets in Appendix A.
9. Sketch approximate frequency-response curves from 10 Hz to 100 kHz for each of the amplifiers you designed in problem 8. Include calculations for the upper and lower critical frequencies, the upper 10% frequency, and the rolloff slope.

10. Sketch output pulses from a 741 op amp for the following conditions. Assume the 741 is used in an amplifier with $A_v = 10$. Make your sketches to scale:
    (a) 100 mV$_{P-P}$, 1 kHz
    (b) 1 V$_{P-P}$, 1 kHz
    (c) 10 V$_{P-P}$, 1 kHz
    (d) 100 mV$_{P-P}$, 10 kHz
    (e) 1 V$_{P-P}$, 10 kHz
    (f) 10 V$_{P-P}$, 10 kHz
    Remember to calculate both bandwidth-limited and slew-rate-limited rise times.

11. Calculate the minimum slew rate for an amplifier that must put out 20 V$_{P-P}$ at 20 kHz for (a) an instrument in which SID doesn't matter, and (b) an audio application in which SID must be avoided. Choose an op amp from the data sheets in Appendix A for each application.

12. Discuss the choice of a compensation network for an LM301.

13. Draw Nyquist plots for the amplifiers whose gain and phase responses are shown in Fig. 3–8. Evaluate each one as to stability. Assume a closed-loop gain of 100.

14. What are the gain and phase margins of the compensated op amp whose characteristics are shown in Fig. 3–8B? Assume a closed-loop gain of 100.

15. By examining the frequency-response plot of Fig. 3–8A, determine:
    (a) for what range of closed-loop gain will the amplifier be stable without compensation.
    (b) if the closed-loop gain decreases at the rate of 20 dB/decade, what is the range of 1-kHz closed-loop gains for which this amplifier will be stable without compensation?

16. List the three sources of internal noise in an op-amp circuit and discuss what affects each of them.

17. Design the following amplifiers, using op amps chosen from Appendix A:
    (a) $R_{IN} = 1$ MΩ, $A_V = 10$, S/N ratio at output at least 50 dB with 1-mV input
    (b) $R_{IN} = 150$ Ω, $A_V = 40$, S/N ratio at output at least 65 dB with 0.5-mV input

18. Discuss the factors that affect noise in an amplifier and how each of them can be reduced by proper design.

LABORATORY EXPERIMENT—BIAS AND OFFSET CURRENT

Objective:

To examine the effects of bias currents on op-amp operation.

Materials:

1 741 op amp
1 10-kΩ potentiometer
miscellaneous resistors

Procedure:

1. Build an inverting amplifier using a 100-kΩ resistor for R_i and a 10-MΩ resistor for R_f. Connect the noninverting input directly to ground. Use a $\pm$15-V power supply.
2. Connect a signal generator to the input of the amplifier. Apply a 100-Hz, 100-mV$_{P\text{-}P}$ signal and measure the AC output. Calculate the gain from these measurements. (Note: If your signal generator has a capacitor-coupled output, you will need to shunt the generator with a 1-kΩ resistor to avoid having the op amp lock up.)
3. After verifying that the gain is about what you would expect, disconnect the signal generator and short the input of the amplifier (*not* the input to the op amp!) to ground.
4. Measure the DC output of the op amp.
5. Turn off the power to the circuit. Calculate the correct value for R_{comp} and install it into the circuit.
6. Apply power again and measure the DC output voltage.
7. Turn off power to the circuit and install the offset nulling circuit shown in Fig. 3–6.
8. Turn power back on and adjust the nulling circuit for zero DC output.
9. Spray the op amp with circuit cooler and remeasure the DC output.

Analysis:

1. From your measurements in step 4, calculate the bias current of your op amp.
2. From your measurement in step 6, calculate the offset current of the op amp.

Laboratory Experiment

(continued)

(continued from page 151)

3. Discuss:
   (a) the effect of circuit resistances upon the need for R_{comp}
   (b) the effect of temperature upon the nulling adjustment
   (c) the effect of circuit resistances upon the output offset voltage that results from a certain value of I_{offset}

LABORATORY EXPERIMENT—FREQUENCY RESPONSE

Objective:

To examine the effects of GBW and slew rate upon the frequency response of op-amp circuits.

Materials:

1 741 op amp
miscellaneous resistors
miscellaneous capacitors
frequency-response graph paper

Procedure:

1. Design a capacitor-coupled inverting amplifier with a gain of 100, an f_{low} of 20 Hz, and an f_c of 20 kHz. Use a 1-kΩ resistor as the load. Use as many stages as you need but not more than you need. Use a $\pm$15-V supply.
2. Build the amplifier you designed. Measure and plot the frequency response using (a) a 10-mV$_{rms}$ input and (b) a 180-mV$_{rms}$ input. For each graph, take measurements at decade multiples of 20, 30, 50, 70, and 100 Hz from 20 Hz to 20 kHz.
3. Apply 20-mV$_{P-P}$ square waves to the input of the amplifier and measure the rise times. Use the following frequencies: 10 Hz, 100 Hz, 1 kHz, 10 kHz. Repeat the measurements using 200-mV$_{P-P}$ square waves.

Analysis:

1. Calculate $f_{10\%}$ and f_c for your circuit. Compare them with the values from your measurements from step 2(a). If they do not agree, it is because the GBW of your amplifier is different from the typical value on the data

(continued from page 152)

sheet. Calculate the actual GBW from your measurements. Verify your calculation based upon your small-signal rise times.

2. Based upon the -3-dB frequency of your large-signal sine-wave measurements, calculate the slew rate of your op amp. Check this calculation by comparing it with the slew rate you calculate from your large-signal rise time measurements.

LABORATORY EXPERIMENT—LOW-NOISE DESIGN

Objectives:

To study the effect of different noise sources upon op-amp output noise level.

Materials:

1 741 op amp
1 SE5534 op amp
1 TL080 op amp
2 100-kΩ resistors
1 10-MΩ resistor
2 1-kΩ resistors
1 metal box large enough to enclose the breadboarding apparatus
1 dual-trace 'scope

Procedure:

1. Build a noninverting amplifier using $R_g = 100$ kΩ, $R_f = 10$ MΩ, and $R_{comp} = 100$ kΩ. Use a 741 with a ± 15-V supply.
2. Apply a 10-mV$_{rms}$, 1-kHz input signal and measure the gain. Verify that it is as expected.
3. Disconnect the signal generator and short the input ("far end" of R_{comp}) to ground. Connect both probes of the scope to the output of the circuit, connect the metal box to the circuit ground, and enclose the circuit in the box.
4. Set the 'scope to 1 ms/cm sweep speed. Adjust the sensitivity of the two vertical inputs so as to get two traces (one from each channel), each about 1 or 2 cm high. Carefully adjust the vertical position of the traces until the two patterns just appear to touch. Switch the inputs of both channels to ground. Measure the voltage represented by the spacing between the

(continued from page 153)

traces. This corresponds to twice the rms noise produced by the amplifier. (This is called the *tangential method* of measuring noise.)

5. Now turn off the power and change R_g to 1 kΩ, R_f to 100 kΩ, and R_{comp} to 1 kΩ. Reapply power and measure the noise again.
6. Repeat steps 1–5 using the TL080 op amp.
7. Repeat steps 1–5 using the SE5534 op amp.

Analysis:

1. Calculate the expected output noise for each of the six circuits you built. Compare your calculated and measured values.
2. The SE5534 is a very-low-noise op amp. Explain why the noise performance of a circuit using a 5534 is not always better than that of a 741.
3. The TL080 is a low-noise op amp. However, its noise-voltage specification is 18 nV/$\sqrt{\text{Hz}}$, which is only slightly better than the 20 nV/$\sqrt{\text{Hz}}$ specified for the 741. Why, then, is the TL080 considered a low-noise device?
4. Compare the noise performance of the high-impedance and the low-impedance circuits and discuss the differences.
5. Discuss the causes and cures of noise in an op-amp circuit.

chapter four

Designing with Real Op Amps

OBJECTIVES

Upon completing this chapter, you will be able to:

- Use the specification sheet for an op amp to optimize your designs.
- Design a complete op-amp amplifier, including
  1. Setting specifications
  2. Choosing an appropriate op amp
  3. Designing your circuit
  4. Connecting your op amps to either a unipolar or a bipolar power supply
- Troubleshoot circuits containing op amps.

UNDERSTANDING THE SPECIFICATION SHEET

Manufacturers of electronic devices publish several types of application literature to help engineers intelligently use their products. The most basic of these is the specification (spec) sheet or data sheet. This gives technical information on a specific device. Most manufacturers also sell data books containing abbreviated data sheets for all their devices of a certain category. For instance, it is common to publish a linear IC data book, a digital IC data book, an interface IC data book, and so on. A few of the most important specifications of best-selling devices are often grouped together in application guides. These are leaflet-sized publications that help in the selection of an appropriate IC. Finally, there are application notes. These give information about some specific aspect of design, such as noise, or about specific applications of a certain device or group of devices. The addresses of the publication offices of several IC manufacturers are listed at the end of Appendix A.

In order to make it easy for you to follow, the data sheet in Appendix A for an SE5534 op amp is given in foldout form. This allows you to look at it while reading the discussion of its contents. The data sheet is headed by a description of the op amp and its special features. The SE5534 is a low-noise op amp, so the noise voltage per $\sqrt{\text{Hz}}$ is given here. It is also a high-slew-rate amplifier, so the slew rate is also given here. Also given are the differences among the various op amps that share the same spec sheet.

The next section of the spec sheet contains the schematic and connection diagrams. Connection diagrams are given for each package in which the IC is available. These units come in an 8-pin dual-in-line (miniDIP) package, a 10-lead flat pack, or a 20-lead chip-carrier package. The type number that must be ordered to obtain a particular package type is also given.

Section three gives the absolute maximum ratings. If these ratings are exceeded, even for a very brief period of time, the op amp is likely to be destroyed. The *continuous maximum power dissipation* requires a bit of explanation, though. First, notice that the allowable power dissipation depends upon the case style. Second, this specification includes not only the dissipation for one op amp—as in this data sheet—but for all op amps within the package. Thus each op amp in a quad package should be allowed to dissipate only one fourth of the specified total. The maximum power dissipated by an op amp is given approximately by

$$P_{\text{DISS,max}} = \frac{V_{\text{OUT,P-P}}}{40R_L} + V_{CC}I_{CC}$$

where $V_{\text{OUT,P-P}}$ is the peak-to-peak output voltage, I_{CC} is the quiescent current drawn by the op amp, as given on the data sheet, and R_L is the load resistance.

The section on electrical characteristics contains most of the information needed for designs. Many of these items will already be familiar to you from your earlier studies. At the top of the section are given the measurement conditions common to all of the stated specs, namely, supply voltage and ambient temperature. More specific test conditions under which each characteristic was derived are stated beside the appropriate characteristic. This allows the designer to determine whether the stated characteristics will be valid for his application. For example, if your application calls for the op amp to operate at 75°C, you would need to use the input offset current spec for T_A = full range, rather than the one for 25°C.

Some of the specifications may need some clarification:

- V_{ICR} = the maximum common-mode voltage that may be applied to the input and still be rejected.
- $V_{\text{OPP}} = V_{\text{supply}} - 2V_{\text{SAT}}$ = the maximum peak-to-peak output voltage swing
- A_{VD} = open-loop gain under large-signal conditions. A gain of 100 V/mV is the same as a gain of 100,000.
- A_{vd} = open-loop small-signal gain. For this particular op amp, this number is smaller than A_{VD} because of the test frequency of 10 kHz, which is well above f_c for this op amp in an open-loop configuration.
- B_{OM} = the highest frequency at which the stated maximum output voltage swing is available. The 5534 is a partially compensated op amp; it is stable for gains above 3 with no additional compensation. For lower gains, more compensation is required. Several values for the additional compensation components are stated, along with the corresponding value of B_{OM}.
- CMRR = the common-mode rejection ratio. This is the ratio of the output voltage resulting from a common-mode input signal to the input voltage of that

signal, expressed in dB. Thus a CMRR of 120 dB (which represents a factor of 10^6) would mean that a 10-V common-mode input would produce an output of $10 \text{ V}/10^6 = 10 \ \mu\text{V}$.

- k_{SVR} = the ratio by which AC noise on the power-supply lines is rejected. For example, if the ± 15-V power supply has 1% rms hum, and k_{SVR} is 100 dB, then the total hum in the op amp's output signal is calculated as follows:

$$V_{\text{hum,supply}} = 1\% \text{ of } 15 \text{ V} = 0.15 \ V_{\text{rms}}$$

$$V_{\text{hum,output}} = 100 \text{ dB less than } 0.15 \text{ V} = 1.5 \ \mu\text{V}$$

- I_{CC} = quiescent current drawn from the power supply.

The operating characteristics are primarily the AC performance characteristics. All of these should be familiar to you except for the overshoot factor and the noise figure F. Overshoot factor is the percentage by which an output square wave exceeds its proper value as it completes its positive transition. Thus, a 20% overshoot factor would mean that a 50-mV square wave would initially rise to 50 mV + 20% = 60 mV, then settle back to the 50-mV value. Noise figure is a measure of how much a certain amplifier degrades the S/N ratio of a signal. If an amplifier has an S/N ratio of 70 dB at the input and 60 dB at the output, then that amplifier's noise figure is 10 dB. Because the F specification is valid only for a certain set of conditions, this specification actually gives less information than the v_n and i_n specs.

Some characteristics of an op amp vary with supply voltage, operating frequency, and/or temperature. The last section of this data sheet includes nine graphs of such characteristics plotted versus the appropriate parameter. These will be discussed by the figure number given in the spec sheet.

- Figure 1—As was mentioned earlier in the chapter, the input bias current and offset current increase as temperature increases. The specified values are for 25°C. If the op amp will be operated at other temperatures, the corresponding values for bias and offset currents can be obtained from this graph. The *normalized* values obtained from the graph are multiplied by the value specified for 25°C to obtain the actual value for use in computations.
- Figure 2—The maximum output-voltage swing varies, as you know, with frequency and with the compensation components selected. This graph shows that variation.
- Figure 3—This is a graph of open-loop gain versus frequency, for two different values of compensation.
- Figures 4 and 5—These graphs show the effects of supply voltage and temperature upon slew rate and GBW. These are normalized graphs, so they are used in the same way as described for Fig. 1.
- Figure 6—Since this op amp is intended primarily for AC applications, the total harmonic distortion is specified along with its dependence upon frequency.
- Figures 7 and 8—These figures plot noise current and voltage as a function of frequency. They permit you to determine not only the values of v_n and i_n, but also f_{corner}, which is about 100 Hz for these units.
- Figure 9—This graph can save a lot of calculation, because it includes the effects of the Johnson noise of the source, the noise voltage resulting from the i_n of

the op amp, the v_n of the op amp, $1/f$ noise, and bandwidth. It provides a total equivalent input noise voltage that can simply be multiplied by the noise gain of the amplifier to yield the output noise voltage. Of course, it is only valid for the conditions specified.

Some op-amp data sheets include other specifications that are not listed for the 5534. Several of these are listed below along with a brief explanation of their meaning.

Input capacitance: The capacitance that exists between inputs. Usually in the low-picofarad range, the input capacitance can nevertheless have significant effects upon the input impedance at high frequencies.

Input offset voltage adjustment range: The range of input offset voltages that can be nulled using the recommended nulling network. For a 741, this range is ± 15 mV. Op amps that do not include internal nulling provisions would naturally not include this spec.

Maximum differential input voltage: As discussed on page 42, the maximum differential input voltage is the greatest voltage that can safely be applied between the inverting and the noninverting inputs of the op amp.

Output short-circuit current: A great many op amps have internal current-limiting circuitry. The output short-circuit current is the maximum current that this circuitry will allow the op amp to deliver. The maximum output voltage of your design divided by the load resistance should never be greater than this value, or the current-limiting circuitry will cause distortion of the output wave.

Power consumption: Power consumption is the product of typical supply voltage and supply current. Sometimes it is given as an alternative to the I_{CC} spec.

Temperature coefficient of input offset current or voltage: The temperature coefficient is the amount by which the input offset current or voltage increases with each degree increase in temperature.

Channel separation or *crosstalk attenuation:* In dual or quad op amps, there is some inevitable coupling of signals between amplifiers. Ideally this coupling should be extremely small. The specification is usually expressed in dB. The 105-dB crosstalk attenuation figure specified for a 4136 op amp means that amplifier 1's signal will not appear in amplifier 2, 3, or 4 at a level greater than 105 dB below the level in amplifier 1. This can be translated into a ratio: a 1-V signal in amplifier 1 will not appear in amplifier 2, 3, or 4 at a level greater than 5.6 μV. Usually the crosstalk is below the op amp's noise level.

SETTING SPECIFICATIONS

It seems obvious that the first part of any design process is setting the specifications, but students often overlook this part since the specifications are usually given in the assignment! It is true that in a professional design assignment as well, the specifications for the completed unit will also be given. However, as the design example for the low-noise audio mixer illustrated, this still leaves quite a lot to the designer. For example, a total gain of 500 may be specified; the designer is left to choose how many stages will be used and how the total gain is to be split among the various stages. A certain noise level may be specified; the designer is left to decide whether bandlimiting should be employed, whether transformer coupling must be used, and so on. In some cases, a designer may be faced with the delicate task of informing a supervisor that a certain specification cannot be met. For example, as of this writing, the quietest monolithic op amp has a noise voltage of 0.5 nV/$\sqrt{\text{Hz}}$. A specification calling for a gain of 100, a bandwidth of 10 kHz, and, say, an output noise of no more than 3 μV would be unrealistic, because the best op-amp would produce an output noise of at least 5 μV under these conditions. So the seemingly simple job of setting specifications includes the following:

1. Setting overall specs
2. Verifying that the overall specs can be met using available devices
3. Deciding upon the number of stages and the specifications (gain, bandwidth, etc.) for each stage

CHOOSING A DEVICE

For most applications, there will be one or two demanding specifications to be met along with some specs that are less demanding. The demanding specs may be low noise, low offset voltage, wide bandwidth, high CMRR, and so on. Manufacturers usually include application charts in their IC data books to help designers choose a device that is appropriate for each application. Table 4–A is National Semiconductors' application guide for their BI-FET™ op-amp family. (BI-FET is a trade name for National Semiconductor's family of FET-input bipolar op amps.) Notice that for each design parameter there are a number of op amps listed, along with the specification for each op amp.

EXAMPLE

Problem

Choose an FET-input op amp for the following specification:

$$A_V = 100 \qquad V_{n,\text{total}} \leq 200\ \mu V \qquad BW = 300\ \text{Hz to } 10\ \text{kHz}$$

$$V_{\text{OUT,max}} = 25\ V_{\text{P-P}}$$

$$R_i = 1\ M\Omega \qquad R_{\text{source}} = 1\ k\Omega$$

Solution

1. The gain and bandwidth call for a GBW of 1 MHz, which is no problem for almost any op amp. The input resistance would be a challenge for a bipolar

COMPARISON OF ELECTRICAL CHARACTERISTICS						
	DC Electrical Characteristics				AC Electrical Characteristics	
Part Number	V_{OS}—Max Offset Voltage (mV) ($T_A = 25°C$)	$\Delta V_{OS}/\Delta T$—TC of V_{OS} ($\mu V/°C$) Typ	I_B—Max Bias Current (pA) ($T_J = 25°C$)	A_{VOL} Large Signal Voltage Gain (V/mV) Min ($T_A = 25°C$)	SR—Slew Rate (V/μs)	e_n—Equiv. Input Noise Voltage (nV/$\sqrt{Hz}$) (Note 2)
MILITARY BI-FET OP AMP (Note 1)						
LF155	5	5	100	50	5	20
LF155A	2	5 (max)	50	50	5	20
LF156	5	5	100	50	12	12
LF156A	2	5 (max)	50	50	12	12
LF157	5	5	100	50	50	12
LF157A	2	5 (max)	50	50	50	12
LF411A	0.5	10 (max)	200	50	10 (min)	25
LF411	2	10	200	50	8 (min)	25
LF441A (low power)	0.5	10 (max)	50	50	1	40
LF412A Dual	1	10 (max)	200	50	10 (min)	25
LF412	3	10	200	50	8 (min)	25
LF442A Dual (low power)	1	10	50	50	1	40
LF444 Quad (low power)	5	10	50	50	1	40
INDUSTRIAL BI-FET OP AMP (Note 1)						
LF255	5	5	100	50	5	20
LF256	5	5	100	50	12	12
LF257	5	5	100	50	50	12
COMMERCIAL BI-FET AND BI-FET II OP AMP (Note 3)						
LF351	10	10	200	25	13	16
LF355	10	5	200	25	5	25
LF355A	2	5 (max)	50	25	5	25
LF356	10	5	200	25	12	15
LF356A	2	5 (max)	50	25	12	15
LF357	10	5	200	25	50	15
LF357A	2	5 (max)	50	25	50	15
LF13741	15	10	200	25	0.5	37
LF411A	0.5	10 (max)	200	50	10	25
LF411	2.0	20	200	50	8	25
LF441A (low power)	0.5	10 (max)	50	50	1	40
LF441 (low power)	5	10	100	50	1	40
BI-FET II DUAL OP AMPS (CHARACTERISTICS FOR EACH AMPLIFIER) (Note 3)						
LF353	10	10	200	25	13	16
LF412A	1	10 (max)	200	50	10 (min)	25
LF412	3	20	200	50	8 (min)	25
LF442A (low power)	1	10 (max)	50	50	1	40
LF442 (low power)	3	20	100	50	1	40
BI-FET II QUAD OP AMPS (CHARACTERISTICS FOR EACH AMPLIFIER) (Note 3)						
LF347	10	10	200	25	13	16
LF347B	5	10	200	25	13	16
LF444A (low power)	5	10	50	50	1	40
LF444 (low power)	10	10	100	25	1	40

BI-FET™ and BI-FET II™ are trademarked terms by National Semiconductor who invented the technology in 1974.
Note 1: DC electrical characteristics are −55°C to +125°C for Military and −25°C to +85°C for Industrial unless otherwise noted; AC electrical characteristics are $T_A = 25°C$, typical specifications unless noted.
Note 2: f = 1000 Hz.
Note 3: DC electrical characteristics are 0°C to +70°C unless otherwise noted; AC electrical characteristics are $T_A = 25°C$, typical specifications unless noted.

(Reprinted with permission of National Semiconductor Corp.)

BI-FET™/BI-FET II™ Op Amp Selection Guide

SELECTION BY DESIGN PARAMETER

Max Input Offset Voltage ($T_A = 25°C$)	0.5 mV	1 mV	2 mV	3 mV	5 mV	10 mV	15 mV
	LF411A LF441A	LF442A LF412A	LF155A/LF355A LF156A/LF356A LF357A	LF412 LF442	LF347B LF155/LF156/LF157 LF255/LF256/LF257 LF444A	LF355/LF356/LF357 LF351 LF353 LF347 LF444	LF13741

Max Input Bias Current ($T_J = 25°C$)	50 pA	100 pA	200 pA
	LF155A/LF156A/LF157A LF355A/LF356A/LF357A LF441A LF442A LF444A	LF155/LF156/LF157 LF255/LF256/LF257 LF441 LF444 LF442	LF355/LF356/LF357 LF351 LF347/LF347B LF353 LF13741 LF411A LF411 LF412A LF412

Typ Equivalent Input Noise Voltage per $\sqrt{Hz}$, f = 1000 Hz $R_S = 100\Omega$	12 nV or Less	15 nV to 20 nV		25 nV to 40 nV		
	LF156/LF156A LF157/LF157A LF256/LF257	LF356 LF356A LF357 LF357A	LF351 LF347 LF347B LF353	LF155 LF155A LF255 LF355 LF355A	LF411A LF411 LF412A LF412 LF441A LF441	LF13741 LF442A LF442 LF444A LF444

Typ Slew Rate	0.5V/μs	1V/μs	5V/μs	12V/μs	13V/μs	15V/μs	50V/μs
	LF13741	LF441A LF441 LF442A LF442 LF444A LF444	LF155/LF155A LF255 LF355/LF355A	LF156 LF156A LF256 LF356 LF356A	LF351 LF353 LF347 LF347B	LF411A LF411 LF412A LF412	LF157 LF157A LF357 LF357A

ADDITIONAL NS PRODUCTS USING BI-FET TECHNOLOGY

- LF111 Comparator
- LF198 Sample and Hold
- LF11201 Series of Analog Switches
- LF11331 Series of Analog Switches
- LF11508 Series of Analog Multiplexers
- LF13300 Integrating A/D Building Block

(Reprinted with permission of National Semiconductor Corp.)

op amp, but will be easy to achieve with the very low bias currents of the FET-input device. The noise and maximum output voltage may require some further examination.

2. A total noise of 200 μV with a gain of 100 implies a total input noise of 2 μV, assuming a noninverting configuration. If we assume 20 dB/decade rolloff slopes, the noise bandwidth is (9.7 kHz)(1.57) = 15.2 kHz. This implies a maximum equivalent input noise voltage of 16 nV/$\sqrt{\text{Hz}}$. The 1-kHz source resistance will not add appreciable noise. Glancing at the spec sheet for a BI-FET op amp, the LF-411 (see Appendix A), we see that f_{corner} is about 100, which is below our passband. Therefore a minimum op-amp noise spec of 15 nV$\sqrt{\text{Hz}}$ should be good enough.

3. The output voltage of 25 $V_{P=P}$ at 10 kHz requires a slew rate of 0.785 V/μs.

4. Looking at Table 4–A, we must find an op amp that meets both the noise and slew-rate specs. Checking the slew-rate category first, we find that no device listed under 1 V/μs or 5 V/μs has low enough noise. However, under 12 V/μs, we find the LF156 and LF256, both of which have noise voltages well under our maximum.

In the absence of application charts, we must resort to a lot of thumbing through data sheets to find a specific op amp. But a little pencil work first to determine which characteristics are most difficult to find will save a lot of effort.

SINGLE-SUPPLY OPERATION

Most op amps are designed for a bipolar power supply. However, providing such a supply entails some difficulties in many cases, such as battery-operated equipment, modifying equipment that already has a unipolar supply, and so on. For these cases, there are three solutions. The first is to use an op amp specifically designed for unipolar operation. Such op amps are usually designed primarily for AC amplification, since they will not be able to handle DC inputs that are negative with respect to ground. The connection of an op amp designed for unipolar operation depends upon its internal circuitry. Some allow the input to be referenced to ground; others provide internal biasing for the input and require capacitor coupling of all input and output connections, including the ground connection of the noninverting input in an inverting amplifier. The LM124, whose data sheet is included in Appendix A, is one of a number of such devices. Because of specially designed input circuits, the LM124 can operate with the inputs biased at 0 VDC. However, the input voltage must be prevented from being made more negative than 0.3 V. For capacitor-coupled applications, the input biasing circuits shown in Fig. 4–1 can be used. However, for applications in which there are only positive excursions of the signal voltage, no such biasing is required. When the output of a 124 is capacitor coupled, a 2-kΩ resistor should be connected from the output to ground to increase output-stage current enough to eliminate crossover distortion. Application circuits for the LM124 are included in the data sheet.

The second solution to the need for a unipolar supply is to use a standard op amp connected as shown in Fig. 4–1. In this circuit, the noninverting input is biased at half the supply voltage by resistors R_{B_1} and R_{B_2}. The inverting input and the output are capacitor isolated from ground. The bias resistors are made equal, and the value of each should equal R_f, if possible. In this way, bias current from the noninverting input will cause the same voltage at that input as will an identical bias current from the inverting input. In the noninverting amplifier, both of these resistors appear in parallel to ground, AC-wise, since the power supply is at AC ground. This means that the bias resistors will determine the input resistance of the amplifier:

$$R_{IN} = R_{B_1} \| R_{B_2} = \frac{R_{B_1}}{2} \qquad (4.01)$$

Therefore these resistors may need to be larger than R_f in many cases. However, if

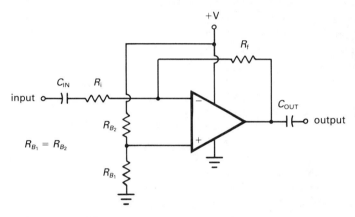

FIGURE 4–1A: Inverting Amplifier

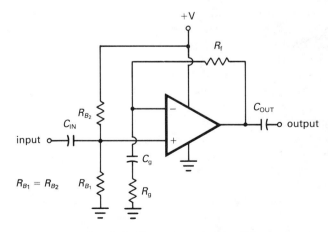

FIGURE 4–1B: Noninverting Amplifier

FIGURE 4–1: Single-Supply Operation

the bias resistors are not made equal to R_f, the resulting offset voltage should be carefully calculated to make sure that it is within allowable limits.

There are three problems with the single-supply-biased op amp. The most obvious is the requirement of additional resistors and capacitors. The second is that half of any hum or noise present on the power-supply lines will appear at the non-inverting input of the op amp. In the inverting amplifier, this can be shunted to ground by a capacitor, but in a noninverting one, the supply must be made extra clean or objectionable hum and noise will appear in the output. The third problem results from the larger resistances from each input to ground. Normally, the resistance through which bias currents must flow is determined primarily by R_g or R_i, since they are usually much smaller than R_f. However, for the single-supply circuits, R_g and R_i are capacitor isolated. This means that the resistance from each input to ground is equal to R_f. Choosing the bias resistors as recommended above will eliminate offset-voltage problems resulting from matched bias currents, but as you remember, we must also contend with offset currents—the mismatch between the two bias currents. The output offset voltage resulting from a given offset current depends directly upon the resistance from each input to ground. Therefore, for the single-supply amplifier, the larger resistances from each input to ground mean that the output offset voltage resulting from offset current will be larger.

The third solution to the single-supply problem avoids these difficulties. It simply converts the single supply into a dual supply by use of a supply splitter. Figure 4–2 shows two circuits for supply splitters and an amplifier circuit using a supply splitter.

The passive splitter shown in Fig. 4–2 can be used for AC amplifiers in which the maximum output current from all of the op amps is 1 mA or less. Using this circuit with larger output currents will cause objectionable levels of AC to appear on the circuit-common lead; in other words, ground won't be ground! The active splitter has no such limitations. In operation, the op amp does as all op amps do—it tries to make the voltages at its inputs equal. Doing this requires that the voltage at the circuit-common point be equal to half the supply voltage, since that is the voltage set by the voltage divider at the noninverting input. The voltage at the circuit-common point is determined by the voltage divider made up of (1) the positive-side load in parallel with the upper transistor, and (2) the negative-side load in parallel with the lower transistor. Since the loads vary, the op amp must vary the base voltages on the transistors in order to continually adjust the resistance presented by the transistors. Thus the upper and lower resistances of the voltage divider are kept equal, and the circuit-common point is kept at the midpoint. The transistors used should be able to handle the maximum short-circuit current of all of the op amps to be fed by the splitter. This means that their power-dissipation capability and maximum collector current must be taken into consideration, as outlined in Chapter 5.

As shown in part C of the figure, all the splitter really does is to provide an AC ground with its DC level located halfway between 0 V and V+. The positive and negative supply connections to the op amps still go to V+ and ground, respectively. Notice once again that inputs and outputs are DC-isolated by the use of capacitors.

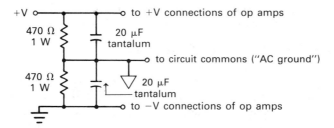

FIGURE 4–2A: Passive Splitter

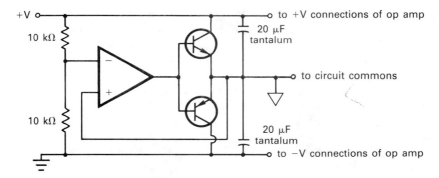

FIGURE 4–2B: Active Splitter

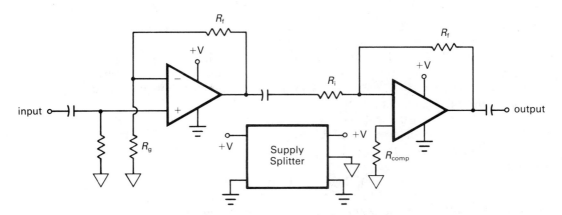

FIGURE 4–2C: Application of Supply Splitters

FIGURE 4–2: Supply Splitters

One other alternative for single-supply operation is the current-differencing amplifiers discussed in Chapter 9.

TROUBLESHOOTING OP-AMP CIRCUITS

Anyone who works very much with op amps, whether as a technician or as a design engineer, will find that a large part of the job is troubleshooting. The job of finding troubles in op-amp circuits splits into two categories: (1) finding troubles in circuits that have previously been working but have stopped, and (2) finding out why a new design does not work. The first category deals primarily with component failures, for which the first step is to examine the circuit visually. Look for signs of overheating, especially near resistors. Look for signs of electrolyte leakage near aluminum electrolytic capacitors. Indications of liquids having been spilled into the circuitry call for circuit-board cleaning. After correcting all obvious faults, power up the circuit. If the circuit still fails to operate, check the power-supply voltages. If these are out of tolerance, the supply should be checked and repaired if necessary. A defective power supply may have damaged other components. Therefore if the supply is OK, or if it was defective and has been repaired, but the circuit still doesn't work, a faulty component can usually be assumed. The first suspect is the op amp itself. Many times op-amp failure is caused by power-supply surges or momentary large inputs that exceed the maximum permissible voltage levels. These conditions usually result in short circuits within the IC. Measuring the voltages at the pins of the IC will give a preliminary indication. If all the voltages are nearly the same, the op amp can be assumed shorted. Inputs and outputs of AC-coupled circuits should be about circuit-common voltage (0 V DC for bipolar supplies, half of V_{CC} for unipolar supplies).

If the voltages at the IC pins are not all the same, the IC may still be bad, but other testing is necessary. The resistors most often used in modern circuits are film types, and these virtually never short. Usually when they open, they leave a telltale burned ring around their middle. Capacitors, however, fail without a sign. They can short, become leaky, or open. Capacitors rarely change value by a great amount. A capacitor that has the same DC voltage on both sides is likely to be shorted. It should be removed from the circuit and tested for leakage under full operating voltage. A capacitor that has AC signal voltage on one side and none on the other may be open. However, if the signal voltage is of a low frequency and the capacitor is small, its reactance will stop most of the signal, so judgment and perhaps a few calculations may be required here.

From the information given in the last paragraph, you can see that a high DC voltage at an op amp input could be caused by either a defective op amp or a leaky capacitor. This will also cause a wrong DC voltage at the output. For example, if the input capacitor of an inverting amplifier is leaky or shorted, so that it allows the DC voltage at the inverting input to be several tenths of a volt positive, the output should then be considerably negative. The exact amount by which it is negative will depend upon the gain of the amplifier. Conversely, if the noninverting input is driven positive, the output will also be positive. For example, if the inverting input measures 0.5 V and the noninverting input measures 0 V, the output should be at some negative voltage. If the gain is large, the output will be at V_{SAT-}. Thus voltage measurements that tell you whether the inputs and outputs have DC voltages that *make sense* will often indicate whether an op amp is good. If the output of the op amp mentioned above were at a positive voltage, a defective IC would be indicated.

If signal is present at the input of an amplifier stage but is not present at the output, and the DC voltages are normal, suspect an open capacitor.

If an op-amp circuit works when first powered up but then quits working, the trouble may be the result of temperature. There is a product manufactured under various trade names that can be sprayed on suspect components to suddenly cool them to subfreezing temperatures. By spraying one component at a time in temperature-sensitive circuits, defective components can usually be located. When you spray the troublemaker, the circuit will begin to work, then will stop working again as the component warms up. When checking for temperature-sensitive effects, remember that the input bias and offset currents also depend upon temperature. Designs having marginal DC stability may behave until the temperature rises. If this is the cause of your problem, spraying the IC with circuit cooler will restore operation, but replacing the IC will not help. In such cases, check the bias-current compensation and/or offset nulling. Occasionally, a minor redesign is needed.

Troubleshooting new designs is different from finding troubles in designs that previously worked. Usually in new designs, the components can safely be assumed to be good. The problems that remain are those of design and construction. Always check the obvious things first, including power-supply voltages and polarity, the presence and proper interconnection of grounds (including the ground return to the power supply!), and the proper connection of the IC pins. Even seasoned engineers occasionally hook up an IC in mirror-image fashion, especially when working from the bottom of the circuit board on a breadboard design. Make sure the ground of your signal source is connected to your circuit's ground; inverting the polarity here will cause lots of problems, especially when you connect your 'scope to the circuit. Having another person check your work is a good idea, because your chances of overlooking your own errors are excellent.

If the circuit is built as designed, the likely remaining problems are lock-up and oscillation. *Lock-up* is the name for the condition in which the output of the op amp is locked at either V_{SAT+} or V_{SAT-}. It can be caused by incorrect DC design, by improper polarity of electrolytic coupling capacitors, or by use of a signal generator with a nonzeroed DC offset voltage. Make sure that all your inputs have bias-current paths; in short, go through your bias-current compensation calculations again. If electrolytic capacitors are used in locations in which there is no DC polarizing voltage or in which the polarizing voltage may vary in polarity, the capacitors should be nonpolar. If none of these are available, one can be made up of two polar capacitors connected negative to negative. Since the capacitors are in series, each of the polar types should be twice the value of the desired nonpolar capacitor.

If a new circuit oscillates the first time it is tried out, there are several steps you should go through. First, check your ground and power connections. These are points that must be at AC ground in order for the circuit to operate properly, and if there are high impedances in the way (poor connections, long lead wires, etc.), these points will not be securely grounded, AC-wise. Second, verify that you have used enough bypass capacitors, located close to the op amp, and that they are securely grounded. Some power supplies sold by reputable test equipment manufacturers have inadequate internal bypassing, and these must be bypassed with a 470-μF capacitor from each side of the supply to ground. To check your supply, just look at the supply pins of the IC with a 'scope while the circuit is powered. If there is *any* AC on the supply leads, more bypassing is needed. The general rule is to start with 0.1-μF bypass capacitors and increase their value until the AC is eliminated from the supply lines. If capacitors larger than 1 μF are needed, use tantalums. These have a much more nearly ideal capacitor action at high frequencies than aluminum electrolytics do. Usually when power-supply bypassing is the source of oscillation, the oscillation will occur at a very low frequency—sometimes a fraction of a hertz. This low-frequency oscillation is often called *motorboating* because of the sound it makes.

At this point it would be wise to mention several things that are *not* oscillation, but that are sometimes mistaken for oscillation. Since an op amp is a very-high-gain device, it is capable of picking up and amplifying a variety of types of interference signals, including radiation from the power line, local radio stations, or even nearby test equipment. Always suspect that power-line-frequency "oscillations" are really interference picked up in a long unshielded input lead, or resulting from crossed ground connections in the input circuit. Always suspect that amplitude-modulated "oscillations" are local radio signals. If you move your circuit to another location several feet away and the "oscillations" change, suspect interference from test equipment.

Having eliminated all AC from the power-supply leads, if you still have genuine oscillation, the cause is unwanted coupling or unexpected phase shifts somewhere in your circuit, causing parasitic positive feedback. Check the frequency of the oscillation. If it is near the unity-gain frequency of the op amp, the problem is likely to be in the feedback loop. Especially in high-resistance feedback loops, stray capacitances or unwanted capacitive coupling from long component leads in a feedback loop can be a problem. With uncompensated op amps, the compensation network, if misdesigned, can cause oscillation.

If moving your hand or your test leads around near the circuit causes the amplitude or frequency of the oscillation to change, the cause of the trouble is likely to be parasitic coupling between the components in your circuit. Make sure that the input and output leads are well separated and are not physically parallel. Potentiometers associated with the input circuit should have as short leads as possible. Shielding of the input leads may be necessary. One useful weapon in the fight against oscillation is the *ground plane*. This is a large, grounded conducting sheet located under the circuit board. (Sometimes the copper on one side of a two-sided circuit board is used as a ground plane.) It tends to break up stray electric fields that can cause unwanted coupling between components in a circuit. When plug-in breadboarding systems are used, be sure that the plastic plug-in strip is mounted on a grounded metal sheet. With other breadboarding systems, it may be necessary to use a sheet of unetched copper-clad board of the type that is used for making printed circuits.

Another cause of oscillation is output-stage instability. This occurs at a frequency much higher than the op amp's unity-gain frequency. One of the most important causes of output-stage instability is capacitive loading at the output. The presence of significant capacitance from the output lead to ground will cause phase shifts at high frequencies. The most common cause of capacitive loading is the use of coaxial cable to transfer the output signal to another circuit or device. The capacitance of coaxial cables is typically 25 to 50 pF/ft. It is true that for cable lengths of the order of a wavelength or greater, the coaxial cable appears as a resistance equal to its characteristic impedance. But for cable lengths much less than a wavelength, the cable looks like a capacitance. The wavelength of an electrical signal in meters is approximately $(3 \cdot 10^8)/f$, where f is the frequency of interest. Thus a 100-kHz wave has a wavelength of about 3000 m. Another source of capacitive loading is the stray capacitance that always exists between the output components and ground. Choice of the best method for stabilizing the circuit against capacitive loading depends upon the frequency of the resulting oscillation. If the frequency is well above the unity-gain frequency, then the oscillation is caused by local instability in the output stage itself. This involves a parasitic "tuned circuit," and can be cured by spoiling the Q of this tuned circuit. This is done by adding a 0.1-µF ceramic capacitor in series with a 3- to 10-Ω resistor from the output line to ground. Some experimentation with the values of the capacitor and resistor may be needed, but these are starting points. Coaxial-cable capacitive loading can cause oscillation within the passband of the amplifier. (The same is true for any other type of cable connected to the output of the op amp.) The loading capacitance can be isolated from the op amp by the use of a modified feedback circuit as shown in Fig. 4–3A. The values

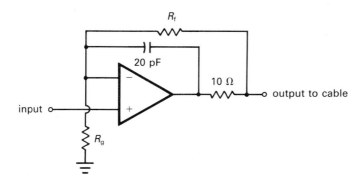

FIGURE 4–3A: Modified Feedback Circuit for Driving Coaxial Cable

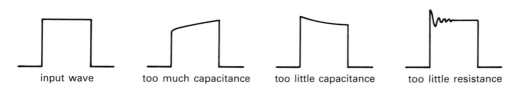

| input wave | too much capacitance | too little capacitance | too little resistance |

FIGURE 4–3B: Square-Wave Responses

FIGURE 4–3: Circuit for Driving Coaxial Cable

given in the figure for the added capacitor and resistor—20 pF and 10 Ω—are approximate. The correct values for any specific application will need to be found experimentally. This is done by connecting the output to the actual length of cable to be driven, then feeding a square wave to the input and observing the output. The frequency of the square wave should be about one-fifth the maximum output frequency of the amplifier. The sketches in Fig. 4–3B show the possible output waveforms, indicating which values, if any, need adjusting.

The final cause of oscillation that we will consider is the existence of stray input capacitance. The stray capacitance that exists between the input-component leads and ground is typically 2 to 5 pF. This small capacitance causes no problems in low-impedance inputs, 100 kΩ or less. However, when large input impedances are encountered, as is often the case with FET-input op amps, the phase shift introduced by the stray input capacitance can cause oscillation. The easiest way to stop this oscillation is to use a small capacitor, typically 5 pF, connected directly in parallel with R_f. This will introduce a small high-frequency loss that can be compensated for by paralleling an identical capacitor across R_i, if the circuit is an inverting amplifier. For noninverting amplifiers, you will just have to accept the high-frequency loss, adding another stage if necessary so that you get adequate bandwidth. You can find the exact value of the necessary capacitors by using the square-wave test discussed above.

DESIGN NOTES

It is not possible to list a step-by-step procedure that will fit every design problem, but a general approach can be given that will help the designer to organize all the sometimes-conflicting considerations of gain, frequency response, output swing, offset voltage, and noise. Such an approach would go more or less as follows:

1. Verify that the specifications can be met by available ICs, and choose specific types as outlined above.
2. Select the gain per stage, remembering that the gain must be less than GBW/f_{high}. Also remember that for multistage amplifiers, the overall critical frequency is less than the lowest f_c of any single stage.
3. Select the inverting or noninverting configuration for the first stage. The noninverting configuration provides a higher input impedance and lower noise gain, and is therefore preferable to the inverting one. The use of an inverting amplifier would be suggested if the input stage is to be a summer or if a low input impedance is required. (Remember that summers have poor noise performance, though, so in low-noise applications it is better to preamplify each channel before applying the signal to the summing stage.)
4. Choose parts values for R_f, R_i or R_g, and C_{IN}, C_{OUT}, and C_g, if used. Remember that keeping resistances as low as the required input impedance allows will help minimize noise and offset voltage.
5. Calculate the expected output offset voltage, and the required R_{comp} if one is needed. In capacitor-coupled circuits, verify that there is a path from each input to ground for bias currents. If output offset voltage is critical, design the nulling circuit.
6. Calculate the expected output noise. If either the output noise or the output offset voltage are too great with the necessary resistor values, consider tee feedback or the isolated R_g circuit.
7. Repeat steps 3 through 5 for the other stages.
8. When designing the physical layout, remember the guidelines given on page 91.

Design
Notes

SUMMARY

An op-amp specification sheet contains virtually all the information needed for designing with that op amp.

Designing an op-amp circuit begins with setting the specifications, including the number of stages and the specs of each stage.

Choosing the best op amp for a circuit involves selecting the most difficult characteristic that the op amp must meet, then finding a device that will meet it. Then one must verify that the chosen device will meet the other necessary specs. Manufacturers of ICs publish tables that help in this process.

Operation of an op amp from a unipolar supply requires one of the following:

- The IC must be designed for a unipolar supply.
- The circuit must contain biasing resistors and coupling capacitors to trick it into thinking that it has a bipolar supply.
- A supply splitter must be used. Passive splitters can be used for low-current loads, but active splitters are needed for larger loads.

Troubleshooting op-amp circuits that have previously worked involves locating defective components. This can usually be done by AC and/or DC voltage measurements.

Troubleshooting new op-amp circuits primarily involves locating design faults and/or curing oscillations. Careful layout helps prevent oscillations. In some cases, special compensation must be added to eliminate oscillation.

REVIEW QUESTIONS

1. A 4136 quad op amp is to be used as four comparators, each driving an LED. No current-limiting resistors are to be used. Will the rated power dissipation of the IC be exceeded? Assume a ±15-V power supply.

2. A 741 op amp is to be used in an application in which common-mode voltages up to 10 V_{rms} must be rejected. The differential-mode input signals will be on the order of 10 mV. If perfect matching of the resistors in the balanced amplifier were achieved, could the 741 do the job?

3. Calculate the output offset voltage for a circuit using a typical 5534 op amp, and having an $R_{mismatch}$ of 15 kΩ. The operating temperature is 75°C, and $A_V = 100$. Ignore offset current effects.

4. What is the maximum frequency at which a 5534 op amp can output a 10-V_{P-P} sine wave if $C_C = 0$ pF and the temperature is 80°C?

5. Set stage-by-stage specifications and choose appropriate devices for the following applications:

   (a) Instrumentation amplifier with $A_V = 1000$, minimum possible noise, and CMRR at least 110 dB. Frequency response must be flat $\pm10\%$ from 0 to 100 Hz.

   (b) Balanced-line amplifier with 10-mA$_{rms}$ output capability into a 600-Ω load, for frequencies from 300 to 3000 Hz. $A_V = 120$.

(c) DC amplifier for voltmeter application. Lowest possible output offset voltage. Lowest possible drift with temperature. Input to op amp is to be fed through a voltage divider so that the input resistance to the voltmeter will be at least 10 MΩ. Input voltage ranges from 100 μV to 1000 V must be accommodated. The op amp must be protected against overvoltage. Frequency response will be limited to 0–10 Hz.

6. Design an active supply splitter using a 741 op amp. Give the beta and the maximum voltage, current, and power specifications for the transistors. The splitter must convert a 30-V unipolar supply to a ±15-V bipolar supply. A maximum output current of 100 mA is required.

7. What are the first two steps in troubleshooting a circuit that was previously known to be working?

8. A 741 IC in an 8-pin dual-in-line package has the following terminal voltages: pin 1, −14 V; pin 2, 0.4 V; pin 3, 0.6 V; pin 4, −15 V; pin 5, −14 V; pin 6, −13V; pin 7, 15 V; pin 8, 0 V. Is the op amp working? Why or why not?

9. In an op-amp amplifier circuit, the DC voltage at the output pin of one op amp is 4 V. The voltage at the input to the following noninverting stage is 3.95 V. This second stage has a 1-kΩ compensation resistor included, but no coupling capacitor is used. Would you suspect a faulty component? If you do, state which one and why.

10. There is no signal at the output of an AC amplifier, but all the DC voltages are normal. What is the likely cause of the problem?

11. A new op-amp circuit appears to oscillate. Name the likely cause of oscillation if the frequency is:
    (a) very low
    (b) about 60 Hz
    (c) about the unity-gain frequency of the op amp
    (d) well above the unity-gain frequency of the op amp

12. Name at least three possible causes of oscillation resulting from the physical construction of the circuit.

LABORATORY EXPERIMENT—
TROUBLESHOOTING

Objective:

To become familiar with the process of eliminating oscillation in a new op-amp circuit.

Materials:

1 709 op amp
1 1-kΩ resistor
1 1.5-kΩ resistor
2 10-kΩ resistors
2 10-μF, 25-V nonpolar capacitors
1 0.001-μF capacitor
1 10-pF capacitor
1 3-pF capacitor
other miscellaneous resistors and capacitors

Procedure:

1. The circuit in Fig. 4–4 contains several design defects. Examine it with the aid of the 709 data sheet in Appendix A and correct all the flaws you

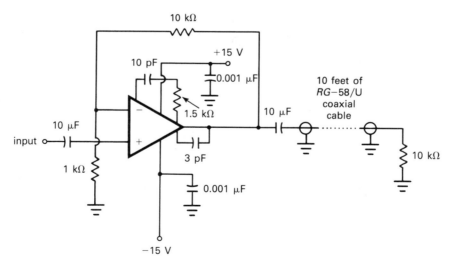

FIGURE 4–4

(continued)

(continued from page 174)

can find. The circuit should have a gain of 10 and should be capable of driving the load with a 24 V_{P-P}, 1-kHz square wave with no appreciable ringing and a rise time not greater than 50 μs.

2. Build your circuit as corrected.
3. If the circuit does not work as designed, use the troubleshooting information given in Chapter 4 and the information from the 709 data sheet to make the circuit work.

Analysis:

In your report, describe all the modifications to the design that were necessary and give the purpose of each modification. Submit a clean copy of your final schematic along with

1. A small-signal ($V_{OUT} = 100$ mV$_{rms}$) sine-wave frequency-response graph
2. A large-signal ($V_{OUT} = 24$ V$_{P-P}$) sine-wave frequency-response graph
3. An accurate sketch of the 24 V_{P-P}, 1-kHz square wave showing rise time, fall time, and peak-to-peak ringing, if any.

chapter five

Power Circuits

OBJECTIVES

Upon completing this chapter, you will be able to:

- Distinguish between small-signal and large-signal amplifier operation.
- Calculate whether a heat sink is necessary for a power device, and specify the characteristics of the heat sink needed.
- Use power ICs in circuits.
- Interface op amps with other semiconductor devices.
- Troubleshoot power op-amp circuits.

COMPARISON OF POWER AND SMALL-SIGNAL OPERATION

Recall from your study of discrete semiconductor devices that amplifiers are often discussed in two categories: small signal and large signal. The difference between the two is the amount of the load line in which the device operates. The reason for this distinction is that an amplifier that operates on only a small portion of its load line will not have serious distortion. Thus the design considerations are different for small-signal discrete amplifiers than for large-signal ones. With op amps, the distinction is a little different. A typical op amp is considered a small-signal device, even though its output stage operates throughout most of its load line. However, the power dissipation is usually not an important consideration, whereas the noise may be. In a large-signal op amp, the power dissipation must be taken into account, and noise is usually of no concern because of the comparatively large input signals.

Figure 5–1 shows a number of IC packages in common use. Notice the heat-sink tabs on the large-signal devices. These are to conduct heat away from the semiconductor chip when the device is dissipating large amounts of power. These tabs are absent from the small-signal packages.

HEAT-DISSIPATION CONSIDERATIONS

Any real device that simultaneously has a voltage across it and a current through it dissipates power. If the device is basically nonreactive (e.g., resistors and semi-

FIGURE 5–1: Linear IC Packages for Small- and Large-Signal Devices

conductor devices), the power equals the product of the voltage and the current. You probably remember from your introductory courses that power is just energy divided by time; in other words, power is the rate at which energy is converted from one form to another. In the case we're discussing, if one joule of electrical energy leaves the circuit each second, the circuit dissipates one watt. Notice that we said that the energy leaves the circuit; we did not say that it is used up. Short of a nuclear reaction, the total amount of energy always remains the same. But what happens in a resistor or semiconductor is that the energy changes from electrical energy to heat energy.

Now heat energy can be compared to current; temperature, to voltage. When current flows in a resistance, a voltage is produced. When heat energy flows in any substance, the temperature rises. And just as there is electrical resistance that determines how much voltage is produced when a certain current flows in a device, there is also a *thermal resistance* that determines how much the temperature of a piece of material rises when a certain amount of heat energy flows in it. Thermal resistance is stated in °C/W. You know from experience that several factors affect the thermal resistance of a piece of material. The difference between a resistor rated at $\frac{1}{2}$ W and one rated at 2 W is primarily the physical size. Obviously the smaller resistor has a greater thermal resistance, because it requires a smaller amount of energy to raise it to a destructive temperature. If you compare a small-signal transistor to a power transistor, you will notice another difference. The small-signal device is likely to be encased in epoxy, while the power transistor is probably in a metal case. So different materials also have different thermal resistances. In fact, when we refer to *good conductors* of heat, we are indicating materials that have low thermal resistance. The concept of thermal resistance is illustrated in Fig. 5–2.

The maximum operating temperature of a semiconductor junction is about 200°C. Depending upon the type of case material, any given semiconductor device may have a lower maximum operating temperature. If this maximum temperature is exceeded, the impurities in the P- and N-type regions tend to diffuse together, turning the device into a rather expensive resistor. An important part of the design process for large-signal semiconductor circuits is making sure that the junction does not rise to a destructive temperature. As you can see from the preceding discussion, you have two variables to work with: the power dissipation and the thermal resistance. Generally, for a specific application, a certain output power is required. For AC operation, the resulting power dissipated in a linear integrated circuit is about 40% of the output power. It is possible to make this generalization because the output stage of nearly all power ICs is a complementary-symmetry stage, and analysis of this type of output stage yields this figure. Of course, in many applications, the output power is not constant. In these cases, it is the *maximum* output power and power dissipation that we are concerned with. The maximum power dissipation of an IC may be approximated from the equation:

$$P_{\text{DISS,max}} = \frac{V_{\text{OUT,P-P}}^2}{20R_{\text{L}}} \tag{5.01}$$

This equation is valid only for sine-wave outputs, but it works reasonably well for any AC outputs except square waves. Thus it will work for most cases. (Strictly,

3. Heat flows from heat sink to air. Number of watts of heat multiplied by thermal resistance between heat sink and air gives number of °C hotter the heat sink is than the air.

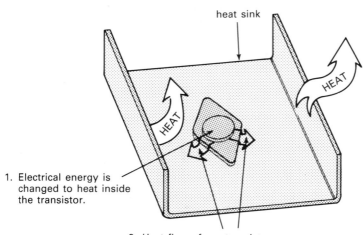

heat sink

1. Electrical energy is changed to heat inside the transistor.

2. Heat flows from transistor to heat sink. Number of watts of heat multiplied by thermal resistance of transistor-to-heat-sink mounting gives the number of °C hotter the transistor is than the heat sink.

FIGURE 5–2: Thermal Resistance

the quiescent power dissipation should be added to the power obtained from equation 5.01, but $P_{\text{DISS,Q}}$ is usually so small that it can safely be ignored.) For amplifiers having a DC output, the power dissipation is just

$$P_{\text{DISS,DC}} = V_{\text{supply}}I_{\text{supply}} - V_L I_L \qquad (5.02)$$

where V_{supply} and I_{supply} are the voltage and current of the power supply, and V_L and I_L are the load voltage and load current. For a constant-resistance load, $P_{\text{DISS,DC}}$ is maximum when $V_L = V_{\text{supply}}/2$.

Once you have the maximum power dissipated by an IC, the only other variable that you can control in order to control temperature is the thermal resistance. So the design process now becomes one of determining how low a thermal resistance is necessary. In order to do this, we must know two things: the maximum allowable temperature for the junction, and the ambient temperature (the temperature of the air surrounding the IC). Just as the total voltage at one end of a resistor depends upon both the current in the resistor and the voltage at the other end, so the temperature of a piece of material depends upon both the temperature rise caused by heat energy flowing in a thermal resistance and the temperature of the surrounding air. Stated mathematically,

$$\text{Temperature} = T_A + P_{\text{DISS}}\theta \qquad (5.03)$$

where θ is the thermal resistance and T_A is the ambient temperature. If we solve this equation to find the necessary thermal resistance to keep temperature from rising above the maximum allowable value, we get

$$\theta = \frac{T_{\max} - T_A}{P_{\text{DISS,max}}} \qquad (5.04)$$

EXAMPLE

Problem

What is the maximum thermal resistance that a linear IC and its mounting can have if it is to deliver maximum possible sine-wave output voltage from a ± 15-V supply to a 20-Ω load? The junction temperature must not rise above 150°C, and the room in which the circuit will be used never becomes hotter than 40°C.

Solution

1. The maximum peak-to-peak output voltage is about 28 V, assuming that the amplifier will swing within 1 V of supply. Thus the maximum power dissipation is

$$P_{\text{DISS,max}} = \frac{V_{\text{OUT,P-P}}^2}{20 R_L} = \frac{(28 \text{ V})^2}{20 \cdot 20 \ \Omega} = 1.96 \text{ W} \qquad (5.01)$$

2. The thermal resistance is

$$\theta = \frac{T_{max} - T_A}{P_{DISS,max}}$$

$$= \frac{150° - 40°C}{1.96\ W} = 56°C/W$$

(5.04)

Many low-power ICs can be operated with no heat sink; the metal tab built into the case gets rid of the heat well enough. When no heat sink is used, the thermal resistance is simply the thermal resistance of the IC. This parameter is given as θ_{JA} (thermal resistance from junction to ambient) on the data sheet, either as a certain number of °C/W or in the form of a graph depicting temperature rise as a function of power dissipated.

Sometimes, though, a heat sink is required. The heat sink may be simply the metal cabinet of the equipment, or it may be an aluminum extrusion designed specifically for the purpose. Several heat sinks are illustrated in Fig. 5–3. When a heat sink is used, the total thermal resistance is made up of three parts:

1. θ_{JC} is the thermal resistance from junction to case. This specifies how many degrees hotter than the case the semiconductor junction will become for each watt dissipated. This is the value specified on the data sheet for the IC or other device.

FIGURE 5–3: Heat Sinks *(Courtesy of Thermalloy, Inc.)*

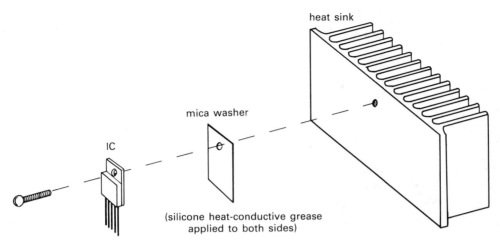

FIGURE 5–4: System for Mounting a Power IC on a Heat Sink

2. θ_{CS} is the thermal resistance from case to heat sink. It specifies how many degrees hotter than the heat sink the case of the device will become for each watt dissipated. When silicone grease is used to ensure good thermal contact between the case and the heat sink, this value is typically about 1°C/W. A common mounting system for a power IC is shown in Fig. 5–4.

3. θ_{SA} is the thermal resistance from heat sink to ambient. It specifies how many degrees hotter than the surrounding air the heat sink will become for each watt dissipated. This is the value that the designer must solve for. Since all three thermal resistances appear in series with the flow of heat energy, the total thermal resistance is just the sum of the three:

$$\theta_T = \theta_{JC} + \theta_{CS} + \theta_{SA}$$

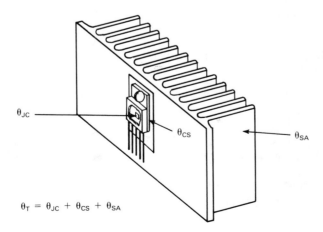

FIGURE 5–5: Thermal Resistance of a Heat-Sinked IC

Figure 5–5 illustrates this concept. Thus we find that

$$\theta_{SA} = \frac{T_{max} - T_A}{P_{DISS,max}} - \theta_{JC} - \theta_{CS} \qquad (5.05)$$

EXAMPLE

Problem

Calculate the necessary θ_{SA} for a heat sink to be used for an LM2005 IC that is to be powered from a unipolar 18-V supply. Each channel will feed a 4-Ω load. Assume T_A is 40°C. The data sheet for the LM2005 is included in Appendix A.

Solution

1. In order to calculate the maximum power dissipated by each channel, we will look at the output-swing-vs-supply-voltage graph on the data sheet. This shows that for an 18-V supply and a 4-Ω load the maximum output swing is 16 V. Thus,

$$P_{DISS,max} = \frac{(16 \text{ V})^2}{(20 \cdot 4 \text{ }\Omega)} = 3.2 \text{ W}$$

   The total dissipation for the package (both amplifier channels) is then twice this value, or 6.4 W.

2. The maximum operating temperature for the IC is 85°C, as shown on page 2 of the data sheet. θ_{JC} is 3°C/W, as shown on page 1 of the data sheet. We will assume $\theta_{CS} = 1$°C/W. Thus the thermal resistance for the heat sink is

$$\theta_{SA} = \frac{T_{max} - T_A}{P_{DISS,max}} - \theta_{JC} - \theta_{CS}$$

$$= \frac{85° - 40°}{6.4 \text{ W}} - 3°\text{C/W} - 1°\text{C/W} = 3°\text{C/W} \qquad (5.05)$$

Table 5–A gives the thermal resistances for the heat sinks shown in Fig. 5–2.

Often, more than one power device is mounted on a single heat sink. In that case, the heat-energy flow through the heat sink is the sum of the individual power dissipations, but each device's junction is made warmer than the heat sink only by its own power dissipation. For instance, if two identical LM2005 ICs were operated under the same conditions as in the above example, the junction temperature of each would be

$$T_{J1} = T_A + P_{DISS,max \text{ }1}(\theta_{JC} + \theta_{CS}) + (P_{DISS,max \text{ }1} + P_{DISS,max \text{ }2})\theta_{SA} \qquad (5.06)$$

TABLE 5–A Thermal Resistances for Some Styles of Heat Sinks

MODEL NUMBER	FOR CASE STYLE	θ (°C/W)
2225	TO-5	46
6010	DIP	60
6011	DIP	68
6038	TO-220	18
6403	TO-3	1.8
6423	TO-3	0.77

Thus θ_{SA} would be found as follows:

$$\theta_{SA} = \frac{T_{max} - T_A - P_{DISS,max\ 1}(\theta_{JC} + \theta_{CS})}{P_{DISS,max\ 1} + P_{DISS,max\ 2}} \qquad (5.07)$$

In cases where the various power devices that share the heat sink have different power dissipations, thermal resistances, and/or maximum junction temperatures, the same method of analysis can be used, but the final equation will come out different.

EXAMPLE

Problem

Find the necessary thermal resistance for a heat sink that is to cool two LM2005's and an LM317T voltage regulator. The LM2005's are connected to produce 10 V_{P-P} into a 4-Ω load, and the LM317T has a quiescent voltage drop across it of 7 V and delivers a current of 400 mA. Ambient temperature is 30°C. Use the data sheets in Appendix A.

Solution

1. The power dissipation of the LM2005's is

$$P_{DISS,max} = \frac{V_{OUT,P-P}^2}{20R_L} = \frac{(10\ V)^2}{20 \cdot 4\ \Omega} = 1.25\ W \qquad (5.01)$$

2. The power dissipation of the LM317T is (7 V)(400 mA) = 2.8 W.
3. From the data sheet, we find that T_{max} for the LM2005 is 85°C, and for the LM317T it is 125°C. θ_{JC} is 3°C/W for the LM2005 and 4°C/W for the LM317T. Let us calculate how many degrees hotter than the heat sink the junction of each device will become. For the LM317T,

$$T_J - T_S = P_{DISS,max}(\theta_{JC} + \theta_{CS}) = (2.8\ W)(4°C/W + 1°C/W) = 14°C$$

where T_S is the temperature of the heat sink. For each of the LM2005's,

$$T_J - T_S = (1.25\ W)(3°C/W + 1°C/W) = 5°C$$

4. In order to keep the LM317T safe, the heat sink must not rise above T_{max} − 14°C, which is 125°C − 14°C = 111°C. For the safety of the LM2005's, the heat sink must not rise above 85°C − 5°C = 80°C. Thus, in spite of the greater power dissipation of the LM317T, the LM2005's safety will set the upper limit on the heat sink temperature. The reason for this, of course, is the much smaller T_{max} of the LM2005.

5. Now we can calculate the thermal resistance for the heat sink:

$$\theta_{SA} = \frac{T_{sink,max} - T_A}{P_{DISS,total}} = \frac{80°C - 30°C}{2(1.25\text{ W}) + 2.8\text{ W}} = 9.4°C/W$$

Notice that in the above example we used the *concept* that was discussed earlier, even though the necessary *equation* was different. This is an important point in any analysis: Learned concepts are far more useful (and memorable) than memorized equations.

HIGH-CURRENT AND HIGH-VOLTAGE OP AMPS

A High-Current Op Amp

Most op amps are small-signal devices: Their maximum supply voltage is no more than ±18 V and their maximum output current is 10 mA or so. There are many applications that require more output current and/or voltage. As technology has advanced, several manufacturers have introduced op amps with greater voltage and current capabilities. One example is the LH0021. As you can see from the data sheet in Appendix A, this device has a maximum output current of one ampere. The other characteristics of the LH0021 are similar to those of any other general-purpose uncompensated op amp. Therefore, the design process that we have already studied applies to this unit as well. However, it is also necessary to consider the maximum output current and power dissipation when working with this type of circuit.

EXAMPLE

Problem

Determine the maximum output current and power dissipation for an LH0021 op amp that is fed by a ±16-V supply and driving a 10-Ω load. Determine whether a heat sink will be needed.

Solution

1. The peak current that can be delivered by any op amp is given by V_{SAT}/R_L. The output-voltage-swing graph on the data sheet in Appendix A shows that

with a 10-Ω load and a ±16-V supply, the LH0021 can deliver a ±13-V output. Thus the peak output current is 13 V/10 Ω = 1.3 A. (Under "DC Electrical Characteristics" on the data sheet, we find that the short-circuit current is typically limited to 1.2 A, with a maximum specification of 1.6 A. This means that large output signals may be clipped due to internal current limiting.)

2. The maximum power dissipation is calculated as we did earlier:

$$P_{\text{DISS,max}} = \frac{V_{\text{OUT,P-P}}^2}{20R_L} = \frac{(2 \cdot 13 \text{ V})^2}{20 \cdot 10 \text{ }\Omega} = 3.4 \text{ W}$$

3. The power derating curve for the LH0021 shown in the data sheet indicates that this power can be handled with no heat sink, as long as the free-air temperature does not exceed 50°C. However, since 3.4 W is fairly close to the 5-W limit shown by the "free-air" curve for a 25°C ambient, we might prefer to use a small heat sink. In general, electronic components of all types last longer if their operating temperatures are minimized.

Very often, high-current loads are not purely resistive. For example, a loudspeaker has an impedance that varies with frequency. For an 8-Ω speaker, the DC resistance is about 6 Ω. In addition to this resistance, there is about 0.1 Ω of "motional resistance," representing the work done in converting electrical energy into acoustical energy. There are also inductive components due to the voice coil and the mechanical mass of the moving cone, and there is a capacitive component corresponding to the stiffness of the suspension. The resulting impedance-vs.-frequency characteristic is shown in Fig. 5–6. At very low frequencies, the impedance is about 5 Ω. Then it rises to a peak of several times the 8-Ω rating at the resonant frequency. Above resonance, the impedance drops to about 8 Ω and maintains that value for an octave or so, then the inductive effects take over and the impedance rises almost in direct proportion to frequency. At extremely high frequencies, interwinding capacitance and various inductive losses begin to reduce the impedance again.

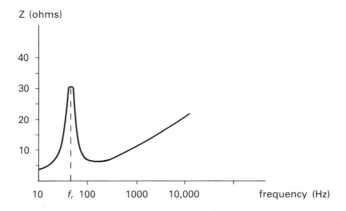

FIGURE 5–6: Impedance of a Loudspeaker Plotted versus Frequency

It is clear from Fig. 5–6 that the specified impedance of a loudspeaker is only a sort of average impedance over the frequency range in which the speaker will be used. The maximum current delivered by the amplifier that drives the speaker, however, is determined by the *lowest* impedance, which is the DC resistance. This is also true for solenoids and many other high-current devices.

For motors, the situation is even tougher on the IC. In motor operation, an internal voltage is generated by the interaction of the motor windings and the magnetic field. This voltage is opposite in polarity from the applied voltage, so it is called the *countervoltage*. The current drawn by a running motor is therefore given by the law of superposition:

$$I_{m,running} = \frac{V_{applied} - V_{counter}}{R_{windings}} \qquad (5.08)$$

When a heavy load causes the motor to slow down, the countervoltage decreases and more current is drawn. When a motor is started from a standstill, there is no countervoltage at first, so the starting current is

$$I_{m,start} = \frac{V_{applied}}{R_{windings}} \qquad (5.09)$$

Many motor controllers provide for forward or reverse operation of the motor. When a motor is running full speed in the forward direction, then is reversed, the countervoltage *adds* to the applied voltage while reversing is occurring:

$$I_{m,reversing} = \frac{V_{applied} + V_{counter}}{R_{windings}} \qquad (5.10)$$

The practical maximum value for the reversing current drawn by a motor is approximately twice the starting current:

$$I_{m,max} = \frac{2V_{applied}}{R_{windings}} \qquad (5.11)$$

For example, a motor having a 10-Ω winding, being operated from a 40-V supply, would draw a starting current of 40 V/10 Ω = 4 A, and a reversing current of about twice this value, or 8 A. This large current draw must be accounted for in the design of the motor controller, both in terms of maximum current and maximum power-dissipation capability.

Another concern that the designer must face in motor-control applications is inductive kickback. When a voltage is suddenly applied to or removed from an inductor, such as a motor's windings, spikes up to about 5 times the applied voltage can result. There are two ways to prevent these spikes from damaging the electronic devices in the controller. One is to use back-to-back Zener diodes connected across the motor to clamp the spikes to a safe value. The other is to use varistors for the same purpose. A varistor is a semiconductor device that functions essentially like back-to-back Zeners, but has somewhat better resistance to damage from high instantaneous currents and voltages. Both of these devices have a high resistance when

Varistor

Zener Transient Suppressor

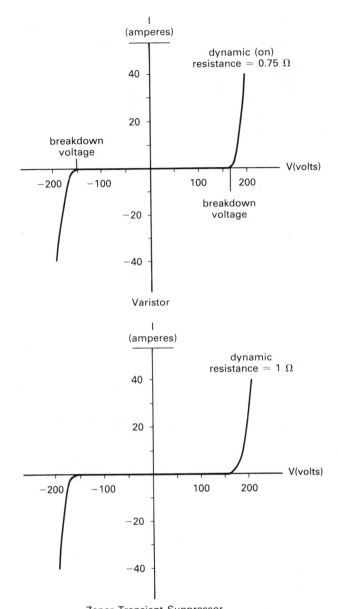

FIGURE 5–7A: Current/Voltage Characteristics

FIGURE 5–7B: Common Symbols

FIGURE 5–7: Two Voltage-Surge Protection Devices

FIGURE 5–7C: Photograph of Varistors (Courtesy of Panasonic Industrial Company, Division of Matsushita Electric Corporation of America)

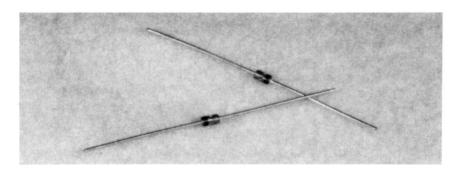

FIGURE 5–7D: Zener Transient Suppressors

the applied voltage is low, but when the voltage rises to the devices' breakdown value, the resistance drops to a very low value, shorting out the spike. The current-vs.-voltage characteristics for both devices are shown in Fig. 5–7A. Back-to-back Zeners and varistors are indicated by the same schematic symbol, as shown in Fig. 5–7B. Photographs of Varistors and Zener Transient Suppressors are shown in Fig. 5–1C and D.

EXAMPLE

Problem

Design an amplifier for use as a reversing permanent-magnet (PM) motor controller. The amplifier is to be capable of applying ± 10 V to the motor. The motor's winding resistance is 40 Ω. The amplifier is to be fed by a tachometer sensor having a ± 1-V output. Include surge-protection devices, and give their breakdown voltage. Calculate the thermal resistance for the heat sink, assuming a maximum ambient temperature of 30°C.

Solution

1. We will use the LH0021C. From the output-voltage-swing graph on the data sheet in Appendix A, we find that a ± 12-V supply is needed. By connecting one lead of the motor to ground, we can apply either positive or negative voltage to the other lead, which will provide forward or reverse operation for a PM motor.
2. The gain of the amplifier should be $V_{OUT}/V_{IN} = \pm 10$ V$/\pm 1$ V $= 10$. We will use a noninverting amplifier with $R_g = 1$ kΩ and $R_f = 9$ kΩ.
3. The maximum output current is

$$I_{m,max} = \frac{2V_{applied}}{R_{windings}} = \frac{(2)(\pm 12 \text{ V})}{40 \text{ }\Omega} = \pm 0.6 \text{ A}$$

This is a safe current for the IC we are using.
4. The maximum power dissipation will occur when the motor is reversing. At that time, there will be a maximum of 24 V across the IC and 0.6 A through it. Thus,

$$P_{DISS,max} = 24 \cdot 0.6 = 14.4 \text{ W}$$

5. The thermal resistance of the heat sink is

$$\theta_{SA} = \frac{T_{max} - T_A}{P_{DISS,max}} - \theta_{JC} - \theta_{CS} \tag{5.05}$$

From the data sheet, θ_{JC} is 2°C/W and T_{max} is 85°C for the LH0021C, so

$$\theta_{SA} = \frac{85°C - 30°C}{14.4 \text{ W}} - 2°C/W - 1°C/W = 0.82°C/W$$

where we have used 1°C/W for θ_{CS}, as we discussed earlier. This is quite a low thermal resistance, but not impossibly low. Also, since we have designed for a continuous power dissipation that is equal to the maximum possible dissipation, there is a possibility that a smaller heat sink (higher θ_{SA}) could be used satisfactorily. This would depend upon how often the motor is to be reversed. If reversing will be seldom, then only occasionally will the IC have to dissipate the maximum power, so the average dissipation will be much smaller than the value we calculated, and a smaller heat sink could be used. But if the motor will be reversed frequently, the average power dissipation will be high, and a heat sink having the low thermal resistance we calculated should be used.

6. Since the largest voltage that will ever be applied to the motor is ± 10 V, we can specify a 22-V varistor for surge protection. It is true that the varistor will place a brief short circuit across the amplifier output each time a surge surpasses its breakdown voltage, but the internal current limiting of the IC will protect it from damage. To protect against possible long-term short-circuits, we will insert a 1-A slow-blow fuse in series with the output. The completed design is shown in Fig. 5–8.

Another example of the application of the LH0021 is shown in Fig. 5–9. The two-way intercom circuit shown there has the advantage of simplicity and low parts count. The circuit is a noninverting amplifier with the gain controllable by the 100-kΩ potentiometer that is used for R_f. A switch is provided so that the speaker at station 1 can be used as the input device and the speaker at station 2 as the output device, or vice versa. This provides for "talk" and "listen" operation. Compensation is provided by a 3000-pF capacitor. (This value was chosen because it is the one specified on the open-loop frequency-response and large-signal frequency-response graphs in the data sheet.) Two 0.5-Ω resistors are used for the positive and negative short-circuit sensing resistors, as suggested by the short-circuit-current-vs.-temperature graphs.

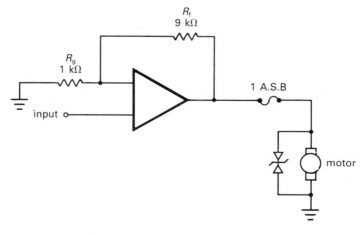

FIGURE 5–8: Reversing Motor-Controller Circuit

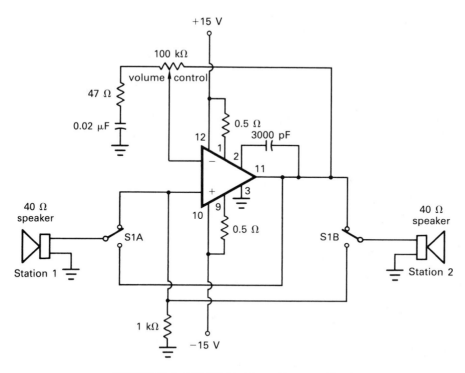

FIGURE 5–9: LH0021 Used in an Intercom Circuit

A High-Voltage Op Amp

There are some applications that call for more output voltage than a general-purpose op amp can deliver, but in which the current requirements are not large. The LH004C is designed for such applications. As you can see from the data sheet in Appendix A, this device can be operated with a ±45-V power supply, delivering 76 $V_{P\text{-}P}$ to a load. But the output current must be held low enough that the 400-mW power-dissipation rating is not exceeded. Internal short-circuit protection is not provided, and the IC can only withstand a maximum 3-second output short. Because of the case style, even heat-sinking only extends the power-dissipation limit to 800 mW. The data sheet includes a suggested circuit for limiting the output current to a safe value. This circuit simply turns off the output stage of the IC when output current exceeds the chosen value.

The LH004C is an uncompensated op amp, requiring two external capacitors for compensation. Typically these include a 39-pF feedback capacitor from pin 10 to pin 1 and a 22-pF capacitor from pin 5 to ground.

EXAMPLE

Problem

It is desired to use the LH004C as a driver for a Darlington transistor pack in a DC motor-control circuit. The maximum voltage to be applied to the motor is 36 V, and the motor has a winding resistance of 9 Ω. Minimum voltage to be applied to the motor under load is 12 V. What is the minimum gain that the Darlington pack must have in order to keep the output current within a safe range? Design a current-limiting circuit for the op amp to protect it against damage in case the output of the Darlington pack is accidentally shorted. The circuit is shown in Fig. 5–10A. It includes a tacho-

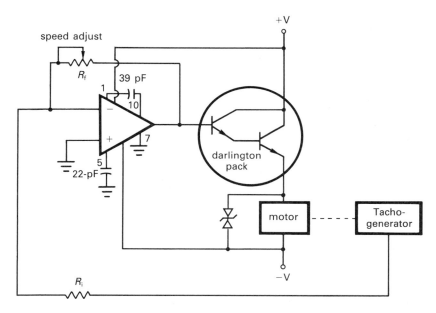

FIGURE 5–10A: Motor Speed-Control Circuit

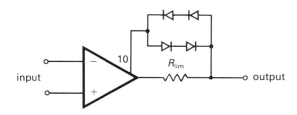

FIGURE 5–10B: Current-Limiting Circuit *(Courtesy of National Semiconductor Corp.)*

FIGURE 5–10: Example Using High-Voltage Op Amp

generator mechanically connected to the motor (dashed line on the schematic). The output voltage from the tachogenerator is directly proportional to the motor speed. Thus this voltage applied to the inverting input of the op amp stabilizes the speed of the motor.

Solution

1. Judging by the output-voltage graph on the data sheet, the LH004C requires at least a 44-V supply in order to provide a 36-V output. We will use ±25 V, which corresponds to a 50-V unipolar supply. This gives us a 40-V output capability. A 2-kΩ load is suggested by the data sheet, giving a maximum output current of 40 V/2 kΩ = 20 mA.
2. The power dissipated by the IC is the product of the voltage across the IC and the current through it. Since this is not a reversible controller, the largest current will be the starting current:

$$I_{m,starting} = \frac{V_{applied}}{R_{windings}} = \frac{36 \text{ V}}{9 \text{ }\Omega} = 4 \text{ A}$$

As mentioned earlier, maximum power is dissipated when V_L is half of V_s, which is 25 V. This means that 25 V will be dropped across the output stage of the op amp. Maximum power dissipation for the IC package at ambient temperatures below 50°C is 400 mW. For long life, let us limit the dissipation to 200 mW. This means that the maximum output current must be limited to 200 mW/25 V = 8 mA. The gain required from the Darlington pack is then given by

$$\beta_{Darlingtons} = \frac{I_{OUT}}{I_{IN}} = \frac{4 \text{ A}}{8 \text{ mA}} = 500$$

This gain must be available at a 4-A collector current.
3. The current-limiting circuit suggested by the data sheet is shown in Fig. 5–10B. The limiting current is

$$I_{lim} = \frac{V_f}{R_{lim}}$$

where V_f is the forward voltage drop of the diodes at a current of 20 to 50 μA. Typically this value is about 0.5 V for each diode, and there are two in series in each polarity, so V_f = 1 V. We will allow a 10% overcurrent before limiting begins, so I_{lim} will be 10% more than 8 mA, which is 8.8 mA. Thus R_{lim} should be 1 V/8.8 mA = 114 Ω. We will use a 120 Ω resistor. Even with maximum overcurrent, the package dissipation is still limited to (25 V)(8.8 mA) = 220 mW, which is quite safe.
4. A 40-V Zener surge protector connected across the motor will prevent damage to the transistors or IC from voltage surges.

AUDIO POWER AMPLIFIERS

Probably the most common application for high-current op amps is audio power amplification. For power output below 20 W, ICs have virtually replaced discrete amplifiers in most audio equipment. In this power range, ICs provide essentially equal performance, lower total parts count (which means lower manufacturing cost), and equivalent total parts cost, when compared to discrete devices.

Distortion

Distortion is an important consideration in audio power amplifier design. Whenever a signal is applied to a nonlinear device, the output signal will not be a faithful reproduction of the input signal. The unfaithfulness is called distortion. (A nonlinear device is one in which the output voltage is not directly proportional to the input voltage. Thus any real amplifier is somewhat nonlinear.) In general, distortion consists of the addition of frequency components that are not present in the input signal. These frequency components are of two varieties. The first variety consists of *harmonics,* or integer multiples of the input frequency. The second variety consists of sum and difference components produced by the unintentional amplitude modulation caused by the nonlinearity. The concept of distortion is illustrated in Fig. 5–11. Notice that in Fig. 5–11A the output wave is slightly clipped at the top, and the whole negative half-cycle is amplified less than the positive half-cycle. Figure 5–11B shows the effect of this distortion in adding harmonic frequencies to the wave. Figure 5–11C shows the effect of intermodulation (IM) distortion. Notice that in the output wave, the high-frequency component is amplified more on the positive half-cycle of the low-frequency wave than on the negative, although the amplitude of the high-frequency component is constant in the input wave. This corresponds to the addition of two extraneous frequencies—the sum and difference of the input frequencies—as shown in Fig. 5–11D. Although harmonic distortion and intermodulation distortion are both produced by the same cause, the exact nature of the nonlinearity can result in more of one or the other. Thus the two forms of distortion are often specified separately. For either kind of distortion, the percentage distortion is calculated as follows:

$$\% \text{ Distortion} = \frac{\text{Extraneous frequency components}}{\text{Total output voltage}} \times 100\% \qquad (5.12)$$

Tolerable distortion levels are shown in Table 5–B.

Output Power

The maximum output power of an AC amplifier depends upon the maximum output voltage swing and the load resistance. Of course, $P = V^2/R$, but in the case of AC, we usually think of average power, which would require that the voltage be

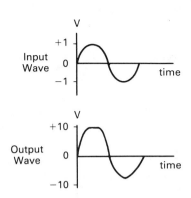

FIGURE 5–11A: Voltage-vs.-Time Graph for Harmonic Distortion

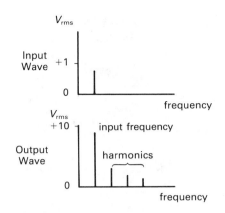

FIGURE 5–11B: Voltage-vs.-Frequency Graph for Harmonic Distortion

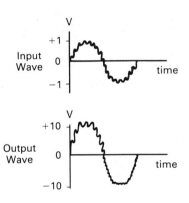

FIGURE 5–11C: Voltage-vs.-Time Graph for IM Distortion

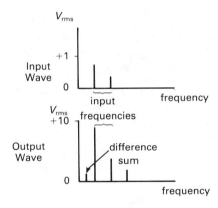

FIGURE 5–11D: Voltage-vs.-Frequency Graph for IM Distortion

FIGURE 5–11: Distortion

TABLE 5–B Distortion Levels

TYPE OF DISTORTION	AUDIBLE LEVEL	TOLERABLE LEVEL	MAXIMUM ALLOWABLE LEVEL
Harmonic	0.1%	3%	10%
IM	0.01%	1%	3%

Note: The amount of distortion that can be tolerated depends upon the application. Somewhat more distortion is tolerable for speech than for music. The figures given in the "Tolerable" and "Maximum" columns above are approximate.

specified in rms volts. We can most easily find the maximum output swing of an IC in peak-to-peak terms. Converting from $V_{P\text{-}P}$ to V_{rms} is simple:

$$V_{rms} = \frac{V_{P\text{-}P}}{2\sqrt{2}}$$

When we square the voltage, as in the power formula, we get

$$V_{rms}^2 = \frac{V_{P\text{-}P}^2}{8}$$

Plugging this result into the power formula, we obtain the output power:

$$P_{OUT} = \frac{V_{OUT,P\text{-}P}^2}{8R_L} \tag{5.13}$$

Power-Amplifier ICs

One of the most popular audio power amplifier ICs is the LM386. As you can see from the data sheet in Appendix A, this circuit is just a specialized op amp. Aside from its maximum output current (300 mA) and power dissipation (1.25 W), the LM386 has three unusual features:

• It is designed for single-supply operation. This is especially handy in mobile or battery-operated use. Because of the design of the input stage, no biasing is needed for the inputs; they can be ground referenced.

• Its open-loop gain is only 20. Actually, the open-loop gain of the circuit inside the LM386 is much greater than 20. However, internal feedback is provided that sets the gain at this value. The reason for this is to lower the external parts count, since in many applications for which the LM386 is used, 20 is very nearly the desired gain. If lower gains are desired, additional feedback can be applied. For higher gains, a 10-μF capacitor can be used to bypass part of the internal R_f, bringing the gain up to 200. A resistor placed in series with the 10-μF capacitor will provide for intermediate values of gain. This is discussed in the data sheet.

• A bypass pin is provided. This pin can be connected to ground through a 10-μF tantalum capacitor to increase power-supply hum rejection, prevent oscillation, and so on.

EXAMPLE

Problem

Design a 1-W amplifier for a portable paging system using an LM386. Specify the power supply voltage, any necessary heat-sinking, and all component values. Use one channel of an LM 381 for the preamplifier. The microphone output voltage is 2 mV$_{rms}$, and a 10-kΩ input impedance is required. Frequency response must be flat from 200 Hz to 10 kHz.

Solution

1. The three device-dissipation-vs.-output-power graphs on the data sheet of the LM386 show that 1-W output power is only available with a 16-Ω load, and that a 16-V power supply is adequate for this output power, so we will choose that value. The necessary rms output voltage is therefore

$$V_{OUT} = \sqrt{P_{OUT}R_L} = \sqrt{(1 \text{ W})(16 \text{ }\Omega)} = 4 \text{ V}_{rms}$$

   The total system gain is

$$A_V = \frac{V_{OUT}}{V_{IN}} = \frac{4 \text{ V}}{2 \text{ mV}} = 2000$$

   The power amplifier provides a gain of 20, so the gain of the preamp needs to be 100.

2. We can now draw the preliminary circuit diagram, which is shown in Fig. 5–12A. Using a noninverting circuit for lower noise, we will select $R_g = 1 \text{ k}\Omega$. This provides the correct input impedance. Because of the design of the LM381's input circuits, a bias-current path from the noninverting input to ground is not needed. R_f is just $A_V R_g = 100 \text{ k}\Omega$.

3. The LM381 data sheet in Appendix A gives 100 kΩ as the input resistance of the noninverting input. Therefore, the input capacitor's value is

$$C_{IN} = \frac{1}{2\pi f R_g} = \frac{1}{2\pi \cdot 200 \text{ Hz} \cdot 100 \text{ k}\Omega} = 0.008 \text{ }\mu\text{F}$$

   We will use a 0.0082-μF capacitor.

4. The output voltage from the preamp is the input voltage multiplied by the gain, which is 200 mV$_{rms}$. The large-signal frequency-response graph on the LM381 data sheet shows that a 10-kHz output at this voltage is no problem. (This saves us from making GBW and slew-rate calculations.) This completes the preamp design.

5. We will use the LM386N-4 version for maximum power capability (see page 2 of the data sheet). Since we are using a gain of 20 in the power stage, no feedback resistors are necessary. The only components whose values we have to calculate are the coupling and output capacitors. We want the reactance of these capacitors to be less than or equal to one-tenth of the resistance of the load they feed. The input resistance of the LM386 is given in the data sheet as 50 kΩ, so

$$C_{coupling} = \frac{10}{2\pi f R_{in}} = \frac{10}{2\pi \cdot 200 \text{ Hz} \cdot 50 \text{ k}\Omega} = 0.159 \text{ }\mu\text{F}$$

$$C_{OUT} = \frac{10}{2\pi f R_L} = \frac{10}{2\pi \cdot 200 \text{ Hz} \cdot 16 \text{ }\Omega} = 497 \text{ }\mu\text{F}$$

   We will use 0.2 μF and 500 μF for the two capacitors. The completed design is shown in Fig. 5–12B.

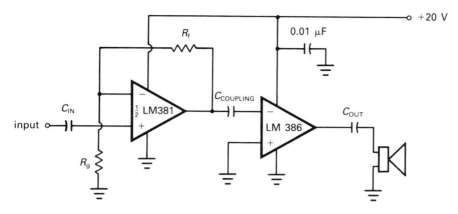

FIGURE 5–12A: Preliminary Diagram

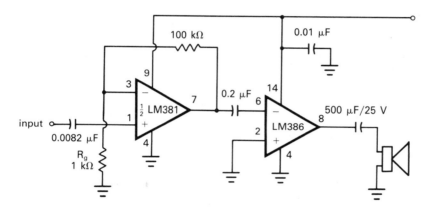

FIGURE 5–12B: Completed Design

FIGURE 5–12: A Power Amplifier Using the LM386

For applications requiring more power, devices such as the LM2005 are available. This is a two-channel amplifier that can deliver up to 10 W per channel. This device incorporates several safety features that are typical of newer-generation power ICs. These include

- Protection from damage caused by brief power-supply overvoltages as high as 40 V. The IC is rated at 18 V maximum.
- Short-circuit protection.
- Protection against "kickback" voltages when driving inductive loads.
- Protection against an accidental open ground in the supply line. This is a common fault in the installation of mobile equipment, and usually results in a heavy current being dumped through the IC and the load to ground, destroying the IC.
- Thermal protection to cut the IC off in case the chip temperature becomes too high.

These features are an example of the advantages of IC power stages, because the number of components that would be required to provide these kinds of protection in a discrete circuit would be quite large, resulting in a very expensive design.

You will notice from the pinout diagram on the data sheet that there is one "bootstrap" pin for each channel. This pin is provided for the connection of an external capacitor to increase the signal voltage fed to the output stage, thereby increasing the maximum output voltage before clipping. (The clipping in earlier stages in the IC limits the output voltage if the bootstrap capacitor is omitted.)

Figure 5–13 shows two power amplifiers connected in a bridge configuration in order to provide increased power output. The bridge configuration consists of two power amplifiers driven out of phase with each other. The load is connected between

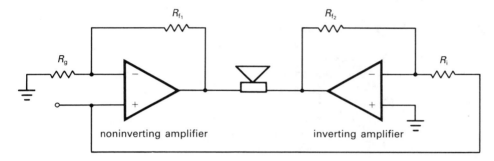

FIGURE 5–13A: Simplified Diagram

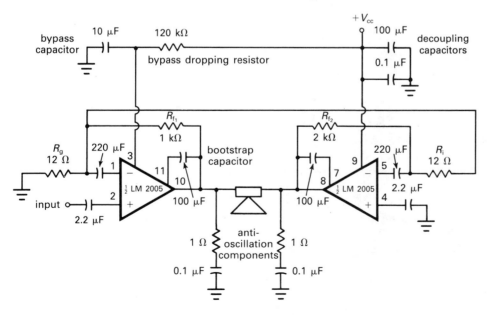

FIGURE 5–13B: Practical Circuit

FIGURE 5–13: Bridged IC Power Amplifiers

the two outputs; neither side of the load is grounded. This arrangement effectively doubles the maximum output voltage. To demonstrate why, we will calculate the maximum output voltage and power available from an amplifier powered by an 18-V supply (the maximum supply for the LM2005). Typically, the output voltage swing would be twice V_{SAT}, or about 16 V_{P-P}. The output power into a 3.2-Ω load would then be

$$P_{OUT} = \frac{V^2_{OUT,P-P}}{8R_L} = \frac{(16 \text{ V})^2}{8 \cdot 3.2 \text{ } \Omega} = 10 \text{ W} \tag{5.13}$$

Now a 16-V_{P-P} output means that the load can be fed ± 8 V with respect to ground. With the practical bridge configuration shown in Fig. 5–13B, if one side of the load is driven 8 V positive by the left-hand amplifier, the other side is driven 8 V negative by the right-hand amplifier. Thus there is 16 V across the load. If the signal reverses polarity, the left-hand amplifier will drive one side 8 V negative while the right-hand amplifier drives the other side 8 V positive. This represents 16 V across the load in the opposite polarity. Thus the bridge circuit can provide 32 V_{P-P} across the load while using an 18-V supply. Now 32-V_{P-P} across a 3.2-Ω load corresponds to 40 W. However, from the total-harmonic-distortion-vs.-power-output (bridge) graph on the data sheet, we see that harmonic distortion increases rapidly when power output exceeds 15 W. The distortion is about 10% when the output reaches 22 W, so although higher output power is available, the distortion would be so severe that it would not be useful for most applications.

INTERFACING OP AMPS WITH DISCRETE DEVICES

Bipolar Transistors

When greater output current and/or voltage are required than an IC can deliver, the IC is often connected to an external device such as a transistor to provide the needed capability. Figure 5–14A shows a simple current booster. This circuit simply uses a complementary bipolar transistor emitter-follower output stage to provide current gain. This stage could be used to increase the current output of a standard op amp, or it could be used with a high-voltage op amp to provide both high voltage and high current. In designing such a circuit, several things must be kept in mind. First, since bipolar transistors require an input current, the maximum load current that can be provided by this circuit is β times the op amp's maximum output current. For a 741, the maximum output current is about 20 mA. With typical output transistors having a β of 50 or so, currents up to 1 A could be provided. For greater output current, Darlington transistors could be used. Second, the transistors' ratings must be chosen properly. In addition to sufficient β, the transistor must have a breakdown voltage ($V_{B,CEO}$) at least as high as the supply (30 V for a $\pm$15-V supply). If the load is highly inductive, such as a motor or a relay, $V_{B,CEO}$ should be 5 times the supply voltage to protect against inductive kickback. If unipolar DC is being

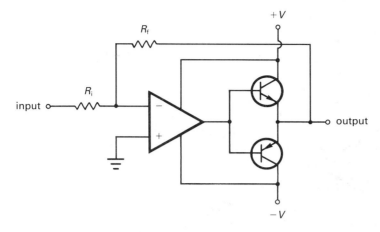

FIGURE 5–14A: Current Booster Circuit

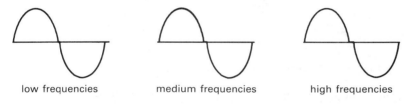

low frequencies   medium frequencies   high frequencies

FIGURE 5–14B: Output Wave

FIGURE 5–14: Current-Boosted Op Amp

applied to the load, a diode in series with the output transistor will help protect against kickback voltages. The transistor must be able to deliver enough current to drive the load. It is surprising how many technicians will attempt to use a small-signal transistor to drive a 2-A load! And of course the power dissipation of the transistors must be calculated, and heat sinks provided if necessary.

You may have noticed that no biasing circuitry is provided for the output transistors in Fig. 5–14A. As shown in Fig. 5–14B, this will result in some crossover distortion because of both transistors being turned off when the output voltage is small. However, because the transistors are included in the feedback loop, the op amp partially corrects for this distortion, making it much less than would be produced by the transistors operating alone. At higher frequencies, the slew rate of the amplifier prevents it from completely correcting for crossover distortion. But for applications in which small amounts of distortion can be tolerated, this simple circuit works quite well.

If greater voltage output is required than an op amp can deliver, the bridge configuration discussed earlier can be used. Of course, bridging does require that neither side of the load be connected to ground. Figure 5–15 shows a booster that provides both increased current and increased voltage output. It does not require that the load "float" with respect to ground. This circuit is simply a complementary two-

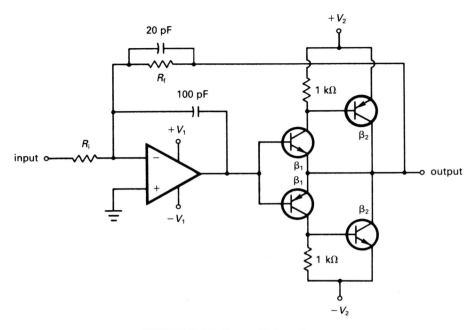

FIGURE 5–15: Current/Voltage Booster

stage common-emitter voltage amplifier. The total voltage gain is determined by the overall feedback loop. The design considerations for this amplifier are similar to those for the current-booster design. In addition, the added voltage gain may require frequency compensation, even if the op amp is internally compensated. The two capacitors shown in Fig. 5–15 are for that purpose. Often the value of these is determined by trial and error, but the values shown in the figure are typical. If the circuit oscillates when built as shown, increase the value of the capacitors until the oscillation is eliminated.

Notice that the booster circuit shown in Fig. 5–15 uses two power supplies. The op amp is supplied by the lower-voltage supply V_1, and the output stage is fed by V_2. The maximum output voltage depends upon the value of supply V_2, as do the necessary ratings of the transistors. The maximum output current is

$$I_{OUT,max} = I_{oa}\beta_1\beta_2,$$

where I_{oa} is the maximum output current of the op amp, and β_1 and β_2 are the current gains of the output transistors.

EXAMPLE

Problem

Design a current/voltage-booster circuit with a maximum output of 80 $V_{P\text{-}P}$ at 100 mA. Assume an 800-Ω resistive load.

Solution

1. We will use the circuit of Fig. 5–15. For each polarity of the supply, we will allow a 2-V margin between V_{SAT} and the supply voltage. This calls for a ± 42-V power supply for V_2.

2. The maximum output current of a 741 op amp is about 20 mA, so the output stage will need a current gain of

$$A_I = \frac{I_{OUT}}{I_{IN}} = \frac{100 \text{ mA}}{20 \text{ mA}} = 5$$

Since the output-stage gain is the product of the gains of the two transistors, the current gain of any transistors will certainly be more than adequate.

3. The maximum power dissipation of the output transistors is

$$P_{DISS,max} = \frac{V^2_{OUT,P-P}}{20 R_L} = \frac{(80 \text{ V})^2}{20 \cdot 800 \text{ }\Omega} = 400 \text{ mW}$$

This means that the output transistors must be able to dissipate 200 mW each.

4. Looking at the data sheet in Appendix A for the TIP31C and TIP32C complementary transistors, we find that the voltage rating, current rating, β, and power dissipation with no heat sink are high enough for our application, so we will specify these.

Triacs, GTOs, SCRs

Other semiconductor devices besides bipolar transistors are sometimes used to interface between op amps and loads. Among these are thyristors—SCRs, triacs, and GTOs. (Figure 5–16 shows the schematic symbols of several common thyristors.) Let's briefly review the operating characteristics of these devices. An SCR has three terminals: anode, cathode, and gate. If the anode is more positive than the cathode, and the gate is then made more positive than the cathode, the device will turn on. When turned on, the SCR acts like a diode; it passes current in one direction. Also, once turned on, an SCR stays on until anode-to-cathode current falls below the "holding value," typically a few milliamps. It cannot be turned off by the gate. In other words, the SCR is a latching device.

The triac also has three terminals, but they are called anode 1 (or main terminal 1), anode 2 (or main terminal 2), and gate. The triac can be turned on in a number of ways. If anode 2 and the gate are at voltages different from that of anode 1, the device will be turned on. Once turned on, a triac will pass current in either direction. Like the SCR, the triac also latches and cannot be turned off by the gate. It can only be turned off by making the anode-1-to-anode-2 current drop below the holding value. Of course, if a triac is used to switch AC, the voltage between anodes falls to zero twice during each cycle, and this usually results in zero current. Therefore, a triac

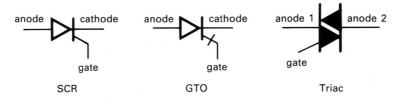

FIGURE 5–16: Thyristor Symbols

that is switching AC must have a steady voltage applied to keep the gate voltage different from the voltage of anode 1. Otherwise, it will turn off at the next zero-crossing of the AC wave.

A device that is similar to the SCR is the gate turnoff device (GTO), or gate-controlled switch (GCS). The GTO operates exactly like an SCR except that it can be turned off by a negative pulse applied to the gate.

The most important ratings of a thyristor are the *maximum forward current* and the *reverse-blocking voltage*. The maximum forward current should be at least twice as high as the expected load current. The reverse-blocking voltage should be at least twice as high as the power-supply voltage if the load is resistive. For inductive loads, the reverse-blocking voltage should be 5 times the supply voltage.

Unlike transistors, thyristors' gate currents are not directly related to the load current. Therefore, a thyristor that switches any current from about 10 to 40 A will typically need about 25 mA of gate current. Sensitive-gate devices are available that require much less gate current than that. So by using a sensitive-gate thyristor, you can connect it directly to the output of an op amp. The penalty for driving a thyristor with insufficient gate current is that it may not turn on, or if it does, it may not latch. The only other consideration is the maximum allowable gate current. If this maximum rating is exceeded, the thyristor will be damaged. If an internally current-limited op amp is used, and its limit current is below the maximum gate current of the thyristor, no further precautions need be taken. However, if the IC can deliver more current than the gate of the thyristor can handle, a current-limiting resistor must be used. There are other important considerations involved in the effective use of thyristors, such as false triggering due to rapid change of output voltage (dV/dt effects). These considerations do not affect the design of the op-amp circuit driving the thyristor, so they are not dealt with in this book. For this information, refer to a good industrial electronics text.

EXAMPLE

Problem

Calculate the value of the current-limiting resistor for the circuit shown in Fig. 5–17. Assume that the maximum gate current for the GTO is 5 mA.

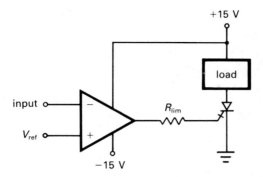

FIGURE 5–17: Op Amp Interfaced with a GTO

Solution

The maximum voltage that the op amp can apply to the GTO is V_{SAT}, which is about
14 V. Ignoring the drop from gate to cathode of the thyristor, we can calculate the
resistor's value using Ohm's law:

$$R_{lim} = \frac{14 \text{ V}}{5 \text{ mA}} = 2800 \ \Omega$$

Power FETs

A semiconductor device that is rapidly gaining popularity in all kinds of power
circuits is the power FET. Sometimes called by various trade names, the power FET
is a MOSFET—that is, an FET whose gate is isolated by a metal-oxide layer from
the channel. In many ways, a MOSFET is similar in operation to a junction FET or
JFET. However, special internal geometries allow the power FET to handle much
greater current than the typical JFET. Unlike the JFET, however, the power FET is
an enhancement-mode device; that is, an N-channel unit requires a positive bias on
the gate to turn it on. (A negative gate bias is required to turn on a P-channel power
FET.) The JFET is normally on and requires a negative bias (for an N-channel unit)
to turn it off. So in respect to turn-on characteristics, the power FET resembles a
bipolar transistor. But it shares other characteristics with the JFET:

1. The input impedance is quite high and almost purely capacitive.
2. The drain current is self-limited to a certain maximum value.
3. It responds to an input voltage rather than an input current as a bipolar transistor
   does. In other words, it is a voltage-sensitive current amplifier or a voltage-
   controlled current source. (A bipolar transistor is a current amplifier.)
4. It is a purely majority-carrier device, so the switching speed is not slowed by
   minority-carrier storage time as in a bipolar transistor. These characteristics
   make the power FET useful for circuits that have a limited driving current but
   must handle a high-current load. They eliminate the need for overcurrent protection and provide greater switching speed.

POWER-IC APPLICATION—PULSE-WIDTH-MODULATED MOTOR CONTROLLER

The speed of a DC motor is proportional to the applied voltage, but the torque diminishes at low voltages. Low-speed performance is usually erratic when analog controllers are used, especially under changing load conditions. Pulse-width-modulated (PWM) controllers offer superior control and operate efficiently at low speeds.

The PWM controller shown below uses complementary half-H peripheral drivers (SN75603, SN75604) with totem-pole outputs rated at 40 V and 2.0 A. These drivers effectively place the motor in a full bridge configuration which has the ability to provide bidirectional control.

Timer U1 operates in the astable mode at a frequency of 80 Hz. The 100-Ω discharge resistor results in an 8-μs trigger pulse which is coupled to the trigger input of timer U2. Timer U2 serves as the PWM generator. Capacitor C1 is charged linearly with a constant current of 1 mA from the IN5297, which is an FET current regulator diode.

Motor speed is controlled by feeding a DC voltage of 0 to 10 V to the control input (pin 5) of U2. As the control voltage increases, the width of the output pulse (pin 3) also increases. These pulses control the on/off time of the two motor drivers. Note that the trigger pulse width of timer U1 limits the minimum possible duty cycle from U2.

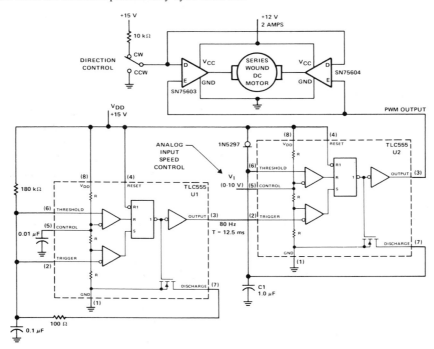

Reproduced from *Linear and Interface Circuits Applications* (Courtesy of Texas Instruments, Incorporated).

The turn-on threshold of a power FET is much higher than the 0.7 V of a bipolar transistor: It is usually in the 2–8-V range. Thus some sort of bias circuit is required in class B output stages in order to avoid severe crossover distortion. The threshold voltage decreases with increasing temperature, so the bias circuit must compensate for this change. Figure 5–18 shows a circuit for interfacing an op amp with a complementary power FET output stage. Notice the MOSFET used for biasing. Since it is mounted on the same heat sink as the output devices, its characteristics track those of the output FETs as temperature changes. In this way, the temperature sensitivity of the threshold voltage is compensated.

The drive current required by a power FET can be calculated using the equation for the current in a capacitor:

$$i = C\left(\frac{dv}{dt}\right),$$

where dv/dt is the time rate of change of the applied voltage. The maximum time rate of change of a sine-wave voltage equals $2\pi f V_P$, where V_P is the peak voltage

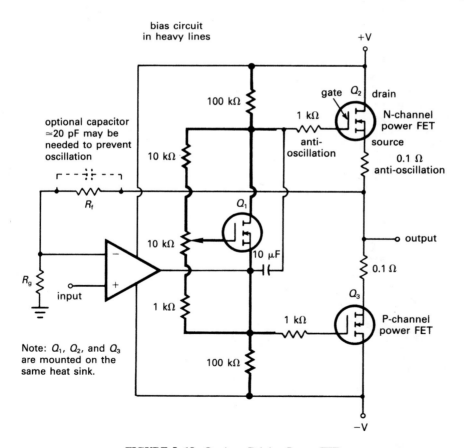

FIGURE 5–18: Op Amp Driving Power FETs

Sidebar

POWER-IC APPLICATION—HIGH-VOLTAGE POWER MOSFET DRIVER

The 1464 is a high-speed, FET input, transconductance amplifier, designed to drive an external power MOSFET output stage. The use of an external output stage makes the 1464 extremely versatile, allowing the users to tailor the part to their requirements. It operates from ±10-V to ±50-V supplies.

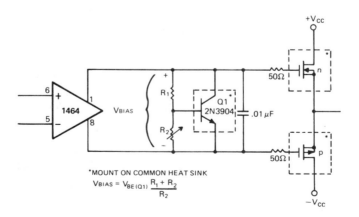

$$V_{BIAS} = V_{BE(Q1)} \frac{R_1 + R_2}{R_2}$$

*MOUNT ON COMMON HEAT SINK

Typical Connection (Courtesy of Teledyne-Philbrick, Inc.)

of the sine wave. Therefore the maximum current would be drawn at the highest frequency:

$$i_{max} = 2\pi f V_P C \tag{5.14}$$

Any additional current drawn by the biasing circuit must be added to this amount.

EXAMPLE

Problem

Calculate the necessary peak driving current for an op amp feeding a complementary power FET output stage. The output requirements are $V_{OUT} = \pm 10$ V$_{P\text{-}P}$, $I_L = 5$ A, C_{IN} for the FETs $= 50$ pF, and $f_{max} = 10$ kHz.

Solution

1. Using the circuit of Fig. 5–18, we see that both FETs appear as a parallel capacitive load on the output of the op amp. Thus the total capacitance is twice the individual capacitance, or 100 pF. Thus,

$$i_{max} = 2\pi f V_P C$$
$$= (2\pi)(10 \text{ kHz})(10 \text{ V})(100 \text{ pF}) = 63 \text{ }\mu A \tag{5.14}$$

2. The bias circuit adds two parallel 100-kΩ resistors to the total load, so the current drawn by this circuit is

$$i = \frac{V_{OUT}}{R} = \frac{10 \text{ V}}{50 \text{ k}\Omega} = 200 \text{ }\mu A$$

3. The total driving current is therefore 63 μA + 200 μA = 263 μA. The load current does not affect this figure.

Since the 63-μA current is drawn by a pure capacitance, it would increase directly with frequency. Thus if f_{max} were increased by a factor of 100, to 1 MHz, 6.3 mA (100 times 63 μA) would have been required.

Because of the thinness of the metal-oxide layer in any MOSFET, discharges of static electricity can easily ruin the device. Although some power FETs contain Zener diodes to protect against such damage, there are still two precautions that should be taken in order to prevent such damage. The first is to keep the leads shorted together or mounted in conductive foam until the device is inserted into a circuit. The second is to always use a grounded-tip soldering iron for soldering MOSFETs.

Relays

Another device that is often driven directly by an IC is a low-current relay. If the operate current of the relay coil is less than the maximum output current of the

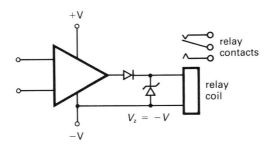

FIGURE 5–19: Op Amp Driving a Relay

op amp, the two can be connected together as shown in Fig. 5–19. The purpose of the diode in series with the op-amp output is to protect the IC against inductive kickback voltages from the relay coil. When voltage is first applied to the relay coil, the inductive kickback can produce spikes of several times the supply voltage. The diodes prevent these spikes from reaching the IC. There is also a Zener diode in Fig. 5–19. This is used to prevent negative voltage spikes from damaging the op amp.

TROUBLESHOOTING POWER OP-AMP CIRCUITS

As with small-signal op-amp circuits, the likely troubles that may develop in power op-amp circuits depend upon whether the circuit is a new one that has never worked or a proven circuit that has failed. In a new circuit, the most common problem is oscillation. The causes of oscillation have been discussed in detail in Chapter 4. However, there is one of those causes that can be particularly troublesome in power circuits. Figure 5–20A shows a circuit that includes a common grounding impedance. Notice that the path to ground for the output current shares an impedance in common with the ground path from the noninverting input. This common path is made of 15 cm of 24-gauge copper wire, which has a resistance of 0.01 Ω. The maximum output current from this circuit is 10 A, so the voltage drop across the common grounding impedance is 0.1 V. This corresponds to a 0.1-V signal, with respect to true ground, applied to the noninverting input. This signal is in phase with the output; in other words, it represents positive feedback. At high frequencies, the inductance of the ground wire becomes important also, increasing the total impedance. Thus it is likely that at some frequency the impedance will become so great that there will be enough positive feedback to cause oscillation. Figure 5–20B shows a corrected connection for this circuit, eliminating the common grounding impedance.

If common grounding impedances are eliminated, the other special consideration for power circuits is decoupling. Capacitors for decoupling were recommended several times earlier in this book. With power circuits, though, because of the larger output currents involved, decoupling becomes more critical. With small-signal circuits, a 0.01–0.1-μF capacitor was recommended for decoupling. With power circuits, as much as 10 μF is sometimes needed. And the type of capacitor used is also important. Ordinary aluminum electrolytics have a resistive component in their impedance that increases substantially with frequency, so that they are not very ideal

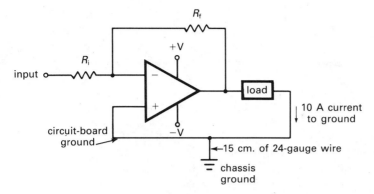

FIGURE 5–20A: Common–Grounding Impedance Problem

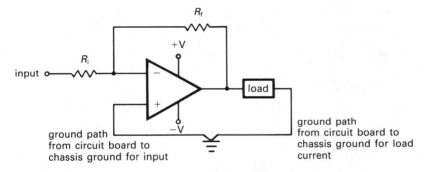

FIGURE 5–20B: The Cure

FIGURE 5–20: Common Grounding Impedance: Example and Correction

at frequencies above 1 kHz. For coupling purposes, where there is a large resistance in series with the capacitor, aluminum electrolytics are fine at frequencies up to the low-megahertz region. But where the capacitor represents the only significant impedance in a circuit, as in a decoupling or filtering application, tantalum capacitors should be used for frequencies above 1 kHz. So in a well-designed power circuit, we would expect to find 1–10-µF tantalum capacitors in place of the smaller disc ceramic capacitors for decoupling purposes.

In power circuits that have been operating successfully for some time but then fail, the most common problem is the power IC itself. The two most likely causes of power IC failure are overheating and reversed supply polarity. If the heat sink has been properly designed, overheating can result from two operator errors. If the person operating the equipment connects a load of too low an impedance, the circuit will be called upon to deliver more power than it was designed for. Naturally, this also means that the circuit will have to dissipate more power than it was designed for. The other operator error is that of restricting air circulation to the heat sinks. If any covering, including a layer of dirt, is allowed to block free circulation of air around the power devices and heat sinks, overheating will result.

One common installation error in any kind of electronic equipment is that of connecting the power supply with the wrong polarity. Although many discrete circuits can survive such an error, ICs almost never can. There are two common methods for protecting a circuit against reversed power-supply polarity. They are shown in Fig. 5–21. The first is to connect a diode in series with each "hot" lead of the supply. Thus reversed current is blocked from the IC. The second method is to connect "crowbar" diodes from the "hot" supply leads to ground. This has the effect of short-circuiting the supply if it is connected in reversed polarity, as though a crowbar were laid across the supply terminals. The result is a blown fuse, which should warn the installer to check his or her work and correct errors.

The disadvantage of the series-diode method is that the diodes introduce an additional 1–2-V drop, reducing the available power-supply voltage, and thus reducing the output swing. Also, for high-current circuits, correspondingly large diodes are needed, adding to the cost. The crowbar circuit avoids these problems at the expense of requiring replacement fuses in the event of reversed polarity. And if the installer responds to the blown fuse by installing an oversize fuse—a very wrong but common fault—it is likely that the diodes' surge current rating will be exceeded and the diodes will be damaged. As you can see, the method chosen depends upon the particular application.

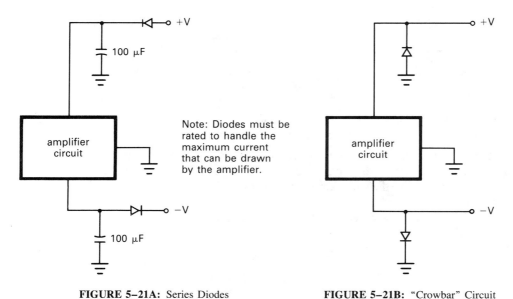

FIGURE 5–21A: Series Diodes   **FIGURE 5–21B:** "Crowbar" Circuit

FIGURE 5–21: The Use of Diodes to Protect Against Reversed Supply Polarity

DESIGN NOTES

Heat-Transfer Calculations

The maximum power dissipation of a device can be calculated as follows:

AC circuit:
$$P_{\text{DISS,max}} = \frac{V^2_{\text{OUT,P-P}}}{20R_L} \tag{5.01}$$

DC circuit:
$$P_{\text{DISS,max}} = V_{\text{supply}}I_{\text{supply}} - V_L I_L \tag{5.02}$$

The maximum thermal resistance of a heat sink is calculated from

$$\theta_{\text{SA}} = \frac{T_{\text{max}} - T_A}{P_{\text{DISS,max}}} - \theta_{\text{JC}} - \theta_{\text{CS}} \tag{5.05}$$

The typical value for θ_{CS} is 1°C/W.

Current and Voltage Booster Designs

Figure 5–20 shows circuits for a current booster and a current/voltage booster. Bias diodes are included to reduce crossover distortion. The output transistors' characteristics are chosen as follows:

$$V_{\text{breakdown}} = 1.1V_{\text{supply}} \qquad \text{(resistive load)}$$
$$V_{\text{breakdown}} = 5V_{\text{supply}} \qquad \text{(reactive load)}$$
$$I_{\text{m,max}} = \frac{2V_{\text{applied}}}{R_{\text{windings}}} \qquad \text{(reversible motors)}$$
$$I_{\text{max}} = \frac{V_{\text{supply}}}{R_{\text{DC}}} \qquad \text{(other loads)}$$
$$\beta = \frac{I_{\text{max}}}{I_{\text{max,op amp}}}$$

$$\tag{5.11}$$

The power-dissipation rating is actually not very important, but the thermal resistance of the transistors must be small enough to allow operation with a real heat sink. If the calculation of heat-sink thermal resistance according to equation 5.05 gives a negative number, a transistor with a smaller θ_{JC} must be used. In the previous equations, V_{supply} means the total voltage from the most

(continued)

(continued from page 213)

positive to the most negative point in the circuit. Thus for a ± 15-V supply, V_{supply} would be 30 V.

Thyristors

When an IC is connected to a thyristor, the maximum output current of the IC should be compared to the maximum trigger current and the maximum safe gate current for the thyristor. If the maximum trigger current is more than the IC can supply, a sensitive-gate thyristor should be used. If the IC can deliver more current than the thyristor's maximum safe gate current, a resistor should be connected in series between the IC output and the thyristor gate. The value of this resistor can be calculated as follows:

$$R_{\text{gate}} = \frac{V_{\text{min}}}{I_{\text{gate,max}}}$$

where V_{min} is the minimum voltage that the IC will supply to turn on the thyristor, measured from the IC output pin to the cathode of the thyristor.

SUMMARY

A small-signal op amp is one in which power dissipation is not an important consideration. A large-signal op amp is one in which power dissipation must be taken into account.

The thermal resistance of a device is the number of degrees Celsius by which the device's temperature rises per watt of power that it dissipates. A semiconductor device has a thermal resistance from junction to case (θ_{JC}), one from case to heat sink (θ_{CS}), and one from heat sink to surrounding air (θ_{SA}). Where no heat sink is used, the thermal resistance from junction to the surrounding air (θ_{JA}) is used for calculations.

The necessary thermal resistance is calculated from the maximum junction temperature, the ambient temperature, and θ_{JC} and θ_{CS} for the device and mounting system used.

For special applications, a variety of high-voltage and/or high-current op amps are available. In using these, you must carefully consider the characteristics of the load in order to correctly determine the current and power that the IC will have to handle. Diodes or transient-protection devices may be needed.

In the design of audio power amplifier circuits, distortion must be minimized for satisfactory operation.

When op amps are interfaced with discrete devices, the current drawn from the op amp must be determined, as well as the required characteristics for the discrete devices. Current-limiting resistors may be required to protect thyristor gates. Special biasing circuits are required for power FETs and may be required for bipolar transistors, to reduce crossover distortion.

Relays and other inductive loads can produce large voltage surges when power is applied or removed. Diodes should be used in series with the output of an IC to protect against damage from these surges. In addition, transient protectors connected across the load provide additional protection.

REVIEW QUESTIONS

1. What is the difference between the use of the terms "small-signal" and "large-signal" in connection with discrete transistors as compared to their use in connection with op amps?
2. Name two physical characteristics that affect thermal resistance.
3. A certain IC dissipates 5 W. It is mounted on a heat sink with a thermal resistance of 3°C/W.
   (a) What is the temperature of the IC's case if the device is operated in a 20°C room?
   (b) If θ_{JC} is 5°C/W, what is the junction temperature?
   Make the normal assumption about θ_{CS}.
4. Calculate the thermal resistance of a heat sink to be used with an IC that dissipates 20 W. $\theta_{JC} = 2°C/W$, $T_{max} = 100°C$, and the room in which the unit will operate is kept at or below 35°C.
5. What thermal resistance will be required for a heat sink that is to cool two devices: one as described in question 4, and one dissipating 10 W and having $\theta_{JC} = 3.5°C/W$? The maximum junction temperature is 100°C.
6. What is the maximum power dissipation for an amplifier that produces a 22-V_{P-P} output into a 6-Ω load?
7. What is the power dissipation of a motor-control amplifier that is operated from a 24-V unipolar supply and that delivers 3 A at 12 V to a motor?
8. If the motor has a winding resistance of 3 Ω, what is the maximum current that would be required from the amplifier described in question 7:
   (a) in a reversible application?
   (b) in a nonreversible application?
9. Draw a circuit using the LM2005 op amp to provide 5 W to an 8-Ω speaker. Indicate the required supply voltage and the thermal resistance of the heat sink. Assume $T_A = 35°C$.
10. From the data sheet in Appendix A, determine the maximum power output of the LM386 for
    (a) an 8-Ω load, distortion within tolerable levels, $V_{CC} = 12V$
    (b) a 4-Ω load, distortion within tolerable levels, $V_{CC} = 16V$
    (c) a 16-Ω load, distortion no more than maximum allowable level, $V_{CC} = 16V$

11. Design a circuit to provide maximum output power from a single channel of an LM2005 IC operated from a 12-V battery. Specify the speaker impedance and the maximum power dissipation of the IC.

12. Design a circuit using the LM386 to drive a small tape-recorder motor from a 12-V supply. The design must provide for reversing the motor. The motor's winding resistance is 36 Ω. Include devices to protect the IC against kickback voltages. Using the graphs on the data sheet, indicate arrangements for dissipating heat from the IC.

13. Repeat the above design using a 741 op amp connected to a current-booster circuit. Include specifications for the transistors and heat sinks.

14. Design a circuit using a 741 op amp driving a triac to control starting and stopping of a 120-V, 5-A AC motor. The triac is a sensitive-gate unit that requires a maximum of 3 mA gate current to switch, and can safely handle a 15-mA gate current. The 741 will be operated from a ±5-V supply.

15. Design a circuit using a 741 op amp to drive a reed relay. The relay has a coil resistance of 1200 Ω and an operating voltage of 10 V. Specify the supply voltage and show any necessary protection devices.

LABORATORY EXPERIMENT—MOTOR CONTROLLERS

Objective:

To become familiar with the operation of reversible DC motor controllers using current-boosted ICs.

Materials:

1 741 op amp
1 miniature 12-V PM motor (Buehler series 16.18 or equivalent)
miscellaneous resistors
1 2.5-A, 400-V diode
1 25-V varistor or Zener transient suppressor
1 TIP 32C transistor
1 TIP 31C transistor
2 small clip-on heat sinks (Thermalloy type 6038 or equivalent)
1 resistor whose resistance equals the motor's resistance, and whose power rating is at least $1152/R_{windings}$ watts

Procedure:

1. Using a low-current ohmmeter such as a digital VOM, measure $R_{winding}$ of the motor.
2. Design a controller using the circuit of Fig. 5–14A to drive the motor. The input voltage is to vary from 0 to ± 5 V, and the output voltage will vary from 0 to ± 10 V. Use a ± 12-V power supply. Calculate the current that must be supplied by the op amp, assuming that the transistors have a β of 40. Using the thermal data on the transistor data sheets in Appendix A, determine whether a heat sink will be required. If a heat sink is required, use the clip-on ones provided.
3. Build your circuit and first verify that it works as expected, using the power resistor as a dummy load.
4. Connect a voltage divider as shown in the figure to provide the proper range of input voltages. Now connect the motor to the controller and verify that varying the input voltage does provide variable speed in both directions.
5. Vary the input voltage as necessary to provide motor voltages in 2-V increments from -10 to 10 V. At each increment, measure the current in the motor. Plot the results on a graph.

(continued)

Laboratory Experiments

(continued from page 217)

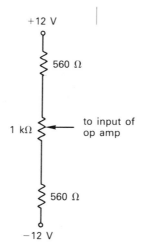

+12 V

560 Ω

1 kΩ — to input of op amp

560 Ω

−12 V

Drawing for Lab Experiment on motor controllers—Step 4

6. After making the measurements, carefully feel the heat sinks of the transistors. A temperature of about 50°C feels hot to the touch. Would you estimate that the transistors are about this temperature, hotter, or cooler? How does your rough impression of their temperature compare with the calculated temperature, based upon the results of step 2? If you have access to a thermometer, measure the transistors' temperature. (Answer in general terms. Since the current in the transistors has been varied rather than staying constant, their temperature will not be exactly as calculated.)

Analysis:

1. Based upon your graph of motor voltage versus current, calculate the power dissipated by the controller at each voltage at which you made a measurement. Plot the power as a function of voltage on a graph. Since the no-load speed of a PM motor is almost directly proportional to the applied voltage, this is also an approximate graph of controller power dissipation versus speed.
2. Describe two or three ways in which an amplifier used for DC motor control is designed differently than one for audio purposes.

(continued from page 218)

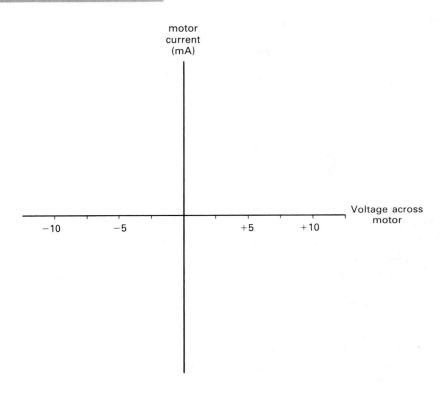

Laboratory
Experiments

LABORATORY EXPERIMENT—DISTORTION

Objective:

To observe the causes and effects of distortion in amplifiers.

Materials:

1 LM386 power-amplifier IC
1 10-kΩ potentiometer
2 0.01-μF, 25-V disc ceramic capacitors
1 2.7-Ω resistor
8 2-Ω, 10-W resistors

(continued from page 219)

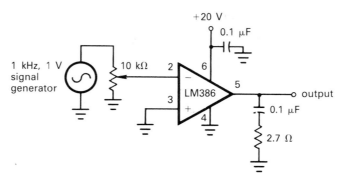

Figure for Distortion Experiment

Procedure:

1. Build the circuit shown in the figure. Use a 20-V power supply.
2. Connect two 2-Ω resistors to the output as a 4-Ω load. Connect an oscilloscope to the output of the op amp. Adjust the 10-kΩ pot for minimum signal to be fed to the LM386. Turn on the power.
3. While observing the output waveform on the scope, increase the setting of the 10-kΩ pot until you can just begin to see clipping of the output. When clipping first becomes visible, the distortion is about 3%. Measure the peak-to-peak output voltage, then return the pot to minimum. Do this procedure quickly so as to avoid overheating the IC.
4. Repeat step 2 for each of the following loads: 6 Ω, 8 Ω, 10 Ω, 12 Ω, 14 Ω, 16 Ω.
5. Connect an 8-Ω load to the amplifier and turn the supply voltage down to 18 V. Measure the peak-to-peak output voltage at the clipping point. Repeat for the following supply voltages: 16 V, 14 V, 12 V, 10 V, 8 V.
6. If a distortion analyzer, wave analyzer, or spectrum analyzer is available, measure the distortion that is present when clipping just becomes visible. Ask your instructor to demonstrate how to operate the particular piece of test equipment you are using.

Analysis:

1. Plot a graph of power output at 3% distortion versus load current, for a supply voltage of 20 V. Use the data you obtained in steps 3 and 4. Convert your voltage measurements to power output by using equation 5.13.
2. Plot the power output at 3% distortion versus supply voltage, using the data you obtained in step 5 plus the 20-V, 8-Ω-load measurement from step 4.

Laboratory Experiments

(continued from page 220)

3. Using equation 5.01, calculate the power dissipation for each measurement you made in steps 2, 3, and 4. Plot a graph of power dissipation at 3% distortion versus load resistance for a 20-V supply. Plot another graph of power dissipation versus supply voltage for an 8-Ω load.
4. Using the graphs in the data sheet in Appendix A, compare your measurements to the specifications for the LM386. Comment upon the agreement or disagreement.

LABORATORY EXPERIMENT—POWER AMPLIFIER USING A VOLTAGE-CURRENT BOOSTER

Objective:

To observe the operation of a voltage/current-boosted amplifier.

Materials:

1 741 op amp
1 SE5534 op amp
1 100-pF, 25-V capacitor
1 20-pF, 25-V capacitor
3 1-kΩ resistors
1 10-kΩ resistor
1 2N2222 transistor (NPN driver)
1 MPSA56 transistor (PNP driver)
1 TIP31C transistor (NPN output)
1 TIP32C transistor (PNP output)
1 220-Ω, 20-W resistor

Procedure:

1. Connect the circuit shown in Fig. 5–15. Use a 1-kΩ resistor for R_i and a 10-kΩ resistor for R_f. Use the 741 op amp. Set the supply voltage at ± 15 V for V_1 and ± 20 V for V_2. Use the 220-Ω, 20-W resistor for the load. Connect a signal generator to the input. Adjust the generator for minimum amplitude and a frequency of 1 kHz.
2. Apply power to the circuit. While observing the output wave on a 'scope, slowly increase the input voltage until clipping is observed. Measure the peak-to-peak output voltage at this point.

Laboratory
Experiments

(continued from page 221)

3. Adjust the input voltage to 100 mV$_{P-P}$. Now change the frequency to 100 Hz and carefully sketch the output wave. Repeat with frequencies of 1 kHz, 10 kHz, and 50 kHz.
4. Turn off the amplifier. Remove the 741 op amp and insert the SE5534. Apply power again and repeat step 3.
5. (Optional) Design a modification to the circuit to reduce the crossover distortion. Install it and verify its operation.

Analysis:

1. Compare the available output voltage and power from the circuit you built with the voltage and power available from an unboosted 741 op amp. Assume 20 mA is the maximum output current from the 741.
2. Calculate the current drawn by the load at maximum output. Assuming β for the 2N2222 and the MPSA56 is about 100, and β for the output transistors is about 50, what is the current supplied by the op amp at maximum output?
3. Calculate the power dissipation:
   (a) of the op amp at maximum output. (The load resistance seen by the op amp is the 220-Ω load multiplied by the product of the 2N2222/MPSA56 β and the TIP31C/32C β.)
   (b) of the output transistors at maximum output.
   (c) of the 2N2222 and MPSA56 at maximum output. (The load resistance seen by these transistors is the 220-Ω load multiplied by the β of the output transistors.) Use equation 5.01, which will give the dissipation for *both* transistors combined.
4. From the data sheets in Appendix A, what is the maximum dissipation of the two output transistors combined, with no heat sink? Based upon this dissipation, what is the minimum load resistance that this circuit could drive without heat sinks? Assume $T_A = 20°C$.
5. What was the effect of frequency upon crossover distortion? Explain why.
6. Comment upon how the choice of op amp affects the amount of crossover distortion. What characteristic of the op amp was responsible for the difference?

chapter six
Voltage Regulators

OBJECTIVES

Upon completing this chapter, you will be able to:

- Design a half-wave, full-wave, bridge, or voltage-doubler power supply.
- Specify the correct filter components for a power supply.
- Design discrete series or shunt voltage regulators.
- Incorporate op amps into discrete voltage regulators to improve their operation.
- Design simple switching power supplies.
- Design IC voltage regulator circuits.
- Interface IC regulators with transistors to increase their output capability.

SUMMARY OF POWER-SUPPLY DESIGN

One of the most important parts of any electronic circuit is the power supply. Not only does the operation of the entire circuit depend upon proper operation of the power supply, but a majority of the troubles in electronic circuits occur in the power supply. The specific role that linear ICs play in power supplies is to regulate the voltage and/or current output. However, in order to provide a firm basis for understanding voltage regulators, we will begin by looking at the design and operation of the rectifier and filter parts of power supplies.

Most electronic equipment requires a fairly stable source of direct current. The voltage required may vary from a few volts to several thousand volts; the current, from milliamperes to hundreds of amperes. We will look at the most common types of supplies: those that supply between 5 and 100 V and deliver a maximum of about 20 A.

As shown in Fig. 6–1, such a supply is made up of three—or sometimes four—components. The first component is the power transformer. The job of the transformer is to change the line voltage to a voltage more appropriate for the application. As we shall see, this voltage also depends upon the type of rectifier, filter, and regulator used. The second component is the rectifier, which changes the transformer's AC output voltage to DC (with an AC *ripple* voltage). The third component of the supply is the filter, which removes most of the ripple. The fourth component is the regulator, which stabilizes the DC output.

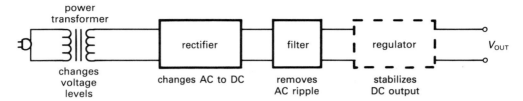

FIGURE 6–1: Block Diagram of Power Supply

There are some power supplies used in low-priced equipment that do not use power transformers but have the rectifiers connected directly to the power line. These "hot-chassis" supplies are somewhat less safe for the user and much less safe for the technician working on the equipment. Consequently, they are seldom used except in lower-priced consumer equipment. We will limit our discussions to the more common "cold-chassis" or transformer-isolated power supplies.

Rectifier Types

Ideal Half-Wave. Figure 6–2 shows the four most common types of rectifiers. Each of these has certain advantages and certain disadvantages for any particular application. The simplest is the half-wave rectifier. The output waveform and characteristics of this rectifier are also shown in the figure. Notice especially the percentage and the fundamental frequency of the ripple. The percentage ripple is

$$\% \text{ Ripple} = \frac{\text{RMS AC output voltage}}{\text{DC output voltage}} \tag{6.01}$$

So 121% ripple indicates that there is actually more AC than DC in a half-wave rectifier's output.

Since the AC portion of the rectifier's output waveform is not a sine wave, it is actually made up of many frequencies; that is, a fundamental and harmonics. But most of the energy in the ripple wave is at the fundamental frequency. When we discuss filters, we'll see why this is important.

Also notice the values of the peak and average output voltages. With a sine wave, the average value is 0.636 times the peak value. But since only half of the half-cycles (every other one) are present in the half-wave rectifier's output, the average voltage is half of that value or 0.318 times the peak value. Now what does this mean? It means that if you connected a transformer with a 10-V secondary to an ideal half-wave rectifier, then read the output voltage with a DC voltmeter, you would read

$$(10 \text{ V}_{\text{rms}})(1.414)(0.318) = (14.14 \text{ V}_{\text{P}})(0.318) = 4.5 \text{ V}$$

Ideal Full-Wave. The full-wave rectifier shown in Fig. 6–2B has an output wave that contains every half-cycle of the input frequency. The result is that every input cycle is converted into two output cycles. Thus the fundamental output frequency is twice the input frequency. The gaps left by the "every-other-half-cycle" conduction pattern of a half-wave rectifier are not there in a full-wave rectifier's output. Since the resulting wave never stays at an instantaneous value of zero, there is proportionally more DC and less AC in the output, yielding a much lower percentage ripple than the half-wave rectifier produces. Thus the average voltage is 0.636 times the peak voltage, just as for a sine wave. However, with this circuit, only half of the transformer is used at a time, so a 10-V transformer secondary only feeds 5 V to each rectifier, and the output is

$$(5 \text{ V})(1.414)(0.636) = 4.5 \text{ V}$$

By the way, this is a good time to notice that a conversion factor from rms to average can be derived very simply: $1.414 \times 0.636 = 0.9$. The same transformer secondary voltage, then, produces the same unfiltered DC output voltage whether used to feed a half-wave or a center-tap-grounded full-wave rectifier. Even though the average output voltages are the same, the peak output voltage of the half-wave rectifier is twice that of the full-wave. With some filters, as we'll see, this fact makes a difference.

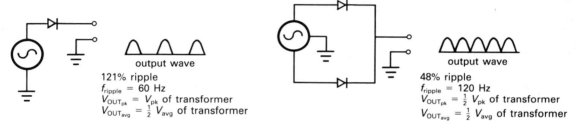

FIGURE 6–2A: Half-Wave

FIGURE 6–2B: Full-Wave Center-Tapped

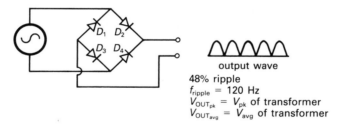

FIGURE 6–2C: Full-Wave Bridge

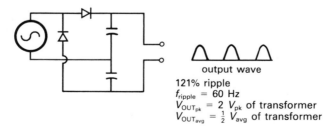

FIGURE 6–2D: Voltage Doubler

FIGURE 6–2: Rectifier Types and Characteristics

Ideal Full-Wave Bridge. The full-wave bridge rectifier (Fig. 6–2C) produces the same output waveform as the center-tapped full-wave rectifier. Thus the ripple frequency and percentage, as well as the peak/average ratio, are the same. However, the full-wave bridge uses the entire transformer secondary for each half-cycle. On the positive half-cycle, conventional current flows through diode D_2, through the load, and back to the source through D_3. On negative half-cycles, conduction is through D_1 and D_4. Thus the DC output voltage of an ideal full-wave bridge rectifier connected to a 10-V secondary would be (10 V)(0.9) = 9 V.

Ideal Half-Wave Voltage-Doubler. The half-wave voltage-doubler (Fig. 6–2D) is a very different form of rectifier than the three we've discussed so far. In order to operate at all, it must have the two capacitors connected as shown. The operation of a half-wave doubler can be thought of as alternate charging of the two capacitors: First the upper one is charged by a positive half-cycle, then the lower one is charged by a negative half-cycle. The result is that the capacitors would be charged to a total voltage equal to twice the peak value of the transformer's secondary, assuming that no load current is drawn. Thus the total voltage is effectively doubled. The ripple frequency is the same as for a half-wave rectifier.

Comparison of Rectifier Types. By far the most commonly used rectifier is the full-wave bridge. The full-wave, center-tapped is second, but it requires a transformer with twice the secondary voltage (more money). The half-wave rectifier has such poor voltage regulation and so much ripple that it is generally used only for applications requiring less than 100 mA. The same can be said for the voltage doubler. For these reasons, we'll concentrate on the full-wave types from now on.

The Real World. The diodes used in a rectifier can be of many varieties. The earliest diodes were vacuum diodes. Then came cold-cathode gas diodes. Both of these types of diodes are still used in some very-high-voltage and/or very-high-current power supplies. The first solid-state diodes to be used in rectifiers were the selenium and the copper-oxide rectifiers. These were more efficient and cooler-operating than vacuum diodes, but were still far from being perfect. By far the majority of power supplies built since 1960 use silicon diodes. The voltage drop across a conducting silicon diode is about 0.6 V, and that voltage is almost independent of the load current. In other words, the *dynamic resistance* of a silicon diode is almost zero. This means much greater efficiency, since the power converted to heat (I^2R) by the diode is also almost zero when R is almost zero. With high efficiency, long lifetime, small size, and low cost, silicon rectifiers' prominence is easily understood. Because they are so overwhelmingly in the majority, we will assume only silicon rectifiers in the supplies discussed in this book.

If silicon rectifiers are so nearly ideal, why do we need a section on "real-world" rectifiers? Because the extent to which silicon rectifiers are not ideal is predictable and easily taken into account to make for a more accurate design. Specifically, as was mentioned, the voltage drop across a conducting silicon diode is approximately 0.6 V. Thus, this "diode drop" can be subtracted in calculations of the output voltage of a rectifier. In a half-wave or full-wave center-tapped rectifier, there is one diode in series with the load. Thus the output voltage is 0.6 V less than the ideal value calculated earlier. A full-wave bridge rectifier has two diodes conducting simultaneously: one in series with the positive output lead, and one in series with the negative lead. The output voltage is therefore 1.2 V less than for the ideal rectifier. The voltage of a doubler is also 1.2 V less than the ideal, because this rectifier also has one diode in series with each output lead, even though they do not conduct simultaneously. In practice, the diode drop is often ignored in voltage calculations except in supplies having output voltages under 10 V. (The power dissipation resulting from diode drop, however, can be quite significant in high-current supplies.)

Filter Types

Most electronic equipment requires essentially pure DC in order to operate correctly. The output from a rectifier contains both DC and AC (ripple). Eliminating most of the ripple is the job of the filter. Another way of saying this is that the DC supply lines must be at *AC ground*. The filter ensures that this condition is met. There are two basic varieties of filters, as shown in Fig. 6–3: the capacitor-input filter and the choke-input filter. We'll look at these one at a time.

Capacitor-Input Filters. The simplest capacitor-input filter is just a capacitor connected from the rectifier output to ground; in other words, in parallel with the load. When the rectifier's output voltage is applied to the capacitor, it charges up to the peak value of that DC + AC voltage wave. *Thus the output voltage of an unloaded, capacitor-input-filtered power supply is the peak value of the AC input voltage, minus the diode drop(s).* This is true whether the filter is a simple capacitor, a capacitor-input *LC* filter, or a pi filter. (Remember, though, that the effective AC input voltage of a center-tapped full-wave supply is half the transformer secondary voltage. But for a half-wave or bridge rectifier, the AC input voltage is the entire transformer secondary voltage.)

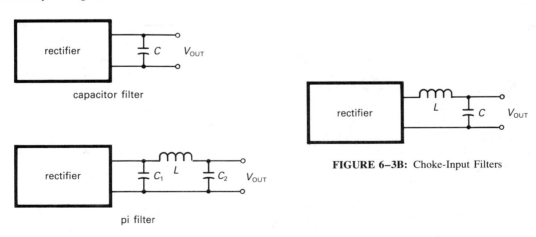

FIGURE 6–3A: Capacitor-Input Filters

FIGURE 6–3B: Choke-Input Filters

FIGURE 6–3: Filter Configurations

The addition of an inductor, or "choke," to a capacitor filter places a large inductive reactance in series with the load. This reactance has no effect on the DC voltage, but it further reduces the ripple. Adding an additional capacitor to ground after the choke provides even further ripple reduction. A filter constructed in this manner is called a pi filter because of the appearance of its schematic diagram. The pi filter has an additional advantage over the capacitor-input LC filter, in that any AC voltages generated in the load are effectively grounded by the second capacitor. Since this prevents coupling of AC voltages generated in one stage into other stages, we say that this capacitor provides *decoupling*.

Choke-Input Filters. The choke-input filter works very differently from the capacitor-input filter. The large inductive reactance of the choke blocks the AC component from the load. *Thus the output voltage of a lightly loaded choke-input filter is the average value of the effective AC input voltage.* (If the load is actually reduced to zero, there will be no current to provide an inductive effect, and the voltage will rise to V_P. This fact is usually ignored in practice, since some load is usually present.)

EXAMPLE

Problem

For an unloaded center-tapped, full-wave rectifier fed by a transformer whose secondary voltage is 10 V, what is the output voltage

(a) with no filter?
(b) with a capacitor-input filter?
(c) with a choke-input filter?

Solution

(a) The effective AC input voltage is half of 10 V, or 5 V. The output voltage is therefore the average value of 5 V_{rms}, or 5 V × 0.9 = 4.5 V. Subtracting the diode drop, we have 4.5 V − 0.6 V = 3.9 V.
(b) The addition of a capacitor-input filter raises the output voltage to the peak value of 5 V_{rms}, which is 5 V × 1.414 = 7.07 V. After we subtract the diode drop, that leaves 7.07 V − 0.6 V = 6.47 V.
(c) The choke-input filter does not raise the output voltage, so it remains at the average value, less the diode drop, or 3.9 V.

The capacitor used in a choke-input filter provides both filtering and decoupling.

Comparison of Filter Types. The choke-input filter has lower ripple than the capacitor-input filter, and, as we shall see, a more constant output voltage, so one might expect it to be the universal first choice. However, chokes are large, heavy, and expensive, especially for high-current applications. Therefore, capacitor-input filters are by far the more widely used. It is usually cheaper to use a large capacitor and add any necessary electronics to stabilize voltage and reduce ripple than it is to use a choke. However, for switching power supplies, choke-input filters are the rule rather than the exception. These supplies will be discussed later in this chapter.

VOLTAGE REGULATION AND RIPPLE OF UNREGULATED SUPPLIES

You've probably noticed that the methods used so far to calculate the output voltages of filtered supplies have specified *unloaded*. There is a reason for this: When current is drawn from a power supply, the output voltage changes. There are two reasons for this change. The first applies only to capacitor-input-filtered supplies. When current is drawn from such a supply, the capacitor discharges somewhat between the peak points of the half-cycles, reducing the time-averaged output voltage, and increasing ripple. Since the peaks never reach the capacitor of a loaded choke-input filter, supplies using these filters do not suffer from this problem. But all supplies suffer from the second weakness, namely, the voltage drop across (1) the resistance of the transformer secondary, (2) the choke, if there is one, and (3) the dynamic resistance of the diode. Increasing amounts of current produce increasing voltage drops, in accordance with Ohm's law.

The amount by which the output voltage of a power supply decreases when the load current goes from zero to maximum is known as the *voltage regulation* of the supply. Voltage regulation is often expressed as a percentage:

$$\%V_{\text{reg}} = \frac{V_{\text{OUT,no load}} - V_{\text{OUT,full load}}}{V_{\text{OUT,full load}}} \times 100\% \qquad (6.02)$$

Figure 6–4 shows typical voltage regulation curves for both types of filters. As you'd expect, the choke-input filter has much better regulation.

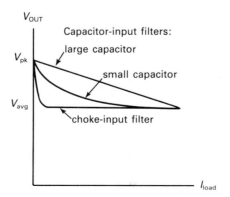

FIGURE 6–4: Voltage Regulation of Capacitor-Input and Choke-Input Filters

Capacitor Filters

For a simple capacitor filter, which is the most common type, the output voltage and percent ripple can be easily calculated if we make a couple of assumptions. These are:

1. The load current is small. (We'll define just how small shortly.)
2. When load current is drawn, the discharge of the filter capacitor is essentially linear; that is, the voltage on the capacitor decreases linearly per unit time.

If the first assumption is valid, the second one is close enough to give answers well within a $\pm 10\%$ tolerance, which is a closer tolerance than most filter capacitors' values have.

Having made these assumptions, let's see what we can do with them. Recall that the voltage on a capacitor is $V = Q/C$, where Q is the charge stored by the capacitor and C is the capacitance. It is also true that the amount of voltage decrease across a capacitor that is being discharged equals the amount of charge removed divided by the capacitance:

$$V_{decrease} = \frac{Q_{discharge}}{C}$$

Now the amount of charge removed is

$$Q_{discharge} = I \cdot t,$$

where I is the discharge current and t is the discharge time. The amount of time that the capacitor discharges is the time from the positive peak of one half-cycle of the rectifier waveform to the next. In other words, t is the period (τ) of the rectifier's output waveform. Thus

$$Q_{discharge} = I(\tau) = I\left(\frac{1}{f}\right) = \frac{I}{f}$$

and

$$V_{decrease} = \frac{I/f}{C} = \frac{I}{fC}$$

As shown by Fig. 6–5, the discharge waveform is essentially a sawtooth wave (which is what you'd expect from the linear discharge we assumed). Therefore, the average DC output voltage is just the peak voltage minus half of $V_{discharge}$:

$$V_{OUT} = V_{peak} - \frac{I}{2fC} \tag{6.03}$$

This equation is valid for either a half-wave or a full-wave rectifier, provided that the proper frequency is used. Remember that for a half-wave rectifier, the fundamental output frequency is line frequency, whereas for a full-wave it is twice line frequency.

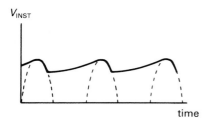

FIGURE 6–5A: Half-Wave

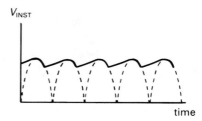

FIGURE 6–5B: Full-Wave

FIGURE 6–5: Waveforms Produced by a Capacitive Filter

This analysis will also allow us to predict the peak-to-peak ripple voltage. It is just the same as V_{decrease}:

$$V_{\text{ripple,P-P}} = \frac{I}{fC} \tag{6.04}$$

This would be of more use if it were converted to % rms ripple. First, let's convert from peak-to-peak into rms. For a triangle wave,

$$V_{\text{rms}} = \frac{V_{\text{P-P}}}{2\sqrt{3}} \tag{6.05}$$

Since

$$\% \text{ ripple} = \frac{V_{\text{rms AC}}}{V_{\text{OUT}}} \times 100\% \tag{6.06}$$

we have

$$\% \text{ ripple} = \frac{I/(2\sqrt{3}fC)}{V_{\text{OUT}}} \times 100\% \tag{6.07}$$

Naturally you recognized $I/V_{\text{OUT DC}}$ as the conductance of the load, that is, $1/R_L$. So our equation for ripple percentage takes the final form of:

$$\% \text{ ripple} = \frac{1}{2\sqrt{3}\,R_L fC} \times 100\% \tag{6.08}$$

Now you can see why the output frequency of the rectifier is important. By using a full-wave rectifier rather than a half-wave, we double the ripple frequency, which cuts the percent ripple in half. Or for the same percent ripple, it lets us use half as large a filter capacitor.

We now define the *ripple factor,* γ, by

$$\gamma = \frac{\% \text{ ripple}}{100} \tag{6.09}$$

$$= \frac{1}{2\sqrt{3}\,R_L fC} \tag{6.10}$$

Now, when are these equations applicable? In other words, when do our two assumptions about small load current and linear discharge hold up? Let's avoid some intricate math and just give the answer. The above equations for output voltage and percent ripple give answers with less than 10% error if the ripple is less than 10%.

EXAMPLE

Problem

Design a power supply using a capacitor filter to deliver 10 V at 2 A with a ripple of 1% or less and voltage regulation of ±2% or better.

Solution

1. Let's choose a bridge rectifier. That's the most common because it doesn't need a center-tapped transformer; and for the same transformer secondary voltage it produces twice the output voltage of the other full-wave configuration. A half-wave supply would be out of the question for this much load current, because of the poor regulation and large amount of ripple that would result.
2. Next we need to decide upon a transformer. To do this, we'll calculate the maximum output voltage allowable and work backward from there. For ±2% regulation, V_{OUT} can be 2% above $V_{nominal}$:

$$V_{OUT,max} = 1.02 \times 10 \text{ V} = 10.2 \text{ V}$$

So 10.2 V is the no-load voltage. For a bridge rectifier, the no-load voltage is the peak value of the transformer secondary voltage, minus two diode drops:

$$V_{peak} = V_{OUT,max} = 1.414 \times V_{sec} - 1.2 \text{ V}$$

Solving for V_{sec}, we get

$$V_{sec} = \frac{V_{OUT,max} + 1.2 \text{ V}}{1.414}$$

$$= \frac{10.2 \text{ V} + 1.2 \text{ V}}{1.414} = 8.06 \text{ V}$$

We'll specify an 8-V transformer. It will need to be rated to deliver at least 2 A.
3. Now we have a choice. We can select the capacitor needed to give the required ripple factor, and then see whether it provides adequate voltage regulation, or we can choose the capacitor to provide good enough voltage regulation, then check the ripple factor. Let's calculate for ripple first.

$$\gamma = \frac{1}{2 \sqrt{3} \, R_L' f C} \tag{6.10}$$

So

$$C = \frac{1}{2\sqrt{3}\,R_L f \gamma} \qquad (6.11)$$

Now

$$R_L = \frac{10\text{ V}}{2\text{ A}} = 5\ \Omega$$

$$C = \frac{1}{2\sqrt{3} \times 5\ \Omega \times 120\text{ Hz} \times 0.01} = 48{,}100\ \mu\text{F}$$

This very large capacitor is required to keep ripple below 1% with a 2-A, 10-V supply. (We'll see later how electronics can help us get by with much smaller capacitors.) Now let's check the full-load output voltage and see if it's within 2%.

$$V_{\text{OUT}} = V_{\text{peak}} - \frac{I}{2fC} \qquad (6.03)$$

$$= 10.2\text{ V} - \frac{2\text{ A}}{2 \times 120\text{ Hz} \times 0.048\text{ F}}$$

$$= 10.0\text{ V}$$

So a 48,000-μF capacitor will work, and our design is complete.

One more thing should be mentioned before we leave the subject of capacitor filters. We have assumed so far that the resistance of the transformer secondary and the dynamic resistance (sometimes called *bulk resistance*) of the rectifiers were zero. Obviously this assumption is false. But how much difference does it make? Well, it depends upon several things. Naturally, the smaller these resistances are, the more valid our approximation is. Also, the smaller the load current is, the less voltage drop will occur across these "charging resistances." Less obvious is a standard practice of transformer manufacturers that bears upon this problem. Most transformers are rated to deliver their stated secondary voltages ±10% *at full rated load current*. This means that the no-load voltage is probably higher than the rated voltage, and when the transformer is delivering full-load current the voltage drop across the secondary resistance will reduce the output to within 10% of the rated voltage. And the diodes' resistance? Usually negligible.

Now that the preliminaries are out of the way, what does all this mean in practice? Well, if we are working with a transformer whose secondary voltage we have measured (with no load), the effect of the secondary resistance upon full-load output voltage can be calculated using the voltage-divider formula:

$$V_{\text{OUT}} = V_{\text{no load}} \left(\frac{R_{\text{load}}}{R_{\text{sec}} + R_{\text{load}}} \right) \qquad (6.12)$$

The other effect of nonzero secondary resistance is to reduce ripple slightly below that calculated for $R_{\text{sec}} = 0 \ \Omega$. However, for ripple percentages below 25%, this effect is negligible.

If we're working only with a transformer's published specifications, we can probably ignore secondary resistance.

Other Filter Types

Because of the much greater popularity of capacitor filters, we will not spend as much time on the other types. But neither will we skip over them completely. First is the *RC* filter, which is a cross between a capacitor filter and a voltage divider. This filter is often used in transistor power amplifiers; a high, capacitively filtered voltage is applied to the output stage, and an *RC* section is added to provide decoupling and further filtering for the input stages. The ripple resulting from such a filter is

$$\gamma_{RC} = \frac{1}{2\,RC}\,(\gamma_{\text{cap}}) \tag{6.13}$$

where γ_{cap} is the ripple factor of the simple capacitor filter, and C is the capacitance of the added capacitor. (See Fig. 6–6A.) The voltage can be calculated using the voltage-divider rule.

For the *LC* filter (Fig. 6–6B),

$$\gamma_{LC} = \frac{1}{6\,\sqrt{2}\,\omega^2 LC}$$

where $\omega = 2\pi f$ is the angular frequency of the ripple. Notice that the ripple does not depend upon the load resistance or current! Why is that? Do you remember that an inductive input filter essentially blocks the AC peaks from reaching the filter capacitor, and therefore the output voltage is just the average value of the rectifier's output voltage? Well, what that means is that the capacitor is receiving more or less constant charging current so that there is no "between half-cycles" during which it can discharge. This also means that the output voltage is also independent of load current as long as charging resistance can be ignored. The actual output voltage of an *LC* filter, taking charging resistance into account, is

$$V_{\text{OUT}} = V_{\text{avg}} - I_{\text{load}}R_{\text{w}} \tag{6.14}$$

where V_{avg} is the average value of the rectifier's AC input voltage, and R_{w} is the winding resistance of the choke. Usually the winding resistance is small. Here, then, we have the secret of the *LC* filter's excellent voltage regulation. Clearly, if it were not for cost, size, and weight, the *LC* filter would be the almost universal choice. However, as things are, it runs a poor second to capacitor filters in popularity.

And finally, there is the pi filter (Fig. 6–6C). This one has more ripple than the *LC* filter but less than the capacitor filter (assuming the same component values and load current):

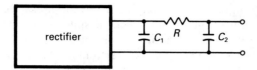

FIGURE 6–6A: *RC* Filter

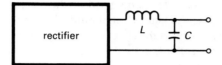

FIGURE 6–6B: *LC* Filter

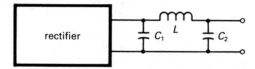

FIGURE 6–6C: Pi Filter

FIGURE 6–6: *RC*, *LC*, and Pi Filters

$$\gamma_\pi = \frac{1}{4\sqrt{2}\ \omega^3 C_1 C_2 L} \qquad (6.15)$$

If an *RC* section is added to either an *LC* or a pi filter, the total ripple factor is just multiplied by the factor $1/2\ RC$, as shown.

Only one question remains: What value of inductance should be used for an *LC* or pi filter? The normal design rule is to make $L \geq R_L/3\omega$.

DISCRETE SHUNT REGULATORS

It should be obvious by now that the design of power supplies to yield a precise voltage output is, at best, a challenge. Even if all the calculations are made correctly, and diode drops and charging resistance are taken into account, it will still be necessary to measure the no-load output voltage of each transformer. And there's no way even the best filter can compensate for the effects of charging resistance. And what about that other bugaboo—low line voltage? In addition to the regulation of voltage against changes caused by load current changes (*load regulation*), supplies must often be regulated against changes caused by varying AC input voltages. This is called the *line regulation:*

$$\%\text{ line regulation} = \frac{V_{\text{DC (high line)}} - V_{\text{DC (low line)}}}{V_{\text{DC (normal line)}}} \times 100\% \qquad (6.16)$$

To give a specific example, many digital systems require a power supply that can deliver 5 V at several amperes, with a regulation of 2%, in spite of line voltage varying as much as ±20%. To do this, an electronic circuit must be added to the output of the filter to regulate the voltage. The simplest electronic voltage regulator is the shunt regulator.

There are two elements in a shunt regulator: the series dropping resistor, and the shunt regulating element. (See Fig. 6–7.) By far the most common shunt regulating element is the Zener diode. Other shunt elements used in the past included neon bulbs and gas-discharge "VR" tubes. All shunt regulating elements have a common characteristic: their resistance is very high as long as the voltage across them is below a certain breakdown voltage. But when that voltage is exceeded, their resistance drops to a very low value. As you are aware, the Zener diode does this when reverse biased. When connected in the circuit shown in Fig. 6–7, a Zener diode will conduct precisely whatever current is required to cause the dropping resistor to drop enough voltage so that the Zener's terminal voltage is at the breakdown value. If the supply voltage is constant, this means that the voltage drop across the resistor will also be constant. Ohm's law tells us that this, in turn, means that the current in the dropping resistor must also be constant. The only way that this current can be constant, when the load current varies, is for the Zener to pass whatever portion of this constant current the load does not draw. Of course, if the line voltage varies, the total current through the dropping resistor will also vary in order to keep the output voltage constant. An additional benefit of any voltage regulator is ripple reduction, since ripple *is* variation in voltage.

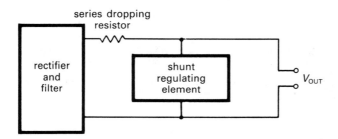

FIGURE 6–7A: General Circuit

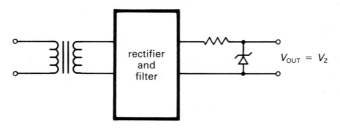

FIGURE 6–7B: Zener Version

FIGURE 6–7: Shunt Regulator

Zener-shunt-regulated supplies can have pretty constant output voltages, that is, line and load regulation around 1%. In fact, only the dynamic resistance of the Zener prevents this regulator from giving perfect regulation. However, from the above discussion you can see that the Zener must be able to carry as much current as the load draws, in order to regulate the voltage when the load isn't drawing current. For a high-current supply, this means that the Zener must dissipate quite a bit of power, and high-power Zeners are expensive. In addition, "dissipating" power really means turning it to heat, and circuits that operate at higher temperatures tend to fail more quickly. And of course there is the question of efficiency. Any shunt-regulated supply will use a constant amount of power no matter how much power the load is using, so with light loads the efficiency is very poor. In spite of these drawbacks, the simplicity of shunt regulators results in their being used for quite a few low-current applications.

So how do you design one? First, using the methods outlined earlier, design the basic supply so that the output is at least 1 V higher than the required output voltage, when the line voltage is at its expected minimum and load current is maximum. Second, choose a dropping resistor so that it drops the difference between V_{supply} and V_{Zener} (at least 1 V) at 110% of maximum load current. The power rating of the resistor equals

$$P_{resistor} = 2\ (V_{no\ load,high\ line} - V_{OUT}) \times 110\% \text{ of } I_{load,max}$$

This is just twice the power that the resistor will be expected to dissipate under worst-case conditions. Finally, select a Zener diode whose breakdown voltage equals the desired load voltage, and whose power rating is at least twice the product V_{load} (1.1 $\times I_{load}$). The 1 V and the extra 10% power are safety factors, as is the factor of 2 in the power rating. Although not actually required, they are a part of the difference between a good design and a marginal one.

EXAMPLE

Problem

Design a shunt regulator to produce 9 V at 100 mA with line voltage variations up to ±10%.

Solution

1. Design the basic power supply to deliver 10 V when the line voltage is 105 V (10% below 117 V).
2. The dropping resistor will have a value of

$$R_{dropping} = \frac{1 \text{ V}}{110 \text{ mA}} \qquad \text{(remember, 110\% of full-load current)}$$

$$= 9.1\ \Omega$$

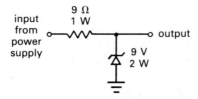

FIGURE 6–8: Zener Regulator Design

Use a 9-Ω resistor. To calculate its power rating, we'll need the no-load output voltage of the basic supply when the line voltage is 129 V. Using the methods discussed earlier in this chapter, let's assume that we come up with 12 V. The power rating is then

$$P_{\text{resistor}} = 2\,(12\text{ V} - 9\text{ V})(110\text{ mA}) = 0.66\text{ W}$$

Use at least a 1-W resistor.

3. The Zener voltage will of course be 9 V, and the Zener's power rating will be

$$P_{\text{Zener}} = 2 \cdot 9\text{ V} \cdot 110\text{ mA} = 1.98\text{ W}$$

It may be necessary to use a 5-W Zener, since Zeners with power ratings greater than 1 W but less than 5 W are not generally available. The completed design is shown in Fig. 6–8.

DISCRETE SERIES REGULATORS

The greatest problem with shunt regulators is that the current that they draw from the power supply is constant, and is slightly greater than the maximum current needed by the load. This can result in poor efficiency, especially for loads whose current demands vary widely. Another approach to regulator design is shown in Fig. 6–9A. Called a *series regulator,* this circuit can be viewed as providing a constant output voltage by inserting an automatically varying resistance in series with the load. The value of this resistance at any given time is exactly the number of ohms required to yield the correct output voltage. In the circuit shown in Fig. 6–9B, the automatically varying resistance is provided by the transistor. When the load current is small, the resistance of the transistor is large; when the load current increases, the transistor's resistance drops. (The comparison of the transistor to a resistor should not be taken too far. It only applies to the collector-to-emitter circuit. When the transistor is viewed from the load side, the transistor's output appears as a constant-voltage source, having a very low internal resistance.)

The operation of the circuit can be understood as follows. The Zener is biased at about 10 mA by resistor R_1. (Typically this is the current at which a Zener's rated voltage is specified.) This keeps the base of the transistor biased at the Zener voltage. As you remember from your study of transistors, there is a fairly constant voltage drop between emitter and base of a conducting transistor. Thus the emitter, which

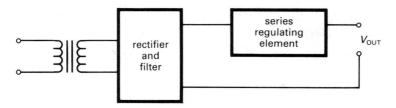

FIGURE 6–9A: General Series Regulator

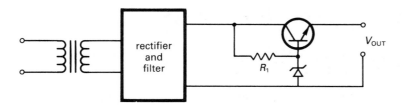

FIGURE 6–9B: Series Regulator Using a Transistor

FIGURE 6–9: The Series Regulator

is the output terminal, is kept at the correct voltage. The drop from collector to emitter varies if the input voltage varies. This varying V_{CE} divided by the varying load current is just the automatically varying series resistance we have been discussing.

EXAMPLE

Problem

Compare the efficiency of a series regulator and a shunt regulator for an output of 9 V, a maximum load current of 100 mA, and an average load current of 50 mA.

Solution

1. We will use the shunt regulator we designed earlier (Fig. 6–8) for this comparison. The power supply of that circuit was designed to deliver 10 V at full load when the line voltage was 105 V. Therefore, with normal-line conditions (117 V), the unregulated output will be

$$V_{\text{unreg}} = \left(\frac{117 \text{ V}}{105 \text{ V}}\right)(10 \text{ V}) = 11.1 \text{ V}$$

A 9-Ω dropping resistor was used. The current necessary to make the voltage at the output equal 9 V is

$$I_{tot} = \frac{11.1 \text{ V} - 9 \text{ V}}{9 \text{ } \Omega} = 233 \text{ mA}$$

The input power to the regulator/load combination will therefore be

$$P_{IN} = V_{IN}I_{IN} = (11.1 \text{ V})(233 \text{ mA}) = 2.6 \text{ W}$$

The output power is just

50 mA: $P_{OUT,50} = V_{OUT}I_{OUT} = (9 \text{ V})(50 \text{ mA}) = 0.45 \text{ W}$

100 mA: $P_{OUT,100} = (9 \text{ V})(100 \text{ mA}) = 0.9 \text{ W}$

The efficiency of this regulator when delivering each value of load current is therefore

$$\text{eff}_{50 \text{ mA}} = \frac{P_{OUT}}{P_{IN}} \times 100\% = \frac{0.45 \text{ W}}{2.6 \text{ W}} \times 100\% = 17\%$$

$$\text{eff}_{100 \text{ mA}} = \frac{0.9 \text{ W}}{2.6 \text{ W}} \times 100\% = 34\%$$

2. If the same power supply is used for the series regulator as for the shunt regulator, the unregulated output voltage will still be 11.1 V. The current drawn from the supply is the output current plus the 10 mA used for biasing the Zener. So for the series regulator

$$P_{IN,50} = (11.1 \text{ V})(60 \text{ mA}) = 0.66 \text{ W}$$

$$P_{IN,100} = (11.1 \text{ V})(110 \text{ mA}) = 1.22 \text{ W}$$

The output power is the same as for the shunt regulator, so

$$\text{eff}_{50 \text{ mA}} = \frac{0.45 \text{ W}}{0.66 \text{ W}} \times 100\% = 68\%$$

$$\text{eff}_{100 \text{ mA}} = \frac{0.9 \text{ W}}{1.22 \text{ W}} \times 100\% = 73.7\%$$

Notice that the efficiency of a series regulator does not vary a great deal as load current varies, but that of a shunt regulator does. As the output current of a shunt regulator is increased, the efficiency increases also. Many times, shunt regulators are not designed as conservatively as the one we designed. With a design that does not allow for much variation in input voltage, it is possible for the efficiency of a shunt regulator to be higher than that of a series regulator, *when delivering maximum output current*. However, over the full range of output current, the series regulator will have a higher average efficiency. When this difference is efficiency is viewed from the standpoint of the power supply, it means that for the same load a power supply feeding a shunt regulator will usually have to deliver more average power than one feeding a series regulator. This, in turn, means larger, more expensive components. And the shunt regulator itself will have to dissipate more heat than the series regulator. For this reason, series regulators are by far the most common choice for load currents greater than a few milliamperes.

The simple series regulator we have been discussing does have a problem, though: The voltage regulation is not good enough for some applications. This is because the base-to-emitter voltage of the transistor is only *approximately* constant. If the base-to-emitter voltage varies by 5% as the load current changes from zero to full-load, then the voltage regulation can be no better than 5%. In fact, temperature variations can cause the Zener voltage to vary somewhat also, making the regulation even poorer. The crux of the problem is that the regulator is operating with no feedback. If we add feedback, the regulator can be made to sense changes in the output voltage and correct for them. A series regulator using an op amp to provide feedback is shown in Fig. 6–10.

In this circuit, the output voltage is sensed by the op amp via the voltage divider formed of R_2 and R_3. A reference voltage is provided by the Zener connected to the noninverting input. Resistor R_S provides initial current to the Zener, so that when the circuit is first turned on, the Zener voltage will be greater than the divided output voltage at the inverting input. This ensures that the op amp's output will go positive upon turn-on, turning on the transistor. A large resistor (typically 10 kΩ or more) is used, so that, once the transistor is turned on, most of the Zener current is provided by the regulated output. This stabilizes the Zener current, preventing Zener-current variations from degrading the regulation.

The op amp acts as a comparator. If the output voltage is too high, the voltage at the inverting input is greater than the voltage at the noninverting input, and the output is driven negative, reducing the base voltage of the transistor. This reduces the output voltage. If the output voltage is too low, the voltage at the inverting input is smaller than the voltage at the noninverting input, and the op amp's output goes positive, increasing the base voltage of the transistor. Thus the regulator's output voltage is increased.

An op amp used in this manner is referred to as an *error amplifier* because it amplifies the error between the correct output voltage and the actual output voltage. The addition of an error amplifier to a series regulator eliminates the dependence of

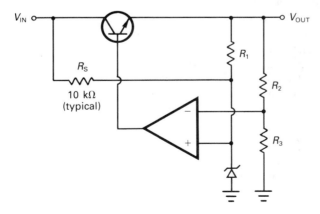

FIGURE 6–10: Series Regulator with Feedback

the voltage regulation upon the base-to-emitter voltage drop of the transistor. The voltage regulation then depends only upon the Zener's temperature characteristics and the offset voltage of the op amp. Regulation of 1% or better is possible using this circuit.

EXAMPLE

Problem

Design a series regulator with an error amplifier to provide an output voltage of 5 V at a load current of 1.5 A. Use a 741 op amp, and specify the Zener voltage, the necessary transistor gain, and the maximum power dissipation of the transistor. Assume that a full-wave rectifier is used, which is fed from a 12.6-V center-tapped transformer feeding a capacitor filter.

Solution

1. We will use a 4.5-V Zener. Since the voltage at each input of the op amp must be the same when the output is correct, this choice of Zener means that the resistors R_2 and R_3 must be in the ratio of 0.5 V/4.5 V. We will use a 500-Ω resistor for R_2 and a 4.5-kΩ resistor for R_3. Both should be 1% resistors, since any error in their values will cause an error in the output voltage.
2. The maximum output current that a 741 can deliver is about 20 mA. If the transistor is to handle 1.5 A, its β must be

$$\beta = \frac{1.5 \text{ A}}{20 \text{ mA}} = 75$$

We will have to choose carefully to find a transistor whose minimum β at a 1.5-A emitter current is at least 75. It may be necessary to use a Darlington transistor. This would make no difference in our design because the op amp will automatically take care of whatever base-to-emitter voltage drop there is.
3. The transistor will draw only as much current as the load does, if we ignore the 1 mA in the R_2–R_3 voltage divider and the 10 mA for the Zener. Therefore, the maximum power dissipation of the transistor will occur when the load current is maximum. The voltage dropped across the transistor is the difference between the unregulated supply voltage and the output voltage. The unregulated supply voltage is

$$V_{\text{unreg}} = \left(\frac{12.6 \text{ V}}{2}\right)(1.414) = 8.9 \text{ V}$$

We have ignored the diode drop. Thus the maximum power dissipation is

$$P_{\text{DISS,max}} = V_{CE}I_E = (8.9 \text{ V} - 5 \text{ V})(1.5 \text{ A}) = 5.85 \text{ W}$$

The completed design is shown in Fig. 6–11.

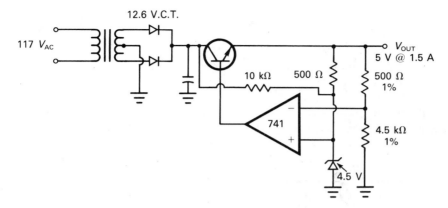

FIGURE 6–11: Regulated 5-V, 1.5-A Power Supply

There is another difference between series and shunt regulators. Because of the series resistor used in a shunt regulator, it is impossible to damage the regulator or power supply by drawing too much current. If a very low-resistance load is connected, there will be excessive voltage drop across the series resistor, resulting in an output voltage that is below the design value, but the output current will be limited to a maximum value of $V_{\text{unreg}}/(R_L + R_{\text{series}})$. However, a series regulator does not provide this inherent current-limiting. If a load of too low a resistance is connected to a series regulator, the regulator will try to deliver the design voltage into the load. The resulting overcurrent can easily destroy the regulating transistor.

There is a way around this problem, though. As shown in Fig. 6–12A, the addition of a transistor and a resistor to the series regulator circuit provides current limiting. It works this way. When too great a current is drawn from the output, transistor Q_2 is turned on, shorting the base-to-emitter circuit of Q_1. This tends to turn off Q_1. If the overload is maintained, the series resistance of Q_1 will drop the output voltage to as low a voltage as necessary in order to keep the current at the limiting value. The limiting value is the amount of current needed to provide enough drop across the sense resistor to turn on Q_2:

$$I_{\text{lim}} = \frac{0.6 \text{ V}}{R_{\text{sense}}} \tag{6.17}$$

Stated differently, the sense resistor is chosen as follows:

$$R_{\text{sense}} = \frac{0.6 \text{ V}}{I_{\text{lim}}} \tag{6.18}$$

EXAMPLE

Problem

Design a current-limiting circuit to add to the regulator shown in Fig. 6–11. The limiting current is 1.5 A.

Solution

Using the circuit shown in Fig. 6–12A, we will need a resistor of

$$R_{\text{sense}} = \frac{0.6 \text{ V}}{I_{\text{lim}}} = \frac{0.6 \text{ V}}{1.5 \text{ A}} = 0.4 \ \Omega \qquad (6.18)$$

A 0.39-Ω resistor would be very close in value. The transistor for Q_2 will only have to handle a small current—the base current of Q_1—so virtually any NPN transistor will do.

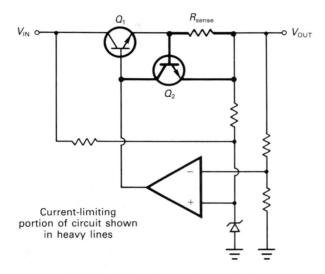

FIGURE 6–12A: Constant-Current Limiting

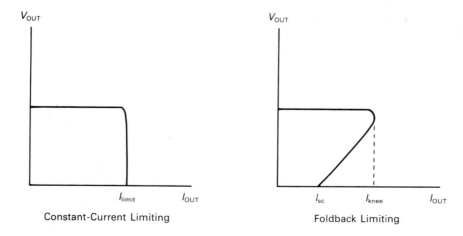

Constant-Current Limiting

Foldback Limiting

FIGURE 6–12B: Characteristic Curves

FIGURE 6–12: Current Limiting

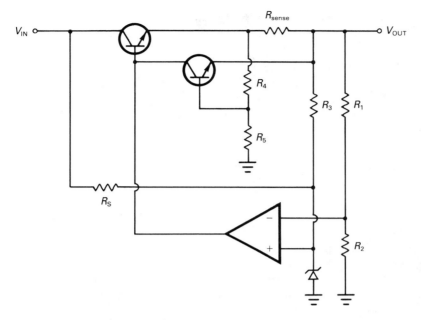

FIGURE 6–12C: Foldback-Current Limiting

Actually, the base-to-emitter turn-on voltage of a transistor is not exactly 0.6 V, and it varies from one transistor to another, so the transistor's data sheet and/ or some trial and error is usually necessary in order to arrive at the correct value for R_{sense}.

Even with current limiting, regulators are not immune to damage from overload. During a short-circuit condition, the regulating transistor has to handle the limiting current as well as having a much greater voltage drop across it. In our example above, the normal full-load power dissipation of the transistor is 5.85 W. If a short circuit appears at the output, the transistor could be required to deliver 1.5 A while dropping the full 8.9 V of the unregulated supply. This would mean a power dissipation of $(8.9 \text{ V})(1.5 \text{ A}) = 13.35$ W. This power dissipation may be too much for the transistor to handle. The solution to this problem is a circuit whose short-circuit current is much less than the limiting-threshold current. Such a circuit provides what is called *foldback limiting*. Figure 6–12B shows the output characteristics of a constant-current-limited and a foldback-limited supply. Figure 6–12C shows a foldback-limiting circuit. The difference between this circuit and the one of Fig. 6–12A is the addition of resistors R_4 and R_5. In order for current limiting to begin, the voltage drop across R_{sense} must be equal to the sum of the drop across R_4 and 0.6 V. Once the current reaches this level, called the *knee current*, Q_2 will be turned on, causing the resistance provided by Q_1 to increase. As a result, the output voltage is lowered. This lowered output voltage decreases the voltage drop across R_4, so now a smaller drop across R_{sense} is required in order to keep Q_2 conducting. Therefore less output current is provided; the value of limiting current becomes inversely dependent upon the load current. A low load resistance will provide a low voltage across R_4 and R_5

and a correspondingly low limiting current. The current that will be fed to a short circuit is called I_{sc}. The knee current of a foldback-limited regulator is

$$I_{knee} = \frac{V_{OUT}R_4 + (0.6 \text{ V})(R_4 + R_5)}{R_{sense}R_5} \qquad (6.19)$$

The short-circuit current is

$$I_{sc} = \frac{(0.6 \text{ V})(R_4 + R_5)}{R_{sense}R_5} \qquad (6.20)$$

In both of these equations, the turn-on voltage of the current-limiting transistor has been assumed equal to 0.6 V.

SWITCHING POWER SUPPLIES

Both of the regulators that we have discussed so far—the shunt regulator and the series regulator—involve power loss in the regulation process; that is, they are less than 100% efficient. Although this is no problem for small power supplies, the power dissipated by a high-current supply is an important consideration. There is one type of power-supply circuit that operates at almost 100% efficiency. A block diagram of a *switching power supply* is shown in Fig. 6–13A. The "brain" of the circuit is the *pulse-width modulator* circuit shown in Fig. 6–13B. This is nothing more than a comparator fed by a triangle-wave generator and a DC error signal. At any instant that the triangle wave is more positive than the error signal, the output of the comparator will be positive and equal to V_{SAT+}. When the error signal is more positive, the output of the comparator will be negative. Thus the value of the error signal controls the fraction of time that the comparator output is positive, which is the pulse width of the output signal. In other words, the pulse width is modulated by the error signal.

The output of the pulse-width modulator is used to alternately turn on two transistors connected in series with the bridge rectifier. When Q_1 is on, electrons flow upward through the transformer, through Q_1, and so back to the rectifier. When Q_2 is on, electrons flow from the rectifier through Q_2, downward through the transformer, and back to the rectifier. The waveform of the signal applied to the primary of the main power transformer is shown in Fig. 6–13C. The width of the positive and negative pulses depends upon the output of the pulse-width modulator. The frequency of the wave at the main transformer primary is determined by the frequency of the triangle-wave generator. Usually, it is above 20 kHz.

Looking back at part A of the figure, we see that the secondary of the main transformer feeds a full-wave rectifier, whose output is filtered by a two-stage LC filter. The voltage is sampled at the output of the filter and fed to the inverting input of the error amplifier. A Zener-regulated reference voltage is applied to the noninverting input. As a result, the output voltage from the error amplifier is negative if the power supply's output voltage becomes too high, and positive if the output voltage becomes too low. This error voltage is used to control the pulse-width modulator.

Let us follow the regulation process. When the power supply is first turned on, there is no output voltage, so the error voltage is at its maximum positive value. This produces the maximum pulse width at the comparator output. Thus Q_1 and Q_2 each operate at about a 50% duty cycle, so that a square wave is fed to the main transformer primary. The rectified, filtered voltage from the secondary appears at the output of the supply. Now a voltage is present at the inverting input of the error amplifier, reducing the error voltage at its output. The pulse width is reduced, and the waveform at the main transformer primary is turned off for part of the time, resulting in a lower average voltage applied to the primary. Of course this means that there is a lower average voltage at the secondary, and since the output of an *LC* filter is proportional to the average input voltage, the output voltage is decreased. Very quickly, the circuit stabilizes the output voltage at the correct value.

In order to justify such a complex power supply, there must be some pretty convincing advantages. Let us see what they are. First, notice that Q_1 and Q_2 are operating in a switching mode; that is, each transistor is always either cut off or saturated. When a transistor is cut off, it dissipates no power because it passes no current. When it is saturated, it dissipates very little power even with very high currents, because the voltage drop across it is only a small fraction of a volt. Thus the regulating part of the supply operates at almost 100% efficiency. Second, because of the high frequency of the AC wave fed to the main transformer, that transformer can be physically small. The reason that most power transformers must be so large is that in order for a transformer to work properly, it must have a large inductive reactance at the frequency of interest. When that frequency is 50 or 60 Hz, this requires many turns and a large core. But when the frequency is 20 kHz or higher, a much smaller transformer can be used. Third, you will remember that earlier in this chapter we discussed the effect of frequency upon the necessary value for a filter capacitor. At that time, we were comparing the value of a capacitor needed for a half-wave rectifier with its 60-Hz fundamental output frequency with that of a capacitor needed for a full-wave rectifier, which has a 120-Hz fundamental. By having a much, much higher fundamental frequency, a switching supply can use a correspondingly smaller capacitor. And fourth, the equation for determining the value of a filter choke was given on page 235 as $R_L/3\omega$. For a 20-kHz supply, 3ω is $3.76 \cdot 10^5$, resulting in a very small value for the choke.

We see, then, that the payback for tolerating the complexity of a switching power supply is much higher efficiency and much smaller (hence lighter-weight and less expensive) components. There are several problems, though. The first is that in general iron-core transformers and chokes cannot be used, because of the large eddy-current losses that would result at such high frequencies. The second is that normal aluminum electrolytic capacitors cannot be used, because they have too much dielectric absorption for use as filters at frequencies above about 1 kHz. The third problem is that the frequencies and waveforms used in switching supplies cause radio-frequency interference unless the supply is carefully shielded. The fourth problem is that optical coupling must be employed if it is desired to isolate the control circuit from the AC line.

In spite of the problems, the advantages of switching power supplies are so great that they are gradually becoming more and more common. As more of these supplies

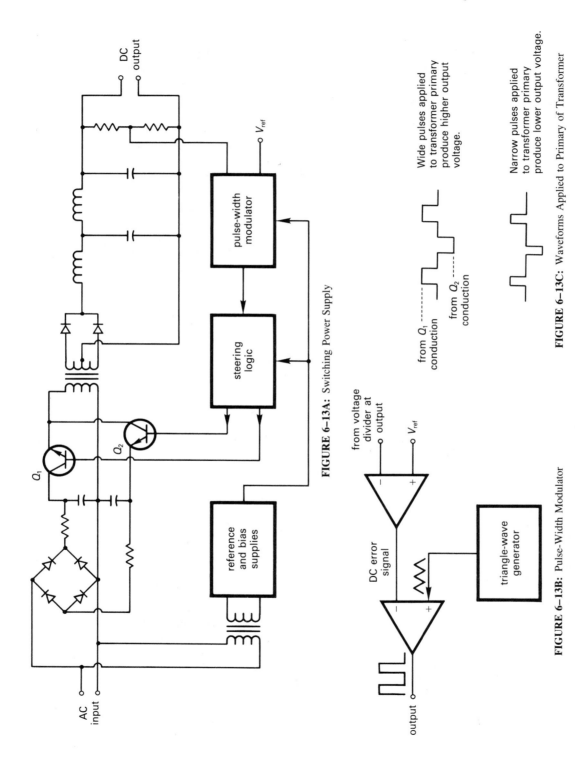

FIGURE 6–13A: Switching Power Supply

FIGURE 6–13B: Pulse-Width Modulator

Wide pulses applied to transformer primary produce higher output voltage.

Narrow pulses applied to transformer primary produce lower output voltage.

FIGURE 6–13C: Waveforms Applied to Primary of Transformer

FIGURE 6–13: A Switching Power Supply

are produced, the price of the special inductors and capacitors used decreases, further encouraging the growth of switching supply use.

A relative of the switching power supply is the switching regulator. A switching regulator is just a particular type of voltage regulator fed by a conventional power supply. Block diagrams of three versions of switching regulators are shown in Fig. 6–14. For each configuration, the pulse-width modulator performs the control function. The modulator, in turn, is controlled by an error voltage that is derived as described earlier. The output of the pulse-width modulator is applied to a switching transistor. In Fig. 6–14A, we see that the transistor is connected as a series element in the current path from the rectifier to the load. It acts as a short circuit when the comparator output is high, and as an open circuit when the comparator output is low. Thus the average value of the voltage at the emitter of the transistor is a function of the pulse width of the signal from the comparator. An *LC* filter is connected to the emitter of the transistor, providing a DC output that is the average value of the input voltage. Diode D_1 prevents inductive kickback voltages from damaging the switching transistor. Now the average voltage of a pulse wave is just the peak value of the wave multiplied by the duty factor:

$$V_{avg} = V_P(\text{Duty factor}) = V_P \left(\frac{t_{on}}{\text{Period}} \right) \tag{6.21}$$

Since the peak voltage of the pulse train applied to the collector of the switching transistor is the input voltage, and the average voltage is the output voltage:

$$V_{OUT} = V_{IN} \left(\frac{t_{on}}{\text{Period}} \right) \tag{6.22}$$

The input current is the same as the load current when the transistor is on, but it is zero when the transistor is off. Thus the *average* input current is actually less than the output current, as would be expected from a step-down regulator whose efficiency is near 100%. The input current is

$$I_{IN} = I_{OUT} \left(\frac{t_{on}}{\text{Period}} \right) \tag{6.23}$$

Thus we see that a step-down switching regulator acts much like a transformer in that it steps down the voltage while stepping up the current.

The operation of the step-up regulator shown in Fig. 6–14B is similar to that of the circuit just discussed. The difference is that the choke is in series with the load-current path, and the transistor is connected from the output of the choke to ground. When the transistor is turned on, a large current flows through the choke. This sets up a magnetic field around the choke; energy is stored in that field. When the transistor turns off, the magnetic field collapses suddenly, inducing a large voltage in the choke. This voltage forward biases D_1 and charges the capacitor. When the transistor turns on again, the capacitor is charged to a higher voltage than the supply voltage, so D_1 is reverse biased, preventing the capacitor from discharging back into the supply.

The time constant of the *RL* circuit formed by the resistance of the rectifier and power transformer and the inductance of the choke is much greater than the period of the pulse-width-modulated wave. Therefore, during the time that the transistor is turned off, the induced voltage across the inductor follows the curve shown to the right of the step-up regulator schematic. The average voltage applied to the capacitor

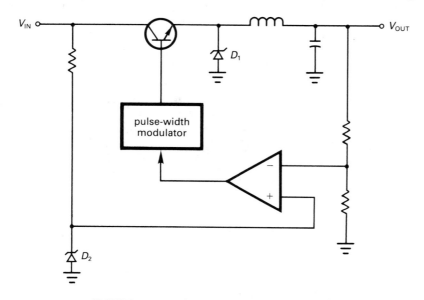

FIGURE 6–14A: Step-Down ("Buck") Regulator

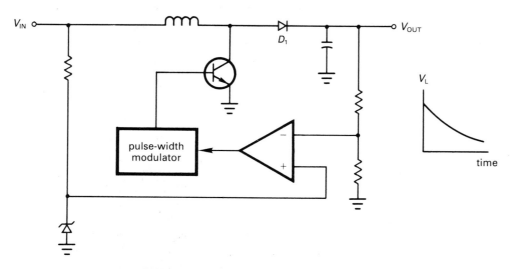

FIGURE 6–14B: Step-Up ("Boost") Regulator

FIGURE 6–14: Switching Regulators

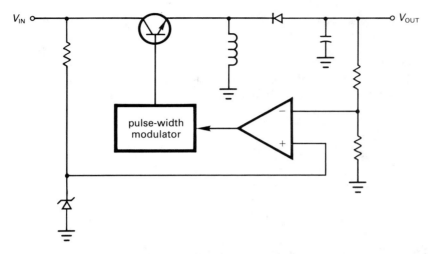

FIGURE 6–14C: Polarity Reverser

is the sum of V_{IN} and the inductor voltage. This total voltage begins at a maximum when the transistor first turns off, then decreases exponentially. But before the inductor voltage drops to zero (at which time just the voltage V_{IN} would be applied to the capacitor), the transistor turns on again, reverse biasing the diode and recharging the inductor. The longer the time the transistor is off, the longer the capacitor can charge from the higher-than-V_{IN} source. Thus, a longer t_{off}—which means a shorter t_{on}—produces a higher output voltage. In other words, the output voltage is inversely proportional to t_{on}:

$$V_{OUT} = V_{IN} \left(\frac{\text{Period}}{t_{on}} \right) \qquad (6.24)$$

As would be expected from the transformerlike action,

$$I_{IN} = I_{OUT} \left(\frac{\text{Period}}{t_{on}} \right) \qquad (6.25)$$

The polarity-reversing switching regulator shown in Fig. 6–14C produces an output voltage that is opposite in polarity from the input voltage. It operates much like the step-up regulator. When the transistor turns on, current from the supply flows through the transistor and the inductor to ground. This current sets up a magnetic field around the inductor. The diode, being reverse biased, prevents the current from reaching the capacitor. When the transistor is turned off, the magnetic field around the inductor collapses, inducing a voltage in the inductor. The polarity of this voltage makes the top end of the inductor positive with respect to ground. This forward biases the diode, charging the capacitor negatively on the top plate. The equations for the output voltage and input current are the same as for the step-up regulator.

All three types of switching regulators share two things in common with the switching power supply: namely, high efficiency and the need for special capacitors that have a low equivalent series resistance at high frequencies.

EXAMPLE

Problem

Calculate the range of output voltages available from (1) a step-down and (2) a step-up switching regulator having $V_{IN} = 15$ V and a duty cycle that can vary from 20% to 80%.

Solution

1. For the step-down regulator:

$$V_{OUT} = V_{IN} \left(\frac{t_{on}}{\text{Period}} \right) \qquad (6.22)$$

Since (t_{on}/Period) is the duty cycle, we can calculate

$$V_{OUT,min} = 20\% \text{ of } 15 \text{ V} = 3 \text{ V}$$
$$V_{OUT,max} = 80\% \text{ of } 15 \text{ V} = 12 \text{ V}$$

2. For the step-up regulator,

$$V_{OUT} = V_{IN} \left(\frac{\text{Period}}{t_{on}} \right) \qquad (6.24)$$

Now (Period/t_{on}) is the inverse of the duty cycle, so:

$$V_{OUT,min} = (15 \text{ V}) \left(\frac{1}{0.8} \right) = 18.75 \text{ V}$$

$$V_{OUT,max} = (15 \text{ V}) \left(\frac{1}{0.2} \right) = 75 \text{ V}$$

THE 723

You may have noticed that the series regulator and all three varieties of switching regulators share several elements, namely, the error amplifier, the voltage reference source, and the pass transistor. This fact led to the introduction of the μA723 precision voltage-regulator IC. This was the first popular voltage-regulator IC to be introduced. Since the introduction of the 723, many other regulator ICs have appeared, most of which are simpler to use and have a lower external parts count. However, the 723 continues to be widely used because of its potential for extremely close regulation (0.01% in some cases) and its versatility. Figure 6–15A shows an equivalent circuit of the 723. Notice that it is not a complete regulator in itself; it just provides building blocks for constructing a regulator. These building blocks include a voltage-reference source (Zener diode fed by a constant-current source), an amplifier to buffer the reference source, an error amplifier, a pass transistor, and a current-limit transistor. In the following circuits using the 723, the components shown in heavy lines are included within the IC. Components shown in standard-weight lines are external parts.

Figure 6–15B shows an example of a common circuit that can be constructed using a 723. It is a low-voltage series regulator for output voltages from 2 to 7 V. Figure 6–15C shows a high-voltage regulator (7 to 37 V) made from a 723. In both circuits, the pass transistor's base is fed from the error amplifier. The inverting input of the error amplifier is taken from the output of the regulator. In the low-voltage version, R_3 is used to provide isolation, but essentially the full output voltage is applied to the error amplifier. The voltage reference source is fed to the noninverting input through a voltage divider. This limits the output of the regulator to the voltage of the reference source, which is about 7.15 V. The R_1–R_2 voltage divider ratio can be adjusted as desired to provide any output voltage up to this maximum value. In the high-voltage circuit, the output voltage is sampled through a voltage divider, and the buffered reference source is fed directly to the noninverting input. This applies a lower voltage to the error amplifier, with the result that output voltages from the value of the reference source up to the maximum rating of the regulator can be obtained. By using a potentiometer for the voltage divider, either circuit could be made into a variable-voltage regulator.

The equation for predicting the output voltage from the circuit in Fig. 6–15B can be derived very easily. Using the voltage-division rule, we find that the voltage present at the noninverting input is

$$V_{IN+} = V_{ref}\left(\frac{R_2}{R_1 + R_2}\right) \tag{6.26}$$

Since an op amp with negative feedback produces whatever output is necessary to provide zero difference between the input voltages, V_{IN+} must equal V_{IN-}, which is just V_{OUT}. Setting equation 6.26 equal to V_{OUT}, we have

$$V_{OUT} = V_{ref}\left(\frac{R_2}{R_1 + R_2}\right) \tag{6.27}$$

For the circuit of Fig. 6–15C, we proceed similarly. In this case, however, making the input voltages equal requires that

$$V_{ref} = V_{OUT}\left(\frac{R_2}{R_1 + R_2}\right) \tag{6.28}$$

Solving for V_{OUT}, we obtain

$$V_{OUT} = V_{ref}\left(\frac{R_1 + R_2}{R_2}\right) \tag{6.29}$$

The value of R_{sense} for use in a current-limited 723 regulator circuit is the turn-on voltage of the current-limit transistor divided by the desired limit current:

$$R_{sense} = \frac{V_{turn\text{-}on}}{I_{lim}} \tag{6.30}$$

The turn-on voltage of the current-limit transistor is about 0.5 V, so

$$R_{sense} = \frac{0.5 \text{ V}}{I_{lim}} \tag{6.31}$$

The equations for the knee current and the short-circuit current are the same as equations 6.19 and 6.20, except that 0.5 V is used as the turn-on voltage of the current-limit transistor:

$$I_{knee} = \frac{V_{OUT}R_4 + (0.5 \text{ V})(R_4 + R_5)}{R_{sense}R_5} \tag{6.32}$$

$$I_{sc} = \frac{(0.5 \text{ V})(R_4 + R_5)}{R_{sense}R_5} \tag{6.33}$$

It is convenient to set the sum of R_4 and R_5 equal to 10 kΩ. Then the value of R_4 determines that ratio of I_{knee} to I_{sc}. This can be seen if we divide equation 6.32 by equation 6.33:

$$\frac{I_{knee}}{I_{sc}} = \frac{[V_{OUT}R_4 + (0.5 \text{ V})(10 \text{ k}\Omega)]/R_{sense}R_5}{(0.5 \text{ V})(10 \text{ k}\Omega)/R_{sense}R_5}$$

Simplifying, we get

$$\frac{I_{knee}}{I_{sc}} = \frac{V_{OUT}R_4 + (0.5 \text{ V})(10 \text{ k}\Omega)}{(0.5 \text{ V})(10 \text{ k}\Omega)}$$

Solving for R_4, we have

$$R_4 = \frac{(0.5 \text{ V})(10 \text{ k}\Omega)(I_{knee}/I_{sc} - 1)}{V_{OUT}} \tag{6.34}$$

Since $R_4 + R_5 = 10$ kΩ,

$$R_5 = 10 \text{ k}\Omega - R_4 \tag{6.35}$$

It only remains to solve either equation 6.32 or 6.33 for R_{sense}. Since 6.33 is simpler,

$$I_{sc} = \frac{(0.5 \text{ V})(10 \text{ k}\Omega)}{R_{sense}R_5} \quad \text{(from 6.33)}$$

$$R_{sense} = \frac{(0.5 \text{ V})(10 \text{ k}\Omega)}{I_{sc}R_5} \tag{6.36}$$

Figure 6–15D shows a sense resistor and the internal current-limit transistor connected to provide a 723-based current-limited voltage regulator. The same circuit modified to include current foldback limiting is shown in Fig. 6–15E.

The maximum current that can be safely drawn from the 723's internal pass transistor is 150 mA. For greater currents, an external transistor must be added. As shown in Fig. 6–16A (page 260), the addition of an external pass transistor changes the circuit very little from the basic low-voltage circuit. The external pass transistor's

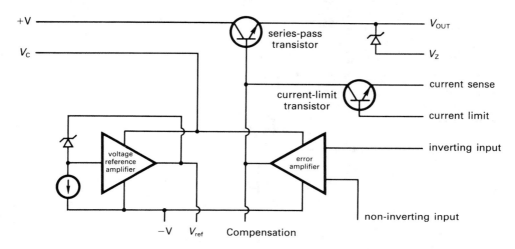

FIGURE 6–15A: Equivalent Circuit of the 723

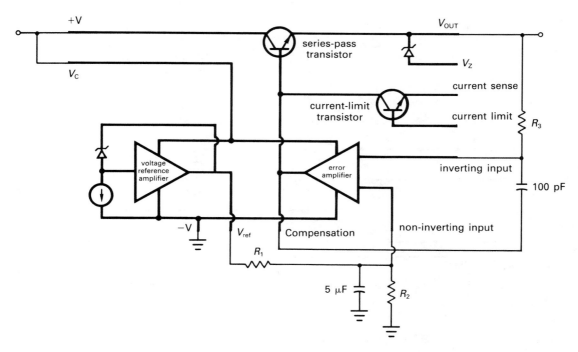

FIGURE 6–15B: Low-Voltage Regulator Circuit

FIGURE 6–15: The 723 Voltage Regulator

base current is supplied by the internal pass transistor, Darlington fashion. The sense resistor and the base of the current-limiting transistor are connected to the output of the external transistor, in order to provide protection for that transistor too.

Figure 6–16B shows a 723 configured as a step-down switching regulator. The 1-MΩ resistor connected from the collectors of the external transistors to the non-inverting input, and the 0.1-μF capacitor connected from the noninverting input to

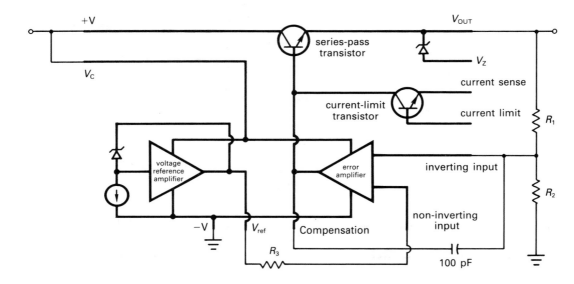

FIGURE 6–15C: High-Voltage Regulator Circuit

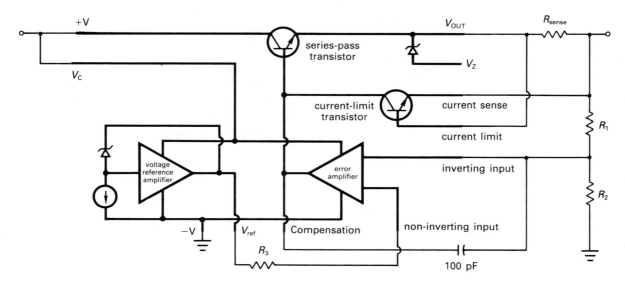

FIGURE 6–15D: High-Voltage, Current-Limited Regulator Circuit

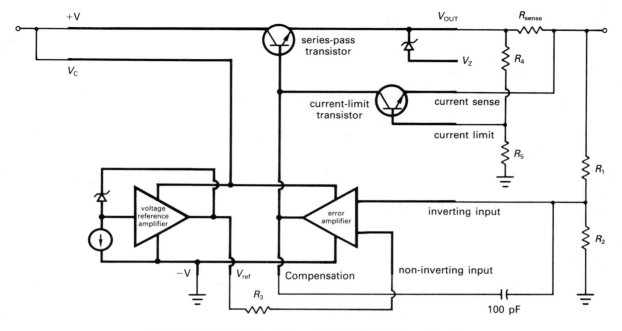

FIGURE 6–15E: Foldback Current-Limited High-Voltage Regulator

ground, provide positive feedback that converts the error amplifier into a sawtooth-wave generator. The output is fed directly to the inverting input, which makes the error amplifier simultaneously perform pulse-width modulation.

EXAMPLE

Problem

Design a low-voltage 723 regulator circuit to provide an output of 5 V at 1.5 A. Provide foldback limiting so that $I_{knee} = 1.6$ A and $I_{sc} = 300$ mA. These current specifications must be held within 5%. Include specifications for all parts, as well as the unregulated input voltage required.

Solution

1. The circuit of Fig. 6–16A will be used. For an output of 5 V, we choose $R_2 = 1$ kΩ and solve for the value of R_1:

$$V_{OUT} = V_{ref}\left(\frac{R_2}{R_1 + R_2}\right) \qquad (6.27)$$

which gives us

$$R_1 = R_2 \left(\frac{V_{ref} - V_{OUT}}{V_{OUT}} \right) = \frac{(1 \text{ k}\Omega)(7.15 \text{ V} - 5 \text{ V})}{5 \text{ V}} = 430 \text{ }\Omega$$

For proper bias-current compensation, we make R_3 equal to the parallel combination of R_1 and R_2:

$$R_3 = \frac{R_1 R_2}{R_1 + R_2} = \frac{1000 \text{ }\Omega \cdot 430 \text{ }\Omega}{100 \text{ }\Omega + 430 \text{ }\Omega} = 811 \text{ }\Omega$$

2. Next, we will design the current-limiting circuit:
   Set $R_4 + R_5 = 10 \text{ k}\Omega$. Then

$$R_4 = \frac{0.5 \text{ V} \cdot 10 \text{ k}\Omega(I_{knee}/I_{sc} - 1)}{V_{OUT}} \tag{6.34}$$

$$= \frac{0.5 \text{ V} \cdot 10 \text{ k}\Omega(1.6 \text{ A}/0.3 \text{ A} - 1)}{5 \text{ V}}$$

$$= 4300 \text{ }\Omega$$

Then $R_5 = 10 \text{ k}\Omega - 4300 \text{ }\Omega = 5700 \text{ }\Omega$, from equation 6.35.

$$R_{sense} = \frac{(0.5 \text{ V})(10 \text{ k}\Omega)}{I_{sc} R_5} \tag{6.36}$$

$$= \frac{0.5 \text{ V} \cdot 10 \text{ k}\Omega}{300 \text{ mA} \cdot 5700 \text{ }\Omega} = 2.9 \text{ }\Omega$$

We will use a 3-Ω resistor for R_{sense}. This resistor will dissipate maximum power when 1.6 A is drawn from the regulator:

$$P_{DISS,max} = I^2 R = (1.6 \text{ A})^2(3 \text{ }\Omega) = 7.7 \text{ W}$$

We should use a resistor with approximately twice this power rating. We will choose a 15-W resistor.

3. Now let us check whether the approximate values we are using for R_{sense}, R_4, and R_5 will keep our limit currents within the required ±5% tolerance.

$$I_{knee} = \frac{V_{OUT}R_4 + (0.5 \text{ V})(R_4 + R_5)}{R_{sense}R_5} \tag{6.32}$$

$$= \frac{5 \text{ V} \cdot 4300 \text{ }\Omega + 0.5 \text{ V} \cdot 10 \text{ k}\Omega}{3 \text{ }\Omega \cdot 5700}$$

$$= 1.55 \text{ A}$$

This is only about 3% low.

$$I_{sc} = \frac{(0.5 \text{ V})(R_4 + R_5)}{R_{sense}R_5} \tag{6.33}$$

$$= \frac{0.5 \text{ V} \cdot 10 \text{ k}\Omega}{3 \text{ }\Omega \cdot 5700 \text{ }\Omega} = 292 \text{ mA}$$

This is less than 3% low.

4. Next, let us find the required unregulated input voltage. The saturation voltage of the external pass transistor will probably be about 0.2 V. The 723 requires a minimum 3-V differential between input and output, as indicated on the data sheet in Appendix A. The voltage drop across R_{sense} when 1.5 A is being drawn is given by Ohm's law as 1.5 A $\cdot$ 3 Ω = 4.5 V. Adding all these voltage drops to the output voltage of 5 V, we have a necessary unregulated input voltage of 12.7 V.

5. The external pass transistor must handle at least the knee current of 1.55 A. Its voltage rating must be at least somewhat higher than the maximum input voltage of 12.7 V. Let us calculate its power dissipation in two ways. First, the dissipation when a short circuit is connected to the output is:

$$P_{DISS,sc} = V_{sc}I_{sc}$$

The voltage dropped across the transistor when the output is shorted is the input voltage, minus the drop across the 723, minus the drop across R_{sense}:

$$V_{sc} = 12.7 \text{ V} - 3 \text{ V} - 0.3 \text{ A} \cdot 3 \Omega = 8.8 \text{ V}$$

In the preceding equation, we have substituted $I_{sc}R_{sense}$ for the drop across R_{sense}. Thus,

$$P_{DISS,sc} = 8.8 \text{ V} \cdot 300 \text{ mA} = 2.64 \text{ W}$$

Second, let us calculate the power dissipated when the regulator is delivering maximum rated current into a normal load:

$$P_{DISS,nominal} = V_{nominal}I_{nominal}$$

We have already said that $V_{nominal}$ is the saturation voltage of the transistor, if the input voltage is 12.7 V. If a higher input voltage is used, $V_{nominal}$ will be increased. Assuming that V_{IN} is 15 V, $V_{nominal}$ would then be 0.2 V + (15 V − 12.7 V) = 2.5 V. Then

$$P_{DISS,nominal} = 2.5 \text{ V} \cdot 1.5 \text{ A} = 3.75 \text{ W}$$

Since this is the greater power, the pass transistor and its heat sink must be chosen to dissipate 3.75 W safely. The β for the pass transistor is given by dividing the maximum required output current by the maximum available input current. Since the input current is supplied by the 723, which can deliver a maximum of 150 mA:

$$\beta_{min} = \frac{1.5 \text{ A}}{150 \text{ mA}} = 10$$

In this example, quite a lot of power was dissipated by the pass transistor and R_{sense}, compared to the power delivered to the load. The power waste could have been reduced if I_{sc} had been set closer to I_{knee}, because this would have resulted in a smaller R_{sense} which would have allowed a smaller unregulated input voltage. However, it would also have necessitated a larger power dissipation capability for the pass transistor, because of the larger current that could flow in a short circuit.

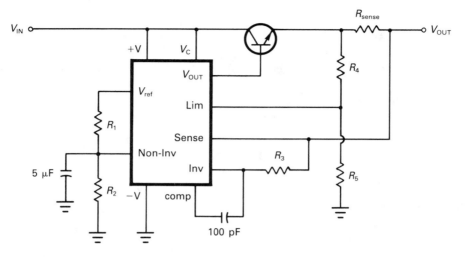

FIGURE 6–16A: 723 Regulator with External Pass Transistor and Foldback Current Limiting

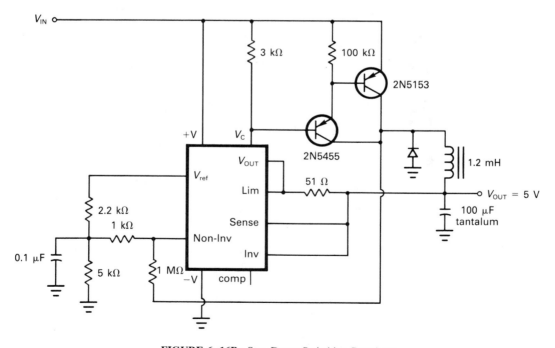

FIGURE 6–16B: Step-Down Switching Regulator

FIGURE 6–16: Two 723 Applications

POWER-SUPPLY IC APPLICATION—COMPLETE FLOPPY-DISK POWER SUPPLY

The floppy-disk power supply shown below uses a pair of TIP34 PNP transistors in a push-pull configuration. The oscillation frequency is set at 25 kHz and -5 V at 500 mA by the .01-μF capacitor on pin 5 and the 5-kΩ resistor on pin 6.

The center connection of the two 5.6-kΩ resistors on pins 13 and 14 establishes a 2.5-V reference voltage on pin 2, which is the inverting input of the voltage control error amplifier. The voltage feedback to pin 1, the noninverting input, comes from the center connection of the two 5.6-kΩ resistors located on the 5-V/2.5-A power supply output terminal. Because this voltage supplies the logic circuits, it requires closer regulation.

The 24-V winding, on the other hand, is not critical as it furnishes voltage for the stepping motor. The -5-V supply is regulated separately with a uA7905 three-terminal regulator.

In choosing components for this circuit, the same precautions taken in the construction of any switching power supply should be observed: Be careful of layout, ground loops, and heatsinking of the power transistors. In the output section, where high frequency rectifiers are needed, either Schottky or fast recovery diodes should be used. For output capacitors, low equivalent series resistance (ESR) types should be considered. The output ripple depends more on the resistance than on the capacitor value.

TRANSFORMER CONSTRUCTION

The transformer for this circuit was wound on a toroid core. The core used was 3C8 ferrite material (F-42908-TC).

Transformer Winding Data
Primary A + B = 28 turns bifilar #20 HNP
Secondary C + D = 28 turns bifilar #20 HNP over A + B
Secondary E + F = 6 turns bifilar #20 HNP over C + D
Secondary G + H = 10 turns bifilar #20 HNP over E + F
NOTE: All windings to be center tapped.

DC Resistance
Winding $1 - 3 = 0.11\ \Omega$
Winding $4 - 6 = 0.11\ \Omega$
Winding $7 - 9 = 0.025\ \Omega$
Winding $10 - 12 = 0.15\ \Omega$

Reprinted from *Linear and Interface Circuits Applications* (Courtesy of Texas Instruments, Inc.)

(continued)

(continued from page 261)

Sidebar

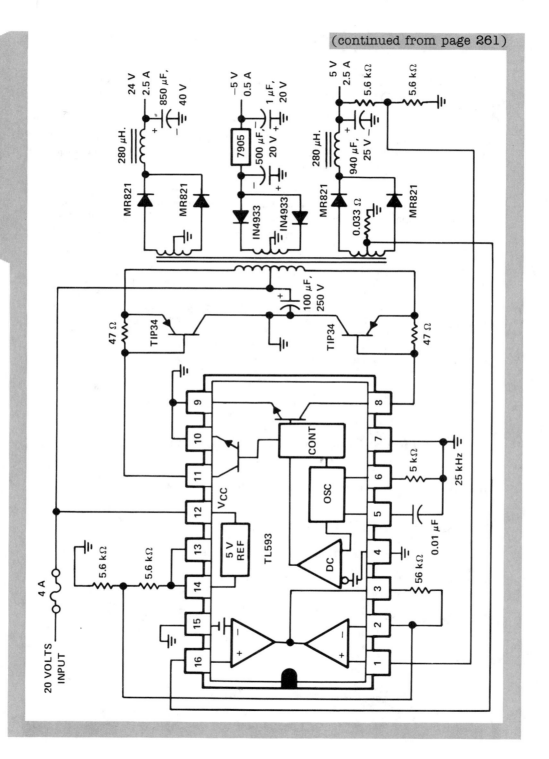

THREE-TERMINAL REGULATORS

Fixed Positive or Negative Regulators

Although the 723 regulator IC is still widely used because of its versatility, the great majority of voltage regulation jobs can be done by a group of ICs that are much simpler to use. These devices have only three terminals—an input, an output, and a ground—and contain complete voltage-regulation circuitry within the IC. Three examples of three-terminal regulators are the 7805, the 7912, and the 317. Data sheets for these are found in Appendix A.

The 7805 and 7912 are members of families that are called the 78XX and 79XX voltage regulators. The 78XX series consists of positive-voltage regulators; the 79XX, of negative regulators. The last two digits of the type number represent the output voltage. Thus a 7805 is a 5-V positive regulator and the 7912 is a 12-V negative regulator. The other characteristics of the 78XX and 79XX families are shared in common. Some of the more important of these characteristics are:

- Output current greater than 1 A without an external pass transistor
- Automatic shutdown in case of overheating
- Internal short-circuit current limiting
- Line and load regulation typically 2%
- Power-supply ripple rejection greater than 60 dB

Figure 6–17A shows a 5-V power supply using a 7805. The characteristics of the supply are given below the figure. Figure 6–17B shows a −12-V supply using a 7912. Notice the input and output capacitors connected to the 7912. The input capacitor is required if the regulator is located more than 3 in. from the filter capacitor, in order to nullify the effects of lead resistance and inductance. The output capacitor is always required for stability.

EXAMPLE

Problem

Design a ±15-V regulator using a 7815 and a 7915 in TO-220 cases. Specify the maximum and minimum input voltages to the regulators for an output current of 1 A. Assume a heat sink of 4°C/W.

Solution

1. The circuit will be as shown in Fig. 6–18. From footnote 1 in the data sheet in Appendix A, we find that the thermal resistance of the 78XX regulators is 4°C/W. For the 79XX types, it is 5°C/W. We will make our calculations based

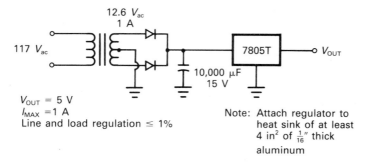

FIGURE 6–17A: Five-Volt Regulated Power Supply

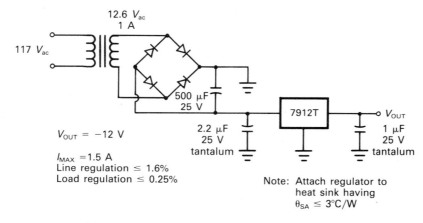

FIGURE 6–17B: Negative-12-V Regulated Power Supply

FIGURE 6–17: Three-Terminal Regulator Applications

on the 79XX, since it has the higher thermal resistance. This means that the total thermal resistance is

$$\theta_{total} = \theta_{JC} + \theta_{CS} + \theta_{SA}$$
$$= 5°C/W + 1°C/W + 4°C/W = 10°C/W$$

where we have assumed that θ_{CS} is 1°C/W.

The maximum operating temperature of the 78XX series is 150°C; for the 79XX series, it is 125°C. Again we will use the characteristics of the 79XX types, since they are more restrictive. Assuming an ambient temperature that does not exceed 40°C:

$$\Delta T = 125°C - 40°C = 85°C$$

Thus the power that each IC can safely dissipate is

$$P_{DISS,max} = \frac{\Delta T}{\theta_{total}} = \frac{85°C}{10°C/W} = 8.5 \text{ W}$$

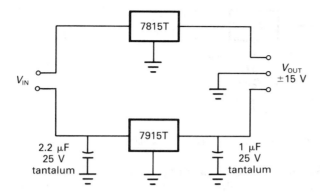

FIGURE 6–18: Bipolar Regulator

2. The maximum input voltage of a regulator IC is determined by dividing the maximum power dissipation of the IC by the load current. Since the load current is to be 1 A, this means that the maximum voltage drop across the IC is 8.5 V. In other words, the maximum input voltage is 8.5 V greater than the output voltage:

$$V_{IN,max} = 15 \text{ V} + 8.5 \text{ V} = 23.5 \text{ V}$$

This same calculation applies for both the positive and the negative regulator, so the maximum input voltage is ±23.5 V.

3. The minimum input voltage is determined by finding the dropout voltage from the data sheet. For the 78XX, it is 2 V; for the 79XX, 1.1 V. In this case, the characteristics of the 78XX are more restrictive, so we will use those. The input must be greater than the output voltage by at least the amount of the dropout voltage. Thus the input voltage must be at least 15 V + 2 V = 17 V. The unregulated input voltages to the regulator must therefore be between ±17 V and ±23.5 V.

Adjustable Regulators

The 317 is a variable-voltage three-terminal regulator. In addition to the convenience of adjustability, the 317 has characteristics that surpass those of the 78XX and 79XX in a number of respects:

- Output currents up to 1.5 A are available.
- Line regulation is typically 0.01%.
- Load regulation is typically 0.1%.
- Ripple rejection is at least 80 dB.
- Output voltages from 1.2 to 37 V are available.

The 317 is used as shown in Fig. 6–19. The unit works as follows. The IC develops a 1.25-V reference voltage between the output terminal and the adjustment

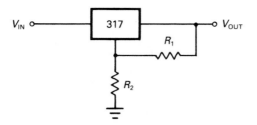

FIGURE 6–19: Application of the 317 Regulator

terminal. This voltage is applied across external resistor R_1. The IC maintains a constant voltage drop across R_1, which results in a constant current in that resistor. Since R_2 is in series with R_1, the current through it must also remain constant. By keeping the current in these two resistors constant, the IC necessarily keeps the output voltage constant. That voltage is approximately the reference voltage multiplied by the inverse voltage-divider ratio:

$$V_{OUT} = V_{ref} \frac{R_1 + R_2}{R_1}$$

More exactly, the 100-μA current that flows from the adjustment terminal also flows through R_2, so

$$V_{OUT} = V_{ref} \frac{R_1 + R_2}{R_1} + 100 \ \mu A \cdot R_2 \qquad (6.37)$$

$$= 1.25 \ V \frac{R_1 + R_2}{R_1} + 100 \ \mu A \cdot R_2$$

Typically, R_1 is made equal to 240 Ω, making the current through R_1 equal to 1.25 V/ 240 Ω = 5.2 mA. This current more or less swamps the 100-μA current from the adjustment terminal, allowing one to ignore it if output voltages can be 2% higher than calculated. If the regulator is to be adjustable, a 10-kΩ potentiometer is usually used for R_2. For many applications, though, a fixed output voltage is required, and an appropriate value of R_2 is calculated:

$$V_{OUT} = 1.25 \ V \frac{R_1 + R_2}{R_1} + 100 \ \mu A \cdot R_2 \qquad (6.37)$$

$$= \frac{1.25 \ V(240 \ \Omega + R_2)}{(240 \ \Omega)} + 100 \ \mu A \cdot R_2$$

$$= (5.2 \ mA)(240 \ \Omega + R_2) + 100 \ \mu A \cdot R_2$$

$$= 1.25 \ V + (5.2 \ mA + 100 \ \mu A)R_2$$

Solving for R_2:

$$R_2 = \frac{V_{OUT} - 1.25 \ V}{5.3 \ mA} \qquad (6.38)$$

In order to avoid having large currents flow through the adjustment terminal, introducing errors, the 317 was designed so that most of the current drawn by the internal circuitry returns to ground through the output terminal. In this respect, the 317 is different from other three-terminal regulators. With most other three-terminal regulators, the current drawn by the internal circuitry flows to ground through a ground terminal. Thus, even if no load is present, the output voltage remains at the specified value. The 317, though, requires a minimum load current of 10 mA. With less output current, the regulating circuitry will not work, and the output voltage will rise.

EXAMPLE

Problem

Design a 28-V regulator circuit using a 317 IC. The load will draw currents ranging from 0 to 100 mA.

Solution

1. We will use a 240-Ω resistor for R_1. R_2 can be selected as follows:

$$R_2 = \frac{V_{\text{OUT}} - 1.25 \text{ V}}{5.3 \text{ mA}}$$

$$= \frac{28 \text{ V} - 1.25 \text{ V}}{5.3 \text{ mA}} = \frac{26.75 \text{ V}}{5.3 \text{ mA}} = 5047 \ \Omega \qquad (6.38)$$

The accuracy of resistors R_1 and R_2 directly affects the accuracy of the output voltage, so 1% resistors should be used. The nearest standard 1% value for R_2 is 5110 Ω.

2. In order to draw a minimum load current of 10 mA, we will connect another resistor in parallel with the load. The value of this resistor will be 28 V/10 mA = 2.8 kΩ. We can use a 2.7-kΩ resistor for this purpose. The power dissipated by this resistor is 28 V · 10 mA = 280 mW, so a $\frac{1}{2}$-W resistor will be sufficient.

3. From the graph on the data sheet, we find that the dropout voltage for a 317 delivering 100 mA is less than 2 V, so the minimum input voltage is 30 V. For a bit of safety margin, we will specify 32 V.

4. The maximum power dissipated by the IC will be

$$P_{\text{DISS,max}} = (V_{\text{IN}} - V_{\text{OUT}})I_{\text{load}}$$

$$= (32 \text{ V} - 28 \text{ V}) \cdot (100 \text{ mA}) = 400 \text{ mW}$$

This small amount of power can probably be dissipated by a 317 in a TO-220 case. However, the value of θ_{JA} is not given on the data sheet. From the 78XX and 79XX data sheets, we find that θ_{JA} is about $10\theta_{\text{JC}}$. Assuming that the thermal resistance of an LM317T (TO-220 case version) is about 50°C/W like its cousins in the 79XX series, 400 mW would only produce a 20°C junction-temperature rise. Since $T_{J_{max}}$ is 150°C for the 317, we can stand a ΔT of 150°C − 40°C = 110°C. Therefore, we will be quite safe in using the 317 with no heat sink for this application.

High-Voltage and High-Current Applications

The 317 can be used to provide output voltages in excess of 37 V, provided that the device is never required to drop more than 37 V and the power dissipation does not become too great. For a typical unregulated 400-V supply, as long as the output voltage is not required to be less than 400 V − 37 V = 363 V, the 317 could be used to provide regulation. Of course, this assumes that 400 V is the maximum that would be applied to the input of the 317. Even with the voltage drop across the IC less than 37 V, when that drop is large, as is normal in a high-voltage supply, the IC must handle less current in order to keep the power dissipation within tolerable limits. Also, it is important to carefully calculate the maximum and minimum unregulated input voltages for high-line, low-load-current and low-line, high-load-current conditions. For a 400-V supply, even a ±5% variation about the nominal output voltage represents a 40-V swing, which is more than a 317 can regulate. (By the way, the 317 is also available in a high-voltage version, the LM317HV, which can handle input/output voltage differentials of up to 57 V.)

When higher output current is required than a standard three-terminal regulator can deliver, an external pass transistor can be added as shown in Fig. 6–20. The value of R_3 is calculated so that the transistor turns on at the desired threshold current. This current is determined by the current and power limitations of the regulator IC. When small output currents are drawn, there is not enough voltage drop across R_3 to turn on the transistor. As the load current increases, a point is reached at which the transistor begins to conduct, shunting current around the IC. Since a transistor is a current source, the collector voltage is not firmly related to the emitter and base voltage, so the collector stays at the voltage set by the regulator IC.

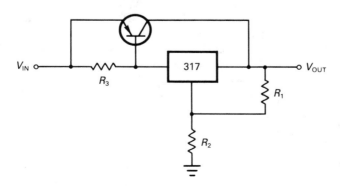

FIGURE 6–20: Current-Boosted 317 Regulator

EXAMPLE

Problem

Design a 5-V, 10-A regulator using a 7805 and a pass transistor.

Solution

1. The 7805 can handle a 1-A output current. Just for a safety margin, let us limit the current in the IC to 500 mA. Assuming that the pass transistor turns on at 0.6-V emitter-to-base, we can select R_1 as follows:

$$R_1 = \frac{0.6 \text{ V}}{500 \text{ mA}} = 1.2 \text{ } \Omega$$

The power dissipation of this resistor is

$$P_{\text{DISS}} = (0.6 \text{ V}) \cdot (500 \text{ mA}) = 0.3 \text{ W}$$

A $\frac{1}{2}$-W resistor could be used, but a 1-W unit would be preferable, in order to provide a 2:1 ratio between power rating and power dissipation.

2. The transistor will have to handle 9.5 A, so we would prefer at least a 12-A unit. The voltage rating only needs to be equal to the input voltage. The β is determined by the maximum allowable base current. Since the base current flows through the 7805 along with 500 mA of the load current, the absolute maximum base current will be 500 mA, because of the 1-A limitation of the 7805. Thus,

$$\beta_{\text{min}} = \frac{9.5 \text{ A}}{500 \text{ mA}} = 19$$

The transistor and its heat sink must be selected so as to dissipate the power given by

$$P_{\text{DISS,max}} = (V_{\text{IN}} - V_{\text{OUT}})I_{\text{max}}$$

The input voltage must be

$$V_{\text{IN,min}} = V_{\text{OUT}} + V_{\text{R1}} + V_{\text{dropout}} = 5 \text{ V} + 0.6 \text{ V} + 2 \text{ V} = 7.6 \text{ V}$$

If we specify a 10-V input, the power dissipation for the transistor becomes

$$P_{\text{DISS,max}} = (10 \text{ V} - 5 \text{ V}) \cdot (9.5 \text{ A}) = 47.5 \text{ W}$$

At the same time, the regulator must dissipate $(10 \text{ V} - 5 \text{ V})(0.5 \text{ A}) = 2.5 \text{ W}$. The thermal resistance calculations are done as usual.

Tracking Regulators

There are many applications involving op amps in DC circuits for which the absolute values of the positive and negative supply voltages must be very nearly equal. Although the regulation provided by three-terminal regulators can be very good, the accuracy of the output voltage compared to the rated voltage is not as good. Usually, if a 12-V regulator is needed that has 0.1% regulation, it is not important if the output voltage of the regulator is only 11.4 V (5% low), as long as that 11.4 V is held constant within ±0.1%. The 78XX series of regulators, for example, has an output-voltage accuracy of 4%, but a regulation of 2%. If a 7812 and a 7912 were used to provide a 12-V bipolar regulator, it is possible that the positive output could be 4% high (12.48 V) while the negative output was 4% low (11.52 V), even though both regulators were in tolerance. This would give almost a 1-V difference between the positive and negative outputs, which would be unacceptable in some cases. The *dual-tracking regulator* circuit shown in Fig. 6–21 avoids this difficulty by providing outputs that have essentially equal absolute values. It does this by using a 317 for the positive regulator and a 337 (negative 317) for the

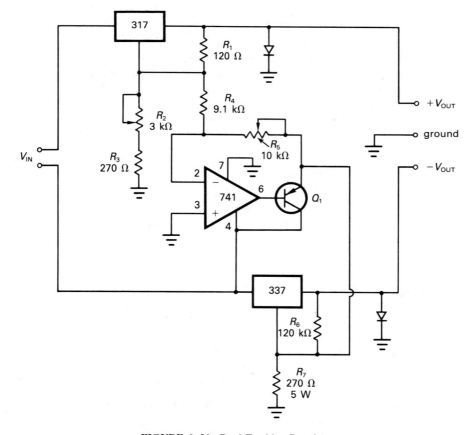

FIGURE 6–21: Dual-Tracking Regulator

negative regulator, with a 741 op amp providing the control voltage to the 337. The op amp senses the voltage at the adjustment terminal of the 317. As you remember, this voltage is always 1.25 V less than the output voltage of the 317. The op amp is connected as a unity-gain inverter, providing at its output a negative voltage whose absolute value is exactly equal to the positive voltage at its input. Resistor R_5 is made variable so that it can be adjusted to make the gain of the 741 exactly unity and to null out any differences in regulator characteristics. By making R_2 variable, the output voltage has been made adjustable. In other words, R_2 simultaneously adjusts the positive and negative output voltage, and R_5 is set to make the absolute value of the outputs equal. Transistor Q_1 is a current booster for the 741. The diodes at the outputs are provided to prevent the momentary application of reverse voltages to the IC outputs at any time, as this would destroy the ICs.

Another way of providing dual-tracking regulation is to use a dual-tracking regulator IC, such as the RC4195, whose data sheet is included in Appendix A.

DESIGN NOTES

Power Supplies

Power-supply design may be summarized as follows (see Fig. 6–22):

1. Choose a rectifier type. For a unipolar supply, the usual choice is either a full-wave center-tapped or a bridge configuration. The choice depends mainly upon the cost and availability of suitable transformers. For a bipolar supply, a bridge rectifier fed by a center-tapped transformer is the almost universal choice. Half-wave and doubler rectifiers are rarely used, except for high-voltage supplies.
2. Calculate the transformer secondary voltage needed, based upon the required output voltage. Since transformer specifications are not very precise, plan on using a regulator if regulation better than about ±10% is needed. The transformer is then chosen so as to give at least the minimum required output voltage. With no regulator,

$$V_{sec} = \frac{1.1 \, V_{OUT,min}}{1.414} \qquad (6.39)$$

This equation is for a bridge rectifier and includes a safety factor for a 5% line-voltage drop and a 5% decrease in output voltage due to discharging of the filter capacitor between peaks at high load currents. For a center-tapped rectifier, use twice the value calculated above. Remember that in this equation, V_{OUT} is the voltage difference between the most negative and the most positive output points of the supply.

For a regulated supply,

$$V_{sec} = \frac{1.1 \, V_{OUT} + V_{dropout} + V_{sense}}{1.414} \qquad (6.40)$$

where $V_{dropout}$ is the minimum input-to-output voltage of the regulator, and V_{sense} equals the maximum current multiplied by R_{sense} if current limiting is used. Use the next higher available transformer secondary voltage.

3. Choose rectifiers rated at least 5 times the peak value of the secondary voltage, and with current rating equal to the maximum output current. This includes a safety margin for both voltage and current ratings.

Design Notes

(continued)

(continued from page 272)

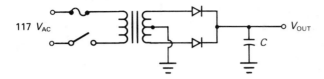

FIGURE 6–22A: Full-Wave Center-Tapped

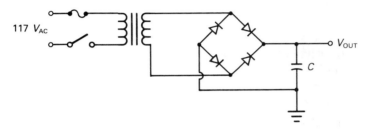

FIGURE 6–22B: Full-Wave Bridge (Unipolar)

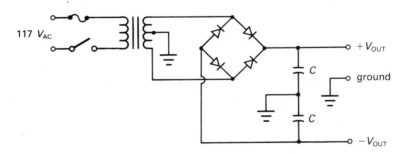

FIGURE 6–22C: Bipolar Bridge

FIGURE 6–22: Unregulated Power Supplies

4. Choose a filter capacitor:

$$C = \frac{1}{2\sqrt{3}R_L f \gamma} \qquad (6.11)$$

$$C = \frac{I_{max}}{0.05\, V_{OUT}2f} \qquad \text{(from 6.03, assuming 5\% regulation)}$$

where γ is the ripple factor. Select the larger of the two values you have

(continued from page 273)

calculated and use the next larger standard value. Remember that all voltage regulators decrease the ripple significantly, so the voltage regulation is the primary criterion in capacitor selection for a regulated supply. The input voltage must not fall so low that the regulator cannot function.

5. Choose a slow-blow fuse with a current rating equal to

$$I_{\text{fuse}} = \frac{I_{\max} V_{\text{sec}}}{115 \text{ V}}$$

where $I_{\max}$ is the smaller of (1) (the rated rectifier current)$V_{\text{sec}}/115$ V, or (2) (the rated transformer secondary current)$V_{\text{sec}}/115$ V. Add a power switch of at least this rating.

Zener Regulators

1. See Fig. 6–23. Choose R_{dropping} as follows:

$$R_{\text{dropping}} = \frac{V_{\text{IN,min}} - V_{\text{OUT}}}{1.1 \, I_{\max}}$$

where $V_{\text{IN,min}}$ is the unregulated input voltage when current is maximum and line voltage is minimum

2. The power rating of the resistor is

$$P_{\text{resistor}} = (V_{\text{no load,high line}} - V_{\text{OUT}})1.1 \, I_{\max}$$

3. The Zener voltage equals the desired output voltage, and the power rating of the Zener is

$$P_{\text{Zener}} = (2 \, V_{\text{Zener}})(1.1 \, I_{\max})$$

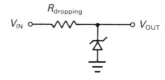

FIGURE 6–23: Zener Regulator

(continued from page 274)

Series Regulator with Feedback

1. See Fig. 6–24. Choose a convenient value of Zener voltage; this must be at least 0.5 V less than the output voltage.
2. The dropping resistor's value is

$$R_1 = \frac{V_{OUT} - V_{Zener}}{10 \text{ mA}}$$

3. The transistor's β is

$$\beta_{min} = \frac{I_{max}}{I_{control}}$$

where $I_{control}$ is the maximum current the op amp can supply. The transistor's maximum current is at least I_{max}; its voltage rating must be greater than V_{IN}.
4. Thermal calculations are performed as discussed in Chapter 5's design notes.
5. Select $R_3 = V_Z/1 \text{ mA}$ and $R_2 = (V_{OUT} - V_Z)/1 \text{ mA}$.

723-Based Regulators

Low-Voltage Circuit. (See Fig. 6–25A.)
Choose $R_2 = 1 \text{ k}\Omega$. Then

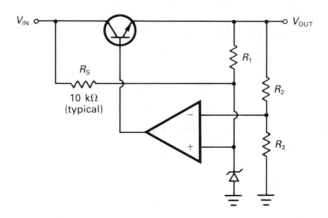

FIGURE 6–24: Series Regulator with Feedback

(continued from page 275)

$$R_1 = R_2 \frac{7.15\ \text{V} - V_{\text{OUT}}}{V_{\text{OUT}}} \qquad \text{(from 6.27)}$$

$$R_3 = R_1 \| R_2$$

High-Voltage Circuit. (See Fig. 6–25B.)
Choose $R_2 = 1\ \text{k}\Omega$. Then

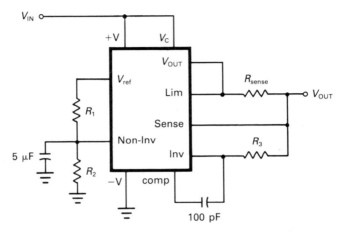

FIGURE 6–25A: Low-Voltage

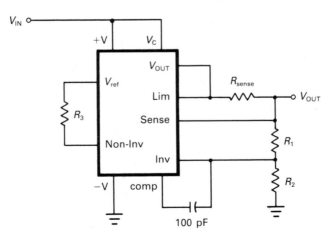

FIGURE 6–25B: High-Voltage

FIGURE 6–25: 723 Regulator Circuits

Design Notes

(continued from page 276)

$$R_1 = (V_{OUT} - 7.15 \text{ V})\left(\frac{R_2}{7.15 \text{ V}}\right) \qquad \text{(from 6.29)}$$

$$R_3 = R_1 \| R_2$$

Constant-Current Limiting. (See Figs. 6–25A and B.)

$$R_{sense} = \frac{0.5 \text{ V}}{I_{limit}} \qquad\qquad (6.31)$$

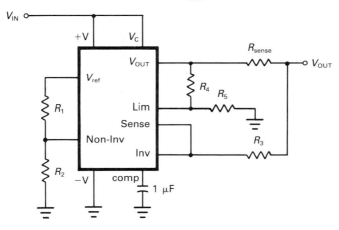

Low-Voltage

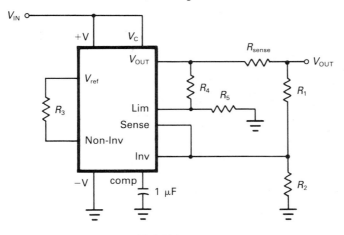

High-Voltage

FIGURE 6–25C: Foldback-Current-Limited

(continued from page 277)

For no limiting, R_{sense} = zero and no connection is made to the *current sense* and *current limit* terminals of the IC.

Foldback Current Limiting. (See Fig. 6–25C.)

$$R_4 = \frac{(0.5 \text{ V} \cdot 10 \text{ k}\Omega)(I_{\text{knee}}/I_{\text{sc}} - 1)}{V_{\text{OUT}}}$$

$$R_5 = 10 \text{ k}\Omega - R_4 \tag{6.34}$$

$$R_{\text{sense}} = \frac{0.5 \text{ V} \cdot 10 \text{ k}\Omega}{I_{\text{sc}}R_{\text{sense}}} \tag{6.35}$$

Adjustable Regulator

(See Fig. 6–26.)
Choose $R_1 = 240 \ \Omega$. Then

$$R_2 = \frac{V_{\text{OUT}} - 1.25 \text{ V}}{5.3 \text{ mA}} \tag{6.38}$$

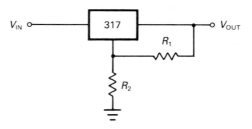

FIGURE 6–26: Adjustable Regulator

SUMMARY

A complete power supply is made up of four components: a transformer, a rectifier, a filter, and a voltage regulator (which is sometimes omitted).

There are four common types of rectifier circuits: half-wave, full-wave center-tapped, full-wave bridge, and doubler. The half-wave and doubler types produce more ripple and have poorer voltage regulation than the full-wave types. The center-tapped full-wave circuit requires a transformer with a center-tapped secondary and produces only half the output voltage with a given transformer that a bridge does. Consequently, the bridge is the most common type of rectifier.

The output voltage of an unfiltered rectifier is the average value of the AC input voltage. (Remember that the AC input voltage for a center-tapped full-wave rectifier is *half* the secondary voltage.)

A capacitor-input filter produces an output voltage that is the peak value of the rectifier's output voltage. This is true whether the filter is a simple capacitor type, a capacitor-input *LC* filter, or an *RC* filter. The output voltage of a capacitor-input filter decreases as the output current increases.

A choke-input filter produces an output voltage that is equal to the average value of the rectifier's output voltage. This voltage is essentially constant, except for ohmic drops caused by resistance in the choke and in the rectifier circuit.

A discrete shunt regulator is made up of a series dropping resistor and a Zener diode connected in parallel with the load. The voltage drop across the resistor is always equal to the difference between the input voltage and the output voltage. The current drawn from the supply by a shunt regulator is constant and equal to the maximum current that the regulator can deliver without the output voltage falling below the rated value.

A discrete series regulator consists of a transistor whose base voltage is fixed by a Zener diode, with the output taken from the emitter. Since the current drawn from the supply by a series regulator is only slightly more than the load current, series regulators are more efficient than shunt regulators.

If an amplifier is added to drive the base of a series regulator's pass transistor, and the amplifier is fed the difference between the actual output voltage and a reference voltage, the result is a series regulator with negative feedback. This type of circuit provides a much more constant output voltage than a simple series regulator.

Switching regulators use pulse-width modulation to supply the exact amount of energy needed by the load. This avoids the need for dissipative components and thereby increases the efficiency of the regulator, compared to a shunt or series regulator. There are three configurations of switching regulator: the step-down, the step-up, and the polarity-inverting versions. It is also possible to build a switching power supply, which adds the advantages of small power transformers to the efficiency of the switching regulator. The use of smaller transformers is possible because the switching supply operates at a higher frequency than a standard power supply.

The 723 IC is a building-block circuit that can be used to make a series, shunt, or switching regulator with or without current limiting. The range of output voltages is from 2 to 37 V, and currents up to 150 mA are possible. For higher currents, an external pass transistor can be used.

Three-terminal regulators provide all regulation functions within a single package. They are available in either fixed or adjustable versions.

REVIEW QUESTIONS

1. Using a 12.6-V center-tapped power transformer, what possible no-load output voltages can you obtain from a filtered, unregulated power supply? (Ignore diode drops.) You should be able to name at least six. State what combination of rectifier and filter you would use to get each one.
2. What are the two most commonly used types of rectifier circuit? Give at least two reasons for their popularity.
3. Design a capacitor-filtered unregulated power supply capable of producing 24 V at 3 A with no more than 1% ripple and with 5% or better regulation.
4. Obtain an electronic distributor's catalog and select specific parts for the circuit designed for question 3: transformer, diodes, and capacitor.
5. What modifications would be necessary for the circuit you designed in question 3 in order to use an *LC* filter? What capacitance would be needed? What inductance would be necessary if the minimum load current is 100 mA? If the choke has 0.75-Ω winding resistance, what would the voltage regulation be? (Ignore the power transformer's resistance and the diodes' bulk resistance.)
6. What fault in a full-wave unregulated, capacitor-filtered power supply would cause the full-load voltage to drop and the ripple percentage to increase, even though the no-load voltage was normal? —
7. What three faults could cause a capacitor-filtered unregulated power supply to blow fuses?
8. Design a discrete shunt regulator for an output voltage of 15 V at 10 mA. Also specify the necessary unregulated input voltage.
9. Obtain an electronics distributor's catalog and find manufacturers' part numbers for the Zener diode and dropping resistor for the regulator you designed in question 8.
10. Calculate the total power dissipation and efficiency of the regulator you designed in question 8, for (a) no load, (b) 5 mA load, and (c) full load.
11. What fault would cause each of the following malfunctions of a discrete shunt regulator?
    (a) No output voltage. Input voltage is OK. Dropping resistor warm.
    (b) High output voltage.
    (c) No output voltage. Dropping resistor cool.
12. Design a discrete series regulator with feedback for an output of 18 V at 5 A. Use TIP31C transistors. Specify all component ratings and the thermal resistance of the heat sink. Calculate the necessary unregulated input voltage.
13. Calculate the efficiency of the regulator you designed for question 12 at loads of: (a) 1 A, (b) 3 A, and (c) 5 A.
14. What faults in the regulator you designed for question 12 could cause
    (a) high output voltage, (b) no output voltage, or (c) output voltage drops after regulator warms up?

15. Suppose 5.5-A constant-current limiting were added to the circuit you designed for question 12:

    (a) What would be the ohmic value of R_{sense}?

    (b) How would the ratings of the pass transistor and the heat sink have to change?

16. Name two advantages of (a) switching power supplies, (b) switching regulators.

17. In your own words, describe the operation of each of the three kinds of switching regulator.

18. What three special design problems are encountered in working with switching regulators that are not of concern in other regulator designs?

19. Design a regulator using a 723 and a pass transistor to meet the specifications listed in problem 12. Include foldback limiting so that $I_{knee} = 5.5$ A and $I_{sc} = 2$ A. Include all component ratings and the thermal resistance of the heat sink.

20. Sketch a circuit for each of the following:

    (a) a ± 15-V nontracking power supply using 78XX and 79XX regulators

    (b) a ± 15-V dual-tracking power supply

    Tell what the maximum output current and the voltage regulation would be for each circuit. Also, for each circuit, what would be the maximum mismatch possible between the absolute values of the positive and negative output voltages?

21. Suppose the output voltage of a three-terminal regulator is very low:

    (a) What faults in the power supply and/or regulator could cause the problem?

    (b) What could cause the problem, even though the power supply and regulator are functioning normally?

LAB EXPERIMENT—POWER-SUPPLY AND VOLTAGE-REGULATOR DESIGN AND OPERATION

Note:

This experiment will require several laboratory periods. Keep careful records so that you can make a complete, accurate lab report.

Objective:

To compare theory to actual measurements for each step of power-supply and voltage-regulator design.

Materials:

1 isolation transformer, 15-VA minimum capacity
1 12.6-V, 1-A power transformer with an AC power cord
4 2.5-A, 1000-V rectifiers
5 100-Ω, 10-W resistors
1 2200-μF, 50-V capacitor
1 7812 IC
1 723 IC
1 317T IC
1 TIP31C transistor
1 4-in.^{2} piece of aluminum drilled for a No. 4 screw, to act as a heat sink
1 No. 4-40 screw and nut
miscellaneous resistors

Procedure:

CAUTION!!!

The transformer used in this experiment will have 115 V AC connected to its primary. Do not touch leads carrying this potentially lethal voltage. Use an isolation transformer to supply the line voltage. Do not touch the AC leads on the secondary side of the transformer while power is applied. Do not depend upon unsoldered leads in the AC portions of this circuit.

1. Construct a bridge rectifier and connect it to the secondary of the power transformer. Carefully plug the transformer cord into the isolation transformer. Measure the DC output voltage. Unplug the transformer cord.
2. Connect the 2200-μF capacitor as a filter for the rectifier. Be sure to observe polarity markings. Apply power and measure the output voltage.
3. Calculate combinations of the 100-Ω, 10-W resistors to make dummy loads for your power supply that will vary from 500 to 20 Ω. Make a

(continued)

(continued from page 282)

chart in which you can record the output voltage for each of the following load resistances: 500 Ω, 400 Ω, 300 Ω, 200 Ω, 100 Ω, 75 Ω, 50 Ω, 33.3 Ω, 20 Ω. Be careful, since the resistors may get rather warm. Now connect the appropriate combinations of resistors, one at a time, and make the measurements. If your isolation transformer is adjustable, make sure that the input voltage to your power transformer stays at 115 V.

4. Mount the 7812 IC to the piece of aluminum, using the No. 4-40 screw. Connect the 7812 to the output of your power supply and repeat the measurements you made in step 3. Disconnect the 7812.

5. Design a circuit using the 723 and a pass transistor (the TIP31C) to duplicate the output characteristics (including constant-current limiting) of the 7812. Mount the transistor instead of the 7812 on the aluminum and connect your circuit to the output of the power supply. Now repeat the measurements you made in step 3. Disconnect your regulator.

6. Design a circuit using the 317T to duplicate the output characteristics of the 7812, except that you should provide for adjustment of the output voltage to exactly 12 V; the adjustment range is to be ±2 V. Mount the 317 T on the aluminum instead of the TIP 31C. Connect your circuit and verify that it works. Now adjust the output voltage to 12 V and repeat the measurements you made in step 3.

Analysis:

1. Calculate the expected output voltage from step 1. In your report, discuss possible causes of differences between the calculated and observed values.
2. Calculate the expected output voltages from step 3. Discuss possible causes for disagreement between actual and measured values.
3. Plot graphs of output voltage versus output current for:
   (a) the unregulated, filtered supply
   (b) the 7812-regulated supply
   (c) the 723-regulated supply
   (d) the 317T-regulated supply
4. From your graphs, determine the output voltage for each of the four circuits for a load current of 500 mA. From this, calculate the voltage regulation of each circuit. Discuss the differences between the circuits from a standpoint of voltage regulation. Also discuss causes of the decrease in the output voltage of the unregulated supply as load current increased.
5. Discuss any other advantages and disadvantages you can think of for each of the three regulator circuits compared to the others. In other words, under what circumstances might you choose the 7812 circuit? the 723 circuit? the 317T circuit?

Laboratory
Experiment

chapter seven

Active Filters

OBJECTIVES

Upon completing this chapter, you will be able to:

- Describe the characteristics of low-pass, high-pass, bandpass, and band-reject filters.
- Predict the operation of *RC* filters.
- Design active filters for the specific characteristics you desire.
- Utilize both standard and specialized ICs to build active filters.
- Troubleshoot active filter circuits.

THE FOUR BASIC FILTER TYPES

So far, when we have examined the frequency response of an op-amp circuit, we have assumed that it was desirable to have a gain that did not vary with frequency; that is, a flat frequency response. However, there are many applications in which certain frequency bands must be emphasized or rejected. An example is the RF and IF stages of a radio. These are tuned to let only a certain band of frequencies pass. When you want to listen to a station, you tune the radio so that the frequency of that station is centered in the band of frequencies that is allowed to pass. A circuit that passes certain frequencies more readily than others is called a *filter*. The frequencies that a certain filter allows to pass through are called that filter's *passband*. Those that cannot pass as easily are referred to as the *stopband*.

There are four basic types of filter circuits:

1. *Low-pass* filters pass low frequencies and reject high frequencies.
2. *High-pass* filters pass high frequencies and reject low frequencies.
3. *Bandpass* filters pass frequencies within a certain band and reject frequencies that fall above or below that band.
4. *Band-reject* or *notch* filters pass all frequencies of interest except for those within a certain band.

Figure 7–1 shows gain-vs.-frequency characteristics for each of the four basic types of filters. Notice that the highest specified gain is 0 dB, which is unity gain. This is because filter characteristics are usually graphed in a *normalized* fashion. This

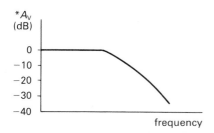

FIGURE 7–1A: Low-Pass

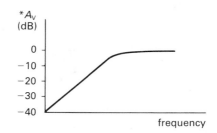

FIGURE 7–1B: High-Pass

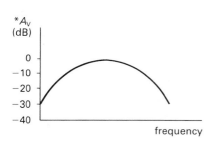

FIGURE 7–1C: Bandpass

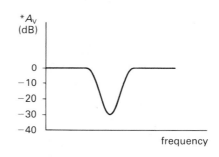

FIGURE 7–1D: Notch

*Normalized

FIGURE 7–1: Gain-vs.-Frequency Curves for Basic Filters

means that the gain shown on the graph at any frequency is referenced to the gain at the center of that filter's passband. Many filter circuits have unity gain at the center of the passband. For those filters that have a gain greater or less than unity, the normalized gain at any frequency is just the actual gain at that frequency divided by the gain at the center of the passband:

$$A_{V.normalized} = \frac{A_{V.actual}}{A_{V.center}} \tag{7.01}$$

Figure 7–2 illustrates this concept. Part A of this figure shows a graph of the gain-vs.-frequency characteristic for a bandpass filter. The center of the passband is 1 kHz. The gain at that frequency is 10. Part B shows a normalized graph for the same filter. Notice that the curve has the same shape, but the vertical axis has been relabeled to show 0 dB normalized gain at 1 kHz. This makes it easy to see by how many dB the filter rejects signals at other frequencies, such as 100 Hz (20 dB in this case) or 10 kHz (40 dB). Often when the gain of a circuit is less than unity, it is referred to as *attenuation*. Thus a gain of −30 dB could also be called a 30-dB attenuation. Sometimes the frequency axis of a response curve is normalized, as shown in Fig. 7–2C. This means that all frequencies on the horizontal axis are expressed as a fraction or multiple of the filter's actual critical frequency.

Filters can be built from very simple components such as resistors, capacitors, and inductors. Remember that the reactance of an inductor varies directly with fre-

Sidebar

FREQUENCY RESPONSES OF FIVE PASSIVE FILTERS

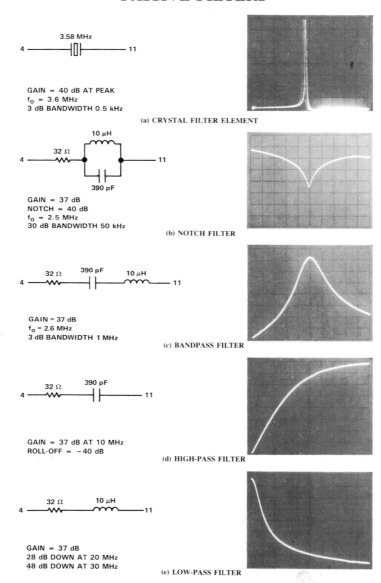

3.58 MHz

4 ———|□|——— 11

GAIN = 40 dB AT PEAK
f_o = 3.6 MHz
3 dB BANDWIDTH 0.5 kHz

(a) CRYSTAL FILTER ELEMENT

10 µH

32 Ω

4 ——/\/\——•——•—— 11

390 pF

GAIN = 37 dB
NOTCH = 40 dB
f_o = 2.5 MHz
30 dB BANDWIDTH 50 kHz

(b) NOTCH FILTER

32 Ω   390 pF   10 µH

4 ——/\/\——|(——∿∿—— 11

GAIN = 37 dB
f_o = 2.6 MHz
3 dB BANDWIDTH 1 MHz

(c) BANDPASS FILTER

32 Ω   390 pF

4 ——/\/\——|(—— 11

GAIN = 37 dB AT 10 MHz
ROLL-OFF = −40 dB

(d) HIGH-PASS FILTER

32 Ω   10 µH

4 ——/\/\——∿∿—— 11

GAIN = 37 dB
28 dB DOWN AT 20 MHz
48 dB DOWN AT 30 MHz

(e) LOW-PASS FILTER

Reproduced from *Linear and Interface Circuits Applications* (Courtesy of Texas Instruments, Incorporated).

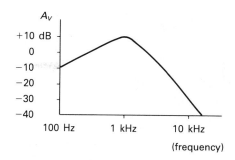

FIGURE 7–2A: Nonnormalized

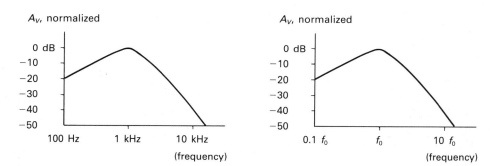

FIGURE 7–2B: Gain Normalized   **FIGURE 7–2C:** Gain and Frequency Normalized

FIGURE 7–2: Normalization of Response Curves

quency, that of a capacitor varies inversely with frequency, and resistance does not vary appreciably with frequency. (It is true that skin effect and electromagnetic losses cause a dependence of resistance upon frequency in certain cases, but these cases can be ignored for our purposes.) The marked dependence of inductive and capacitive reactance upon frequency enable them to be used in filters. Figure 7–3 shows schematics of simple low-pass and high-pass filters, made in each of three different ways: as *RC* circuits, as *RL* circuits, and as *LC* circuits. Notice that each filter is just a voltage divider. In fact, the gain of each filter at any frequency can be calculated by using the voltage-divider rule. For example, the output of the low-pass filter is taken across the capacitor. Thus, according to the voltage-divider rule, the output voltage is

$$V_{OUT} = V_{IN} \frac{X_C}{Z}$$

$$= V_{IN} \frac{X_C}{\sqrt{R^2 + X_C^2}} \angle -\arctan(X_C/R)$$

Since $A_V = V_{OUT}/V_{IN}$,

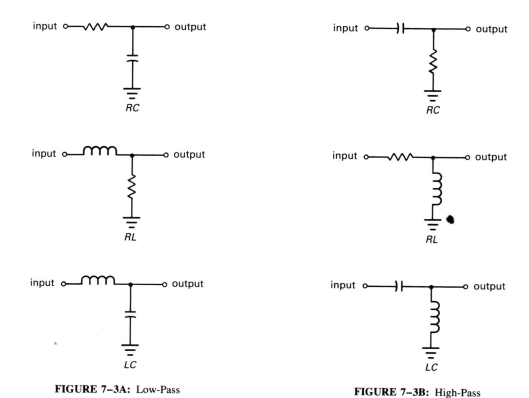

FIGURE 7–3A: Low-Pass

FIGURE 7–3B: High-Pass

FIGURE 7–3: Passive Low- and High-Pass Filters

$$|A_V| = \frac{X_C}{\sqrt{R^2 + X_C^2}} \tag{7.02}$$

The gain equations for each of the other configurations can be derived similarly.

EXAMPLE

Problem

Calculate the gain at 10 kHz of a low-pass filter made up of a 1.5-nF capacitor and a 10-kΩ resistor.

Solution

1. The reactance of the capacitor at 10 kHz is

$$X_C = \frac{1}{2\pi f C} = 10.6 \ \text{k}\Omega$$

2. Using equation 7.02, we find that

$$|A_v| = \frac{(10.6 \text{ k}\Omega)}{\sqrt{(10 \text{ k}\Omega)^2 + (10.6 \text{ k}\Omega)^2}} = 0.727$$

There is an easier way to learn the basic filter configurations than just memorizing the circuits shown in Fig. 7–3. Notice that each filter has a component that is in series between input and output (the *series element*) and a component that is in parallel with the load (the *shunt element*). Capacitors have a low reactance at high frequencies. Thus, filters in which a capacitor is the series element will pass high frequencies. Conversely, if a capacitor is the shunt element, high-frequency current will be shunted to ground, resulting in a low-pass output characteristic. Inductive reactance is low at low frequencies. Therefore, if an inductor is the series element, low frequencies are passed; if it is the shunt element, lows are shunted to ground.

There are two ways to build a bandpass or notch filter from passive components. The first is to use a low-pass and a high-pass filter. In Fig. 7–4A, a low-pass filter that passes frequencies below 1 kHz is connected in cascade with a high-pass filter that passes frequencies above 800 Hz. The result is a bandpass filter that passes frequencies between 800 Hz and 1 kHz. In part B of the figure, a twin-tee filter is shown. In this filter, R_1 and C_3 function as a low-pass filter. This low-pass filter is connected in parallel with a high-pass filter made up of C_1 and R_3. There is a narrow band of frequencies that are not passed by either the low-pass or the high-pass filter,

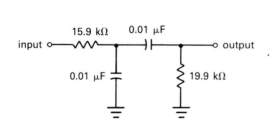

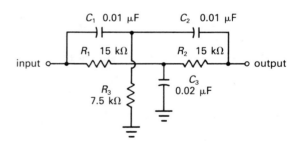

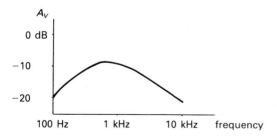

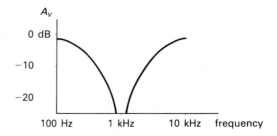

FIGURE 7–4A: *RC* Bandpass Filter   **FIGURE 7–4B:** *RC* Notch Filter

FIGURE 7–4: Passive Bandpass and Notch Filters

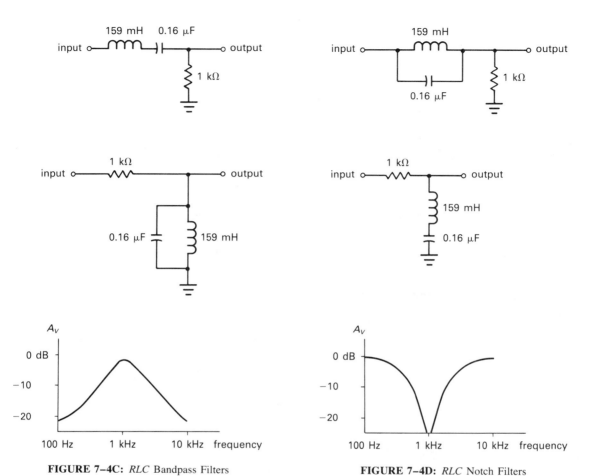

FIGURE 7–4C: *RLC* Bandpass Filters

FIGURE 7–4D: *RLC* Notch Filters

giving a notch filter response. This filter rejects frequencies centered about 1 kHz. R_2 and C_2 provide isolation to keep the low-pass and high-pass sections from interacting.

The second way of building passive bandpass and notch filters is to use resonant circuits. Figure 7–4C shows a series-resonant circuit used as the series element of one type of bandpass filter, and a parallel-resonant circuit used as the shunt element of another type. Figure 7–4D shows notch filters made from resonant circuits.

FILTER SPECIFICATIONS

Break Frequencies

In addition to the type of filter (low-pass, high-pass, bandpass, or notch), there are several other important characteristics by which filters are specified. The most obvious is the frequency at which the filter takes effect. In Fig. 7–1, the low-pass and high-pass filters each had a small frequency range in which their response began to deviate from unity. With filters, as with amplifiers, the frequency at which the filter is considered to begin to have an effect is that frequency at which the gain is 3 dB lower than the gain in the middle of the passband. This frequency is variously called the *break frequency,* the *critical frequency,* the *cutoff frequency,* or the *half-power point* of the filter. For simplicity, we will refer to this frequency as the break frequency.

Also notice in Fig. 7–1 that bandpass and notch filters each have two break frequencies, an upper and a lower one. These are also −3-dB frequencies. *A break frequency, then, defines a point at which the passband meets the stopband for any filter.*

The value of the components needed to build a simple filter with a certain break frequency can be calculated from the gain equation for that filter. For example, using the *RC* low-pass filter, we have

$$|A_V| = \frac{X_C}{\sqrt{R^2 + X_C^2}} \tag{7.02}$$

Taking the inverse $\log_{10}$ of −3 and dividing by 20, we find that a gain of −3 dB is a numerical gain of 0.707. Thus the gain at the break frequency is 0.707, and

$$0.707 = \frac{X_C}{\sqrt{R^2 + X_C^2}}$$

Squaring both sides of this equation, we obtain

$$0.5 = \frac{X_C^2}{R^2 + X_C^2}$$

Clearing the fraction and collecting terms gives us

$$0.5X_C^2 = 0.5R^2$$

or,

$$X_C = R \tag{7.03}$$

We can now substitute $1/(2\pi f C)$ for X_C and solve for f_b, the break frequency:

$$\frac{1}{2\pi f C} = R$$
$$2\pi f R C = 1$$
$$f = \frac{1}{2\pi R C} = f_b \tag{7.04}$$

EXAMPLE

Problem

Find the break frequency of an *RC* filter with $R = 10\ \text{k}\Omega$ and $C = 1.5\ \text{nF}$.

Solution

Using equation 7.04,

$$f = \frac{1}{2\pi RC} = \frac{1}{2\pi \cdot 10 \text{ k}\Omega \cdot 1.5 \text{ nF}} = 10.6 \text{ kHz}$$

This correlates well with our earlier calculation in which we found that the gain at 10 kHz, just below the break frequency, is 0.727.

By the way, it turns out that equations 7.03 and 7.04 also work for the *RC* high-pass filter.

Since most active filters use only resistive and capacitive elements, we will not develop the equations for *RL* and *LC* filters here. They are available from any standard text on passive filters.

Cutoff Slope, Q, and Notch Depth

A second characteristic of all filters is the rate at which the gain changes as frequency is changed beyond the break frequency. Table 7–A lists the gain of the low-pass filter that we used for our examples (10 kΩ and 1.5 nF) for frequencies from $0.1f_b$ to $20f_b$. Notice that the gain is inversely proportional to frequency once the break point is passed. For instance, the gain at $2f_b$ is 0.44, which is very close to twice the gain at $4f_b$. Since a doubling of frequency represents one octave, and a halving of gain represents a change of −6 dB, we say that the *cutoff slope* of the gain curve for this filter is −6 dB/octave. Also notice that the gain at $20f_b$ is very close to one-tenth of the gain at $2f_b$. A factor of ten in frequency is referred to as a *decade*. A factor of one-tenth in voltage gain is −20 dB. Thus we can also describe the cutoff slope of this filter as −20 dB/decade. Both methods of description are used.

TABLE 7–A Gain versus Frequency for a 10.6-kHz Low-Pass Filter

FREQUENCY	GAIN
$0.1 f_b$	0.99
$0.2 f_b$	0.98
$0.3 f_b$	0.95
$0.4 f_b$	0.92
$0.7 f_b$	0.81
f_b	0.71
$2 f_b$	0.44
$3 f_b$	0.31
$4 f_b$	0.24
$7 f_b$	0.14
$10 f_b$	0.099
$20 f_b$	0.049

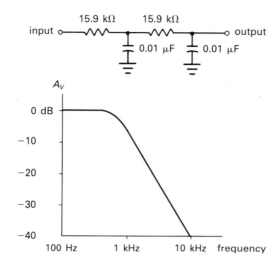

FIGURE 7–5: Second-Order *RC* Low-Pass Filter

Figure 7–5 shows two *RC* low-pass filter sections cascaded together. Since they have identical components, each has the same break frequency. Let us calculate the gain of the composite filter at $2f_b$, $4f_b$, and $20f_b$. Since the gains of each filter section are already tabulated in Table 7–A, we can simply multiply the gains of the two sections at each frequency together to obtain the composite gain. This is the same approach as we take when figuring the gain of a multistage amplifier:

$$2f_b: \quad 0.44 \cdot 0.44 = 0.19$$
$$4f_b: \quad 0.24 \cdot 0.24 = 0.058$$
$$20f_b: \quad 0.049 \cdot 0.049 = 0.0024$$

Notice that the gain at $4f_b$ is about one-fourth of the gain at $2f_b$. Since a factor of one-fourth in voltage gain corresponds to -12 dB, this implies a slope of -12 dB/octave. Likewise, the gain at $20f_b$ is about one one-hundredth of the gain at $2f_b$, implying a slope of -40 dB/decade. (The deeper you move into the stopband of a filter, the more nearly the actual cutoff slope matches the theoretical slope: 6 dB/octave for one section, 12 dB for two sections, and so on).

An *RC* filter having two sections, as shown in Fig. 7–5, is called a *second-order* filter. A single-section *RC* filter is a first-order filter. *The order of a filter corresponds to the number of reactive devices in the filter*. Therefore, a single-section *LC* filter is a second-order filter, because it has two reactive devices, even though it only has one section. As we observed above, *the ultimate cutoff slope of a filter in dB/octave is just 6 dB multiplied by the order of the filter. The cutoff slope in dB/decade is 20 dB multiplied by the order of the filter.* Thus, for example, a fourth-order filter would have a cutoff slope of 24 dB/octave or 80 dB/decade.

Cutoff slopes become essentially constant at frequencies above $5f_b$ for low-pass filters, and below $0.2f_b$ for high-pass filters. However, the slopes for bandpass and

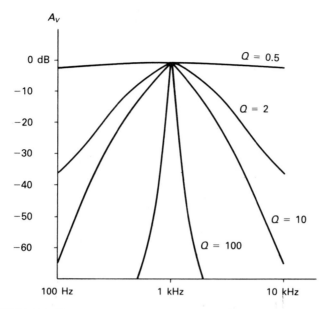

FIGURE 7–6A: Response Curves of Bandpass Filters with Different Q's

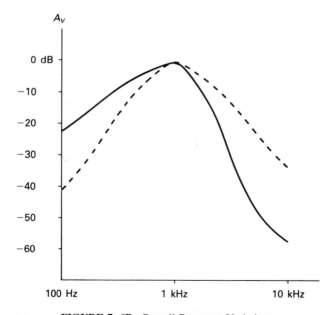

FIGURE 7–6B: Overall Response Variations

FIGURE 7–6: Bandpass Filter Characteristics

notch filters are not always so simple. Rather than attempting to specify the cutoff slopes of these kinds of filters, another method is used. It is to specify the Q of the filter. Recall from your study of resonant circuits that Q (which stands for *quality factor*) is the ratio of the center frequency (f_0) to the bandwidth of a resonant circuit:

$$Q = \frac{f_0}{\text{BW}} \qquad (7.05)$$

Figure 7–6A shows several response curves for bandpass filters. Each has the same center frequency, but they have different Q's. Notice that the higher the Q is, the narrower is the passband. Figure 7–6B shows two response curves that have the same center frequency and Q but different overall shapes. This graph shows that while f_0 and Q do not completely describe the response curve of a bandpass filter, they do pretty well define the extent of the passband and the general shape of the passband response. Where more information is needed about the response skirts outside the passband, approximate cutoff slopes are sometimes given. Although the graphs in Figs. 7–6A and B are drawn for bandpass filters, the same concepts also apply to notch filters.

EXAMPLE

Problem

(a) What is the bandwidth of a filter whose f_0 is 5 kHz and whose Q is 40?
(b) What are the upper and lower break frequencies of the filter described in (a)?

Solution

(a) Since $Q = f_0/\text{BW}$,

$$\text{BW} = \frac{f_0}{Q} = \frac{5 \text{ kHz}}{40} = 125 \text{ Hz} \qquad (7.05)$$

(b) For high-Q circuits, the break frequencies are located approximately symmetrically about f_0, so the lower break frequency would be

$$f_{b1} = f_0 - \frac{\text{BW}}{2} = 5000 \text{ Hz} - 62.5 \text{ Hz} = 4937.5 \text{ Hz}$$

Similarly,

$$f_{b2} = f_0 + \frac{\text{BW}}{2} = 5062.5 \text{ Hz}$$

(To be precise, f_0 is geometrically rather than arithmetically centered, as discussed later in this chapter. However, for high-Q circuits, there is little difference between the two methods of calculating f_b.)

Notch filters have another specification in addition to f_0, passband gain, and Q. This specification is *notch depth,* or the maximum rejection (in dB) of signals at frequency f_0.

Passband Flatness and Pulse Response

The response curves of simple filters change gradually from straight horizontal lines to straight sloped lines. (That is, the sloped lines are straight if the graphs are plotted with a logarithmic frequency scale, as is usually done.) However, some more complex filters have some variation in response near the break frequency, as shown in Fig. 7–7. Because of its appearance on the graph, this sort of variation is called *passband ripple*. Passband ripple (as well as stopband ripple, for that matter) can occur in any second- or higher-order filter in which the break frequencies of the individual sections are not the same. In the early theoretical investigations of passive filters, it was found that certain modifications of the response near the break frequency were possible. These modifications were named after the engineers who first described their properties. The most common are Bessel, Chebyshev, and Butterworth filters. The response curves of low-pass second-order filters of each type are shown in Fig. 7–8. Notice that the ultimate cutoff slope (above $2f_0$) of each of these filters is the same: -40 dB/decade. However, the Bessel filter begins a significant rolloff at a frequency far below f_0. The Butterworth filter has the flattest response of the three within the passband, so it is sometimes called a *maximally flat* filter. The various Chebyshev filters are named in accordance with their total passband gain variation, or *peak-to-peak ripple*. They all provide a more rapid rolloff just above f_0 at the expense of having gain ripples within the passband.

Because all filters contain reactive components, and reactive components store energy, all filters cause some distortion of pulse waves. Naturally, since a pulse is composed of a fundamental frequency and harmonics, a filter that attenuates any of these frequency components would be expected to change the waveshape. However, in addition to the effects caused by attenuation of certain frequency components, there are other effects caused by the phase response of the filter. Back on page 287, when we were developing equation 7.02, we wrote a complete expression for the output voltage of a first-order low-pass filter; this expression included a phase term:

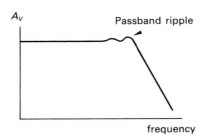

FIGURE 7–7: Filter Curve with Passband Ripple

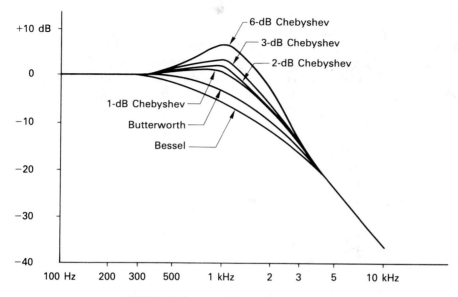

FIGURE 7–8: Second-Order Filter Responses

$$\theta_{LP} = -\arctan\left(\frac{X_C}{R}\right)$$

This can be simplified using the trig identity $-\arctan(A/B) = \arctan(B/A)$; Thus

$$\theta_{LP} = \arctan\left(\frac{R}{X_C}\right) = \arctan(2\pi fRC) \qquad (7.06)$$

As an interesting sideline, notice that the argument of the phase term, $2\pi fRC$, can be factored into $(f)(2\pi RC)$. And since the second factor is just the inverse of the expression for f_b (from equation 7.04), the phase angle can also be expressed as

$$\theta_{LP} = \arctan\left(\frac{f}{f_b}\right) \qquad (7.07)$$

The phase angle of a high-pass RC filter can be predicted in the same way. The phase angle is

$$\theta_{HP} = \arctan\left(\frac{X_C}{R}\right) = \arctan\left(\frac{1}{2\pi fRC}\right) \qquad (7.08)$$

$$= \arctan\left(\frac{f_b}{f}\right) \qquad (7.09)$$

Figures 7–9A and B show the results of calculating and plotting the values for the phase shift of a first-order low-pass filter for frequencies from $0.1f_b$ to $10f_b$. Notice that the phase shift at f_b is 45°, and that the maximum phase shift approaches

90°. If we cascade two first-order low-pass filters to make a second-order filter, the phase response will depend upon the exact values for the f_b's of the individual sections. Thus Bessel, Butterworth, and the various Chebyshev filters will have different phase responses, as shown in Fig. 7–9B. Notice that for all these second-order filters, the phase shift at f_b is 90°, and the ultimate phase shift approaches 180°. However, the rate at which the phase changes near f_b is quite different for the different

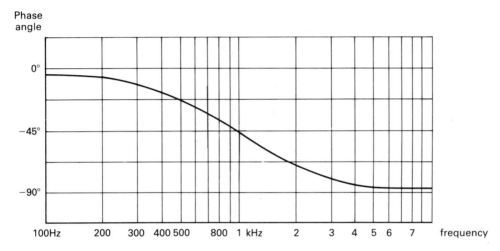

FIGURE 7–9A: Phase Response of First-Order Low-Pass Filters

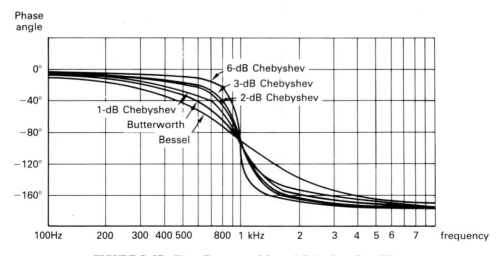

FIGURE 7–9B: Phase Response of Second-Order Low-Pass Filters

FIGURE 7–9: Phase Response of Low-Pass Filters

filters. Since phase shift is really a representation of the time response of a circuit, you can readily understand that a wave made of many frequency components will have the time relations of those components changed when the wave is passed through a circuit having a frequency-dependent phase shift. These changes in the time relationships cause overshoot in a pulse wave. Figure 7–10 shows the overshoot produced in a 5 kHz square wave when it is passed through a 10-kHz second-order low-

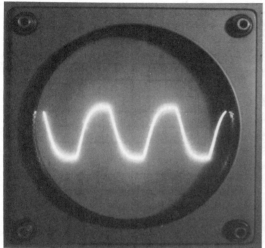

FIGURE 7–10A: Bessel

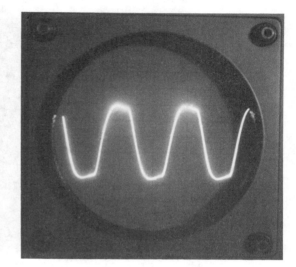

FIGURE 7–10B: Butterworth

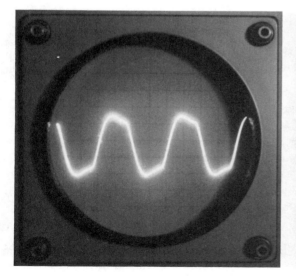

FIGURE 7–10C: 1-dB Chebyshev

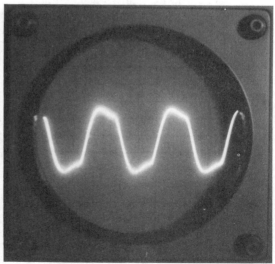

FIGURE 7–10D: 2-dB Chebyshev

FIGURE 7–10: Square-Wave Distortion by Low-Pass Filters

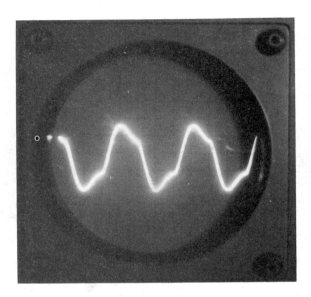

FIGURE 7–10E: 3-dB Chebyshev

pass filter. Oscilloscope traces are shown for Bessel, Butterworth, and 1-, 2-, and 3-dB Chebyshev filters. Notice that the Bessel filter causes the least distortion of the pulse wave, and the 3-dB Chebyshev causes the greatest distortion. In fact, if you compare Fig. 7–10 with Fig. 7–9, you will notice that the sharper the initial cutoff slope a filter has, the greater the pulse distortion will be. (Bessel filters are sometimes called *maximally flat time-delay filters*.)

Because of its maximally flat in-band response, and because it has the second-best pulse response, the Butterworth filter is the most widely used type of second- or higher-order filter. Later in this chapter, tables will be given that will allow you to design Bessel, Butterworth, or Chebyshev filters if you need to for a particular application.

HOW ACTIVE FILTERS WORK—BASIC CONCEPTS

So far all the filters that we have discussed have been built entirely with passive components; that is, components that have no gain. While a great many passive filters are used, especially for high frequencies, the majority of filters used at audio frequencies or below are active filters. *An active filter is one that includes some sort of amplifying device.* There are two main reasons for the use of active filters. The first is that in order for a passive filter to perform properly, it must feed its output into a very high impedance. A low-impedance load connected to the output of a passive filter acts as a resistor in parallel with the shunt element, thus changing the tuning of the filter. Figure 7–11 shows a basic low-pass and a basic high-pass active filter. As you will notice, each of these filters simply consists of a simple *RC* filter followed by a buffer amplifier. The buffer amplifier provides the required high input

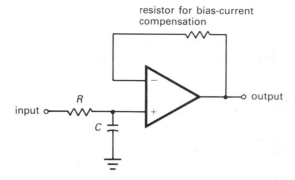

FIGURE 7–11A: First-Order Low-Pass Active Filter

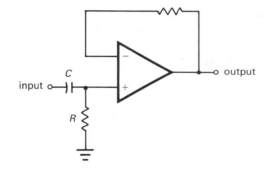

FIGURE 7–11B: First-Order High-Pass Active Filter

FIGURE 7–11: First-Order Active Filters

impedance needed to make the *RC* filter section perform as designed. (In virtually all active filters, capacitors are used exclusively as the reactive components, thus eliminating the bulk and expense of inductors.)

Since the frequency characteristic of each of the active filters shown in Fig. 7–11 is determined by the *RC* section, equation 7.04 can be used to find or determine the break frequency. The passband gain is simply the gain of the amplifier: $1 + R_f/R_g$. Since a unity-gain amplifier is shown in Fig. 7–11, these particular filters will have unity passband gain. And since the circuit only has one reactive component, it is a first-order filter and has a cutoff slope of 6 dB/octave or 20 dB/decade.

EXAMPLE

Problem

Design a first-order high-pass filter that will have a break frequency of 3 kHz and a passband gain of 50.

Solution

1. We will use the circuit of Fig. 7–11B, but with R_g added so as to provide gain. Let us choose $R = 10$ kΩ. Then we find C by solving equation 7.04:

$$f_b = \frac{1}{2\pi RC} \tag{7.04}$$

$$C = \frac{1}{2\pi Rf} = \frac{1}{(2\pi \cdot 10\ \text{k}\Omega \cdot 3\ \text{kHz})} = 0.0053\ \mu\text{F}$$

These components set the break frequency.

2. For bias-current reasons we will set $R_g = R = 10$ kΩ. This choice makes $R_f = 50R_g = 500$ kΩ.

PRACTICAL REALIZATIONS OF HIGHER-ORDER ACTIVE FILTERS

Second-Order Filters

Very often the cutoff slope required for an active filter is greater than that provided by a first-order filter. For these applications, the addition of another RC section converts the circuit to a second-order filter. As shown in Fig. 7–12, there is no need to add another op amp. These circuits utilize positive feedback through C_1 (low-pass) or R (high-pass) to provide the additional frequency-response shaping. In order to prevent the positive feedback from causing the circuit to oscillate, sufficient negative feedback is provided by R_f and R_g so that the net feedback remains negative at all frequencies. The passband gain of either circuit is just $1 + R_f/R_g$. The break frequency of either circuit is

$$f_b = \frac{1}{2\pi\sqrt{R_1C_1R_2C_2}} \tag{7.10}$$

Recall that the tuning of the two RC pairs, R_1C_1 and R_2C_2, determines not only the break frequency of the final filter, but also the filter family (Butterworth, Bessel, Chebyshev, and so on). The particular characteristic of a second- or higher-order filter that determines the family is called the *damping factor*. The Bessel filter has a damping factor of 1.732; the Butterworth, 1.414, and the 1-, 2-, and 3-dB Chebyshev, 1.06, 0.866, and 0.766, respectively. Higher damping factors imply three things: less steep cutoff slopes near f_b, less square-wave distortion, and less sudden changes of phase as frequency is changed near f_b. The equations for the damping factor of the circuits shown in Fig. 7–12 are as follows:

$$\alpha_{LP} = \frac{R_2C_2 + R_1C_2 + R_1C_1(1 - A_0)}{\sqrt{R_1R_2C_1C_2}} \tag{7.11}$$

$$\alpha_{HP} = \frac{R_1C_1 + R_1C_2 + R_2C_2(1 - A_0)}{\sqrt{R_1R_2C_1C_2}}$$

(7.12)

where α_{LP} and α_{HP} are the damping factors for low-pass and high-pass filters, respectively, and A_0 is the passband gain.

Because the passband gain of a feedback filter affects the filter performance, designing a filter using the circuits shown in Fig. 7–12 can present formidable difficulties. In addition, there is more than one combination of components that can be used to provide a given filter characteristic. Fortunately, pioneering work has been done that allows us to greatly simplify the design process. In particular, in a paper published in the early 1950s, Messrs. Sallen and Key suggested the advisability of making both resistors equal in a second-order active filter, and making both capacitors equal also. Doing so simplifies equation 7.10 to

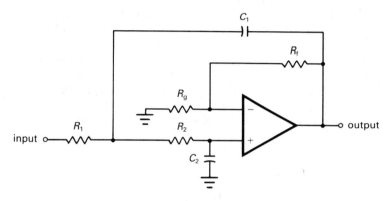

FIGURE 7–12A: Low-Pass

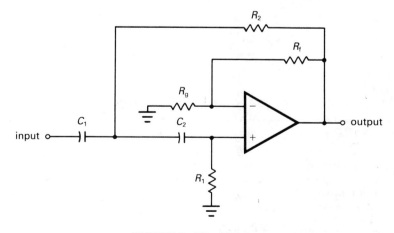

FIGURE 7–12B: High-Pass

FIGURE 7–12: Second-Order Active Filters

$$f_b = \frac{1}{2\pi RC} \qquad (7.13)$$

A side effect of the simplicity provided by the Sallen-Key equal-component circuit is that the passband gain is no longer an independent variable. Once you have specified the filter family, you have tacitly agreed to a certain passband gain. This is because the damping factor of this circuit is controlled only by the gain:

$$\alpha = 3 - A_0 \qquad (7.14)$$

Of course, the gain is set by the choice of R_f and R_g, as mentioned earlier. Thus the value of these two resistors sets the damping factor of a Sallen-Key equal-component filter.

If you look carefully at Fig. 7–8, you will notice another difference between the different filter families besides the response shape near f_b. Only the Butterworth filter has a gain reduction of exactly 3 dB at f_b. In fact, the gain is *greatest* at f_b for the Chebyshev filters! And yet all of the curves are supposed to represent filters having the same break frequency. This peculiarity is caused by the fact that each filter family's tuning has an effect upon the attenuation at the break frequency. Since all of the characteristic curves match at frequencies above $5f_b$, all these filters can legitimately be considered to be 1-kHz filters. In order to account mathematically for this peculiarity, *frequency-correction factors* have been introduced. There are frequency-correction factors for both low-pass and high-pass filters; they are denoted by k_{LP} and k_{HP}, respectively. The low-pass and high-pass factors are related by

$$k_{HP} = \frac{1}{k_{LP}}$$

The frequency-correction factors for each type of filter are given in Table 7–B. With the use of these factors, equation 7.13 can be rewritten to accurately express the break frequency of any family of filter:

$$f_b = \frac{k}{2\pi RC} \qquad (7.15)$$

TABLE 7–B   Second-Order Filter Damping and Correction Factors

FAMILY	α	k_{LP}*
Bessel	1.732	0.786
Butterworth	1.414	1
0.5-dB Chebyshev	1.158	0.574
1-dB Chebyshev	1.054	0.673
2-dB Chebyshev	0.866	0.779
3-dB Chebyshev	0.766	0.841

*$k_{HP} = 1/k_{LP}$

EXAMPLE

Problem

Design a second-order Butterworth active low-pass filter having a break frequency of 10 kHz. Then indicate what design modifications would be necessary to change the design to a 3-dB Chebyshev filter. Finally, repeat the designs for corresponding high-pass filters.

Solution

1. First, we will select a convenient value for C, since it is easier to match desired values of resistance than capacitance. Let $C = 0.01$ μF. Then we can solve equation 7.15 for R:

$$R = \frac{k_{LP}}{2\pi f C}$$

$$\textit{Butterworth:} \quad R = \frac{1}{2\pi \cdot 10^4 \text{ Hz} \cdot 10^{-8} \text{ F}} = 1592 \ \Omega$$

$$\textit{3-dB Chebyshev:} \quad R = \frac{0.841}{2\pi \cdot 10^4 \text{ Hz} \cdot 10^{-8} \text{ F}} = 1338 \ \Omega$$

2. Next, we will set the gain. Let $R_g = 1$ kΩ. The required gain is $A_0 = 3 - \alpha$.

$$\textit{Butterworth:} \quad A_0 = 3 - 1.414 = 1.586, \quad \text{so} \quad R_f/R_g = 0.586.$$

This means that $R_f = 0.586$ kΩ.

$$\textit{3-dB Chebyshev:} \quad A_0 = 3 - 0.766 = 2.234, \quad \text{so} \quad R_f = 1.234 \text{ kΩ.}$$

3. For the high-pass filters, the gains are the same, so R_f and R_g will be the same. Also, we can use the same value for C. In fact, the Butterworth design will use the same value of R also. However, since $k_{HP} = 1/k_{LP}$, the Chebyshev design will require a different value of R:

$$R_{\text{Chebyshev}} = \frac{1/0.841}{2\pi \cdot 10^4 \text{ Hz} \cdot 10^{-8} \text{ F}} = 1893 \ \Omega$$

As shown by the above example, active filters can require odd-valued resistors. The importance of the resistors having the correct values depends upon the application. An error of -10% in R_f in the preceding design for the 3-dB Chebyshev filter would result in a gain of

$$A_0 = 1 + \frac{R_f}{R_g} = 1 + \frac{(0.9)(1.234 \text{ kΩ})}{1 \text{ kΩ}} = 2.111$$

From equation 7.14, we find that this would give a damping factor of

$$\alpha = 3 - A_0 = 0.889 \qquad (7.14)$$

As you can see from table 7–B, this would essentially change the design to a 2-dB Chebyshev filter. Errors in the values of R and C will affect the accuracy of the break frequency in direct proportion to the percentage error. Thus, for accurate designs, resistors having tolerances of $\pm 2\%$ or closer are needed. Using close-tolerance resistors, in turn, eases the problem of finding the odd values that the equations often call for.

An often-overlooked part of the component-tolerance problem as related to active filters is the tolerance of the capacitors used. Some capacitors in common use have tolerances as great as $\pm 20\%$. Using an off-value capacitor will result in a shifting of the break frequency; it will not affect the family of the filter. But if the break frequency must be carefully controlled, the capacitors should be low-tolerance types or should be individually measured.

Third-Order and Higher-Order Filters

Active filters of orders higher than second can be built using combinations of the first-order and second-order circuits already discussed. It is not practical to build a third- or higher-order filter with a single op amp. In order to design higher-order filters, you can use the configurations and damping and correction factors provided in Table 7–C.

The response curves for higher-order 3-dB Chebyshev high-pass filters are illustrated in Fig. 7–13. Notice that the number of ripples in the passband increases as the order of the filter is increased.

EXAMPLE

Problem

Design a filter to reject induced 60-Hz hum by at least 50 dB, while passing signals above 120 Hz with essentially no attenuation. Maximum passband ripple is 3 dB.

Solution

1. We will use a Chebyshev filter, since the rejection at $0.5f_b$ of the other families is not as great. From Fig. 7–13, we can see that a fifth-order filter is required. From Table 7–C, we find that a fifth-order filter can be built from two second-order filters and a first-order filter.
2. Using a 0.1-μF capacitor for C in the first-order filter, we can solve equation 7.04 for the correct value of R to give $f_b = 120$ Hz:

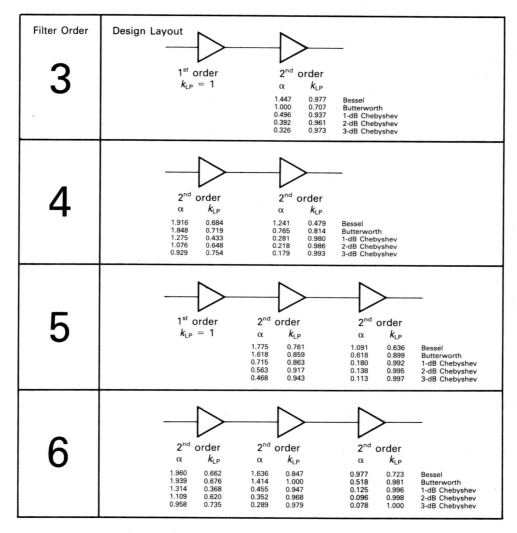

TABLE 7–C Third- and Higher-Order Alpha and k Factors

$$f_b = \frac{1}{2\pi RC} \tag{7.04}$$

$$R = \frac{1}{2\pi f_b C} = \frac{1}{2\pi \cdot 10^{-7}\,\text{F} \cdot 120\,\text{Hz}} = 13{,}263\;\Omega$$

We will also use a 13,263-Ω feedback resistor for bias-current compensation. No R_g will be used, so the gain of the first-order filter will be unity.

3. For the first second-order filter, the table tells us that α will be 0.468, so the passband gain becomes

$$A_0 = 3 - \alpha = 3 - 0.468 = 2.532$$

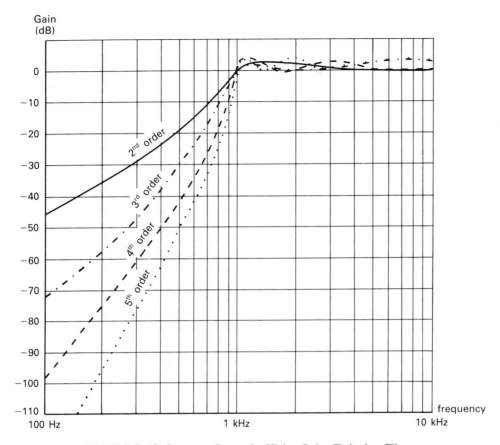

FIGURE 7–13: Response Curves for Higher-Order Chebyshev Filters

Since the gain is $1 + R_f/R_g$, if we use 1 kΩ for R_g, R_f becomes

$$R_f = R_g(A_0 - 1) = (1 \text{ k}\Omega)(2.532 - 1) = 1.532 \text{ k}\Omega$$

Using 0.1 μF for C in the filter network, we can solve equation 7.15 for R:

$$R = \frac{k}{2\pi f C} = \frac{0.943}{2\pi \cdot 120 \text{ Hz} \cdot 10^{-7} \text{ F}} = 12.5 \text{ k}\Omega$$

4. For the second second-order filter, α is 0.113, making the gain

$$A_0 = 3 - \alpha = 3 - 0.113 = 2.887 \tag{7.14}$$

If we use $R_g = 1$ kΩ, this calls for $R_f = 1.887$ kΩ. Again we will use 0.1 F for C; thus

$$R = \frac{0.997}{2\pi f C} = 13.22 \text{ k}\Omega$$

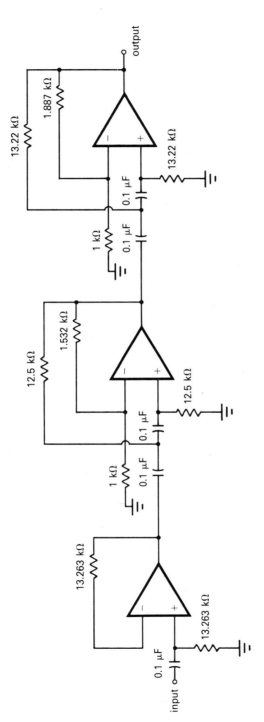

FIGURE 7–14: Fifth-Order 120-Hz High-Pass 3-dB Chebyshev Filter

The total gain is the product of the two stage gains:

$$A_{tot} = 2.532 \cdot 2.887 = 7.309$$

The completed circuit is shown in Fig. 7–14.

Notch and Bandpass Filters

There are many applications in which a filter is required to eliminate or select a certain narrow band of frequencies. For these applications, notch and bandpass filters are needed. It is possible to make either of these types of filter by cascading a high-pass and a low-pass filter. Cascaded filters are occasionally used in order to obtain a very wide-bandwidth notch or bandpass. For these purposes, the design is performed just as was illustrated in the previous section. For most purposes, though, the bandwidth required of a notch or bandpass filter is small. There are simpler designs for narrowband filters than those involving the low-pass/high-pass combination.

Figure 7–15 shows a circuit and corresponding response curves for a single-op-amp bandpass filter. The bandpass filter consists of a high-pass section (R_3C_2) and a low-pass feedback section (R_1C_1). By controlling the break frequencies of the two *RC* sections, filters can be built having Q's from unity up to a practical maximum of about 20. Figure 7–15B shows response curves for this type of filter, for a center frequency of 1 kHz, and for Q's from 1 to 20. Notice that regardless of the Q, the ultimate cutoff slope is 6 dB/octave. This is to be expected, since the low-pass and high-pass filters are both first-order types. The higher-Q versions, however, do have a steeper initial cutoff slope for the first 20 dB of attenuation. In fact, the filter whose Q is 20 has an initial slope of over 60 dB/octave.

The equations for analyzing this filter are as follows:

$$f_0 = \frac{1}{2\pi C} \sqrt{\frac{R_1 + R_2}{R_1 R_2 R_3}} \tag{7.16}$$

$$Q = \pi f_0 R_3 C \tag{7.17}$$

$$A_0 = \frac{-R_3}{2R_1} \tag{7.18}$$

where $C_1 = C_2 = C$ for ease of design and analysis. With a great deal of manipulation, these equations can be solved to obtain the design equations:

$$R_1 = \frac{Q}{2\pi f_0 C A_0} \tag{7.19}$$

$$R_2 = \frac{Q}{(2Q^2 - A_0)2\pi f_0 C} \tag{7.20}$$

$$R_3 = \frac{Q}{\pi f_0 C} \tag{7.21}$$

In these equations, it was assumed that the value of C was chosen first. Also, there

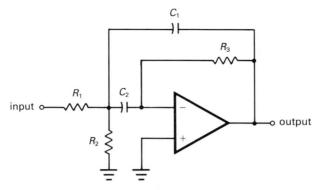

FIGURE 7–15A: Circuit

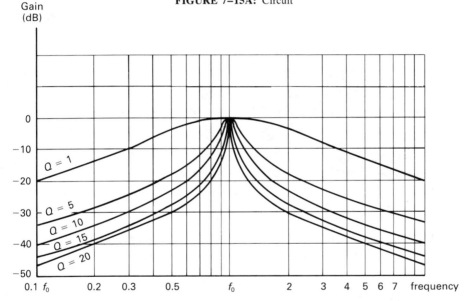

FIGURE 7–15B: Response Curves

FIGURE 7–15: Single Op-Amp Bandpass Filter

are two restrictions that must be met in order for the design to be possible. The first is that A_0 must be less than $2Q^2$. The second is that the op amp's GBW must be greater than or equal to $(20Q^2 \cdot f_0)$.

The characteristics of a bandpass filter can be specified in several ways. Very narrow-band filters usually have the center frequency and the Q given. Wider-band filters often have upper and lower break frequencies specified instead. In this case, the center frequency is not the arithmetical average of the upper and lower break frequencies. Instead, it is given by

$$f_0 = \sqrt{f_{\text{low}} f_{\text{high}}} \qquad (7.22)$$

This is the *geometrical center frequency*.

EXAMPLE

Problem

Design an active bandpass filter with upper and lower break frequencies of 600 Hz and 400 Hz, respectively, and a passband gain of 10.

Solution

1. The bandwidth of this filter will be 600 Hz − 400 Hz = 200 Hz. The center frequency is

$$f_0 = \sqrt{f_{low}f_{high}} = \sqrt{400 \text{ Hz} \cdot 600 \text{ Hz}} = 490 \text{ Hz} \tag{7.22}$$

The Q is therefore

$$Q = \frac{f_0}{\text{BW}} = \frac{490 \text{ Hz}}{200 \text{ Hz}} = 2.45 \tag{7.05}$$

2. Next we will verify that the design meets the two restrictions given above. The gain of 10 is indeed less than $2Q^2$, which is 12. The GBW must be at least

$$20Q^2 + f_0 = 20(2.45)^2 \cdot 490 \text{ Hz} = 58,825 \text{ Hz}$$

Any op amp will meet this requirement.

3. We will try a 0.1-μF capacitor. Then we can calculate the resistor values:

$$R_1 = \frac{Q}{2\pi f_0 C A_0}$$

$$= \frac{2.45}{2\pi \cdot 490 \text{ Hz} \cdot 10^{-7} \text{ F} \cdot 10} = 796 \text{ } \Omega \tag{7.19}$$

$$R_2 = \frac{Q}{(2Q^2 - A_0)2\pi f_0 C}$$

$$= \frac{2.45}{(2 \cdot 2.45^2 - 10)2\pi \cdot 490 \text{ Hz} \cdot 10^{-7} \text{ F}} = 3969 \text{ } \Omega \tag{7.20}$$

$$R_3 = \frac{Q}{\pi f_0 C}$$

$$= \frac{2.45}{\pi \cdot 490 \text{ Hz} \cdot 10^{-7} \text{ F}} = 15,915 \text{ } \Omega \tag{7.21}$$

When higher-Q bandpass filters are required than can be built using this circuit, or when the 6 dB/octave ultimate cutoff slope is not steep enough, two or more filters of this type can be cascaded. The maximum practical Q attainable from this method is 50. When designing multistage single-op-amp bandpass filters, you must use the same center frequency for each stage, and the components must be carefully matched ($C_{\text{stage }1} = C_{\text{stage }2}$, and so on). Otherwise, the completed filter will not perform as desired. Each stage should be designed for a Q given by

$$Q_{\text{stage}} = Q_{\text{overall}}\sqrt{2^{1/n} - 1} \qquad (7.23)$$

where n is the number of stages.

Figure 7–16A shows a simple notch filter circuit. Notice that it is just a one-op-amp bandpass filter and a summing amplifier. It works this way. The input signal contains all frequencies. The bandpass filter inverts the input signal, passing only a certain band of frequencies. This inverted, band-limited signal is summed with the entire input signal. The frequencies that are passed by the bandpass filter are 180°

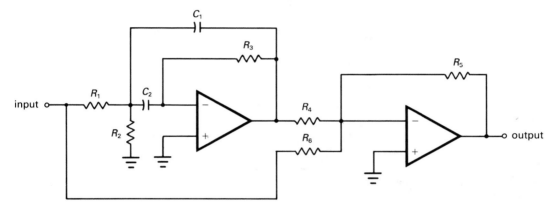

FIGURE 7–16A: Bandpass/Summer Notch Filter

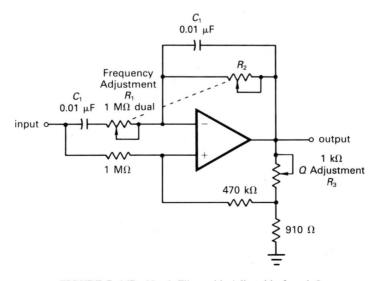

FIGURE 7–16B: Notch Filter with Adjustable f_0 and Q

FIGURE 7–16: Notch Filters

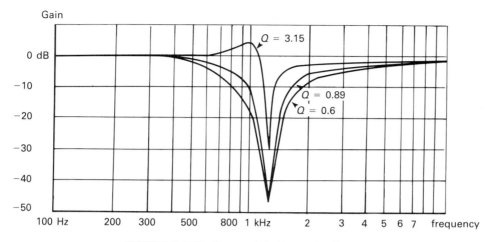

FIGURE 7–16C: Characteristic Curves for Circuit B

out of phase with the input signal, so those frequencies are canceled out in the summing process.

In order for this scheme to work well, resistors R_4 and R_6 must be exactly the proper values, and the gain of the bandpass filter must be exactly as calculated. The best way to ensure these conditions is to use a potentiometer for part of R_6. Then when the filter has been built, this potentiometer is tuned for maximum rejection at the notch frequency.

EXAMPLE

Problem

Design a notch filter whose notch extends from 400 to 600 Hz, and whose passband gain is 10.

Solution

1. The specifications for this filter are the same as for the bandpass filter designed earlier. Therefore, that same circuit can be used for the bandpass portion of the notch filter.
2. In order to obtain the maximum notch depth, the overall gain of the center-frequency signal through the bandpass filter must be the same as the overall gain of the signal that does not go through the bandpass filter. The gain of the bandpass filter at the center frequency is 10, by our previous design. Therefore, the summing amplifier must have unity gain for the filtered signal. This means that $R_5/R_4 = 1$, or $R_4 = R_5$. The gain of the summing amplifier for the unfil-

tered signal is R_5/R_6. This must also equal 10, so R_6 must equal $0.1R_5$. If we choose $R_5 = 1$ kΩ, then R_4 will also = 1 kΩ, and R_6 calculates as 100 Ω. We will use a 250-Ω potentiometer for R_6, to allow adjustment for maximum notch depth.

Often a notch filter is needed whose frequency and Q can be adjusted. Figure 7–16B shows such a circuit. The center frequency is adjustable from 100 Hz to about 1 MHz and is given by

$$f_0 = \frac{1}{RC}$$

The Q can be adjusted from 0.6 to about 4 by adjusting R_3. Figure 7–16C shows response curves for this filter for $f_0 = 1.3$ kHz and for various Q's.

For either type of notch filter, the notch depth depends upon how well R_1 matches R_2, and upon how well C_1 matches C_2.

State-Variable Filters

The concept of adding and subtracting the outputs of simple filters to produce other types of filters has already been explored in connection with the notch filter. This concept is carried further in a type of filter called the *state-variable filter*. The circuit of such a filter is shown in Figure 7–17. As you can see, A_1 is an inverting buffer amplifier, and A_2 and A_3 are integrators. The gain of an integrator is

$$A_V = \frac{-X_C}{R} = \frac{-1}{2\pi f CR}$$

This gain is high at low frequencies and low at high frequencies; the response has a -6 dB/octave slope. The unity-gain frequency is derived as follows:

$$A_V = \frac{-1}{2\pi f CR} = -1$$

$$f_0 = \frac{1}{2\pi CR}$$

In a state-variable filter, two integrators are cascaded, giving an overall -12 dB/octave slope. The addition of amplifier A_1 and the overall feedback loop provides a "shelving" effect so that the gain becomes independent of frequency at frequencies below f_0. Thus, f_0 acts as a sort of break frequency for the state-variable filter. Adding and subtracting the unfiltered input and the integrator outputs makes the filter produce a second-order low-pass or high-pass output and a second-order bandpass output as well. The addition of one more op amp, as shown by the dashed lines, provides a notch output. Resistors R_A and R_B control the damping factor, permitting

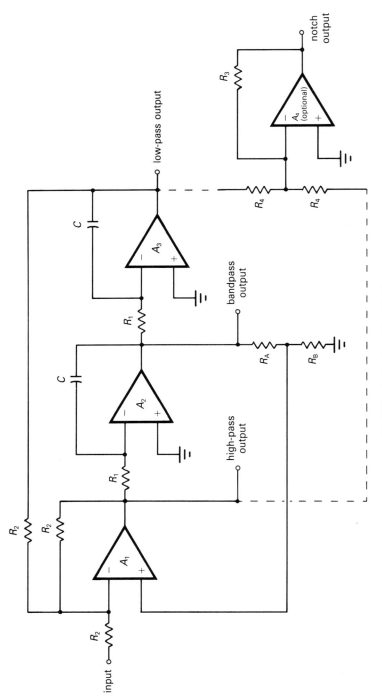

FIGURE 7–17: State-Variable Filter

selection of any desired filter family. The design equations are

$$f_0 = \frac{1}{2\pi R_1 C} \qquad (7.24)$$

$$\alpha = \frac{3R_B}{(R_A + R_B)} \qquad (7.25)$$

$$A_0 = Q = \frac{1}{\alpha} = \frac{R_A + R_B}{3R_B} \qquad (7.26)$$

For the notch filter, after R_4 is arbitrarily selected, R_3 adjusts the passband gain:

$$A_{PN} = \frac{A_0 R_3}{R_4}$$

As you can see from the above equations, a high Q corresponds to a low damping factor. Thus even a lightly-damped low- or high-pass response like a 3-dB Chebyshev will only give a moderately low Q. To verify this, we look up the α for a 3-dB Chebyshev filter in Table 7–B; it is 0.766. The corresponding Q is therefore $1/0.766 = 1.3$. Much higher Q's are certainly possible, up to a maximum of about 100 for this circuit, but these result in badly peaked low-pass and high-pass responses. In other words, a state-variable filter can be designed for any desired second-order low-pass, high-pass, or bandpass response, but it is unlikely that the bandpass output and the low-pass/high-pass outputs will be useful simultaneously.

EXAMPLE

Problem

Design a state-variable filter to perform the notch-filtering function specified in the previous example: $f_{low} = 400$ Hz, $f_{high} = 600$ Hz. The gain is not critical.

Solution

1. We will choose a 0.1-μF capacitor. Then we can solve equation 7.24 for the value of R:

$$f_0 = \frac{1}{2\pi RC} \qquad (7.24)$$

$$R_1 = \frac{1}{2\pi f_0 C} = \frac{1}{(2\pi \cdot 490 \text{ Hz} \cdot 10^{-7} \text{ F})} = 3250 \text{ }\Omega$$

2. We will choose a 1-kΩ resistor for R_B. Then we can solve equation 7.26 for the value of R_A:

$$Q = \frac{R_A + R_B}{3R_B} \tag{7.26}$$

$$R_A = R_B(3Q - 1) = (1 \text{ k}\Omega)(3 \cdot 2.45 - 1) = 6.35 \text{ k}\Omega$$

3. The value of R_2 is chosen for correct bias compensation:

$$R_2 \| R_2 \| R_2 = R_A \| R_B$$

or

$$R_2 = 3(R_A \| R_B) = 3(6.35 \text{ k}\Omega \| 1 \text{ k}\Omega) = 259 \text{ }\Omega$$

4. We will choose $R_4 = 1$ kΩ and use a 10-kΩ potentiometer for R_3 in order to provide adjustable gain.

As with the other notch and bandpass filter circuits, good performance in a state-variable filter depends upon accurate component values. In practice, this often means that the two R_1 resistors are made up of a fixed resistor and a potentiometer, to allow trimming for the desired response. In the example above, 2.7-kΩ resistors would probably be used in series with 1-kΩ potentiometers.

SPECIALIZED ACTIVE-FILTER ICs

There are two general families of ICs designed especially for active-filter use. The first contains ICs that are intended for use as state-variable filters. These ICs, called *universal active filters*, contain four op amps that are interconnected to form a state-variable filter. In this way, they can be made into any of the four basic second-order filter types by the addition of a few resistors and capacitors. The second family is newer. It uses a combination of analog and digital technology to make filters whose break frequencies are externally programmable. These *switched-capacitor filters* are available in second-order through sixth-order versions.

Universal Active-Filter ICs

The National Semiconductor AF100 is a universal active-filter IC available in a 16-pin DIP. The block diagram of the device is shown in Fig. 7–18A. Part B of the figure shows an application example using the AF100. Notice that four resistors are all that are needed to make the device into a usable state-variable filter. The two resistors R set f_0 or f_b:

$$f_0 = \frac{\sqrt{0.1}}{2\pi RC} = \frac{0.316}{2\pi \cdot 10^{-9}R} \tag{7.27}$$

$$R = \frac{0.316}{2\pi \cdot 10^{-9}f_0} = \frac{5.0 \cdot 10^7}{f_0} \tag{7.28}$$

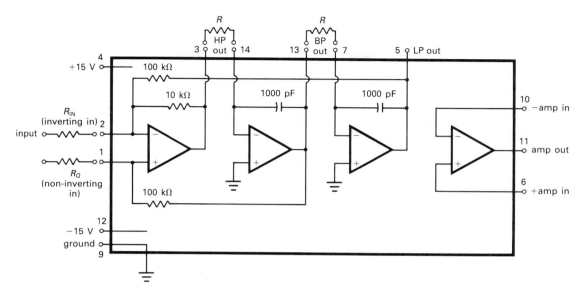

FIGURE 7–18A: AF100 Circuit

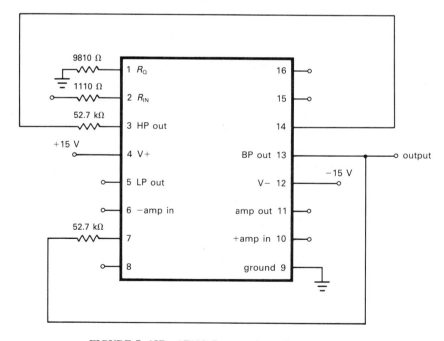

FIGURE 7–18B: AF100 Connected as a Bandpass Filter

FIGURE 7–18: Universal Active-Filter IC

The passband gains of the low-pass output and the high-pass output are different:

$$A_{LP} = \frac{-10^5}{R_{IN}} \tag{7.29}$$

$$A_{HP} = \frac{-10^4}{R_{IN}} \tag{7.30}$$

In both of these equations, the minus sign indicates an inversion of the signal at the outputs. The passband gain at the bandpass output is

$$A_{BP} = \frac{(10^4/R_{IN})(1 + 10^5/R_Q)}{1.1 + 10^4/R_{IN}} \tag{7.31}$$

The Q is

$$Q = \frac{0.316(1 + 10^5/R_Q)}{1.1 + 10^4/R_{IN}} \tag{7.32}$$

This can be solved for R_Q:

$$R_Q = \frac{10^5}{(Q/0.316)(1.1 + 10^4/R_{IN}) - 1} \tag{7.33}$$

Equations 7.30 and 7.31 are interrelated, but the design problem is eased if you notice that

$$A_{BP} = -A_{HP}\left(\frac{Q}{0.316}\right) \tag{7.34}$$

which leads to

$$A_{HP} = \frac{-0.316A_{BP}}{Q} \tag{7.35}$$

The fourth amplifier of the AF100 can be connected as a summing amplifier to provide a notch output, or it can be used as a gain stage for the filter. Alternatively, the fourth amplifier can be connected to external capacitors and resistors to make a first- or second-order filter that can be cascaded with the state-variable filter section to provide a total third- or fourth-order characteristic. Of course, the proper damping and frequency correction factors must be used, as shown in Table 7–C.

EXAMPLE

Problem

Use the AF100 IC to design a second-order bandpass filter for limiting the signal from a telephone set to a range from 300 Hz to 3 kHz. Design for a gain of 10.

Solution

1. First, we must find the center frequency of the filter:

$$f_0 = \sqrt{f_{low}f_{high}} = \sqrt{300 \text{ Hz}(3 \text{ kHz})} = 949 \text{ Hz} \qquad (7.22)$$

2. Next, we find the Q:

$$Q = \frac{f_0}{BW} = \frac{949 \text{ Hz}}{3000 \text{ Hz} - 300 \text{ Hz}} = 0.35 \qquad (7.05)$$

3. Then, we find R:

$$R = \frac{5.0 \cdot 10^7}{f_0} = \frac{5.0 \cdot 10^7}{949 \text{ Hz}} = 52.7 \text{ k}\Omega \qquad (7.28)$$

4. To find R_{IN}, we must first solve for A_{HP}:

$$A_{HP} = \frac{-0.316 A_{BP}}{Q} = \frac{-0.316 \cdot 10}{0.35} = -9.02 \qquad (7.35)$$

Now

$$A_{HP} = \frac{-10^4}{R_{IN}} \qquad (7.30)$$

So

$$R_{IN} = \frac{-10^4}{-9.02} = 1110 \ \Omega$$

5. Finally, we find R_Q:

$$R_Q = \frac{10^5}{(Q/0.316)(1.1 + 10^4/R_{IN}) - 1} \qquad (7.33)$$

$$= \frac{10^5}{(0.35/0.316)(1.1 + 10^4/1110 \ \Omega) - 1} = 9810 \ \Omega$$

This is the circuit shown in Fig. 7–18B.

Switched-Capacitor Filters

The use of integrators as the frequency-dependent gain element in a state-variable filter opens the door to a novel idea. The time constant of an integrator—and therefore the frequency response—depends upon the resistor and the capacitor. More specifically, it depends upon how rapidly the resistor allows the capacitor to charge and discharge. If a method could be found that caused a certain capacitor/resistor combination to charge and discharge at different rates, this method would have the effect of changing the time constant of the circuit, without any change in component values. This is the idea behind the switched-capacitor filter. Figure 7–19 shows the general idea.

On page 315, we discussed how the term $1/2\pi RC$ acts as a break frequency for the state-variable filter. The R and C correspond to the resistor and capacitor of the conventional integrator shown in Fig. 7–19A. The input current to that integrator is given by

$$i_{IN} = \frac{V_{IN}}{R} \tag{7.36}$$

In the switched-capacitor integrator shown in Fig. 7–19B, the switch is changed back and forth between positions A and B. In position A, the switch allows C_{IN} to charge from V_{IN}. In position B, C_{IN} discharges into the virtual ground represented by the op amp's inverting input. This causes the op amp's output voltage to change, charging C. The input current to the switched-capacitor integrator can be determined as follows:

$$i_{IN} = \frac{\Delta q}{\Delta t} \tag{7.37}$$

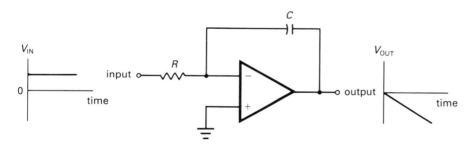

FIGURE 7–19A: Conventional Integrator

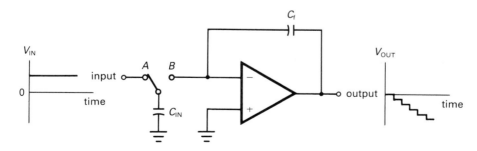

FIGURE 7–19B: Switched-Capacitor Integrator

FIGURE 7–19: Operation of a Switched-Capacitor Integrator

where Δq is the change in the charge on C_{IN}, and Δt is the amount of time that the switch remains in position A. Since $C = q/V$ by definition, $q = CV$, and

$$i_{IN} = \frac{C_{IN} V_{IN}}{\Delta t}$$

Now if we use a clock having a 50% duty cycle to electronically operate the switch, then Δt is one-half the clock period:

$$\Delta t = \frac{1}{2f_{CLK}}$$

Thus,

$$i_{IN} = 2C_{IN} V_{IN} f_{CLK} \qquad (7.38)$$

Comparing equation 7.38 to equation 7.36, we find that an equivalent input resistance has been created:

$$i_{IN} = \frac{V_{IN}}{R} = 2C_{IN} V_{IN} f_{CLK}$$

$$R_{equiv} = \frac{1}{2C_{IN} f_{CLK}}$$

This means that f_0 of a state-variable switched-capacitor filter is given by:

$$f_0 = \frac{1}{2\pi R_{equiv} C_f} = \frac{2C_{IN} f_{CLK}}{2\pi C_f}$$

$$= \frac{C_{IN} f_{CLK}}{\pi C_f} \qquad (7.39)$$

Of course, this approach produces a stepped (distorted) output wave. But since the switching occurs at a frequency far above the maximum signal frequency, the lowest-frequency component of the distortion introduced will also be above the signal range. In this way, the use of a variable-frequency clock to connect and disconnect the capacitor provides the same effect as a continuously-variable resistor. Thus precision-matched fixed capacitors and resistors can be built into the integrated circuit, and their *effective* values—hence, f_0—can be controlled by the clock frequency.

The National Semiconductor MF10 is a universal dual switched-capacitor filter. Figure 7–20 shows the block diagram of the MF10. As you can see from the figure, the MF10 contains two separate state-variable filters. These can be used separately, or they can be cascaded to provide a fourth-order response. In function, then, the MF10 resembles the AF100. However, the actual operation of the filter is very different, as is the design process.

A look at the pin identifications in Fig. 7–20 will emphasize some of the differences between designing with conventional filters and designing with switched-capacitor filters. A bit of explanation is in order concerning some of the pins.

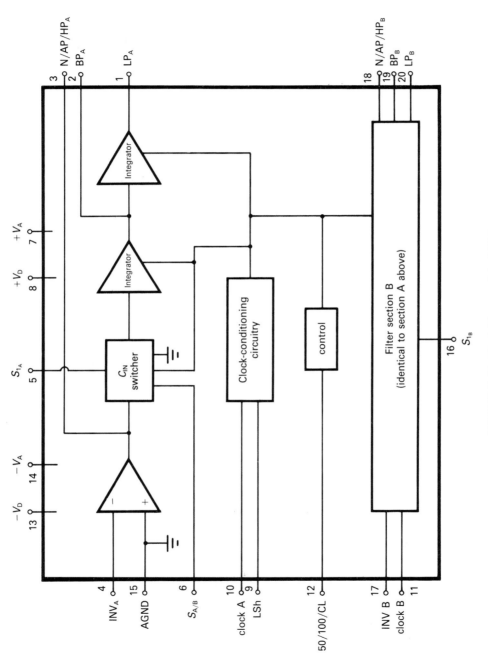

FIGURE 7–20: Block Diagram of the MF10

• V_{A+}, V_{A-}, V_{D+}, V_{D-}—The analog and digital power-supply pins are interconnected inside the IC. However, the analog circuitry is connected to the internal power bus near the points where the V_{A+} and V_{A-} connections are brought out; likewise for the digital circuitry and the V_D pins. This is done to allow separate bypassing capacitors for the analog and digital supplies, to prevent interaction of the two systems.

• 50/100/CL—When this pin is tied to the positive power supply lead, $f_{CLK}/f_0 = 50$. When the pin is connected to $V_+/2$, $f_{CLK}/f_0 = 100$. When it is grounded, the filtering action is defeated.

• AGND—If a bipolar power supply is used, this pin is grounded, V_{A+} and V_{D+} are connected to V_+, and V_{A-} and V_{D-} are connected to V_-. If a unipolar supply is used, AGND should be connected to a voltage-divider delivering $V_+/2$. In this case, the connection to AGND should be thoroughly decoupled.

• N/AP/HP—This pin is used for either a notch output (mode 1 and 2), a highpass output (mode 3), a low-pass output (mode 6), or an all-pass output (mode 4). An all-pass filter is one that provides a frequency-independent time delay and attenuation characteristic. (For details on the various modes of operation, see the data sheet.)

• L Sh—For CMOS clock levels (± 5 V), a ± 5-V bipolar supply should be used, AGND should be grounded, and the L Sh pin can be tied either to ground or to -5 V. For TTL clocks (0 and 5 V), a 10-V unipolar supply should be used, AGND should be connected to a 5-V, decoupled voltage divider, and V_{A-}, V_{D-}, and L Sh should be grounded.

The complete data sheet for the MF10 is included in Appendix A. It lists six modes of operation. In order to illustrate the use of this circuit, we will look at the one identified as mode 1. This circuit is shown in Fig. 7–21. When used in this mode, the MF10 provides notch, bandpass, and low-pass outputs. The design equations are given below:

$$f_0 = \frac{f_{CLK}}{100} \quad \text{or} \quad \frac{f_{CLK}}{50}, \qquad \text{selected by pin 12} \qquad (7.40)$$

$$A_{0,LP} = \frac{R_2}{R_1} \qquad \text{(low-pass passband gain)} \qquad (7.41)$$

$$A_{0,BP} = \frac{R_3}{R_1} \qquad \text{(passband gain of bandpass filter)} \qquad (7.42)$$

$$A_{0,\text{notch}} = \frac{R_2}{R_1} \qquad \text{(passband gain of notch filter)} \qquad (7.43)$$

$$Q = 1/\alpha = \frac{R_3}{R_2} \qquad (7.44)$$

These equations are somewhat interlocked. Some manipulation shows that

$$A_{0,BP} = A_{0,LP}Q \qquad (7.45)$$

326 Chapter Seven

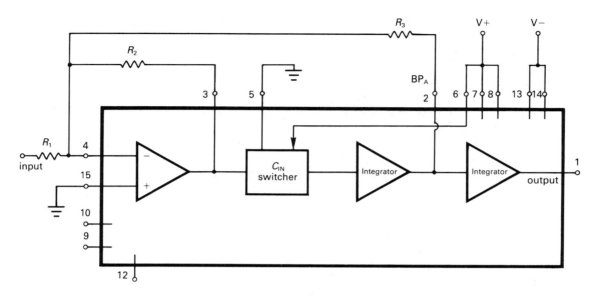

FIGURE 7-21: The MF10 Connected in Mode 1

Also, the maximum low-pass gain occurs at the peak produced at f_0 of a Chebyshev filter. This maximum gain is

$$A_{0,\text{peak}} = A_{0,\text{LP}}Q \tag{7.46}$$

In addition to showing how the design equations are interdependent, these last two equations are useful in avoiding clipping at the outputs of the amplifiers. By calculating these gains, you can determine the maximum permissible input signal.

EXAMPLE

Problem

Use the MF10 to design a bandpass filter like the one designed earlier using the AF100: $f_{\text{low}} = 300$ Hz, $f_{\text{high}} = 3000$ Hz, $A_0 = 10$.

Solution

1. The variables that we must determine are R_1, R_2, R_3, L Sh, AGND, V_+, V_-, f_{CLK}, and 50/100/CL. We will use a TTL clock, which will determine $V_+ = 10$ V, $V_- = 0$ V, L Sh = grounded, and AGND = 5 V. We will use two 1-kΩ resistors decoupled by a 1-μF tantalum capacitor to make the biasing circuit for AGND.

2. We can arbitrarily choose f_{CLK}/f_0, so we will set that ratio equal to 100. Since f_0 was determined in our previous example to be 949 Hz, this means that f_{CLK} = 100 f_0 = 100(949 Hz) = 94,900 Hz. It also means that the 50/100/CL pin should be tied to the 5-V point to which AGND is connected.

3. The Q of 0.35 (also determined in the previous example) sets the ratio of R_3/R_2:

$$Q = \frac{R_3}{R_2} \quad \text{and} \quad \frac{R_3}{R_2} = 0.35 \tag{7.44}$$

If we choose R_2 = 10 kΩ, this makes R_3 = 3.5 kΩ.

4. The passband gain of 10 sets the ratio of R_3/R_1:

$$A_{0,BP} = \frac{R_3}{R_1} \quad \text{and} \quad R_3/R_1 = 10 \tag{7.42}$$

Since R_3 has already been chosen as 3.5 kΩ, R_1 must be 350 Ω.

5. The values of $A_{0,BP}$ and $A_{0,peak}$ will allow us to calculate the maximum allowable input voltage. We already know that $A_{0,BP}$ = 10. Then

$$A_{0,peak} = A_{0,LP}Q \tag{7.46}$$

$$= \frac{R_2}{R_1}Q \tag{from 7.41}$$

$$= \frac{10 \text{ k}\Omega}{350 \text{ }\Omega}(0.35) = 10$$

Thus the greatest gain existing anywhere in the circuit is 10. Since the supply is 10 V unipolar, this means that the maximum undistorted output is ± 4 V$_{peak}$ (page 2 of the data sheet in Appendix A). Therefore the maximum peak input voltage is one-tenth of that value, or ± 0.4 V.

APPLICATION EXAMPLE

Figure 7–22 shows a schematic of an octave-band room equalizer for audio applications. This circuit includes a noise generator that generates a noise signal having equal energy per octave. This characteristic is referred to as *pink noise*. In use, the noise generator is connected to a sound system input through the set of bandpass filters. To equalize the response of a room, one filter section is switched in at a time. Thus the sound system gets energy in only a one-octave frequency range. The signal from the speakers is picked up by a microphone, preamplified, and then fed to a metering circuit. Usually the 1-kHz octave band is used as a reference and the potentiometers of the other bands are adjusted to produce the same meter indication when each band is tried. This provides the ability to adjust the frequency response of the system in order to provide a frequency-independent acoustical gain in the room in which it is installed.

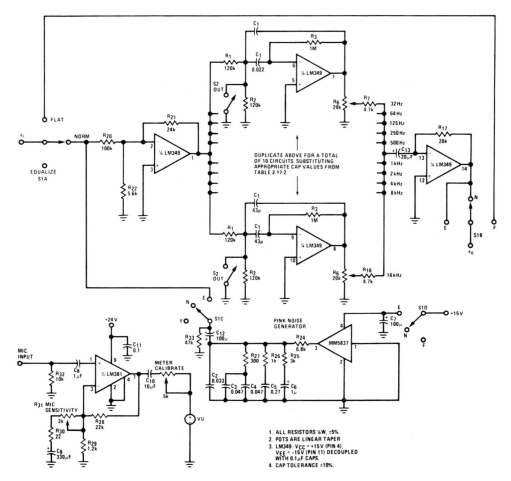

FIGURE 7–22: Room Equalizing Instrument *(Reprinted from* <u>Audio Handbook</u> *by permission of National Semiconductor Corp.)*

The heart of the circuit itself is just a set of ten bandpass filters, each having a one-octave bandwidth, and each centered about the frequency indicated on the diagram. The input and output of the filter sections are fed by unity-gain inverting buffer amplifiers in order to provide a low driving impedance and output isolation. The microphone amplifier is an adjustable-gain noninverting amplifier.

TROUBLESHOOTING ACTIVE FILTERS

Troubleshooting active filter circuits that have previously worked properly is not very different from troubleshooting op-amp amplifier circuits. The one symptom that active filters can have that amplifiers are unlikely to have is failure to exhibit the proper frequency response. This can be broken into several categories. If there is no filtering action at all, it is likely that one or more capacitors are open, since capacitors are the frequency-dependent element in active filters. If the circuit does filter, but the filtering action takes place at the wrong frequency, it is likely that one or more resistors have changed value or have broken loose from the circuit board. (Especially in hand-built circuits, it is possible to make a cold-solder joint whose effects do not show up for years. Then one day the circuit can suddenly malfunction "for no reason.") In the case of bandpass and notch filters, the response—especially the notch depth—depends heavily upon component matching. There are some instruments whose operation relies upon the rejection of certain frequencies by a certain number of dB. If, for example, a circuit must reject 20-kHz signals by at least 50 dB, then very good component matching is essential. Any component is subject to some *drift*, or change in value over a period of time. A drift of even 1% can cause a malfunction in a notch filter with such stringent requirements. For measuring components for precise matching, digital test equipment having at least three or more digits resolution must be used, and the equipment must be properly calibrated.

If the response of an active filter is the complement of what you expect, an op amp is probably defective. Since many active filter circuits operate by subtracting a certain response from the input, if the amplifier performing the subtraction were defective, you would get the complement of the expected response. For example, a state-variable notch filter whose final summing amplifier is defective can produce a low-Q bandpass response.

DESIGN NOTES

General Notes About Active Filters

The sections below give design methods for various types of active filters. Two points are important in any active filter design, though. The first is that the operation of active filters depends upon accurate component values. Hand-selected components or components with tolerances of 2% or closer should be used. In some cases, trimmer resistors may have to be used in order to adjust the circuit operation to meet frequency, bandwidth, or Q specifications. For labor reasons, however, hand adjustments are to be avoided whenever possible. The second point is that for active filters to perform properly, a low driving impedance is necessary. This often requires the inclusion of a buffer amplifier stage preceding the filter.

First-Order LP and HP Filters

A single-pole low-pass or high-pass filter is just an *RC* filter with a buffer amplifier. Therefore, to design one, you pick a convenient value for C and solve for

$$R = \frac{1}{2\pi f_c C} \qquad \text{(from 7.13)}$$

Then you select R_f and R_g for the desired gain. See Fig. 7–23.

Second-Order and Higher-Order LP and HP Filters

The easiest way to design a low-pass or high-pass filter with order greater than one is to use the *equal-component Sallen-Key* configuration (Fig. 7–24). You begin by deciding upon the type of response: Bessel, Butterworth, and so on. Then look at Table 7–B (second-order) or 7–C (third- or higher-order) for the appropriate values for k_{LP} and α. The most common choice is the Butterworth response. For high-pass filters, you must convert:

$$k_{HP} = \frac{1}{k_{LP}}$$

Then you pick a convenient capacitor value and calculate:

(continued)

Design Notes

(continued from page 330)

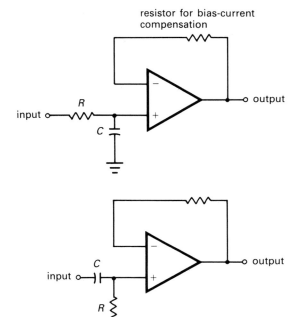

resistor for bias-current
compensation

input

R

C

output

C

input

R

output

FIGURE 7–23: First-Order Active Filters

$$R = \frac{k}{2\pi f_b C} \qquad \text{(from 7.15)}$$

Finally, you select R_f and R_g to give a gain of

$$A_V = 3 - \alpha \qquad (7.14)$$

Notice that the gain determines α. If some other value of gain is needed, you can add a voltage divider to the input or output, or another amplifier stage, as necessary. This process is followed for each stage of a third- or higher-order filter.

Bandpass Filters

Bandpass filters are usually specified in terms of center frequency (f_0), passband gain, and Q. If low and high break frequencies are specified instead,

(continued from page 331)

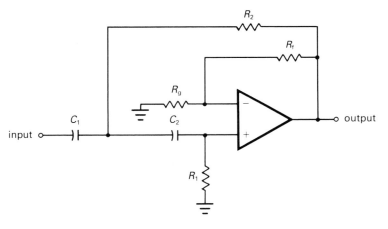

FIGURE 7–24: Second-Order Active Filters

first find f_0 and Q:

$$f_0 = \sqrt{f_{low}f_{high}} \qquad (7.22)$$

$$Q = \frac{f_0}{f_{high} - f_{low}} \qquad \text{(from 7.05)}$$

One way to design a bandpass filter is to cascade a low-pass and a high-pass filter, with overlapping responses. This has the advantage that any desired response shape (cutoff slopes) can be had, but it has the disadvantage that at least two op amps are required.

Design Notes

(continued from page 332)

Another way to design a bandpass filter is to use one low-pass and one high-pass feedback network on the same amplifier, as shown in Fig. 7–25. First, choose a convenient value of C. Then calculate

$$R_1 = \frac{Q}{2\pi f_0 C A_0} \tag{7.19}$$

$$R_2 = \frac{Q}{(2Q^2 - A_0)(2\pi f_0 C)} \tag{7.20}$$

$$R_3 = \frac{Q}{\pi f_0 C} \tag{7.21}$$

The performance of this circuit depends heavily upon the accuracy of the component values. Therefore, the values of R_2 may need to be adjusted ("trimmed") in order to achieve the calculated value of Q.

Notch Filter

One way to design a notch filter is to cascade low-pass and high-pass filters, with nonoverlapping passbands. This approach is probably the best if the stopband required is fairly wide, because it gives independent control of the lower and upper response skirts. However, for a narrow notch, very precise component tolerances would be required. An easier way to build a notch filter is to use a bandpass filter and a summing amplifier, as shown in Fig. 7–26. The bandpass filter is designed as described above, then the feedback and input resistor values are chosen for the summing amplifier to provide the required gain. (The two input resistors are always made equal, for maximum notch depth.)

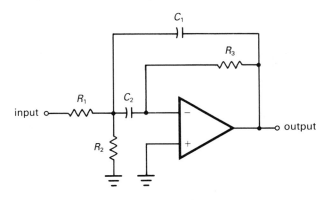

FIGURE 7–25: Bandpass Filter

(continued from page 333)

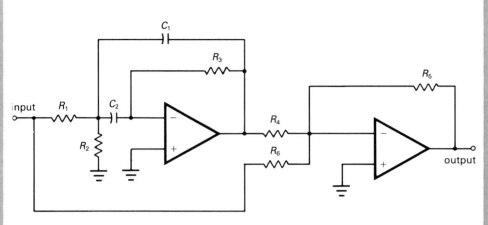

FIGURE 7–26: Notch Filter

State-Variable Filter

The state-variable filter (Fig. 7–17, page 316) has low-pass, high-pass, and bandpass outputs, and with the optional circuitry shown, it can also provide a notch output. The value of Q can be as high as 100, without critical matching of components. To design such a filter, first choose a convenient C, R_4, and R_B. Then solve for

$$R_1 = \frac{1}{2\pi f_0 C} \quad \text{(from 7.24)}$$

$$R_A = R_B(3Q - 1) \quad \text{(from 7.26)}$$

$$R_2 = 3(R_A \| R_B)$$

If the notch circuit is added, choose a value for R_3 to set the desired gain:

$$R_3 = A_0 R_4$$

where A_0 is the passband gain of the notch filter.

Specialized IC's

For designs using specialized active-filter ICs such as universal and switched-capacitor filters, the complete data sheet of the specific IC in question should be consulted.

Design Notes

(continued from page 334)

Frequency Scaling

You may have noticed that all the types of filters that we have discussed have been associated with some form of the equation $f = 1/2\pi RC$. This implies that once you have designed a filter for a certain frequency, you can modify that filter for other frequencies as follows:

Using the same capacitors: $\qquad R_{\text{new}} = R_{\text{old}}\left(\dfrac{f_{\text{old}}}{f_{\text{new}}}\right)$

Using the same resistors: $\qquad C_{\text{new}} = C_{\text{old}}\left(\dfrac{f_{\text{old}}}{f_{\text{new}}}\right)$

These equations are only applied to the frequency-determining components. If Q, α, and A_0 do not change, there is no need to change the values of the other resistors in the circuit.

SUMMARY

There are four basic types of filter circuits:

1. *Low-pass* filters pass low frequencies and reject high frequencies.
2. *High-pass* filters pass high frequencies and reject low frequencies.
3. *Bandpass* filters pass a certain band of frequencies.
4. *Band-reject* or *notch* filters reject a certain band of frequencies.

The band of frequencies that a filter passes is called the *passband;* the band that it rejects is called the *stopband*.

Passive filters can be built from any combination of resistors, capacitors, and inductors. *RC* passive filters form the basis for most active filters.

Low- and high-pass filters have a frequency at which the gain is 3 dB less than the passband gain. This is called the *break frequency* (f_b).

Bandpass and notch filters have a low and a high break frequency. The difference between these frequencies is the passband of a bandpass filter; it is the stopband of a notch filter. The geometrical center frequency of a bandpass or notch filter is called f_0.

The Q of a bandpass filter is the ratio of f_0 to the passband. The Q of a notch filter is the ratio of f_0 to the stopband.

The *notch depth* of a notch filter is the number of dB by which the filter rejects signals whose frequency is f_0.

The slope of the gain-vs.-frequency curve in the stopband of a filter is called the *cutoff slope*. The number of reactive components of a filter is called the *order* of the filter. The cutoff slope of a filter equals 6 dB/octave (20 dB/decade) multiplied by the order of the filter.

Second- and higher-order filters can be constructed in a number of ways, resulting in a number of different frequency and phase responses in the vicinity of f_b. Some of these different ways have names; *Bessel, Butterworth,* and *Chebyshev* are the most common.

Active filters are filters that include an amplifying device in addition to the frequency-selective components. Usually the amplifying device is an op amp. The op amp may be used simply as a buffer, to provide the necessary input and output impedances, or it may include reactive components in its feedback loop.

Low- and high-pass feedback sections can be used to make a single-op-amp bandpass filter. The addition of a summing amplifier to subtract the passband of a bandpass filter from the input signal results in a two-op-amp notch filter.

A universal active filter using two integrators and a summing amplifier can be built. Called a *state-variable filter*, this circuit provides low-pass, high-pass, and bandpass outputs. With the addition of another summing amplifier, a notch output is also possible.

ICs are available that include all necessary circuitry for a state-variable filter, except for four resistors. These *universal active-filter* ICs simplify construction and decrease manufacturing costs.

A modified state-variable filter using the *switched-capacitor* principle provides any desired filter response, tunable by varying the clock frequency.

REVIEW QUESTIONS

1. Sketch rough response curves for:
   (a) a first-order 1-kHz low-pass filter
   (b) a first-order 1-kHz high-pass filter
   (c) a second-order 1-kHz low-pass filter
2. What is the break frequency of an *RC* filter using a 15-kΩ resistor and a 0.022-μF capacitor?
3. What frequencies are included in the stopband of a notch filter having $f_0 = $ 19 kHz and $Q = 50$?
4. From your study of earlier chapters in this book, explain which of the following capacitors you would choose if you were designing a 10-kHz low-pass filter: 100 pF, 0.01 μF, 10 μF.
5. Design a second-order Butterworth low-pass filter with $f_b = $ 100 kHz. Include GBW and slew-rate calculations for selection of an appropriate op amp.
6. Design a third-order 2-dB Chebyshev high-pass filter with $f_b = $ 7 kHz. If the highest frequency of interest is 30 kHz, what GBW and slew rate are required for the op amp?
7. For the filter designed in question 5, what would be the worst-case response error if the capacitors and resistors had $\pm 10\%$ tolerances and were at their minimum values? Their maximum values? What if one *RC* pair was at min-

imum and the other at maximum? Your answers should include consideration of both f_b and damping factor (i.e., filter family).

8. Design a bandpass filter to pass the octave band extending from 707 Hz to 1414 Hz. Design for a Q of 1.12.
9. Repeat question 5 using a state-variable filter.
10. Repeat question 5 using the AF100 IC.
11. Using the various graphs in this chapter, estimate gain at (a) 1.2 kHz, (b) 1.3 kHz, and (c) 4.8 kHz for a second-order, 3-dB Chebyshev 1.2-kHz high-pass filter having $A_0 = 5$.

LABORATORY EXPERIMENT—PASSIVE FILTERS

Objective:

To measure the performance of a passive filter with various driving and load impedances.

Materials:

1 0.01-µF capacitor
1 10-kΩ resistor
1 1-MΩ potentiometer
1 10-kΩ potentiometer

Procedure:

1. Construct a low-pass filter using the capacitor and the resistor.
2. Connect a signal generator to the filter's input and a 'scope to its output. Measure the frequency response of the filter at the following multiples of f_b: 0.1, 0.2, 0.3, 0.5, 0.8, 1, 2, 3, 5, 8, and 10.
3. Connect the 1-MΩ pot as a variable load resistance from the output of the filter to ground. Repeat the measurements of frequency response at each of the following pot settings: 1 MΩ, 500 kΩ, 100 kΩ, 10 kΩ, 1 kΩ.
4. Disconnect the load potentiometer and connect the 10-kΩ resistor in series with the signal generator to simulate a nonzero driving resistance. Repeat the measurements of frequency response at the following pot settings: 100 Ω, 1 kΩ, 5 kΩ, 10 kΩ.

Analysis:

1. Plot and label each response curve you obtained.
2. Write a discussion of the effect of nonzero driving resistance and finite load resistance upon passive filter performance. Also discuss what bearing this has upon the desirability of using active filters and the design of circuits containing active filters.

Laboratory Experiments

(continued)

(continued from page 338)

LABORATORY EXPERIMENT—SECOND-ORDER ACTIVE FILTERS

Objective:

To observe the effect of component tolerances upon active filter performance.

Materials:

2 741 op amps
various resistors and capacitors

Procedure:

1. Build the circuit you designed for question 5. Use 10% tolerance components, not selected for matching.
2. Measure the response carefully, especially around f_b. Graph the response, and compare your graph with the graphs in this chapter to see whether your filter is indeed a Butterworth filter and whether f_b is as calculated.
3. Using measured values of components, experimentally verify the calculations of question 7.

LABORATORY EXPERIMENT—STATE-VARIABLE FILTERS

Objective:

To examine the versatility of the state-variable filter.

Materials:

1 4136 op amp
2 0.1-μF capacitors
various resistors

Procedure:

1. Build the state-variable notch filter designed in the example on page 317. Measure the values of the components, adding resistors as necessary to achieve ±1% accuracy.
2. Measure the frequency response of the low-pass, high-pass, bandpass, and notch outputs at 20 frequencies in the range from 40 to 4000 Hz.

Laboratory
Experiments

(continued from page 339)

3. Measure the maximum voltage before the onset of clipping at:
   (a) the input
   (b) the LP output
   (c) the HP output
   (d) the BP output
   (e) the notch output
4. Change the value of R_A as necessary to achieve a Q of 100. The value of f_0 will not be changed. Remeasure the response at each output as in step 2.
5. Remeasure the maximum voltage before clipping as in step 3.

Analysis:

1. Discuss how useful you think each output from this filter would be, based upon your measurements in steps 2 and 4. In other words, which of the curves you obtained seem that they would ordinarily be useful?
2. Discuss the effect of Q upon maximum input before clipping. At which outputs does clipping occur with the lowest input level, or is there any difference?

chapter eight

Signal Generation and Shaping

OBJECTIVES

Upon completing this chapter, you will be able to:

- Design monostable, bistable, and astable circuits using IC timers.
- Design rectangular-wave generators using op amps.
- Design sine-wave generators using either LC or RC networks.
- Design adaptive-feedback circuits to avoid waveform distortion.
- Apply voltage-controlled oscillators.
- Apply amplitude and frequency modulation to sine, rectangular, or triangle waves.
- Troubleshoot wave-generation circuits.

INTRODUCTION

When the term *signal generator* is mentioned, most technicians think of a piece of laboratory equipment. Although it is true that a signal generator is a valuable piece of test equipment, it is also true that there are many other applications for specific types of signal generators. The clock signal in a computer is generated by a crystal-controlled square-wave generator. Many pulse-width-modulated systems, such as switching power supplies, employ triangle-wave generators. Radio transmitters and receivers, RF heating equipment, remote-control units, industrial position sensors, robotic proximity sensors, and metal detectors use sine-wave generators. So a technician working in any area of electronics needs to understand signal generators.

Virtually all signal generators function as amplifiers with positive feedback at one frequency. The particular waveshape produced by the signal generator depends upon the way in which the circuit responds to that positive feedback. In some cases, it is easier to understand the operation of a particular circuit in terms of how the wave is formed rather than in terms of an amplifier with positive feedback. So the method of explanation that is clearest for the particular application will be used in this chapter.

The way in which positive feedback causes an amplifier to oscillate can be explained as follows. Let us assume that we have an amplifier with feedback as shown in Fig. 8–1. For a normal amplifier circuit, the feedback would be connected to the inverting input; it would be negative feedback. But in this case the feedback is connected to the noninverting input, so we have positive feedback. The gain provided by the amplifier without the positive feedback loop is represented as A_{ol}, and the fraction of the output signal that is fed back is β. (β is often just a voltage-divider ratio, as in the case of an inverting amplifier, where $\beta = R_i/(R_f + R_i)$.) If we assume that there is a small input signal, v_n, to our amplifier, such as a noise voltage, then the signal v_i presented at the amplifier input is the sum of v_n and the signal v_f from the feedback loop:

$$v_i = v_n + v_f \tag{8.01}$$

The value of v_f is v_i multiplied by the amplifier gain, then multiplied by the feedback ratio:

$$v_f = A_{ol}\beta v_i \tag{8.02}$$

The total gain provided by the loop including the amplifier and the feedback network is called the *loop gain,* and this is just the output signal from the loop divided by the input signal to the loop:

$$A_{loop} = \frac{v_f}{v_i} = \frac{A_{ol}\beta v_i}{v_i} = A_{ol}\beta \tag{8.03}$$

The output voltage from the amplifier is v_i multiplied by the gain:

$$V_{OUT} = A_{ol}v_i \tag{8.04}$$

We can now calculate the gain of the amplifier, A_{cl}, with the positive feedback loop connected:

$$A_{cl} = \frac{V_{OUT}}{v_n} = \frac{A_{ol}v_i}{v_n} \qquad \text{(from 8.04)}$$

$$= \frac{A_{ol}v_i}{v_i - v_f} \qquad \text{(from 8.01)}$$

$$= \frac{A_{ol}v_i}{v_i - A_{ol}\beta v_i} \qquad \text{(from 8.02)}$$

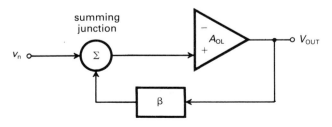

FIGURE 8–1: Positive-Feedback Analysis

Canceling v_i from the numerator and denominator, we have

$$A_{cl} = \frac{A_{ol}}{1 - A_{ol}\beta} \tag{8.05}$$

Now if the loop gain is less than unity, A_{CL} will be greater than A_{ol} but still finite.

EXAMPLE

Problem

An amplifier with a gain of 9 has a positive feedback loop made up of a 9-kΩ feedback resistor and a 1-kΩ resistor from the input to ground. What is the gain of the amplifier?

Solution

1. The feedback ratio is calculated from the voltage-divider formula:

$$\beta = \frac{1\ k\Omega}{9\ k\Omega + 1\ k\Omega} = 0.1$$

2. The value of $A_{ol}\beta$ is $(9)(0.1) = 0.9$. Thus,

$$A_{cl} = \frac{A_{ol}}{1 - A_{ol}\beta} = \frac{9}{1 - 0.9} = 90 \tag{8.05}$$

If $A_{ol}\beta$ is greater than unity, the assumptions used in deriving in equation 8.03 break down, and the equation is no longer valid. If $A_{ol}\beta$ is exactly unity, the denominator of equation 8.05 is zero, and the results are indeterminate. But if we rewrite 8.05 in terms of v_n and V_{OUT} and clear the fractions, we obtain the useful result

$$\frac{V_{OUT}}{v_n} = \frac{A_{ol}}{1 - A_{ol}\beta}$$

$$V_{OUT}(1 - A_{ol}\beta) = A_{ol}v_n \tag{8.06}$$

If we now assume that v_n is zero, as it is for an oscillator, then the right side of equation 8.06 is zero. In order to still have an output from the oscillator (meaning V_{OUT} is not zero), the quantity $(1 - A_{ol}\beta)$ must be zero. This means that for an oscillator the loop gain must equal unity:

$$A_{loop} = A_{ol}\beta = 1$$

Since an oscillator is by definition a device that produces an AC output, there is one other essential consideration. As you probably remember, in Chapter 3, when we were discussing op-amp compensation, we mentioned that the phase shift introduced by an amplifier and/or its feedback network affects the "positiveness" or "negativeness" of the fed-back signal. In other words, a signal with a 180° phase shift in the feedback loop, even though connected to the inverting input, is in fact a positive-feedback signal. To be more specific, for an oscillator to work, the total of all phase shifts in the amplifier and feedback network must be an integral multiple of 360°, so that the feedback will stay positive. These two criteria that must be satisfied in order for oscillation to exist—proper loop gain and proper phase—can be restated in a single polar equation called the *Barkhausen criterion:*

$$A_{\text{loop}} = 1\underline{/k360°}$$

where A_{loop} is the phasor form of the loop gain, and k is any integer, including zero.

SINE-WAVE GENERATORS

One of the most common waveforms needed in many branches of electronics is the sine wave. There are basically two ways to generate sine waves. The first is to use an oscillator that produces only one frequency at its output. Remember that any nonsinusoidal waveform is made up of more than one frequency: a fundamental and harmonics. If the Barkhausen criterion is met for more than one frequency, or if it is only met for one frequency but the amplifier is driven into saturation, the output will not be a sine wave. Thus, the direct method of generating sine waves involves:

1. An amplifier with positive feedback that meets the Barkhausen criterion
2. A feedback network that causes the criterion to be met at only one frequency
3. Some way of preventing the amplifier from being overdriven and causing distortion

The indirect method of generating sine waves is often used at low frequencies when the frequency needs to be easily varied. It involves generating triangle waves, then shaping them into sine waves. Because it is easy to build triangle-wave generators whose frequency can be changed by changing a control voltage, this method offers versatility, which for some applications offsets its greater complexity and slightly less perfect output waveform.

LC Oscillators

One of the most common methods of producing a frequency-selective feedback network is to use an *LC* circuit. Figure 8–2 shows five different ways to build a sine-wave oscillator using *LC* circuits. These circuits were originally developed for vacuum tubes, and bear the names of their inventors, except for the last circuit. That one, by the way, was formerly called the "tuned-plate-tuned-grid oscillator," then

IC TIMER APPLICATION—CAPACITANCE-TO-VOLTAGE METER CONVERTER

Voltage Meter Converter

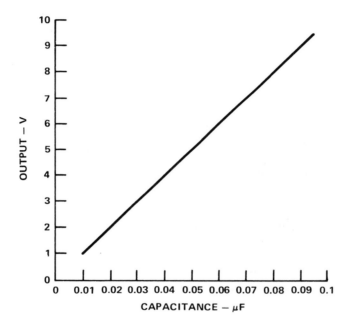

This circuit converts an unknown capacitance value to a voltage, as shown by the graph above. Timer U1 operates as a free-running oscillator at 60 Hz, providing trigger pulses to timer U2 which operates in the monostable mode. Resistor R_1 is fixed and C_X is the capacitor being measured. While the output of U2 is 60 Hz, the duty cycle depends on the value of C_X. U3 is a combination low-pass filter and unity-gain follower whose DC output voltage is the time-averaged amplitude of the output pulses of U2. If the value of C_X is small, the duty cycle is low. Larger values of C_X result in a larger duty cycle, making the output pulses at U2 wider; thus the average DC output level at U3 is greater.

(continued)

Sidebar

(continued from page 345)

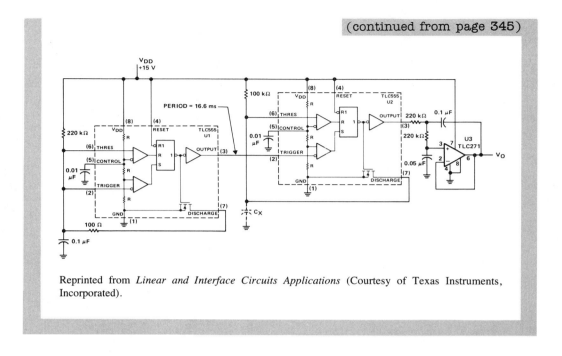

Reprinted from *Linear and Interface Circuits Applications* (Courtesy of Texas Instruments, Incorporated).

the "tuned-base-tuned-collector oscillator," then sometimes the "tuned-gate-tuned-drain oscillator." To avoid continued renaming of this circuit, we use the name *double-tuned oscillator*.

For each of these oscillators, the *LC* "tank" circuit only passes enough signal at the selected frequency, and also allows the correct phase relationship only at that frequency. The operation of each circuit can be briefly described as follows:

Hartley: When the output end of the coil is driven positive by the op-amp output, the grounded center-tap causes the input end to go negative. This produces a 180° phase shift which, when added to the phase shift of the inverting amplifier, totals 360°. The capacitor resonates with the coil, producing additional phase shift at all frequencies except the resonant frequency. In addition, the high impedance that occurs at resonance causes maximum voltage drop across the coil at resonance, so that the signal at the input end is greatest at resonance. The frequency of oscillation is

$$f_0 = \frac{1}{2\pi\sqrt{LC}} \tag{8.07}$$

where L is the total inductance of the coil. Hartley oscillators are seldom used for variable-frequency operation because of the difficulty and expense of obtaining coils whose inductance can be varied over a wide range.

Colpitts: This circuit operates very much like the Hartley, except that the centerpoint of the "composite capacitor" (C_1, C_2) is grounded. A variation on this circuit that

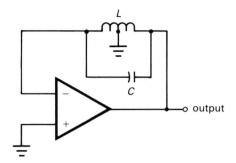

FIGURE 8–2A: Hartley

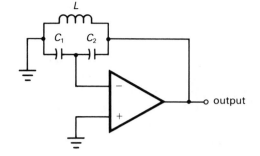

FIGURE 8–2B: Colpitts

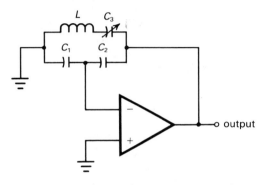

FIGURE 8–2C: Clapp

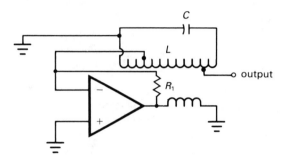

FIGURE 8–2D: Armstrong

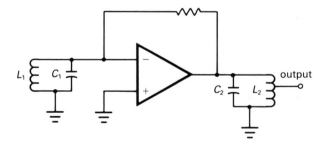

FIGURE 8–2E: Double-Tuned

FIGURE 8–2: *LC* Sine-Wave Oscillators

is sometimes used at high frequencies is to use a transformer primary for the coil, and the secondary (lightly loaded) for the output connection. This can provide a clean sine wave even when the op amp saturates, if the Q of the LC circuit is high enough. The frequency of oscillation is given by equation 8.07, in which C is the total capacitance; that is,

$$C = \left(\frac{1}{C_1} + \frac{1}{C_2}\right)^{-1}$$

Colpitts oscillators can provide a wide range of frequency variation, if a double-ganged tuning capacitor is used.

Clapp: This variation on the Colpitts circuit provides frequency tuning over a limited range, using a single variable capacitor. It works by using the capacitive reactance of C_3 to cancel part of the inductive reactance of the coil, thus changing the resonant frequency. The frequency of oscillation can be calculated by equation 8.07, except that the value of C_3 is included in the value of C; that is,

$$C = \left(\frac{1}{C_1} + \frac{1}{C_2} + \frac{1}{C_3} \right)^{-1}$$

Armstrong: This design uses inductive coupling between the op amp's output and its input, via a "tickler" coil. Phase inversion is provided by the transformer. A certain amount of negative DC feedback is also provided by R_1 to stabilize the DC operation of the circuit. This is another circuit in which the output is taken directly from the tank circuit, so that saturation of the op amp does not prevent it from producing a clean sine wave. The oscillating frequency is given by equation 8.07, in which L is the inductance of the transformer secondary.

Double-tuned: This circuit looks as though it simply provides positive feedback at a single frequency, but it is actually a bit more involved. The input circuit is tuned slightly below the desired output frequency, and the output circuit is tuned slightly above. Thus, each produces a certain amount of phase shift. When both circuits are tuned correctly, exactly 180° of phase shift is added to the phase shift of the inverting amplifier, at only one frequency. Thus the circuit oscillates at that frequency. This circuit can also produce sine waves even when the op amp is saturating on peaks. Both tuned circuits of this circuit are designed according to equation 8.07. Then the capacitors are slightly changed so that the tuning described above is accomplished. Usually the output circuit is tuned first, slightly above f_0, then the input circuit is tuned until oscillation is established. If the output frequency is not correct, the tuning process is repeated until the correct frequency is obtained.

The *frequency stability* of an oscillator refers to how exactly the output frequency remains at the same value over a period of time, and with changing temperature. The stability of an *LC* oscillator depends upon two things: the Q of the *LC* circuit and the temperature coefficient of the inductor and capacitor. A discussion of temperature coefficients can be found in any good electric circuits text. There are several aspects affecting Q, though, that bear mentioning here.

The Q of a passive circuit depends upon the ratio of reactance to resistance in the circuit. Therefore, anything which increases resistance lowers Q. Each capacitor or inductor has a Q.

$$Q_{\text{component}} = \frac{X}{R} \tag{8.08}$$

The Q of virtually all capacitors is quite high. The exception is electrolytics; these capacitors have a significant resistance that increases with frequency. Therefore, electrolytics are not appropriate for use in high-Q tank circuits. The Q of an inductor depends upon the wire gauge with which it is wound and the efficiency of the magnetic circuit. If small (high-resistance) wire is used, and/or there is quite a bit of magnetic leakage, the Q will be low. The resistance or Q of inductors for tank-circuit use is usually specified by the manufacturer.

There is another way in which the Q of a tuned circuit can be reduced. Any circuit that is in parallel with the tank circuit, such as the input circuit of the op amp, lowers the Q. The higher the resistance that is in parallel with the tank circuit, the less the Q is degraded. In circuits in which the output is taken via a secondary winding on the inductor, resistance is reflected back into the tank circuit by the transformer action, lowering the Q. Therefore, the secondary winding should feed into a very high resistance to minimize this effect. The use of a buffer amplifier to provide very-high-impedance loading is helpful.

The Q of the tank circuit also has an important effect upon the output waveform. As we mentioned earlier, the amplifiers used with oscillators often tend to saturate, introducing harmonics into the waveform. High-Q tuned circuits reject these harmonics more effectively than do low-Q circuits. Figure 8–3 shows the effect of the tank-circuit Q upon the harmonic content of the output from an LC oscillator. Notice that a minimum Q of about 20 is desirable.

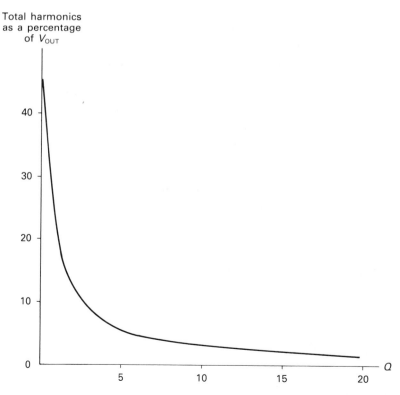

FIGURE 8–3: Harmonic Content of LC Oscillator Using Saturated Op Amp versus Q

EXAMPLE

Problem

Design a Hartley oscillator for an output of 100 kHz. For a minimum Q of 20, specify the maximum resistance for the inductor, ignoring magnetic losses.

Solution

1. We will choose a 1-nF capacitor. Then, solving equation 8.07 for the inductance, we have

$$f = \frac{1}{2\pi\sqrt{LC}}$$

$$f^2 = \frac{1}{4\pi^2 LC}$$

$$L = \frac{1}{4\pi^2 f^2 C} = \frac{1}{4\pi^2(10^{10}\ \text{Hz}^2)(10^{-9}\ \text{F})} = 2.5\ \text{mH} \qquad (8.07)$$

2. The reactance of this coil at 100 kHz is

$$X_L = 2\pi f L = 2\pi(10^5\ \text{Hz})(2.5 \cdot 10^{-3}\ \text{H}) = 1570\ \Omega$$

The resistance that would give a Q of 20 can be calculated from equation 8.08:

$$Q = \frac{X}{R}$$

$$R = \frac{X}{Q} = \frac{1570\ \Omega}{20} = 79\ \Omega \qquad (8.08)$$

In fact, the magnetic leakage of a coil cannot usually be ignored, because it is often as great as 50% or more. Therefore, it is a good rule of thumb to specify a maximum resistance of 1/4 the calculated value; in this case, about 20 Ω.

Crystal Oscillators

It was discovered many years ago that certain materials, notably quartz and Rochelle salts crystals, had the property of *piezoelectricity* (pronounced pie-ee-zoe-electricity, from the Greek verb *piezon*, to press). This means that when these crystals were mechanically stressed, they produced a voltage, and when excited by a voltage they changed their shape. Further, these crystals can act as very high-Q resonant circuits. Thus a crystal can replace capacitors and/or coils in the tank circuit of an oscillator, causing it to produce a very clean, stable output. Figure 8–4A shows a drawing of a crystal, and 8–4B shows its equivalent circuit.

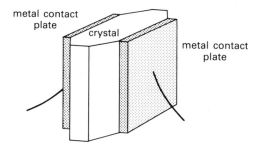

FIGURE 8–4A: Physical Appearance

equivalent circuit of crystal material (heavy lines)

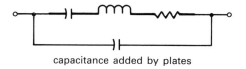

capacitance added by plates

FIGURE 8–4B: Equivalent Circuit

FIGURE 8–4: Crystals

Crystals can be used in oscillators in a number of ways. Figure 8–5 shows a circuit in which the crystal is connected in the positive feedback loop of an op amp. The crystal acts as a parallel-resonant circuit, providing a high impedance and a nonzero phase shift to frequencies other than the resonant frequency.

Crystals are available for frequencies from about 1 to 100 MHz. But their extremely high Q and stable temperature characteristics make crystal oscillators the only choice for oscillators of any frequency if extreme stability is required. Therefore, crystal stabilization is often needed for low- or high-frequency oscillators for frequencies at which no crystal is available. Low-frequency crystal-stabilized oscillators are made by using digital counters to act as frequency dividers, dividing the higher frequency generated by the crystal. For example, a very stable 400-Hz os-

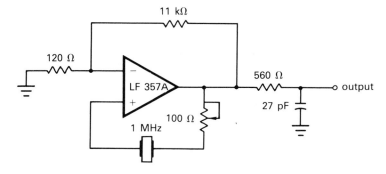

FIGURE 8–5: Crystal Oscillator

cillator can be built from a 3.2768-MHz crystal oscillator (a standard-frequency crystal) and a divide-by-8192 counter. The design of counters and their use as frequency dividers is covered in any good digital electronics text. The output of the frequency divider will be a square wave, so a sine shaper must be added if a sine-wave output is required.

High-frequency crystal oscillators are made by making a lower-frequency crystal oscillator, feeding the output to a Schmitt trigger to square it, and then using a tuned amplifier circuit to amplify the desired harmonic. At present, there are no op amps with sufficient frequency response to be used at frequencies above those for which crystals are available, so this type of circuit would be built from discrete components.

RC Sine-Wave Generators

In sine-wave generator design, as in most other areas of electronics, tradeoffs are necessary. *LC* oscillators, while providing good stability and a reasonably low-distortion waveform in spite of amplifier clipping, are difficult to tune over a wide frequency range. Also, they are inappropriate at audio frequencies because of the large inductors that would be required. Crystal oscillators, while providing the greatest stability, are not tunable at all, and require digital divider circuits and sine shapers in order to produce low-frequency outputs. For these reasons, *RC* oscillators are usually used to generate audio-frequency sine waves. Although requiring special measures to avoid amplifier distortion and lacking the stability of either *LC* or crystal oscillators, *RC* oscillators do provide low-frequency operation without inductors or frequency dividers, and one type of *RC* oscillator is also tunable over a wide range.

The circuit of an *RC phase-shift oscillator* is shown in Figure 8–6. It simply consists of an inverting amplifier with three *RC* high-pass networks connected in the feedback loop. At one frequency, each *RC* network will provide a 60° phase shift, resulting in a total 180° phase shift for the three networks. Added to the inversion produced by the amplifier, this results in a 360° phase shift at the selected frequency.

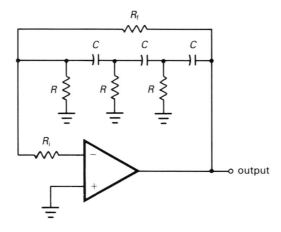

FIGURE 8–6: *RC* Phase-Shift Oscillator

It is more difficult to satisfy the gain requirement of the Barkhausen criterion. In fact, a special *adaptive feedback* circuit is required to keep the loop gain exactly unity for this circuit. (This circuit will be discussed in more detail later in this chapter.) Without adaptive feedback, the op amp will saturate, producing square waves at the desired frequency. The loss provided by the phase-shift network at f_0 is approximately 0.034. This means that in order to have unity loop gain, the op amp must have a minimum gain of $1/0.034 = 29$. Slightly more gain is usually provided, then automatic adjustment is made by the adaptive feedback circuit.

The output frequency of a phase-shift oscillator is given approximately by

$$f_0 = \frac{1}{2\pi\sqrt{6}RC} \tag{8.09}$$

It is possible to vary the frequency of a phase-shift oscillator by varying any of the resistances or capacitances. However, the capacitor values necessary for audio-frequency oscillation are generally so large that variable versions are not available. If a single or double-ganged variable resistor is used, the frequency equation becomes:

$$f_0 = \left(\frac{1}{2\pi\sqrt{6}C}\right)\left(\frac{1}{\sqrt[3]{R_1 R_2 R_3}}\right) \tag{8.10}$$

However, since each of the RC networks is loaded by the remainder of the circuit, the maximum phase shift of each section is well under 90°. Using unequal components will result in more phase shift being required of some sections than of others. Since there is not a lot of margin available between the 60° provided by each of three equal networks and the maximum phase shift required if unequal networks are used, attempting to obtain much frequency variation by varying only one, or even two, of the three resistors may well result in a circuit that fails to oscillate. For this reason, phase-shift oscillators, while the most stable of the RC oscillators with respect to frequency, are seldom used for applications requiring wide frequency variations.

EXAMPLE

Problem

Design a phase-shift oscillator to provide a stable 1-kHz sine wave. Provide for a ±50-Hz variation about f_0.

Solution

1. We will use a 0.01-μF capacitor. Using equation 8.09, we can solve for R:

$$f_0 = \frac{1}{2\pi\sqrt{6}RC}$$

$$R = \frac{1}{2\pi\sqrt{6}fC} = \frac{1}{(2\pi\sqrt{6}\cdot 1000\ \text{Hz}\cdot 10^{-8}\ \text{F})} = 6497\ \Omega \tag{8.09}$$

2. Since ±50 Hz is a small variation, we will try using a single potentiometer to provide tuning. Rather than solving equation 8.10 to find the value of the potentiometer, let us analyze the equation for the information we need. Varying a single resistor by a proportion R_{new}/R_{old} causes a frequency variation proportional to $\sqrt[3]{R_{new}/R_{old}}$. Since 1050 Hz/1000 Hz = 1.05, and 950 Hz/1000 Hz = 0.95, the resistance ratios must be

$$\frac{R_{min}}{6497\ \Omega} = (0.95)^3 = 0.857$$

Therefore, $R_{min} = 0.857 \cdot 6497\ \Omega = 5568\ \Omega$.

$$\frac{R_{max}}{6497\ \Omega} = (1.05)^3 = 1.16$$

Therefore, $R_{max} = 7537\ \Omega$.
A 5000-Ω resistor in series with a 5000-Ω potentiometer will provide more than the required variation.

3. In order to prevent loading of the phase-shift network, we will let $R_i = 10R = 65$ kΩ. Then in order to have a minimum gain of 29, we would need a 1.9 MΩ resistor for R_f. Using a 2.2-MΩ resistor will give a small gain margin, which will be taken care of by the adaptive feedback.

Figure 8–7 shows the circuit of a *bridged-tee* (sometimes called a *twin-tee*) oscillator. The frequency-determining element in this circuit was discussed in Chapter 7; it is a passive notch filter. When this filter is connected in the negative feedback loop of an op amp, it provides negative feedback with little attenuation at all frequencies except the notch frequency. At that frequency, there is no negative feedback; the phase shift in the network is also zero at the notch frequency. The addition of a small amount of positive feedback to provide unity net loop gain completes the circuit. The output frequency of a bridged-tee oscillator is given approximately by

$$f_0 = \frac{1}{5RC} \tag{8.11}$$

Like the phase-shift oscillator, the bridged-tee oscillator requires adaptive feedback to avoid amplifier saturation.

The most popular *RC* oscillator is the *Wien-bridge* (pronounced "veen-bridge") oscillator, shown in Fig. 8–8. Part A of the figure shows the bridge configuration. In part B, the circuit is redrawn to show its operation more clearly. The positive feedback loop consists of a series *RC* circuit and a parallel *RC* circuit. Usually the values of *R* and *C* are equal in these circuits, although they do not need to be. Each circuit provides a phase shift of the fed-back signal. At one frequency, the phase shift provided by the series circuit cancels that provided by the parallel circuit. At this frequency, the total phase shift in the feedback loop is 0°. R_f and R_g provide enough gain to offset the loss of the *RC* networks at f_0, which is 0.33. Thus a gain of 1/0.33 = 3 is required.

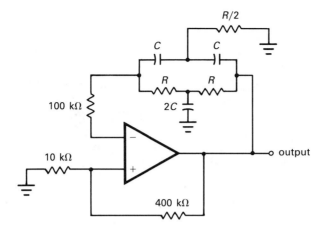

FIGURE 8–7: Bridged-Tee Oscillator

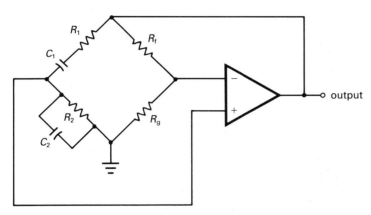

FIGURE 8–8A: Basic Circuit

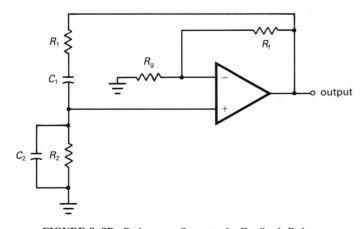

FIGURE 8–8B: Redrawn to Separate the Feedback Paths

FIGURE 8–8: Wien-Bridge Oscillator

The frequency can be determined by

$$f_0 = \frac{1}{2\pi RC} \tag{8.12}$$

Equation 8.12 assumes that both resistors and both capacitors are equal. The Wien-bridge oscillator can provide frequency tuning over a range of three decades, if a dual-ganged potentiometer is used for the resistors. In this application, the inability of dual pots to track perfectly is of no particular importance. (Tracking is the ability of one potentiometer of a dual unit to have exactly the same resistance as the other potentiometer at each position of rotation. Typical tracking for most dual pots is no better than about ±10%.)

EXAMPLE

Problem

Design a Wien-bridge oscillator to produce an output frequency that can be varied from 20 Hz to 20 kHz.

Solution

1. Let us try a 0.1-μF capacitor and see whether it will allow practical resistance values.

$$f_0 = \frac{1}{2\pi RC} \tag{8.12}$$

$$R_{min} = \frac{1}{2\pi f_0 C} = \frac{1}{2\pi \cdot 20 \text{ kHz} \cdot 10^{-7} F} = 79 \ \Omega$$

$$R_{max} = \frac{1}{2\pi \cdot 20 \cdot 10^{-7} F)} = 80 \text{ k}\Omega$$

This would require a 100-kΩ potentiometer, since that is the next standard value. Theoretically, the potentiometer will adjust all the way down to zero ohms, so we should use a 68-Ω resistor in series with the pot to provide a lower limit. However, real pots may not go below 50 Ω or thereabouts, so the series resistor will probably not be necessary.

2. The choice of R_g will depend upon bias-current considerations. The average value of resistance from the noninverting input to ground will be the half-rotation resistance of the 100-kΩ potentiometer, which is 50 kΩ. Therefore, the parallel combination of R_g and R_f should be 50 kΩ. The gain of a noninverting amplifier is given by

$$A_V = 1 + \frac{R_f}{R_g} \tag{2.10}$$

Since the gain is to be 3, we have

$$3 = 1 + \frac{R_f}{R_g}$$

$$\frac{R_f}{R_g} = 2$$

$$R_f = 2R_g$$

Now if we combine this last equation with the bias-current compensation conditions, we have

$$R_g \parallel 2R_g = 50 \text{ k}\Omega$$

$$\frac{R_g \cdot 2R_g}{R_g + 2R_g} = 50 \text{ k}\Omega$$

$$\frac{2R_g^2}{3R_g} = 50 \text{ k}\Omega = \frac{2R_g}{3}$$

$$R_g = \frac{50 \text{ k}\Omega \cdot 3}{2} = 75 \text{ k}\Omega$$

Then $R_f = 150 \text{ k}\Omega$.

3. These are rather large resistors, so now let us check to see whether we will have bias-current problems. The greatest mismatch we will have between the resistance to ground at the inverting and noninverting inputs will be when the pot is set at maximum; the mismatch will then be 50 kΩ. The bias maximum current of a 741C op amp is 1.5 μA over the full operating temperature range. This will give us a worst-case input offset voltage of 50 kΩ · 1.5 μA = 75 mV. With a gain of 3, the output offset voltage will only be 3 · 75 mV = 225 mV. This is acceptable, because the circuit is for AC use, and this offset voltage will not significantly affect the maximum output voltage.

The last type of *RC* oscillator we will discuss is the *quadrature oscillator*. This one is unusual in that it provides two outputs in quadrature; that is, 90° out of phase. These are shown in Fig. 8–9 as the *sine* and *cosine* outputs. There are certain types of electronic communication that require 90° out-of-phase waves—notably narrow-band FM (used for police and emergency communications) and single-sideband (used in many point-to-point services). The circuit's operation can be described as follows. Amplifier A₂ is an integrator. As you probably remember, an integrator with a sine-wave input produces a cosine-wave output. In other words, an integrator produces a 270° phase shift. It also produces unity gain. Amplifier A₁ looks like an integrator, except that it has the signal applied to the noninverting input. This changes it from a true integrator into a low-pass filter. Its operation can be easily analyzed. First, we must remember that the gain of an inverting amplifier, although usually written as $1 + R_f/R_g$, can also be written as

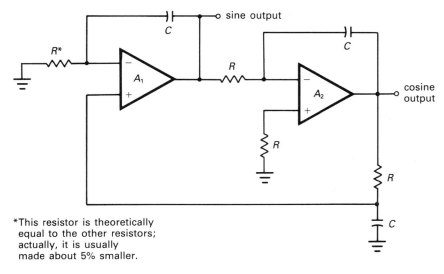

*This resistor is theoretically
equal to the other resistors;
actually, it is usually
made about 5% smaller.

FIGURE 8–9: Quadrature Oscillator

$$A_V = \frac{R_f + R_g}{R_g} \tag{2.10}$$

Since the feedback element in A_1's circuit is a capacitor, this becomes

$$A_V = \frac{\sqrt{X_C^2 + R_g^2} \,/\underline{\text{arctan}\ (X_C/R_g)}}{R_g}$$

Let us investigate only the frequency at which X_C and R_g are equal in magnitude. At that frequency, the gain is

$$A_V = \frac{\sqrt{2}\, R_g \,/\underline{\text{arctan}\ (1)}}{R_g} = \sqrt{2} \,/\underline{45°}$$

So we see that amplifier A_1 provides a 45° phase shift at the frequency at which the magnitudes of X_C and R are equal. We will call this frequency f_0. The remaining portion of the overall feedback loop consists of an RC low-pass filter. Since this filter consists of the same components as the local feedback loop of A_1, it contributes a 45° phase shift at f_0. Thus the phase shift around the loop is 270° from the integrator, plus 45° from A_1, plus 45° from the RC network, for a total of 360°. The loss factor introduced by the RC filter at f_0 is

$$A_{RC} = \frac{X_C}{\sqrt{R^2 + X_C^2}} = \frac{1}{\sqrt{2}}$$

Thus the total loop gain of the circuit equals the integrator's gain, multiplied by A_1's gain, multiplied by the gain of the RC network:

$$A_{\text{loop}} = 1 \cdot \sqrt{2} \cdot \frac{1}{\sqrt{2}} = 1$$

So the Barkhausen criterion is satisfied.

Normally, in order to provide a bit of gain margin to ensure that the circuit will oscillate, the resistor used for R_g of A_1 is made about 5% smaller than the other three resistors. With that slight change, component values are chosen in accordance with equation 8.11.

The Amplitude Problem and Adaptive Feedback

The term *adaptive feedback* has already been introduced. It is a special form of feedback used to stabilize the output of an oscillator at some value below the saturation level of the op amp. Adaptive feedback is necessary because of the impossibility of maintaining a loop gain of exactly unity. With a loop gain smaller than unity, no oscillation will occur. But with a loop gain greater than unity, the oscillations will very rapidly grow in amplitude until they are limited by saturation of the op amp. Of course, the output of the oscillator is then almost a square wave rather than a sine wave.

All forms of adaptive feedback use some variety of nonlinear resistance in the feedback loop. The earliest form, and one that held favor for many years, simply used an incandescent lamp. If the active device of the oscillator was a vacuum tube, the lamp was connected between the cathode and ground. A resistor connected at that point decreased the gain of the tube stage, just as an unbypassed emitter resistor does in a common-emitter transistor amplifier. When the tube began to saturate, the current increased, heating up the filament in the lamp. This heating increased the resistance of the filament, thus reducing the stage gain. An equilibrium point was reached just short of saturation, allowing the oscillator to provide maximum output without distortion. This same approach can be used with transistor circuits, provided that the transistor draws enough current to operate the lamp. (A few milliamps are required.) However, the technique is seldom used with op amps because there is usually not enough current available in the feedback loop to operate the lamp, where a varying resistance would make a difference. Besides, the response of the lamp is slow, requiring a few seconds to stabilize after oscillator frequency is changed.

Incandescent lamps provide a resistance that is almost linearly proportional to the filament current. This is ideal for amplifiers having limited gain, as do single-stage vacuum-tube or transistor amplifiers. However, because of their extremely high open-loop gain, op amps can make use of a component that provides nonlinear resistance in a much more abrupt fashion. This component is a Zener diode. Figure 8–10A shows the characteristic curve of a Zener diode. This curve is a graph of current versus voltage. Therefore, the slope of the curve at any point is the conductance of the diode at the corresponding value of voltage. Stated differently, the inverse of the slope at any point equals the resistance of the diode at that point. Notice that at the knee (threshold of conduction), the resistance changes very rapidly but continuously from almost infinity to almost zero. If two Zeners are connected

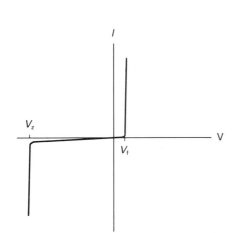

FIGURE 8–10A: Characteristic Curve of a Zener Diode

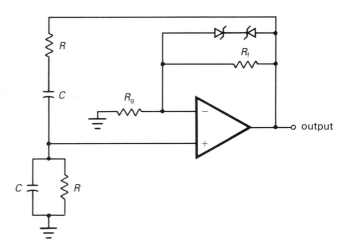

FIGURE 8–10B: Wien-Bridge Oscillator with Zener Adaptive Feedback

FIGURE 8–10: Zener Adaptive Feedback

back-to-back, then placed in parallel with the negative-feedback resistor R_f, as shown in Fig. 8–10B, then at the point at which the output voltage of the op amp approaches the Zener voltage, the resistance of the Zeners will begin to decrease rapidly, reducing the gain of the circuit. This abrupt change in feedback resistance would cause its own distortion if it were not for two facts. First, the gain without the Zeners is limited by design to a value only slightly above that required for unity loop gain, so that a small decrease in gain is all that is required to provide stabilization. This means that the Zeners operate only barely in the knee region. And second, the distortion produced by the Zeners is added *in the feedback loop,* rather than in the output of the amplifier, as would be the case with distortion produced by saturation. This distortion can show up in the output only if it passes through the oscillator circuit. But since the distortion consists of harmonics (frequencies other than f_0), the frequency-selective feedback elements cause the loop gain to be very low at the distortion frequencies. As a result, the amount of distortion added to the output by the adaptive feedback is very small.

There are other ways to build adaptive-feedback circuits. One is to use signal diodes connected in antiparallel (Fig. 8–11A). These act similarly to Zeners, except that the peak limiting voltage is the forward conduction threshold of the diodes (about 0.6 V).

Although Wien-bridge oscillators have been used in the examples showing adaptive-feedback circuits, these techniques can be applied to any oscillator circuit. For the Zener or signal-diode methods, the diodes are placed in parallel with the feedback resistors of most oscillators. For the quadrature oscillator, they are placed in parallel with the feedback capacitor of amplifier 2.

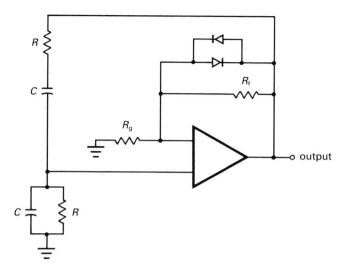

FIGURE 8–11: Signal-Diode Adaptive Feedback

TRIANGLE-WAVE GENERATORS

Although they function in the same sort of way that sine-wave oscillators do, circuits that generate other waveforms are usually called *generators* rather than *oscillators*. Triangle waves are useful for many applications in which a linear voltage change with time is needed. There are two basic waveforms that can be classed as triangle waves. The symmetrical wave shown in Fig. 8–12A is the one usually called a triangle wave. The ramp or sawtooth wave shown in Fig. 8–12B is another waveform of the same family, and is generated similarly.

Figure 8–13A shows the idea behind a triangle-wave generator. Notice that it is just an integrator with a polarity-reversing circuit. As you remember from Chapter 2, when a DC voltage is applied to the input of an integrator, a negative ramp is generated at the output. (Review Fig. 2–29 if you need to.) If we use an automatic

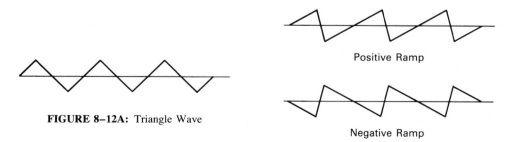

FIGURE 8–12A: Triangle Wave

Positive Ramp

Negative Ramp

FIGURE 8–12B: Sawtooth or Ramp Wave

FIGURE 8–12: The Triangle-Waveform Family

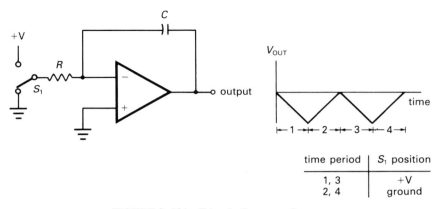

FIGURE 8–13A: Triangle-Generator Concept

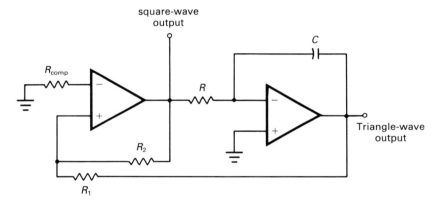

FIGURE 8–13B: Triangle-Generator Circuit

FIGURE 8–13: Triangle-Wave Generator

switch to invert the polarity of the DC voltage when the output voltage reaches a certain value, the ramp will also reverse. Again reversing the polarity at the top of the new ramp will once again produce a negative ramp. Figure 8–13B shows a practical circuit that includes the polarity inverter. Notice that the added circuit is just a Schmitt trigger—a comparator with an upper and a lower trigger level. This circuit was illustrated earlier in Fig. 2–6. The circuit works as follows. When power is first applied to the circuit, the comparator will come up in either the high or the low state. Let us assume that the comparator comes up in the high state. This means that the integrator begins to produce a negative ramp at its output. When the integrator's output voltage reaches the Schmitt trigger's lower threshold voltage, the output of the comparator will switch to the low state. Now the integrator's output will assume the form of a positive ramp. This condition will continue until the output of the integrator reaches the upper threshold voltage of the trigger circuit, at which time the output will switch again.

The operating frequency of the generator depends upon how rapidly the integrator output changes from the upper to the lower threshold point. This, in turn, depends upon the resistor and capacitor used in the integrator, the supply voltage, and the two resistors used in the Schmitt trigger. The slope of the integrator's output ramp is just V_{SAT}/RC Volts/second. The threshold points of the Schmitt trigger are given by

$$V_{threshold} = V_{SAT\pm}\left(\frac{R_1}{R_2}\right)$$

where V_{SAT} can be either V_{SAT+} or V_{SAT-}. This equation differs from equation 2.03 because we are using the noninverting input. This means that the difference between the upper and lower threshold voltages is

$$V_{P-P} = 2V_{SAT}\left(\frac{R_1}{R_2}\right) \tag{8.13}$$

If we divide this voltage difference by the slope (in volts/second) of the integrator's output ramp, we will have the amount of time that is required for the waveform to go from a positive to a negative peak, or vice versa. This will be one half the period of the triangle wave:

$$\frac{t}{2} = \frac{V_{P-P}}{\text{slope}}$$

$$= \frac{2V_{SAT}\, R_1/R_2}{V_{SAT}/RC} = \frac{2R_1RC}{R_2} \tag{8.14}$$

If we multiply this equation by 2, we will have the period of the output wave. Inverting the result will give us the frequency:

$$f_{triangle} = \frac{R_2}{4R_1RC} \tag{8.15}$$

The peak-to-peak output voltage of the triangle-wave generator is equal to the voltage difference between the trigger points, or V_{P-P}, as given in equation 8.13.

EXAMPLE

Problem

Design a triangle-wave generator for a frequency range of 100 to 10,000 Hz, with an output voltage of 10 V_{P-P}.

Solution

1. Let us use a ± 15-V supply, so that V_{SAT} will be about ± 14 V. Then we can solve equation 8.14 to find the values for R_1 and R_2.

$$V_{P-P} = \frac{2V_{SAT}R_1}{R_2}, \therefore R_2 = \frac{2V_{SAT}R_1}{V_{P-P}} \qquad (8.13)$$

We will use a 1-kΩ resistor for R_1. Then R_2 becomes

$$R_2 = \frac{2 \cdot 14 \text{ V} \cdot 1 \text{ k}\Omega}{10 \text{ V}_{P-P}} = 2.8 \text{ k}\Omega$$

2. The value of R_{comp} is

$$R_{comp} = R_1 \parallel R_2 = 1 \text{ k}\Omega \parallel 2.8 \text{ k}\Omega = 667 \ \Omega$$

We will use a 680-Ω resistor for R_{comp}.
3. Now we can choose $C = 0.1 \ \mu\text{F}$ and use equation 8.15 to find R:

$$f_{triangle} = \frac{R_2}{4R_1RC} \qquad (8.15)$$

$$R = \frac{R_2}{4R_1 f_{triangle}C}$$

Of course a potentiometer must be used for R in order to provide a variable frequency. The minimum and maximum values are as follows:

$$R_{min} = \frac{2.8 \text{ k}\Omega}{(4 \cdot 1 \text{ k}\Omega \cdot 10 \text{ kHz} \cdot 10^{-8} \text{ F})} = 7 \text{ k}\Omega$$

$$R_{max} = \frac{2.8 \text{ k}\Omega}{(4 \cdot 1 \text{ k}\Omega \cdot 100 \text{ Hz} \cdot 10^{-8} \text{ F})} = 700 \text{ k}\Omega$$

We can therefore use a 1-MΩ potentiometer in series with a 7-kΩ resistor for R.

You may have noticed that the triangle-wave generator has a no-cost side benefit: it also produces a rather good square wave at the output of the comparator. By introducing a variation into the circuit, the positive and negative slopes of the triangle wave can be made to be different, which will also vary the duty cycle of the square wave. This variation consists of a diode and resistor in parallel with R, allowing the integrator capacitor to charge and discharge at different rates. Depending upon the direction in which the diode is inserted, either the positive or the negative slope of the triangle wave can be varied. This also provides for varying the duty cycle of the square wave. A circuit with its corresponding output waveforms is shown in Fig. 8–14. Notice that the positive slope of the output stays the same, but the negative slope varies as R_3 is varied. Thus the frequency depends upon R_3 also:

$$f_{sawtooth} = \frac{R_2}{2R_1C(R + R_3)} \qquad (8.16)$$

Sweep circuits for oscilloscopes and similar instruments require triangle waves with very rapid fall times. The circuit shown in Fig. 8–14 can produce fairly rapid fall times if R is allowed to be reduced to zero ohms. However, the switching time

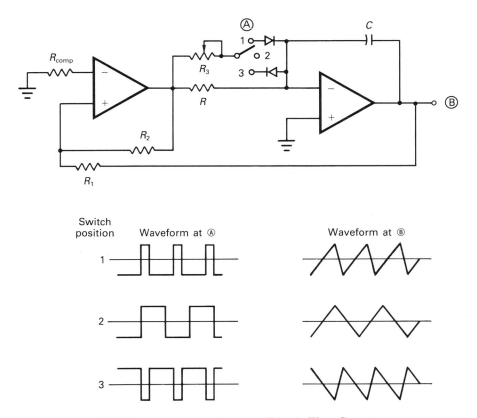

FIGURE 8–14: Variable-Symmetry Triangle-Wave Generator

and output resistance of the comparator still provide a practical limit on the minimum fall time. Figure 8–15A shows a circuit for generating a sweep waveform that not only has a rapid fall time, but also has a variable *holdoff*. Before discussing the circuit, let us first review the functions of the three portions of a sweep wave in an oscilloscope. The positive ramp (segment 1 in Fig. 8–15B) is the portion of the wave that causes the electron beam to sweep across the CRT screen. The falling portion (segment 2 in the figure) causes the beam to return quickly to its original position. It is called the *retrace* portion of the sweep wave. The portion during which the instantaneous voltage remains zero (segment 3) is the time during which the oscilloscope is waiting for the proper trigger signal to begin another sweep. This is the holdoff portion.

The sweep generator shown in Fig. 8–15A is just an integrator with a transistor connected in such a way as to short out (discharge) the capacitor. In use, the transistor's base would be fed from a timing circuit that produces a pulse train similar to the one shown in Fig. 8–15C. Notice that when the control voltage goes high, the transistor is turned on, discharging *C*. The output quickly falls to zero volts and stays there during the holdoff period, which lasts until the control voltage is dropped to zero, turning off the transistor.

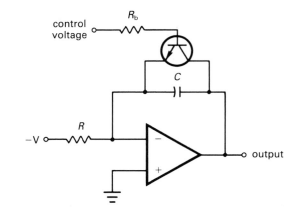

FIGURE 8–15A: Sweep-Generator Circuit

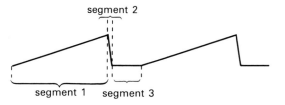

FIGURE 8–15B: Sweep Waveform

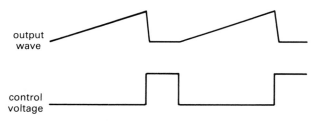

FIGURE 8–15C: Control Voltage Timing

FIGURE 8–15: A Sweep Generator

RECTANGULAR-WAVE GENERATORS

Op-Amp Circuits

We have already discussed one type of rectangular-wave generator—the triangle-wave generator. This circuit is often used to generate square waves in applications in which both square and triangle waves are needed, and in which very fast rise and fall times are not essential. If output levels no greater than 5 V_{P-P} are needed, faster transition times can be obtained by feeding the output of any waveform generator into a digital Schmitt trigger buffer or inverter, such as the 74LS14.

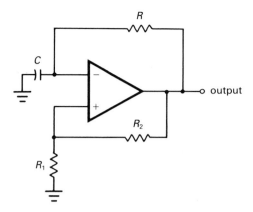

FIGURE 8–16: Op-Amp Square-Wave Generator

Another form of square-wave generator is shown in Fig. 8–16. This circuit is an oscillating version of a Schmitt trigger and is called an *astable multivibrator*. In order to examine its operation, let us assume that the circuit output begins in a high state when power has just been applied. This causes C to charge through R. When the voltage on C reaches the upper threshold point of the Schmitt trigger, the output will switch to a low state, because the capacitor is connected to the inverting input. The output being low will cause the capacitor to begin to discharge through R. When the voltage on the capacitor drops to the lower threshold point, the output will switch to a high state again. Since the capacitor is not in the feedback loop of the IC, it is not charged by a constant current, as it would be in an integrator circuit. Constant-voltage charging of a capacitor results in a voltage that changes in an inverse exponential fashion. Therefore, the equation for the output frequency is rather complex:

$$f_0 = \frac{1}{2RC \ln[(2R_1 + R_2)/R_2]} \qquad (8.17)$$

This equation can be considerably simplified by making the natural log term in the denominator equal unity: If

$$\ln[(2R_1 + R_2)/R_2] = 1 \qquad (8.18)$$

then

$$f_0 = \frac{1}{2RC} \qquad (8.19)$$

In solving equation 8.18 to find the relation of R_1 to R_2, we must first clear the ln function. Then we have

$$\frac{2R_1 + R_2}{R_2} = e^1 = e$$

where e is the root of natural logs (approximately 2.72). Solving for R_2 in terms of R_1 gives:

$$2.72R_2 = 2R_1 + R_2$$

$$R_2 = \left(\frac{2}{1.72}\right)R_1 = 1.16R_1 \qquad (8.20)$$

EXAMPLE

Problem

Design a square-wave generator to provide a 100-kHz output for use as a TTL clock.

Solution

1. Letting $R_1 = 1\ k\Omega$, R_2 must be $1.16\ k\Omega$, from equation 8.20.
2. Choosing $C = 1$ nF, we can solve for R:

$$f_0 = \frac{1}{2RC} \qquad (8.19)$$

$$R = \frac{1}{2f_0C} = \frac{1}{2\cdot 10^5\ \text{Hz}\cdot 10^{-9}\ \text{F}} = 5\ k\Omega$$

3. We can limit the output voltage to levels appropriate for TTL (i.e., 0 V and 5 V) by using diodes connected as shown in Fig. 2–8.

IC Timers

One of the most versatile circuits for building rectangular-wave generators is the IC timer. There are basically two families of timers, the 555 and the 2240. The 555 is the first IC timer that was introduced, and it is still quite popular in both existing and new designs. Its internal circuitry is illustrated in the block diagram of Fig. 8–17. The heart of the device is an RS (reset-set) flip-flop. When the S input to this flip-flop is made high, the Q output becomes high and the Q' output becomes low. This is called the *set* condition. (The Q' output is always the complement of the Q output, so its level will not be mentioned further. This output has no effect on the other workings of the IC and is not available as an output from the chip.) After the flip-flop is set, changing the S input has no further effect on it; the Q output remains high. If the R (reset) input is then made high, the Q output will become low (reset condition), remaining low until the flip-flop is again set. The flip-flop is operated by two comparators; comparator A feeds the S input and comparator B feeds the R input. The reference input to each comparator is fed from a voltage divider that is powered through supply pin 8, which is connected to V_{CC}. Comparator A's reference is $\frac{2}{3}V_{CC}$; comparator B's reference, $\frac{1}{3}V_{CC}$. Thus if the input to pin 6 (threshold) is greater than $\frac{2}{3}V_{CC}$, the flip-flop will be set. If the input to pin 2 (trigger)

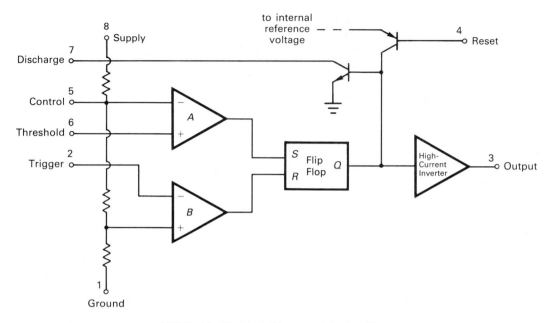

FIGURE 8–17: Block Diagram of the 555 Timer

is made greater than $\frac{1}{3} V_{CC}$, the flip-flop will be reset. An additional input (control) to comparator A is available to allow direct control of both comparators' switching levels. The flip-flop can also be reset by a ground connection at the system reset input at pin 4. In most circuits, this feature is not used, and pin 4 is tied to V_{CC}. The output of the flip-flop is inverted before appearing at pin 3. The inverter used is a high-current unit that can supply or sink up to 200 mA. Also connected to the flip-flop output is a transistor that has an open-collector output and is usually used to provide a discharge path for an external timing capacitor; when the flip-flop's output is high, the transistor is turned on. The "high" output voltage is about 1.5 V less than V_{CC}. The "low" output voltage is about 0.1 V. The output of the 555 can be used either to source or to sink output current. For loads connected between the power supply and the output, the 555 acts as a normally on device, turning off the load when the output goes high. For loads connected between the output and ground, the 555 is normally off, and turns on the load when the output is high.

The assortment of building blocks in the 555 make it an extremely versatile IC. Figure 8–18 shows four circuits using the 555. They are briefly discussed below:

Monostable: A monostable multivibrator (usually just called a monostable) is a circuit that, when triggered, responds with an output pulse of a preset width and height. In other words, it is a pulse shaper. Such circuits are useful at the receive end of a digital communication link. Incoming pulses that have been distorted and attenuated by noise and line capacitance can be reformed by a monostable. Another name for a monostable is a *one-shot*. The trigger pulse must be a negative-going pulse whose level is less than $\frac{1}{3}V_{CC}$ during the pulse's "on" time. (An inverter can be used to convert a positive-going pulse if necessary.) When the circuit is first powered up, the flip-flop output is high, causing the internal discharge transistor to keep the capacitor shorted. The internal inverter makes the output low when the flip-flop output is high. When an input voltage less positive than $\frac{1}{3}V_{CC}$ is applied to the trigger input, the flip-flop switches to the low state, turning off the discharge capacitor, and switching the output to the high state. Now the capacitor charges through R_A. When the charge on the capacitor reaches $\frac{2}{3}V_{CC}$, the flip-flop again switches to the high state,

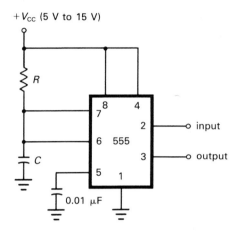

FIGURE 8–18A: Monostable

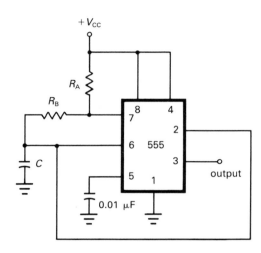

FIGURE 8–18B: Astable

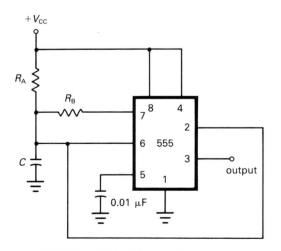

FIGURE 8–18C: 50% Duty-Cycle Astable

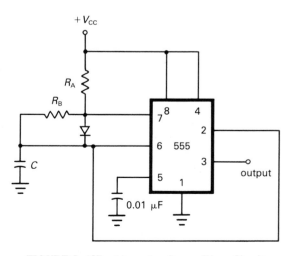

FIGURE 8–18D: Alternative Square-Wave Circuit

FIGURE 8–18: 555 Timer Applications

H. W. Bode, who discovered the connection between the gain and phase of feedback amplifiers and oscillators (Courtesy of AT&T).

discharging the capacitor, and bringing the output low. The pulse width is given by

$$\text{P.W.} = 1.1RC \tag{8.21}$$

The reason that this voltage does not depend upon the supply voltage is that both the trigger voltage and the capacitor's charge rate depend upon the supply voltage, so that dependence cancels out.

Astable: The term *astable multivibrator* has already been introduced as another name for a rectangular-wave generator. This circuit is also often called a *free-running multivibrator*. The circuit operates similarly to the monostable circuit. The difference is that the trigger input is fed from the same point as the threshold input: the top of the timing capacitor. Also, the capacitor discharges through a timing resistor R_B, rather than directly into the discharge transistor. Thus when the flip-flop output is high, the transistor discharges the capacitor through R_B until the voltage at the top of the capacitor (V_C) equals $\frac{1}{3}V_{CC}$. Then the flip-flop is reset: Its output goes low, the 555's output goes high, and the discharge transistor is turned off. Now the capacitor charges through R_A and R_B in series. When the capacitor voltage reaches $\frac{2}{3}V_{CC}$, the flip-flop is set: its output goes high, the 555's output goes low, and the discharge transistor is turned on, allowing the capacitor to discharge again through R_B. The time during which the output is high is the time when the capacitor is charging:

$$t_{\text{charge}} = 0.693(R_A + R_B)C \tag{8.22}$$

The time while the output is low is the discharge time of the capacitor:

$$t_{\text{discharge}} = 0.693R_BC \tag{8.23}$$

The period is the sum of these two times:

$$t = t_{\text{charge}} + t_{\text{discharge}} = 0.693(R_A + 2R_B)C \tag{8.24}$$

The inverse of this equation gives the frequency of oscillation:

$$f = \frac{1}{0.693(R_A + 2R_B)C} = \frac{1.44}{(R_A + 2R_B)C} \tag{8.25}$$

This circuit cannot generate square waves, since the discharge time must always be greater than the charge time.

50%-Duty-Cycle Astable: In this circuit, R_B is placed in series with the discharge pin so that it is not in the capacitor's charging circuit. Therefore,

$$t_{\text{charge}} = 0.693R_AC \tag{8.26}$$

However, the equation for "low" time is more complex:

$$t_{\text{discharge}} = (R_A \| R_B)C \ln\left(\frac{R_B - 2R_A}{2R_B - R_A}\right)$$

In order for this to be equal to the "high" time, the right side of this equation must equal the right side of equation 8.22:

$$0.693R_A C = (R_A \| R_B)C \ln \left(\frac{R_B - 2R_A}{2R_B - R_A} \right)$$

or

$$0.693R_A = (R_A \| R_B) \ln \left(\frac{R_B - 2R_A}{2R_B - R_A} \right)$$

This type of equation is rather difficult to solve, but the correct ratio of R_A/R_B = 2.36, for a 50% duty cycle. This circuit is rather sensitive to errors in resistor values; a 1% error in the value of R_A or R_B can cause a 3% error in the discharge time. The easiest way to achieve the correct resistance ratio is to use a potentiometer for part of either R_A or R_B, then adjust for the correct duty cycle as observed on a 'scope. In using this circuit for other duty cycles, notice that the circuit will not work for ratios of R_A/R_B equal to or less than 2, because the logarithmic term of the equation would then have zero in the denominator. The physical result is that the voltage at the junction of R_A and R_B cannot drop to $\frac{1}{3}V_{CC}$ to trigger comparator B.

Alternate Square-Wave Circuit: This circuit simply uses a diode to bypass R_B during the charging time of the capacitor. Since the dynamic resistance of a diode is very low, this makes the duty cycle very nearly 50%.

A related IC is the 556 dual timer. This is simply two 555's in the same package, independent except for shared V_{CC} and ground connections.

EXAMPLE

Problem

Design a circuit to generate pulses with a 75% duty cycle and a frequency of 400 Hz.

Solution

1. Let us choose a 0.1-μF capacitor and solve the frequency equation for the sum of R_A and $2R_B$:

$$f = \frac{1.44}{(R_A + 2R_B)C}$$

$$R_A + 2R_B = \frac{1.44}{fC} = \frac{1.44}{400 \text{Hz} \cdot 10^{-7} \text{ F}} = 36 \text{ k}\Omega \qquad (8.25)$$

2. For a 75% duty cycle, the discharge time ("high" time) must equal three times the charge time ("low" time):

$$t_{\text{charge}} = 3t_{\text{discharge}}$$

This means that

$$0.693(R_A + R_B)C = 3(0.693R_B C) \qquad \text{(from 8.22 and 8.23)}$$

or

$$R_A + R_B = 3R_B$$
$$R_A = 2R_B$$

3. We can substitute the result of step 2 into the result of step 1:

$$4R_B = 36 \text{ k}\Omega$$
$$R_B = 9 \text{ k}\Omega$$

Then

$$R_A = 2R_B = 18 \text{ k}\Omega.$$

Another very versatile timer is the 2240 programmable counter-timer. As shown in Fig. 8–19, the 2240 consists of a time-base oscillator, a flip-flop, an eight-stage digital counter, and a voltage regulator. Figure 8–20A shows the 2240 connected as an astable. As shown by the output waveforms, in addition to the output from the time base, outputs can be taken from the counters, which act as frequency dividers. The counter chain can divide the time-base frequency by any integer factor from 2 to 128. In actual practice, only one output is used (or perhaps a few), and the other pullup resistors are omitted. In this circuit, the charge and discharge times are equal:

$$t = \frac{RC}{2}, \text{ where } t = \text{charge time} = \text{discharge time} = \frac{\tau}{2}. \qquad (8.27)$$

The 10-kΩ resistor and 0.047-μF capacitor connected to the trigger input are required to ensure that the oscillator will start upon power-up. Alternatively, a 5-V input pulse can be applied to the trigger input to cause oscillations to start.

Figure 8–20B shows the 2240 connected as a programmable monostable. The resistor, capacitor, and diode connected to the trigger input form a passive differentiator circuit with a negative clipper. This circuit prevents long input pulses from keeping the trigger input high during the time that the reset pulse occurs. Since the trigger input overrides the reset input, this would prevent the circuit from resetting properly. The differentiator changes the input pulse into a spike, preventing this problem. The pulse width is

$$\text{P.W.} = 1.09RC \qquad (8.28)$$

For long delays, the output can be taken from the counter outputs. This allows the use of reasonably sized timing resistors and capacitors, while achieving very long time delays. For example, a monostable circuit with a 5-minute pulse width, used as a time-delay unit, would require a 2.7-MΩ resistor and a 100-μF capacitor in a 555 circuit. Large low-leakage capacitors are difficult to obtain. Using a 2240, we could obtain the same delay with a 540-kΩ resistor and a 4-μF capacitor, using a

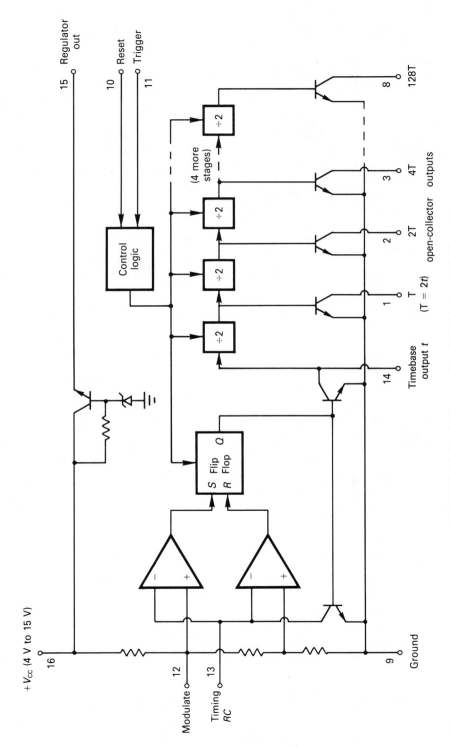

FIGURE 8–19: Block Diagram of the 2240 Programmable Timer

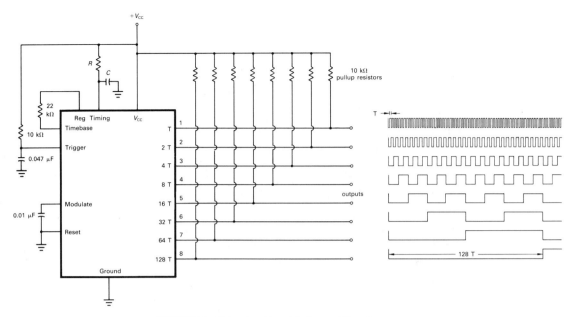

FIGURE 8–20A: Astable with Output Waveforms

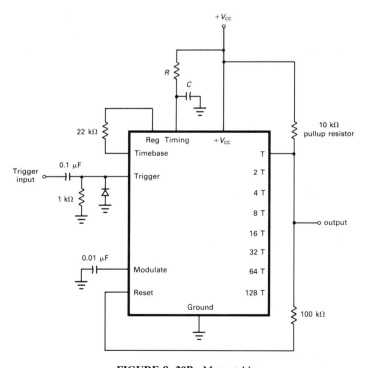

FIGURE 8–20B: Monostable

FIGURE 8–20: 2240 Timer Applications

divide-by-128 configuration. In fact, two or more 2240's can be cascaded, providing delays of up to three years!

The 2240 monostable circuit shown in Fig. 8–20B operates differently from the 555 monostable circuit. The input pulse causes the circuit to begin operating as an astable; it then operates until a negative-going transition of the output activates the reset input, making the 2240 turn off. Depending upon which combination of output connections is used, the T output can execute from one to 255 pulses before a reset occurs. Because the outputs of the counter stages are of the open-collector type, tying two of them together makes a wired AND circuit; that is, a circuit that acts like an AND gate. Thus the total frequency-division factor equals the sum of the factors of the outputs wired together. In other words, to divide the time-base frequency by 41, you could tie together the following outputs: 32T, 8T, and T. The sum of $32 + 8 + 1$ equals 41. You have probably noticed that we have just tied together the outputs corresponding to the binary digits 101001_2, which equals 41_{10}.

EXAMPLE

Problem

Design a circuit to turn on a car's headlights for a one-minute period after a trigger switch is depressed. Use the 2240.

Solution

1. We will use the circuit shown in Fig. 8–20B, and add the appropriate divider connections. To achieve a one-minute delay, we can use a 1-s time-base delay, then divide by 60. We will choose a 1-μF tantalum capacitor. From equation 8.28, we can solve for the resistance R.

$$\text{P.W.} = 1.09RC \qquad (8.28)$$

$$R = \frac{\text{P.W.}}{1.09C} = \frac{1 \text{ s}}{1.09 \cdot 10^{-6}\text{F}} = 917 \text{ k}\Omega$$

2. The divide-by-60 function is selected by tying together the output pins corresponding to the binary representation of 60_{10}, which is 111100_2. Thus we tie together pins 32T, 16T, 8T, and 4T. Using a solid-state relay in parallel with the 10-kΩ pull-up resistor to connect these pins to the power supply, we end up with the completed circuit shown in Fig. 8–21.

VOLTAGE-CONTROLLED OSCILLATORS

Op-Amp VCOs

There are many applications in which it is desirable to be able to control the output frequency of a waveform generator by means of a control voltage. One ex-

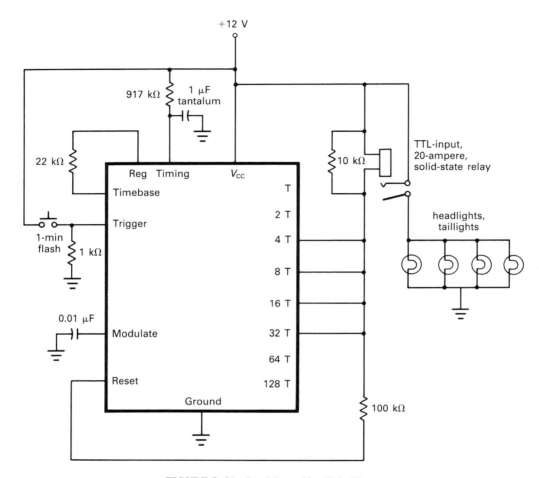

FIGURE 8–21: One-Minute Headlight Timer

ample is in electronic music synthesizers; one function that many of these provide is the ability to sweep or *glissando* from one note to another. By having the starting and ending notes represented by voltage levels, and using the charging of a capacitor to create a voltage ramp from the lower to the higher level, one can create a *glissando,* provided that one has a *voltage-controlled oscillator* (VCO) to respond to the changing voltage with a changing frequency. Many types of test equipment use VCOs also.

The heart of most VCOs is a triangle-wave generator. One way to obtain voltage control of the frequency is to use a voltage-variable resistance for any of the three resistors R_1, R_2, or R in the triangle-wave generator. A linear optocoupler with a photoconductive output device is shown replacing R in Fig. 8–22. When the control voltage is greater, more current flows in the LED, making it brighter, and thereby making the resistance of the photoconductive cell lower. This allows the integrator capacitor to charge more rapidly, decreasing the amount of time required for the output of the integrator to change from the lower threshold point of the comparator

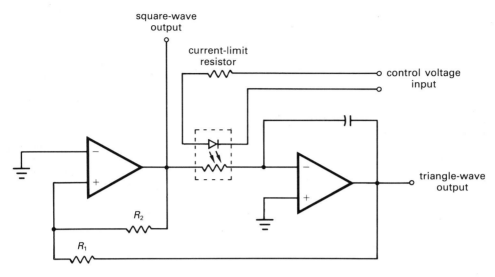

square-wave
output

current-limit
resistor

control voltage
input

triangle-wave
output

R_2

R_1

FIGURE 8–22: Optocoupler-Type VCO Circuit

to the upper threshold point. This, in turn, increases the frequency. An FET could be used as a voltage-controlled resistor, but the fact that neither terminal of resistor R is grounded would make biasing difficult.

Figure 8–23 shows another VCO circuit. This is just an ordinary triangle-wave generator with four changes:

1. Both inputs of the integrator are biased by the control voltage.
2. The polarity switching of the integrator is accomplished through a transistor rather than directly.
3. The Schmitt trigger is reconnected using the inverting input and biasing the noninverting input to $V_{CC}/2$.
4. A single-supply op amp (the LM124) is used.

The circuit functions by using the control voltage as a source from which the integrator capacitor charges. When the output from the Schmitt trigger is high, the transistor is saturated, so the voltage at the inverting input of the integrator is $V_C/3$, as a result of the voltage divider made up of resistors R and $R/2$. The noninverting input is set at $V_C/2$, so the output of the integrator is a positive-going ramp. When the ramp reaches the upper threshold point of the (inverting) Schmitt trigger, the output of the trigger switches to the low state, turning the transistor off. Now the inverting input of the integrator is biased at the full control voltage, while the non-inverting input is still biased at $V_C/2$. This causes the integrator output to form a negative-going ramp. When this ramp's voltage reaches the lower threshold point of the Schmitt trigger, the output switches again. Thus the trigger points of the Schmitt trigger depend upon V_{CC}, but the charging voltage of the integrator capacitor depends only upon V_C. As a result, the output frequency depends upon both the supply voltage and the control voltage. In order to remove the unwanted dependence of frequency upon supply voltage, a well-regulated supply is used.

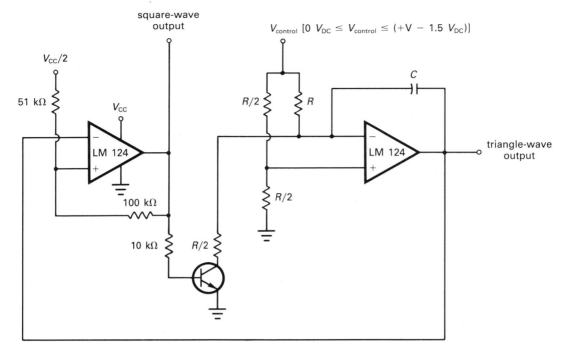

FIGURE 8–23: Single-Supply VCO Circuit

The 566 VCO

There are many ICs that are specifically designed as VCOs. The most basic of these is the 566. This unit provides both triangle and square waves at frequencies from the millihertz range up to 1 MHz. The range of output frequencies is selected by means of a timing capacitor and resistor. Then the output frequency can be varied over a 10:1 range by means of the control voltage. The relationship between control voltage and frequency is linear within less than 1%. The 566 requires a unipolar voltage supply between 10 and 24 V.

Figure 8–24 shows a typical connection of the 566. The output frequency is

$$f_0 = \frac{2(V_{CC} - V_C)}{RCV_{CC}} \tag{8.29}$$

where V_C is the control voltage between pin 5 and ground. The timing resistor must have a value between 2 and 20 kΩ.

EXAMPLE

Problem

Design a VCO circuit to switch the output of a 566 between the FSK (frequency-shift-keying) frequencies used for a binary 1 and 0 in serial data communication and

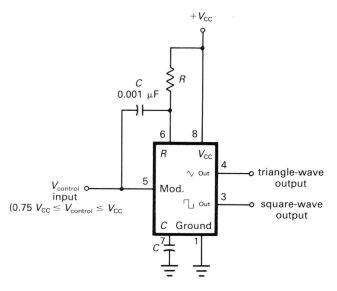

FIGURE 8–24: 566 VCO Application

digital cassette recorders. These frequencies are 1200 Hz = 0 and 2400 Hz = 1. The input will be provided from a TTL circuit having 0.3 V = 0 and 4.5 V = 1.

Solution

1. TTL circuits use a 5-V supply, which is too low for a 566. However, many digital circuits also incorporate a +12-V supply, which is appropriate for the 566. In order to provide the necessary control voltage (between $0.75V_{CC}$ and V_{CC}), an op amp will be needed. The LM124 op amp can operate from a 12-V unipolar supply, so we will use it.

2. We must select R and C for the 566. The maximum frequency occurs at the minimum control voltage, which is $0.75V_{CC}$:

$$f_{max} = \frac{2(V_{CC} - 0.75V_{CC})}{RCV_{CC}} \qquad \text{(from 8.29)}$$

$$= \frac{2(0.25V_{CC})}{RCV_{CC}} = \frac{0.5}{RC}$$

or, solving for RC gives

$$RC = \frac{0.5}{f_{max}}$$

The range of frequencies available for a given R and C is about a decade. Therefore, we want f_{max} to be greater than 2400 Hz, but we also want one-tenth of f_{max} to be less than 1200 Hz. Then both of our required frequencies will be within the available range. Choosing f_{max} = 3 kHz will meet this requirement. Then

$$RC = \frac{0.5}{3 \text{ kHz}} = 1.67 \cdot 10^{-4} \text{ s}$$

If we choose C = 0.01 μF, then

$$R = \frac{1.67 \cdot 10^{-4} \text{s}}{10^{-8} \text{ μF}} = 16.7 \text{ k}\Omega$$

The nearest standard value is 15 kΩ, which we will use.

3. The input voltage to the LM124 will be 0.3 V for a zero and 4.5 V for a one. Let us calculate the required output voltage:

$$f_0 = \frac{2(V_{CC} - V_C)}{RCV_{CC}} \tag{8.29}$$

Solving for V_C, we obtain

$$2V_{CC} - 2V_C = f_0 RCV_{CC}$$
$$-2V_C = V_{CC}(f_0 RC - 2)$$
$$V_C = \frac{V_{CC}(2 - f_0 RC)}{2}$$

Substituting the values for V_{CC}, R, C, and f_0 = 2400 Hz, we find

$$V_{C,2400} = \frac{(12 \text{ V})(2 - 2400 \text{ Hz} \cdot 15 \text{ k}\Omega \cdot 10^{-8} \text{ F})}{2} = 9.84 \text{ V}$$

Likewise, for 1200 Hz,

$$V_{C,1200} = \frac{(12 \text{ V})(2 - 1200 \text{ Hz} \cdot 15 \text{ k}\Omega \cdot 10^{-8} \text{ F})}{2} = 10.92 \text{ V}$$

4. Due input voltages to the op-amp stage have a ratio of 4.5 V/0.3 V = 15. The output voltages have a ratio of 10.92 V/9.84 V = 1.11. Therefore, a simple amplifier stage will not be enough; we will need to use a summer to provide both gain and offsetting. Using an inverting summer, we first calculate the needed gain:

$$A_{V,signal} = \frac{\Delta V_{OUT}}{\Delta V_{IN}} = \frac{10.92 \text{ V} - 9.84 \text{ V}}{4.5 \text{ V} - 0.3 \text{ V}} = 0.26$$

If we let R_f = 1 kΩ, then R_{i_1} is 1 kΩ/0.26 = 3.85 kΩ. This will make the resistance seen by the TTL circuit equal to 3.85 kΩ, which is satisfactory. We can use the 5-V supply for our offsetting input. The output voltage produced by this input is

$$V_2 = V_{OUT\,low} - V_{IN\,low}A_{V,signal} \qquad \text{(from 2.09)}$$
$$= 9.84 \text{ V} - 0.3 \text{ V} \cdot 0.26 = 9.76 \text{ V}$$

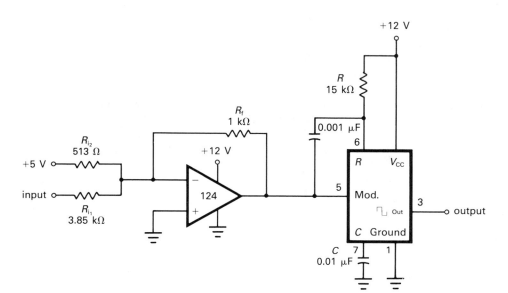

FIGURE 8-25: TTL Binary to Standard FSK Adapter

The gain for the offsetting input is therefore

$$A_{V,\text{offsetting}} = \frac{V_2}{V_{\text{IN,offsetting}}} = \frac{9.76 \text{ V}}{5 \text{ V}} = 1.95$$

Therefore $R_{i_2} = R_f/A_{V,\text{offsetting}} = 1 \text{ k}\Omega/1.95 = 513 \text{ }\Omega$. The completed circuit is shown in Fig. 8-25.

The 2206 Monolithic Function Generator

A much more versatile VCO IC is the 2206 monolithic function generator. This IC provides sine, square, and triangle outputs at frequencies from 0.01 Hz to over 1 MHz. The range of output frequencies is established by one capacitor and two resistors. The VCO function provides a 2000:1 ratio of highest to lowest frequency within a given range. For example, if the timing resistor and capacitor are chosen to provide a maximum frequency of 20 kHz, the output could be swept from that value down to 10 Hz, by means of the VCO function. Alternatively, the frequency can be controlled by means of a potentiometer connected as a timing resistor. For such operation, the frequency is

$$f_0 = \frac{1}{RC} \tag{8.30}$$

Because of the versatility of the 2206, we can use it to introduce several important functions. The circuits for these are illustrated in Fig. 8-26.

Frequency Modulation. When a waveform's frequency is varied in proportion to the instantaneous voltage of another waveform, the result is called frequency modulation (FM). This is the principle used for adding audio information to the high-frequency *carrier* wave for your FM radio. For example, if the *unmodulated* carrier frequency is 100 MHz, and the instantaneous voltage of the audio-frequency modulating wave is positive, then the *modulated* carrier's frequency will be greater than 100 MHz. Conversely, if the instantaneous voltage of the audio wave is negative, the carrier's frequency will be less than 100 MHz. Frequency modulation is used in many kinds of instrumentation and communication circuits besides radio and television audio.

The output frequency of the 2206 is actually controlled by the current drawn from its timing pins. (The active pin is chosen by a logic signal at pin 9, as will be discussed later.) The equation is

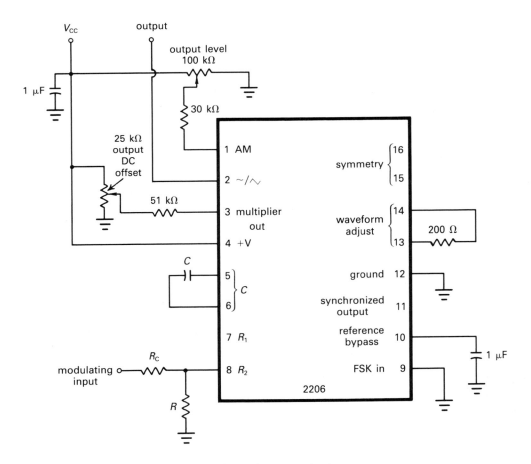

FIGURE 8–26A: FM Circuit

FIGURE 8–26: Applications of the 2206 Function Generator

$$f = \frac{320I}{C} \tag{8.31}$$

where I is the timing current in milliamps and C is the capacitance in microfarads. This equation applies for currents from about 1 μA to 3 mA. (The maximum current that can safely be drawn from the timing pins is 3 mA). The timing pins are internally biased at 3 V, so that a resistor connected from a timing pin to ground determines the current. But a control voltage less than 3 V, applied as shown in Fig. 8–26A, can also control the timing current. Since the timing pins represent a very low impedance, the resistance R_C constitutes the load on the control-voltage source. The complete equation for the output frequency of the circuit shown in the figure is

$$f = \frac{1}{RC[1 + (R/R_C)(1 - V_C/3)]} \tag{8.32}$$

where V_C is the control voltage, and the other quantities are as identified in Fig. 8–26A. By taking a partial derivative with respect to V_C, we can obtain an equation for the "voltage-to-frequency conversion gain":

$$K = \frac{-0.32}{RC} \tag{8.33}$$

(It is not necessary to understand the process of partial differentiation to use the result given above; simply understand that K is the conversion from control volts to frequency in hertz/volt.)

EXAMPLE

Problem

Design a circuit to provide a frequency swing of ± 1 kHz about a 10-kHz center frequency, using a 100-Hz, 2-V_{P-P} modulating signal.

Solution

1. The center frequency is determined from equation 8.30:

$$f_0 = \frac{1}{RC} \tag{8.30}$$

Thus:

$$RC = \frac{1}{f_0} = \frac{1}{10 \text{ kHz}} = 10^{-4} \text{ s}$$

If we choose C as 0.01 μF, then R becomes 10^{-4}s/10^{-8} F = 10 kΩ.

2. Since the voltage swing of the input is 1 V above and below the zero level, we need a voltage-to-current conversion gain of

$$K = \frac{\text{Maximum frequency deviation}}{\text{Maximum control voltage}}$$

$$= \frac{1 \text{ kHz}}{1 \text{ V}} = 1000 \text{ Hz/V}$$

We can now solve for the necessary value of R_C:

$$K = \frac{0.32}{R_C C} \qquad\qquad (8.33)$$

$$R_C = \frac{0.32}{CK} = \frac{0.32}{10^{-8} \text{ F} \cdot 1000 \text{ Hz/V}} = 0.32 \cdot 10^5 = 32 \text{ k}\Omega$$

3. Now let us verify that the maximum current drawn from the timing pin is less than 3 mA. The maximum current will be drawn when the control voltage is minimum, that is, -1 V. The timing current is then the sum of the current through R and the current through R_C, by Kirchoff's current law. Remembering that the timing pin is biased at 3 V:

$$I_T = \frac{3 \text{ V}}{R} + \frac{3 \text{ V} - (-1 \text{ V})}{R_C} = \frac{3 \text{ V}}{R} + \frac{4 \text{ V}}{R_C}$$

Substituting the values for R and R_C gives

$$I_T = \frac{3 \text{ V}}{10 \text{ k}\Omega} + \frac{4 \text{ V}}{32 \text{ k}\Omega} = 0.425 \text{ mA}$$

This is a safe value of current.

A version of frequency modulation that is often used in testing is the sweep-frequency generator. This is simply an FM circuit driven by a ramp control waveform. During the positive slope of the ramp, the frequency increases steadily from its minimum to its maximum value, then returns suddenly to the minimum value during the ramp's rapid negative slope. Some sweep-frequency generators use a logarithmic positive slope, so that the frequency increase with time will be logarithmic, rather than linear. If the output of this sort of circuit is fed to a filter, the output of the filter is fed to an oscilloscope, and the 'scope is triggered from the ramp waveform, the 'scope will display the frequency response of the filter on a linear-voltage-vs-logarithmic-frequency plot.

Frequency-Shift Keying (FSK). Many serial digital communications systems transmit information as a series of discrete frequencies. The design example on page 380 made use of this principle. In FSK systems, a binary zero (a "space," in communications parlance) is represented by one frequency, usually 1200 Hz, and a binary 1 (a "mark") is represented by another frequency, typically 2400 Hz. Because the

2206 has two timing pins, FSK generation using that IC is greatly simplified. The circuit is shown in Fig. 8–26B. If pin 9 is open-circuited or connected to a voltage of 2 V or more, pin 7 acts as the timing pin, and components connected to pin 8 have no effect on the circuit. If pin 9 is biased at 1 V or less, pin 8 is active and pin 7 is ignored. Thus the digital logic levels can be applied directly to pin 9, provided that V_{CC} for the 2206 is greater than the highest logic voltage. Then the appropriate frequencies for binary 1 and 0 can be chosen by the timing resistors at pins 7 and 8, respectively. The correct values for these resistors and for the capacitor can be selected from equation 8.30.

Amplitude Modulation. When the instantaneous amplitude of a carrier wave is varied in proportion to the instantaneous amplitude of another wave, the result is amplitude modulation (AM). This is the principle used in AM radio. An amplitude-modulated wave can be analyzed to indicate the frequency components of which it is made. If a sinusoidal carrier is modulated by a sinusoidal modulating wave, the output contains three frequencies: the carrier frequency, the sum of the carrier and

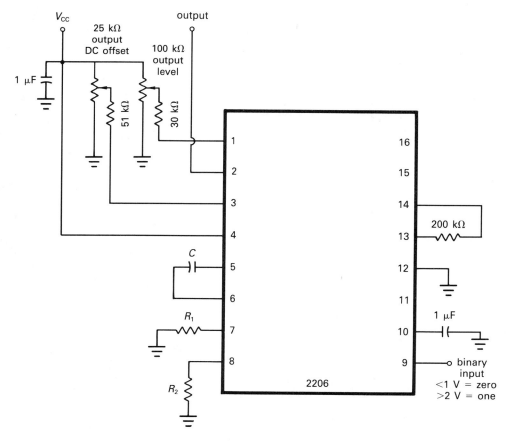

FIGURE 8–26B: FSK Circuit

modulating frequencies, and the difference between the carrier and modulating frequencies. AM can be performed with the 2206 by the use of the AM input, which is pin 1. The output amplitude varies linearly with the voltage applied at that pin. As long as the voltage at pin 1 is less than $V_{CC}/2$, the result is normal amplitude modulation. If the modulating voltage is made to swing above and below $V_{CC}/2$, the result will be double-sideband suppressed-carrier modulation. This is a form of modulation in which the output contains only the sum and difference frequencies; the carrier frequency is suppressed. Figure 8–26C shows a simple AM transmitter circuit with a carrier frequency of 800 kHz, which is in the AM broadcast band. For satisfactory operation, a power amplifier would be needed. The amplifier would have to be capable of driving a 50–300-Ω antenna, depending upon antenna and feed-circuit design. (Maximum legal power for unlicensed operation of a transmitter in the broadcast band is 100 mW.) Even without the amplifier, though, this circuit can be connected to a 5-foot length of wire and can then transmit a signal to a nearby AM radio.

If the AM function is not used, pin 1 can be fed from the wiper of a potentiometer to provide output level control, as shown in Fig. 8–26D.

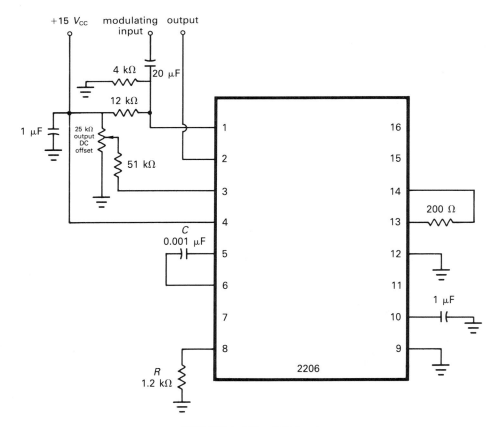

FIGURE 8–26C: AM Circuit

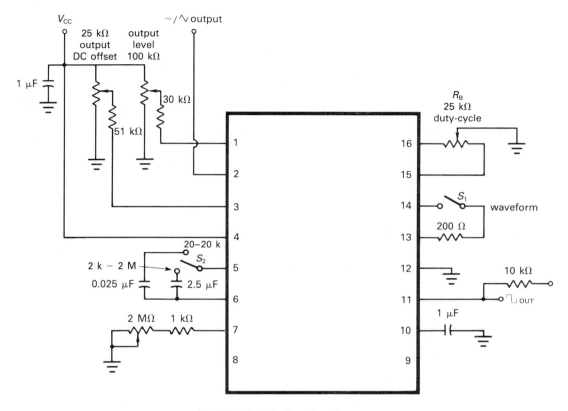

FIGURE 8–26D: Function Generator

Waveform Generation. Figure 8–26D shows the 2206 connected to produce sine, square, and triangle waves in two frequency ranges: 20 Hz to 20 kHz, and 2 kHz to 2 MHz. The output range is controlled by switch S_2, which selects the timing capacitor. For sine waves, switch S_1 is closed. This produces sine waves having a total distortion no greater than 2.5%. Lower-distortion sine waves can be generated using the circuit given in the data sheet for the 2206, which is in Appendix A. If switch S_1 is opened, the output is a triangle wave. The triangle can be changed to a sawtooth wave by adjustment of R_B. A square-wave output is available from pin 11. The duty cycle of the square wave is controlled by R_B.

WAVESHAPING CIRCUITS

We have already mentioned the use of a circuit to change a triangle wave into a sine wave. While such a circuit is contained within the 2206, there are other VCOs that require an external triangle-to-sine-wave converter (or *sine shaper*) if a sine-wave output is to be had. More generally, there are many industrial sensors that do not provide a linear output, but whose associated control circuits require a linear input. For example, as shown in Fig. 8–27, an unbalanced measuring bridge produces an output voltage that depends upon the percentage of unbalance, but the dependence is not a linear function. By using an amplifier having a complementary nonlinearity, a linear output can be obtained. It may seem a long way from sine shapers to bridge linearization, but the same approach is used in designing circuits for both purposes. This approach has already been introduced in the section on adaptive feedback. As you remember, the signal-diode version of adaptive feedback used a diode connected in parallel with the feedback resistor of an op amp. When the output voltage became high enough to turn on the diode, its low dynamic resistance reduced the effective feedback resistance, and hence the gain, to a low value. Figure 8–28A shows a slight variation on this idea. The antiparallel diodes are part of a tee feedback circuit. Resistors R_{t_1} and R_s form a voltage divider, determining the fraction of the output voltage that is applied to the diodes. Each diode will turn on when the voltage at the R_{t_1}–R_s junction becomes 0.6 V greater than the voltage at the input. When a diode turns on, the remainder of the tee network is connected into the circuit. This provides a lower effective value of R_f and, therefore, a lower gain. Figure 8–28B shows the transfer curve of this type of circuit. Remember that the slope of the transfer curve is equal to the gain. Notice that the gain of this circuit has one value as long as the output voltage is below the level at which the diodes begin to

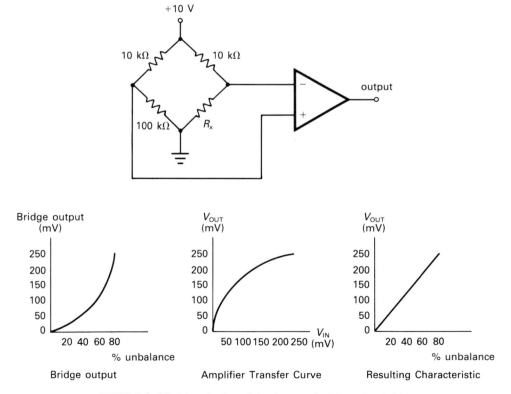

FIGURE 8–27: Linearization of the Output of a Measuring Bridge

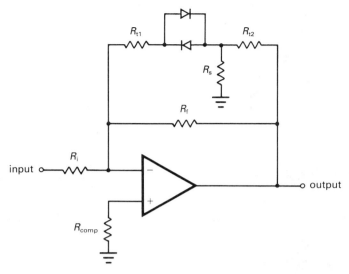

FIGURE 8–28A: Basic Nonlinear-Feedback Circuit

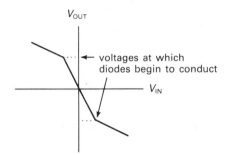

FIGURE 8–28B: Transfer Curve

FIGURE 8–28: Basic Shaping/Linearizing Circuit

conduct, and the gain has a lower value for larger output voltages. By repeating this procedure, we can make a multisegment *piecewise-linear* curve approximating any desired transfer curve. Figure 8–28B shows an approximation of the curve required to convert a triangle wave into a sine wave. Since the piecewise-linear approximation method of providing sine shaping supplies a transfer curve that changes slope at fixed voltage levels, it only works if the input triangle wave has the correct amplitude.

EXAMPLE

Problem

Design a sine-shaping circuit with a three-section piecewise-linear approximation of the correct function to change a triangle-wave input to a 5-V_P sine-wave output.

Solution

1. Let us compare the input (triangle-wave) instantaneous amplitudes with those for a sine wave. We will assume both waves to have a peak voltage of 5 V. We will calculate values at 10° increments up to 90°. Since a sine wave has bilateral symmetry about the 90° point and also has bipolar symmetry, calculation of values up to 90° will be sufficient.

Waveform	10°	20°	30°	40°	50°	60°	70°	80°	90°
Triangle	0.55	1.11	1.67	2.22	2.78	3.33	3.89	4.44	5.0 volts
Sine	0.86	1.71	2.50	3.21	3.83	4.33	4.70	4.92	5.0 volts
$A_V(V_{OUT}/V_{IN})$	1.58	1.54	1.50	1.45	1.38	1.30	1.21	1.11	1.0

These values of calculated gain are graphed in Fig. 8–29A.
2. Without applying curve-fitting techniques, which are beyond the scope of this book, we can see that for angles up to 50°, the gain is approximately 1.5; for angles of 50° to 70°, the gain averages about 1.3; and for angles from 70° to 90° the gain is about 1.1. Therefore, we will choose 50° (V_{OUT} = 3.83 V) and 70° (V_{OUT} = 4.7 V) as the voltages at which the gain changes.
3. We will use the circuit shown in Fig. 8–29B. It is clear that the *initial gain* A_{V_1}, the gain when none of the diodes are turned on, should be 1.5. Let us select R_i = 50 kΩ. This means that $R_f = R_i A_{V_1}$ = 50 kΩ · 1.5 = 75 kΩ. The reasons for choosing such high values will be made clear as we go along. The correct values for the other two gains require a bit more analysis. If we simply used A_{V_2} = 1.3, then our output voltage would be too great. Let us see why. The first 2.78 V of input (the 50° input amplitude) will be amplified by a factor of 1.5, producing an output of 4.17 V. If we then amplify the next 1.11 V (up to the 70° amplitude) by 1.3, then the total output voltage with a 3.89-V (70°) input will be 5.61 V, rather than the correct value of 4.70 V. Instead, we must calculate the *incremental gain* thus:

$$A_{V_2} = \frac{\Delta V_{OUT}}{\Delta V_{IN}}$$

$$= \frac{\text{Correct } V_{OUT} \text{ at } 70° - (V_{IN} \text{ at } 50°)(A_{V_1})}{V_{IN} \text{ at } 70° - V_{IN} \text{ at } 50°}$$

$$= \frac{4.70 \text{ V} - 4.17 \text{ V}}{3.89 \text{ V} - 2.78 \text{ V}} = 0.48$$

Notice that by using the calculated V_{OUT} as the second term in the numerator rather than the 50° value in the table, we have corrected for the error introduced by the initial gain being only *approximately* correct.
4. The equivalent feedback resistance for tee circuit 1 in Fig. 8–29B must be that resistance which, when paralleled with the 75-kΩ R_f, will yield a value of

$$R_{\|2} = R_i A_{V_1} = 50 \text{ kΩ} \cdot 0.48 = 24 \text{ kΩ}$$

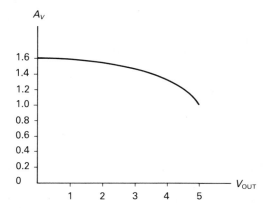

FIGURE 8–29A: Gain versus Output Voltage for Three-Segment Sine Shaper

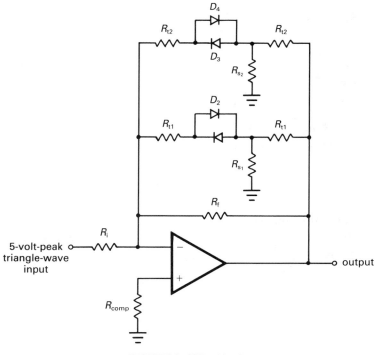

FIGURE 8–29B: Circuit

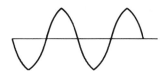

FIGURE 8–29C: Output Waveform

FIGURE 8–29: Three-Segment Sine Shaper

The necessary value of the equivalent feedback resistance can be found from the parallel-resistance formula:

$$R_{\|2} = \frac{R_f R_{eq_1}}{R_f + R_{eq_1}}$$

Solving for R_{eq_1}, we have

$$R_{eq_1} = \frac{R_f R_{\|2}}{R_f - R_{\|2}} = \frac{75 \text{ k}\Omega \cdot 24 \text{ k}\Omega}{75 \text{ k}\Omega - 24 \text{ k}\Omega} = 35.3 \text{ k}\Omega$$

We also know that D_1 should turn on when $V_{OUT} = 3.83$ V. This means that the forward voltage across the diode should be about 0.6 V when $V_{OUT} = 3.83$ V. When the diode is off, its cathode is at the voltage of the inverting input, which is a virtual ground. Therefore, we can design the voltage divider made of the right-hand R_{t_1} and R_{s_1} to give 0.6 V when 3.83 V is present at the amplifier output. Thus, from the voltage-divider formula,

$$(3.83 \text{ V}) \frac{R_{s_1}}{R_{s_1} + R_{t_1}} = 0.6 \text{ V}$$

Solving for R_{s_1}, we have

$$\frac{R_{s_1}}{R_{s_1} + R_{t_1}} = \frac{0.6 \text{ V}}{3.83 \text{ V}}$$

$$3.83 \text{ V} \cdot R_{s_1} = 0.6 \text{ V} \cdot R_{s_1} + 0.6 \text{ V} \cdot R_{t_1}$$

$$R_{s_1} = \frac{(0.6 \text{ V}) R_{t_1}}{3.23 \text{ V}} = 0.186 R_{t_1}$$

The equation for R_{eq_1} in terms of the tee resistors is

$$R_{eq_1} = \frac{R_{t_1}^2 - 2 R_{s_1} R_{t_1}}{R_{s_1}} \qquad \text{(from 3.08)}$$

Substituting the expression we just derived for R_{s_1}, we obtain

$$R_{eq_1} = \frac{R_{t_1}^2 - 2 \cdot 0.186 R_{t_1}^2}{0.186 R_{t_1}}$$

$$= \frac{0.628 R_{t_1}^2}{0.186 R_{t_1}} = 3.38 R_{t_1}$$

Now we solve for R_{t_1} and substitute to determine the value:

$$R_{t_1} = \frac{R_{eq_1}}{3.38} = \frac{35.3 \text{ k}\Omega}{3.38} = 10.44 \text{ k}\Omega$$

Then $R_{s_1} = 0.186 R_{t_1} = 1.94 \text{ k}\Omega$

5. When D_1 turns on, the left-hand R_{t_1} is effectively placed in parallel to ground with R_{s_1}, from the point of view of the voltage divider. Let us see whether this will shift the turn-on voltage of D_1 significantly. The new output voltage required to produce 0.6 V at D_1's anode will be the output voltage at which D_1 will turn off on the negative slope of the sine wave. It can be derived from the voltage-divider formula:

$$V_{\text{OUT}} \frac{R_{s_1}}{R_{t_1} + R_{s_1} \| R_{t_1}} = 0.6 \text{ V}$$

$$V_{\text{OUT}} = (0.6 \text{ V}) \frac{R_{t_1} + R_{s_1} \| R_{t_1}}{R_{s_1}}$$

$$= (0.6 \text{ V}) \frac{10.4 \text{ k}\Omega + (1.94 \text{ k}\Omega \| 10.4 \text{ k}\Omega}{1.94 \text{ k}\Omega} = 3.72 \text{ V}$$

This value is only 2.8% in error, so it will not significantly affect symmetry.

6. Following the same process for R_{t_2} and R_{s_2}, we find that the incremental gain when both tee sections are operating is

$$A_{V_3} = \frac{\Delta V_{\text{OUT}}}{\Delta V_{\text{IN}}} = \frac{V_{\text{OUT}_{90°}} - V_{\text{OUT}_{70°}}}{V_{\text{IN}_{90°}} - V_{\text{IN}_{70°}}} = \frac{5 \text{ V} - 4.7 \text{ V}}{5 \text{ V} - 3.89 \text{ V}} = 0.27$$

Thus the total feedback resistance when tee section 2 is operating must be:

$$R_{\|3} = A_{V_3} \cdot R_{\text{i}} - 0.27 \cdot 50 \text{ k}\Omega = 13.5 \text{ k}\Omega$$

Thus

$$R_{\text{eq}_2} = \frac{24 \text{ k}\Omega \cdot 13.5 \text{ k}\Omega}{24 \text{ k}\Omega - 13.5 \text{ k}\Omega} = 30.86 \text{ k}\Omega$$

We used 24 kΩ in this equation since that is the equivalent feedback resistance in parallel with tee network 2 when that network turns on. The output voltage when D_2 turns on must be 4.70 V. Thus, proceeding as we did earlier:

$$R_{s_2} = \frac{0.6 \text{ V} \cdot R_{t_2}}{4.70 \text{ V} - 0.6 \text{ V}} = 0.146 R_{t_2}$$

and

$$R_{\text{eq}_2} = \frac{R_{t_2}^2 - 2 \cdot 0.146 R_{t_2}^2}{0.146 R_{t_2}} = 4.85 R_{t_2}$$

$$R_{t_2} = \frac{R_{\text{eq}_2}}{4.85} = \frac{30.86 \text{ k}\Omega}{4.85} = 6.36 \text{ k}\Omega$$

$$R_{s_2} = 0.146 R_{t_2} = 929 \text{ }\Omega$$

7. The necessary bias-current compensation resistor can be calculated from the initial conditions (all diodes off) because it is at small values of V_{OUT} that offset

voltage will make the greatest difference. Thus,

$$R_{\text{comp}} = R_f \| R_i = 75 \text{ k}\Omega \| 50 \text{ k}\Omega = 30 \text{ k}\Omega \qquad \text{(from 3.03)}$$

8. Now we must make sure that the total resistance to ground from the op-amp output is not so low as to cause distortion. Distortion produced by current limiting can occur in many op amps if the output current exceeds 10 mA. Our maximum output voltage is designed to be 5 V. This will produce a 10-mA output current if the resistance from the output to ground is 500 Ω or less. In order to preserve some safety margin, let us make sure the resistance is at least 1 kΩ. The total resistance to ground from the output, neglecting the small contribution due to the left-hand tee resistors, is

$$R_G = R_f \| (R_{s_1} + R_{t_1}) \| (R_{s_2} + R_{t_2})$$
$$= 75 \text{ k}\Omega \| (1.94 \text{ k}\Omega + 10.4 \text{ k}\Omega) \| (929 \ \Omega + 6.36 \text{ k}\Omega) = 4.32 \text{ k}\Omega$$

This value is sufficiently high. However, if we had used a much smaller R_f and R_i, as is done for other circuits, all the tee resistors would have been correspondingly reduced, with the possibility of distortion as a result. Figure 8–29C shows the actual output wave produced by the circuit we have designed. Although not by any means a good sine wave, it bears sufficient resemblance that you can easily see how the addition of several more segments to the transfer curve could complete the conversion.

TROUBLESHOOTING WAVE GENERATORS

We have now discussed the most common types of circuits used for generating sine, square, and triangle waves. Based upon your familiarity with basic op-amp circuits, you can see that these circuits all fall into the categories of specialized amplifiers, integrators, or comparators. Troubleshooting these kinds of circuits has been discussed earlier in the book. There are several kinds of troubles that are peculiar to wave generators, though. These include failure to oscillate, oscillation at the wrong frequency, frequency instability, and distortion in the output.

When an oscillator fails to oscillate, the cause is invariably a failure of the circuit to meet Barkhausen's criterion. Anything that reduces the gain of an amplifier, such as a change in resistance values, can be a cause of trouble. Especially when potentiometers are used in the feedback circuits, vibration and/or dirt accumulation can affect their settings. Just as commonly, an open capacitor can affect either the gain or the phase relations necessary to produce oscillation. In *LC* oscillators, misadjustment of variable inductors is an unusual but possible offender. A final point to check is any decoupling capacitors on the power-supply leads. Improper decoupling can result in either negative or positive feedback through the supply leads, causing oscillation where there should be none, or causing a failure to oscillate when the circuit should oscillate.

Oscillation at the wrong frequency involves components whose values have changed. The components to suspect in any circuit are the ones that appear in the frequency equations for that particular circuit: the *R, C,* and supply voltage of the integrator in a triangle-wave generator, for example. There is a problem that is sometimes mistaken for oscillation at the wrong frequency: the pickup and amplification of an extraneous frequency. This can include inductive pickup of power-line-frequency noise as well as pickup of frequencies generated elsewhere in the equipment. In circuits in which shielding must be removed to do troubleshooting, the lack of shielding can cause power-line-induced noise to occur in the circuit. Power-supply faults can also be the culprit. Pickup of frequencies generated elsewhere in a piece of equipment can be caused by poor shielding, but is more likely the result of improper grounding or decoupling.

Frequency instability in a waveform generator usually shows up as a slow variation in output frequency. Usually this variation is temperature related. Any component can become unusually temperature sensitive if the internal connections become defective. As with oscillators operating at the wrong frequency, the first place to look is at the components that determine the frequency of operation. With the use of spray circuit cooler and a soldering pencil, suspected components can be temperature cycled. When the faulty components are found, changing their temperature will change the output of the circuit quite noticeably. Be careful when using the soldering pencil to heat components; the coating on many components cannot withstand the temperature of a hot soldering tip, so the tip must just be held near, but not touching, the component being tested. Also be aware that some output variation is likely to occur even with normal components when they are heated or cooled to temperatures far removed from their normal operating temperatures. The trick of distinguishing between normal and abnormal variation depends heavily upon judgment and will improve with practice.

Distortion in the output is often caused by power-supply problems. Low supply voltage is a common cause. Distortion can also be caused by conditions in the circuit that uses the wave generator's output, causing the load impedance seen by the generator to be too low. In fact, this can also cause failure to oscillate, in extreme cases. The most likely internal cause of distortion is a defect in the adaptive-feedback circuit or a changed feedback-resistor value.

DESIGN NOTES

General Considerations

In the design of any type of signal generator, there are three points that must be considered. The first is to make sure that the op amps used have a high enough GBW to provide the required gain at the highest frequency to be generated. A rough guideline is that the GBW should be at least ten times the highest frequency of interest.

The second consideration is the slew rate: It must be high enough to produce the desired output wave at the highest frequency and amplitude without attenuation or distortion. The necessary slew rate is:

- Triangle wave $2V_{\text{P-P}} f_{\max}$
- Sine wave $2\pi f V_{\text{P}}$
- Square wave $\dfrac{2V_{\text{P-P}}}{\text{Rise time} + \text{Fall time}}$

If the rise time and fall time are not known, an approximation for a good square wave is to make sure the slew rate is at least 10 times that required for a sine wave of the same amplitude and frequency.

The third point to remember deals with capacitors used as frequency-determining elements for low-frequency oscillators. Generally, for values greater than 1 μF, electrolytics must be used. However, most op-amp circuits do not provide a polarizing voltage for capacitors used in the feedback loop. Therefore nonpolar electrolytics should be used, or two polarized ones of twice the desired value, connected in series, positive-to-positive. Also, it is generally true that anything an aluminum electrolytic (the normal kind) will do can be done better by a tantalum electrolytic. This includes more accurate and stable capacitance, less leakage, and less equivalent series resistance. Therefore, tantalums should be specified for use in applications in which these characteristics are critical. However, it must be remembered that tantalum capacitors, being electrolytics themselves, are polarized.

Sine-Wave Generators

Space does not permit a discussion of the design of each of the many types of sine-wave generators we have introduced. Therefore, we will concentrate upon the most popular: the Wien-bridge oscillator with Zener adaptive feed-

Design Notes

(continued)

(continued from page 398)

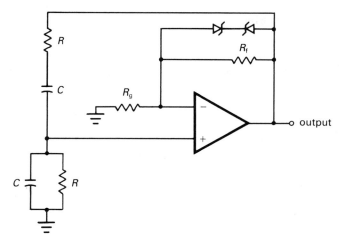

FIGURE 8–30: Wien-Bridge Oscillator with Zener Adaptive Feedback

back. The circuit is shown in Fig. 8–30. After selecting the appropriate op amp, select an appropriate value for C. Then solve for R:

$$R = \frac{1}{2\pi f C} \qquad \text{(from 8.12)}$$

If the calculated value of R is less than 1 kΩ or more than 1 MΩ, select a different capacitor and try again. Next, set R_g equal to R. Then make $R_f = 5R_g$. Finally, select the Zener voltage of the diodes equal to the desired peak output voltage.

Triangle-Wave Generators

Use the circuit shown in Fig. 8–31. If a variable-duty-cycle function is not needed, then the diode, switch, and potentiometer can be omitted. Use a 1-kΩ resistor for R_1. Then choose an appropriate value for C. The other components can be calculated as follows:

$$R_2 = \frac{2V_{\text{SAT}}R_1}{V_{\text{P-P}}} \qquad \text{(from 8.13)}$$

$$R_{\text{comp}} = R_1 \| R_2$$

$$R = \frac{R_2}{4R_1 f C} \qquad \text{(from 8.15)}$$

(continued from page 399)

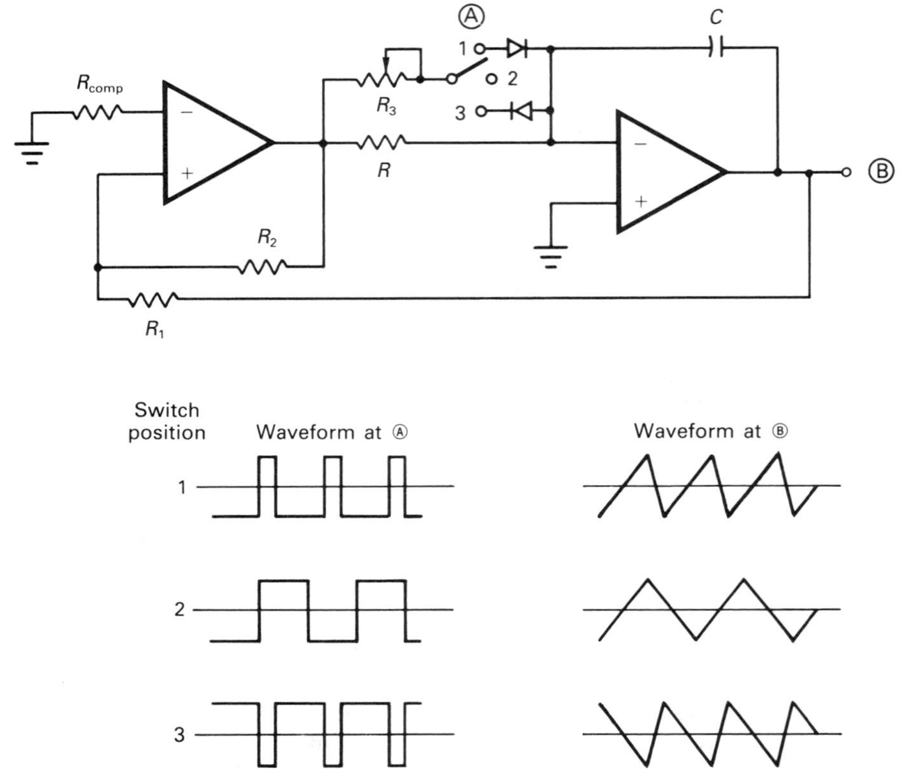

FIGURE 8–31: Variable-Duty-Cycle Triangle-Wave Generator

where V_{SAT} is the saturation voltage of the op amp, V_{P-P} is the peak-to-peak output voltage of the generator, and f is the output frequency when the duty cycle is 50%.

Resistor R should be between 1 kΩ and 1 MΩ; otherwise, try a different value of C. If the variable-duty-cycle function is used, the signal diode should be oriented as shown for a steep negative slope; it should be reversed to produce a steep positive slope. Since only one slope is varied, the output frequency will also vary when R_3's setting is changed. R_3 should be equal to $10R$, to allow smooth control of duty cycle. An op amp having internal current limiting should be used for this circuit; otherwise, the charging current into the integrating capacitor can be so great as to damage the output devices within the op amp.

Design Notes

(continued from page 400)

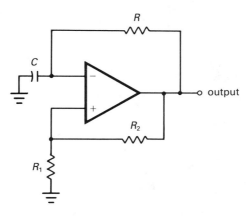

FIGURE 8–32: Square-Wave Generator

Square-Wave Generator

The circuit described above for a triangle-wave generator has a square-wave output also, and is a good circuit to use if variable duty cycle is needed. For a simple square-wave generator, use the circuit of Fig. 8–32. To select the component values, let R_1 equal 1 kΩ and $R_2 = 1.16$ kΩ. Then choose an appropriate value for C and calculate

$$R = \frac{1}{2f_0 C} \quad \text{(from 8.19)}$$

If R is not between 1 kΩ and 1 MΩ, choose another C and recalculate.

555 Circuits

Figure 8–33 shows a monostable and an astable circuit using a 555 timer. There are several general design guidelines that apply to both circuits:

- In order for your circuits to perform as you expect, always select a timing capacitor greater than 500 pF, and timing resistor (R for the monostable, R_A and R_B for the astable) between 1 kΩ and 3.3 MΩ.
- Do not omit the 0.1-μF capacitor that bypasses supply to ground at pin 5; even though the circuit may work without it, it may be unstable.
- Bypass the power-supply input with at least a 0.1-μF capacitor paralleled by a 1-μF electrolytic connected from pin 8 to ground.
- The minimum pulse width the circuit can deliver is 10 μs.

Design Notes

(continued from page 401)

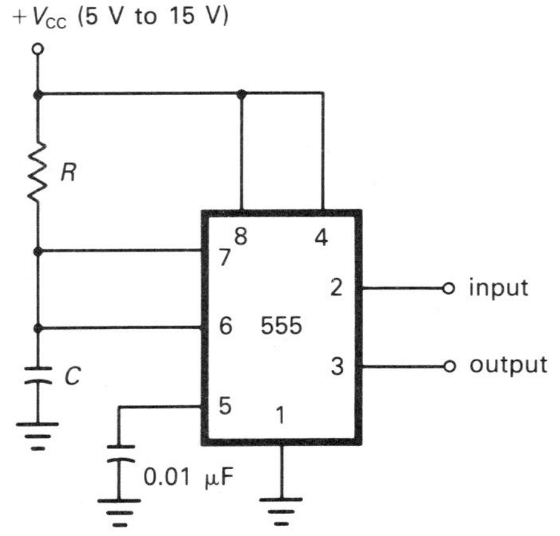

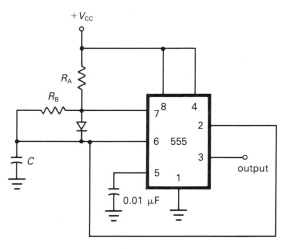

FIGURE 8–33A: Monostable

FIGURE 8–33B: Astable

FIGURE 8–33: 555 Circuits

Design Notes

• If output currents greater than 200 mA are needed, use a separate booster stage.
• Normally on loads should be connected between supply and pin 3; normally off loads are connected between pin 3 and ground.

For the monostable circuit, choose an appropriate value for C and calculate

(continued from page 402)

$$R = \frac{P.W.}{1.1C} \qquad \text{(from 8.21)}$$

where P.W. is the pulse width. If R is not within the range prescribed earlier, choose another C and recalculate. For an astable in which the duty cycle is greater than 50% omit the diode, choose C and calculate

$$M = \frac{\text{Duty cycle}}{1 - \text{Duty cycle}}$$

$$R_B = \frac{1.44}{(M + 1)fC} \qquad \text{(from 8.22, 8.23, and 8.25)}$$

$$R_A = R_B(M - 1)$$

where M is called the *duty-cycle multiplier*. For an astable having a 50% duty cycle, choose C and calculate

$$R_A = R_B = \frac{1.44}{2fC}$$

2240 Programmable Timer Applications

Figure 8–34 shows a 2240 timer connected as an astable and a monostable. Since the timer portion of this circuit is similar to the 555, the same restrictions on the size of timing resistor and capacitor apply. After choosing C, calculate

$$\text{monostable:} \qquad R = \frac{P.W.}{1.09C} \qquad \text{(from 8.28)}$$

where P.W. is the pulse width.

$$\text{astable:} \qquad R = \frac{1}{fC} \qquad \text{(from 8.27)}$$

The monostable can be wired to provide multiples of the basic pulse width. This is done by connecting the counter outputs together to arrive at a sum equal to the desired multiple. Thus for a 1-s time-base pulse width and a 53-s output pulse, outputs 32T, 16T, 4T, and T would be connected together through a single 10-kΩ pull-up resistor ($32 + 16 + 4 + 1 = 53$). The astable can also be connected to make use of the counter outputs, but only one output should be used at a time: They should not be used in multiples.

Design Notes

(continued from page 403)

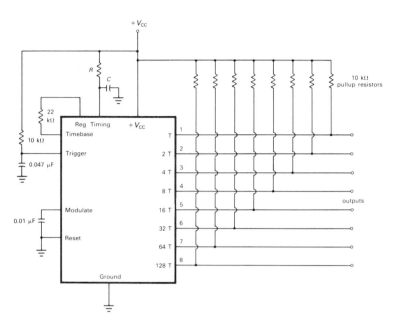

FIGURE 8–34A: Astable

566 VCO

Figure 8–35 shows the basic VCO circuit using a 566 IC. There are several general design considerations:

- The maximum output current is 200 mA, peak.
- The maximum VCO frequency ratio (f_{max}/f_{min}) for a given value of R and C is 10.
- The control voltage must be between $0.75V_{CC}$ and V_{CC}.
- The timing resistor must be between 2 and 20 kΩ.

To use this circuit, select a value of C that uses an R between 2 and 20 kΩ, according to the following equation:

$$R = \frac{2(V_{CC} - V_C)}{f_0 C V_{CC}} \quad \text{(from 8.29)}$$

where V_C is the control voltage applied to pin 5.

It is convenient to use the minimum control voltage and the maximum fre-

(continued from page 404)

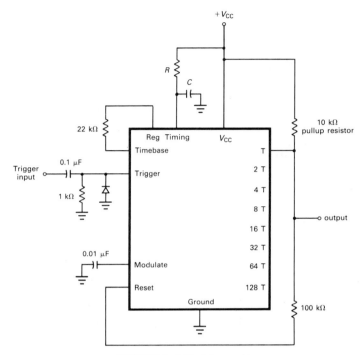

FIGURE 8–34B: Monostable

FIGURE 8–34: 2240 Circuits

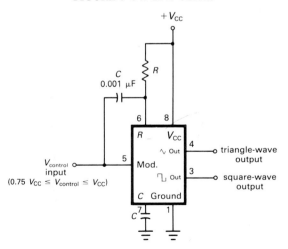

FIGURE 8–35: 566 VCO Circuit

Design
Notes

Design
Notes

(continued from page 405)

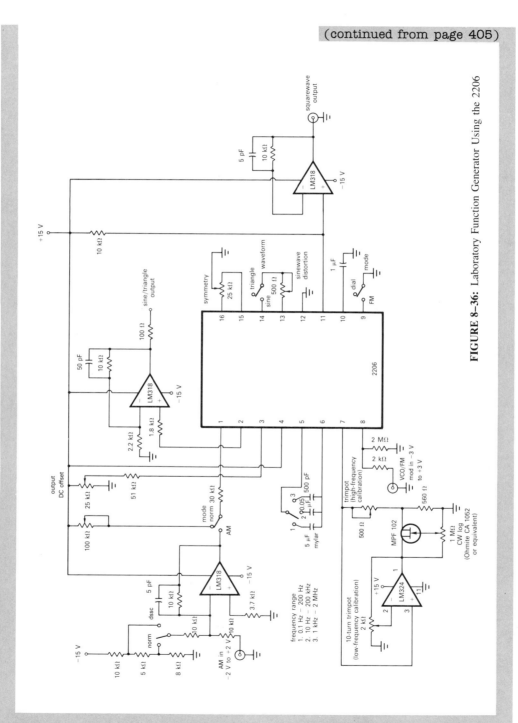

FIGURE 8–36: Laboratory Function Generator Using the 2206

(continued from page 406)

quency in the above equation, then after selecting R, recheck by calculating

$$f_{\min} = \frac{2(V_{CC} - V_{C,\max})}{RCV_{CC}} \qquad \text{(from 8.29)}$$

This will verify that the desired range of frequencies is available from your circuit.

2206 Function Generator

Figure 8–36 shows a complete circuit using the 2206 as a wide-range, low-distortion, sine-, square-, triangle-wave generator with VCO, FM, AM, and variable-duty-cycle capabilities. For further applications information, see the data sheet in Appendix A.

SUMMARY

The term *signal generator* refers to any waveform generator; *oscillator* is usually used only for sine-wave generators.

Most signal generators are amplifiers having positive feedback and meeting the *Barkhausen criterion:* unity loop gain and a loop phase shift equal to an integral multiple of 360°.

Sine-wave oscillators can use *LC* circuits as their frequency-determining elements. *LC* oscillator types include Hartley, Colpitts, Clapp, Armstrong, and double-tuned circuits. All of these can produce clean sine waves with good frequency stability, and are used mainly at high frequencies.

Crystal oscillators are used whenever very stable frequencies are needed. They operate at frequencies from about 1 to 100 MHz, and can be used with frequency multipliers and dividers to produce lower or higher frequencies.

RC sine-wave generators offer the advantage of eliminating the weight, bulk, and expense of large inductors when used for generating low-frequency waves. *RC* sine-wave generators include the phase-shift, twin-tee, Wien-bridge, and quadrature circuits. Of these, the Wien bridge is by far the most commonly used.

Adaptive feedback is a form of nonlinear feedback that results in a gain reduction when the output voltage increases. It is used to stabilize the output amplitude of sine-wave generators at some point short of saturation.

A triangle-wave generator consists of an integrator and a Schmitt trigger. The frequency depends upon the resistor and capacitor used in the integrator, and also upon the supply voltage. The symmetry or duty cycle of a triangle wave can be adjusted by using a diode/resistor network in parallel with the integrator's resistor.

A square-wave output is available from a triangle-wave generator. Square waves can also be generated by use of a Schmitt trigger with positive feedback. Such a circuit is called an *astable multivibrator*.

IC timers are used as astables to generate square waves and also as monostables to create pulses of a certain selectable, repeatable width. The most common timer is the 555, or its dual-timer cousin, the 556. The 2240 is a programmable timer incorporating digital counters for use as frequency dividers.

Voltage-controlled oscillators, or VCOs, have an output frequency that can be varied by means of a control voltage. VCOs can be built from modified triangle-wave generators, or they can use VCO ICs such as the 566 or the 2206.

Waveshaping circuits use nonlinear feedback in a fashion similar to adaptive feedback. By use of enough segments, virtually any waveform can be synthesized from a triangle wave.

REVIEW QUESTIONS

1. Describe the meaning of the Barkhausen criterion in your own words.
2. What is the resonant frequency of a Colpitts oscillator using a 50-μH inductor and a 0.1-μF capacitor?
3. The coil of a Hartley oscillator operating at 2 MHz has an inductance of 10 μH. What capacitance should be used?
4. Explain how the Barkhausen criterion is satisfied in a double-tuned oscillator.
5. Sketch a block diagram of a circuit that could be used to generate 19-kHz square waves with extreme frequency stability. Include as much detail about each block as you can.
6. Design a phase-shift oscillator to operate at a frequency of 2.5 kHz.
7. Based upon your understanding of RC circuits, predict the operating frequency of a four-section phase-shift oscillator using 0.022-μF capacitors and 15-kΩ resistors. Ignore the effects of loading upon the performance of the four RC sections.
8. Design a circuit for a Wien-bridge oscillator that is tunable from 100 Hz to 10 kHz. Include Zener adaptive feedback. The output voltage is to be 5 V_{P-P}.
9. What is the unusual feature of the quadrature oscillator, and in what kind of equipment would one likely be used?
10. Modify the circuit you designed in question 8 to use an FET adaptive feedback circuit.
11. Design a triangle-wave generator that feeds a four-segment sine shaper, to produce a 5-V_{P-P} quasi-sine-wave output at 10 kHz.
12. If the circuit you designed in question 11 oscillated at the incorrect frequency, what component(s) would you check first?
13. If the output wave of the circuit you designed in question 11 were improperly shaped, even though your design was correct, what fault would you suspect in the circuit?
14. If the output of the circuit you designed in question 11 were badly clipped, what two things would you check?

15. How could you modify the circuit you designed in question 11 to make it into a VCO? Would the sine shaper's operation be affected?
16. What changes would you make to the circuit you designed in question 11 to allow adjustment of symmetry or duty cycle?
17. Sketch three circuits that could be used to build a 100-kHz clock (square-wave) generator. Include component values.
18. Design a circuit using the 555 to regenerate 12-V pulses used in serial digital communication after they have been distorted by transmission on a long coaxial cable. The correct pulse width is to be 100 μs.
19. Design a circuit using the 2240 to provide a 1-Hz wave using a capacitor no larger than 0.1 μF and a resistor no larger than 100 kΩ.
20. Using a 566 IC, design a voltage-to-frequency converter circuit that can be used to change voltages in the range of 5 to 15 V into frequencies in the range of 5 to 15 kHz. (This circuit, with the addition of a frequency counter, is one method of designing a digital voltmeter.)
21. Fill in the blanks:
    In FM, the _____ of the carrier is varied according to the _____ of the modulating wave. In AM, the _____ of the carrier is varied according to the _____ of the modulating wave. FSK is a binary form of _____ (FM or AM?).

LABORATORY EXPERIMENT—Wien-Bridge Oscillator

Objective:

To observe the operation of a Wien-bridge oscillator with and without adaptive feedback.

Materials:

1 741 op amp
1 signal diode
2 5-V Zener diodes
miscellaneous resistors and capacitors

Procedure:

1. Design a 1-kHz Wien-bridge oscillator using the circuit in Fig. 8–11, but omitting the two Zener diodes. Use a potentiometer slightly larger than the calculated value for R_g; use a carbon-composition resistor for R_f.
2. Build your circuit and then carefully adjust R_g to produce the best sine wave you can obtain.
3. While observing the sine wave on a 'scope, heat up R_f. (Hold the iron near, but not touching, R_f.) What happens to the waveform?

_____

4. Allow R_f to cool; readjust R_g if necessary, and then heat R_g. What happens to the waveform? _____
5. Adjust R_g so that the output is barely clipped. Now connect the two Zener diodes across R_f, as shown in Fig. 8–11. Again heat R_f and R_g (one at a time) and note the results.

_____

6. Measure the peak-to-peak output voltage.
7. If a spectrum analyzer, wave analyzer, or distortion meter is available, measure the harmonic distortion of the sine wave.

Analysis:

1. Why did the effects you observed in steps 3 and 4 occur? Why is this undesirable?
2. Explain how the addition of the Zeners prevented the problem you observed in steps 3 and 4.
3. Was the output voltage amplitude the value you expected it to be? Explain.

(continued)

(continued from page 410)

LABORATORY EXPERIMENT—Triangle-Wave Generator and Sine Shaper

Objective:

To examine the operation of a triangle-wave generator and the dependence of a sine shaper's performance upon the input voltage.

Materials:

2 741 op amps
8 signal diodes
miscellaneous resistors and capacitors

Procedure:

1. Build the circuit you designed in problem 11.
2. Adjust the amplitude of the triangle-wave generator so that it is the value you designed the sine shaper to handle.
3. Sketch the output wave of the sine shaper. If a wave analyzer, spectrum analyzer, or distortion meter is available, measure the distortion in the sine shaper's output.
4. Now increase the amplitude of the triangle wave by 50% by changing the resistors in the Schmitt trigger. Observe the output of the sine shaper and measure the distortion if possible.
5. Reduce the amplitude of the triangle wave and observe the sine shaper's output, again measuring distortion if possible.

Analysis:

1. What can you say about the effect of input level upon the accuracy of the sine shaper's output waveform?
2. How does your waveform compare with that shown in Fig. 8–29? Why is it better or worse?

Laboratory
Experiments

(continued from page 411)

LABORATORY EXPERIMENT—Voltage-to-Frequency Converter

Objective:

To investigate the operation of a VCO-type digital voltmeter.

Materials:

1 566 IC
miscellaneous resistors and capacitors

Procedure:

1. Build the circuit you designed for problem 20.
2. Connect a frequency counter to the output of your circuit. Now apply input voltages in 1-V increments from 5 to 15 V (as read on a digital voltmeter) and read the output on the counter.

Analysis:

1. Graph the actual input voltage versus the measured voltage (from the counter output).
2. Graph the percent deviation of the measured value from the correct value. The percent deviation is

$$\frac{\text{Measured value} - \text{Correct value}}{\text{Correct value}} \cdot 100\%$$

The zero-percent deviation line of the graph should be in the center. Then positive deviations (too-large measured values) will be above the line and negative percent deviations (too-small values) will be below the line. The horizontal axis will be labeled with the actual voltage.
3. Calculate the average percent deviation of your "voltmeter" circuit. This is obtained by adding the percent deviation at each measurement, without regard to sign, and dividing by the number of measurements. A good voltmeter should have an average percent deviation of well under 5%. How does yours compare?

Laboratory Experiment

(continued from page 412)

LABORATORY EXPERIMENT—555 Timer

Objective:

To gain experience with the 555 timer in a monostable circuit.

Materials:

1 555 timer
1 TIP122 Darlington transistor
1 12-V lamp
miscellaneous resistors and capacitors

Procedure:

1. Design a 555 circuit to turn on a burglar-alarm sounder one minute after a trigger switch is depressed. The sounder requires 12 V DC at 2 A. You will need to use the TIP122 Darlington transistor to provide enough current gain to drive this unit. Use a 1-kΩ resistor in series with the base of the transistor to protect it against excessive base current.
2. Build your circuit and connect the lamp to act as a dummy load. It will not draw 2 A, but it will indicate whether the circuit is working, and will not require the transistor to have a heat sink. Verify correct operation.

Analysis:

1. How could you change your circuit to make the time delay variable from 15 s to 1 min?
2. How could you change your circuit to prevent operation of the sounder after the trigger switch had been depressed if a safety switch were then energized?
3. Considering the maximum values of the timing resistor and capacitor in a 555 circuit, what is the maximum time delay you could obtain using this circuit?

Laboratory
Experiments

chapter nine

Specialized Analog Functions

OBJECTIVES

Upon completing this chapter, you will be able to:

- Design circuits using programmable op amps, operational transconductance amplifiers, current-differencing amplifiers, analog multipliers, rms converters, phase-locked loops, and compandors.
- Design precision rectifiers, clipper and clamper circuits, logarithmic amplifiers, and signal-processing and conversion circuits, including sample-and-hold circuits, and voltage/current converters.
- Understand the operation and use of several different kinds of A/D and D/A converters.

INTRODUCTION

We have now completed the discussion of the most common linear IC circuits and applications. By far most of these applications have centered around op amps. However, there are several specialized circuits using op amps that we still need to cover. Also, there are a number of circuits that are fairly complex to build from individual components, but that are needed frequently enough that they have been made available in IC form. Not only does this large-scale integration greatly simplify construction of equipment, but it simplifies the design process also, because what were complex designs can now often be reduced to a few relatively simple design rules.

SPECIALIZED DEVICES

Programmable Op Amps

A programmable op amp is one that has an external connection for setting the GBW, slew rate, supply current, input bias current, input offset current, and input

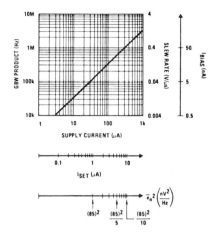

FIGURE 9–1: Programmable Amplifier Characteristics *(Reprinted with permission of National Semiconductor Corp.)*

noise level. This allows the designer to optimize the noise characteristics for a given source resistance, to gain increased bandwidth at the expense of greater noise, or to make other tradeoffs that a particular design may require. Figure 9–1 summarizes the effects of the control current I_{SET} upon supply current, equivalent input noise, bias current, GBW, and slew rate. To use the graph, first select a particular value of I_{SET}. Find that value on the horizontal axis. Then look vertically below the I_{SET} value to find the noise voltage; look above the I_{SET} value to find the resulting supply current. Next, find the intersection of the vertical line corresponding to your I_{SET} value with the diagonal line on the graph, then look horizontally to determine the GBW, slew rate, and bias current. Figure 9–2 shows an LM146 connected as a

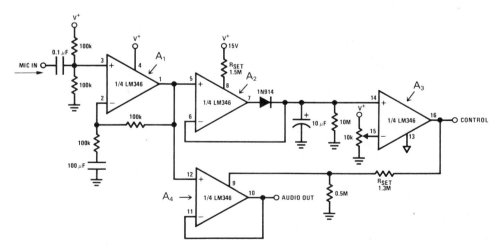

FIGURE 9–2: Voice-Operated Switch and Amplifier Using the LM146 *(Reprinted with permission of National Semiconductor Corp.)*

voice-operated switch and amplifier. In this circuit, amplifier A_1 is used as a pream-plifier, and A_4 is the output amplifier. The output signal from A_2 is rectified and used to charge the 10-μF capacitor. A_3 acts as a comparator: Its output is high when the average signal from the rectifier is higher than the set-point value at A_3's in-verting input. Otherwise, the output is low. The output of the comparator is used as the control voltage for A_4. When the control voltage is dropped to V_{SAT-}, A_4 shuts down. The purpose of this circuit is to provide an output only when there is a sig-nificant input voltage. With a low input voltage, there is no output. Turning the output amplifier on or off according to the amplitude of the signal at A_1's output provides this function. An example of this circuit's use would be in mobile radio transmitters. Even if the transmitter were keyed (transmitting) continuously, it would only receive an input signal when the operator spoke into the microphone. During pauses in the operator's speech, the circuit would prevent the lower-amplitude road and engine noise from passing to the transmitter.

Operational Transconductance Amplifiers

An operational transconductance amplifier (OTA) is a special type of op amp with programmable gain. The way in which it is special is revealed in the name of the device. Most op amps' gain is specified as a ratio of output voltage to input voltage; thus the gain has the units of volts per volt, making it a pure number. Another way of looking at this is to say that op amps, in the circuits in which they are normally used, are voltage-controlled voltage sources. They are voltage con-trolled because the input quantity is a voltage; no input current is drawn by an ideal op amp. They are voltage sources because they have ideally zero internal impedance (or zero output resistance), and thus produce a constant output voltage into any load. A transconductance amplifier is a voltage-controlled current source. Its input is a voltage with, ideally, no input current. But its output acts as a current source; that is, it attempts to deliver a constant current to any load, regardless of load resistance. You have probably had experience with at least one voltage-controlled current source, and perhaps two, because FETs and vacuum tubes both fall into this category.

The gain of a voltage-controlled current source cannot be expressed in terms of V_{OUT}/V_{IN}; instead, it must be expressed as the ratio I_{OUT}/V_{IN}. This ratio has the units of amperes/volts, which is conductance. Since the amperes and the volts are mea-sured at different points—namely the output and the input, respectively—the gain characteristic is called a *transconductance*. Transconductance was originally called *mutual conductance,* so it is represented by the symbol g_m. Any device whose gain is a transconductance has a voltage gain that depends upon the load resistance:

$$A_V = g_m R_L \qquad (9.01)$$

An analogous situation exists for a common op amp: the transconductance would depend upon the load resistance, and could be derived from $g_m = A_V/R_L$. However, this relation is not often very useful. The distinction, though, is helpful: For a com-mon op amp, the voltage gain is a constant and the transconductance varies inversely with the load resistance; whereas, for a transconductance amplifier, g_m is a constant and the voltage gain varies directly with the load resistance.

Another characteristic common to OTAs is their ability to be controlled by a bias current, I_{ABC}. This current varies the input resistance, transconductance, noise level, and the bias and offset currents.

The LM13600 is a dual OTA incorporating separately accessible buffer transistors in the same package. It has a typical transconductance of 9600 μS (microsiemens), maximum output current of 500 μA, and a maximum buffer output current and voltage of 2 mA and 10 V, respectively. The input resistance can be set at any value from 10 kΩ to 4 MΩ. Complete specifications are given in Appendix A. Let us look at what these specifications mean, by comparison with the op amps with which we are familiar. The maximum output current is about one-fifth that of a 741, and although it is sufficient for many applications, some applications may require separate buffer amplifiers in order to produce sufficient output voltage into the load. The maximum output voltage and current specifications imply a minimum load resistance of 5 kΩ. Of course, it is important to remember that the output resistance of the OTA is quite high; that is a necessary result of the output acting as a current source.

The input voltage required to produce maximum unbuffered output current may be determined from

$$V_{IN} = \frac{I_{OUT}}{g_m} \qquad \text{(from definition of transconductance)}$$

$$= \frac{500 \text{ μA}}{9600 \text{ μS}} = 52 \text{ mV}$$

This does not look like a great deal of sensitivity. Let us investigate further. Since the voltage gain depends upon the load resistance, a voltage gain equal to the open-loop gain of a 741 (about 200,000) could be obtained by using a load resistance of

$$A_V = g_m R_L$$

$$R_L = \frac{A_V}{g_m} = \frac{200,000}{9600 \text{ μS}} = 20.8 \text{ MΩ} \qquad (9.01)$$

This great a load resistance is impractical. Therefore we may conclude that an OTA has less available gain than a common op amp.

The input resistance of the 13600 is controllable, and at its highest value it is higher than that of the 741.

One peculiarity of OTAs is the fact that they do not respond linearly to differential input voltages greater than about 10 mV. Although the LM13600 has linearizing diodes that reduce the distortion, it is still a good idea to limit the maximum input voltage to 10 mV.

Figure 9–3A shows a voltage-controlled amplifier circuit using an LM13600. Notice that there is no feedback resistor in the circuit; the gain is controlled by the bias current instead. The 13-kΩ resistor connected from supply to the junction of the linearizing diodes is used to bias the diodes, reducing distortion. The 1-kΩ po-

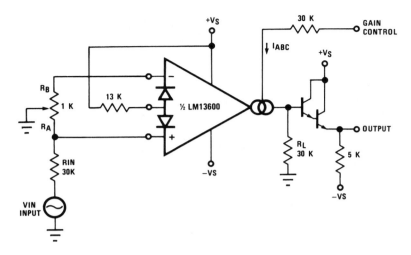

FIGURE 9–3A: Voltage-Controlled Amplifier

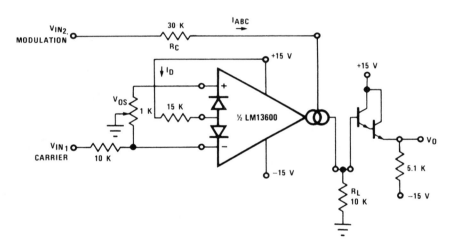

FIGURE 9–3B: Amplitude Modulator

FIGURE 9–3: OTA Applications *(Reprinted with permission of National Semiconductor Corp.)*

tentiometer provides a means of limiting the maximum input voltage to 10 mV. Varying the voltage applied to the 30-kΩ resistor at the point marked *gain control* varies the transconductance of the amplifier, and hence, the voltage gain. The transconductance can be varied from zero (off) to 9600 μS, giving a voltage gain that is variable from zero to 288. This range of variation requires a control voltage range from V^- to V^+. At maximum gain, the output voltage can be as much as 2.88 V, with a maximum input of 10 mV.

Figure 9–3B shows an OTA used as an amplitude modulator. In this circuit, the control voltage that varies the gain is the modulating signal. The carrier is fed to the input of the circuit. Thus its amplitude is varied in proportion to the instantaneous amplitude of the modulating signal.

The OTA, then, is a unique device whose special properties include a large range of controllability by means of the bias current. Although not suitable for use as a general-purpose op amp in many applications, it nevertheless provides functions that are difficult to obtain in any other way.

Current-Differencing Amplifiers

In order to provide an op amp that would operate from low-voltage, unipolar supplies, and that would show little parameter variation over a wide range of supply voltages, Tom Frederiksen of National Semiconductor Corp. designed the current-differencing amplifier (CDA). Although a number of more conventional op amps, such as the LM124, have since been developed to meet these requirements, the CDA is still used for some applications. The CDA is a current-controlled voltage source. That is, the input quantity is a current, or more precisely, a difference between the currents at the inverting and noninverting inputs. The output acts as a voltage source, as in a conventional op amp. Because the input responds to current rather than voltage, the CDA is sometimes called a *Norton* amplifier. As a result of this current-sensitive nature, the inputs of a CDA cannot be driven directly from a voltage-source input device. A voltage-to-current converter is needed. This usually takes the form of a large resistor. The variation in voltage applied to the resistor produces a corresponding current variation at the input to the amplifier. When the negative-feedback loop is closed, the sum of the feedback current and the input current produce a theoretical zero-current point at the input to the amplifier, just as a normal op amp has a zero-voltage point at the input. The maximum input of a standard op amp is defined by the maximum differential input voltage. The maximum input of a CDA is defined by a maximum differential input current. The open-loop voltage gain, maximum output current, and other characteristics of the CDA are similar to those of a common op amp.

Figure 9–4 shows the methods of biasing a CDA. Although any of the four methods can be used, the current-mirror biasing circuit shown in part A of the figure is the most common. Since both of the inputs are about 0.5 V above ground, the reference current into the noninverting input is

$$I_1 = \frac{V^+ - 0.5 \text{ V}}{R_B} \tag{9.02}$$

Because the negative-feedback loop will cause the currents into the two inputs to be equal, the current in R_f must be equal to I_1. This means that the output voltage must be exactly enough to cause that amount of current to flow in R_f:

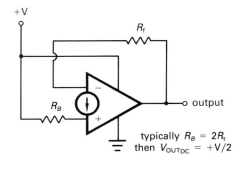

FIGURE 9–4A: Current-Mirror Biasing

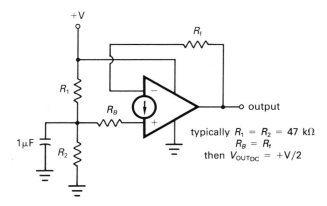

FIGURE 9–4B: Current-Mirror Biasing with Noise Filtration

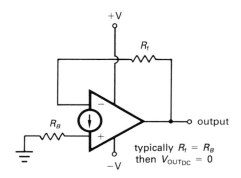

FIGURE 9–4C: Dual-Supply Current-Mirror Biasing

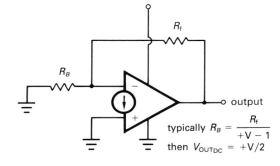

FIGURE 9–4D: V_{BE} Multiplier Biasing

FIGURE 9–4: CDA Biasing Methods

$$V_{OUT} = I_1 R_f = (V^+ - 0.5 \text{ V}) \frac{R_f}{R_B}$$

Optimum quiescent output voltage for maximum undistorted output swing is half of the supply voltage, $V^+/2$. Approximately this voltage will result if $R_B = 2R_f$. Ignoring the 0.5-V term in the previous equation, we get

$$V_{OUT} = \frac{V^+ R_f}{R_B} = \frac{V^+ R_f}{2R_f} = \frac{V^+}{2}$$

The other biasing arrangements achieve the same result through different means.

Figures 9–5A, B, and C show the basic inverting, noninverting, and differential amplifier circuits using a CDA. The equations for gain and input impedance of the inverting and differential amplifiers are the same as for standard op amps. For the

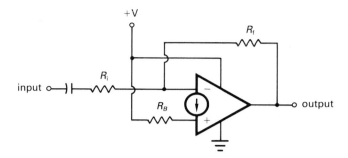

FIGURE 9–5A: Inverting Amplifier

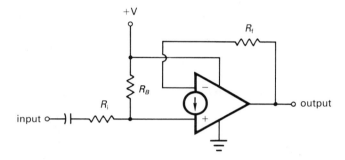

FIGURE 9–5B: Noninverting Amplifier

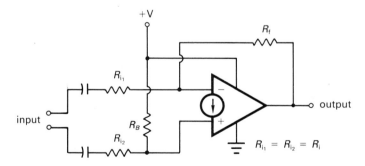

FIGURE 9–5C: Differential Amplifier

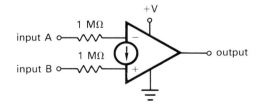

FIGURE 9–5D: CDA Comparator

FIGURE 9–5: CDA Applications

noninverting amplifier, the presence of a small dynamic-resistance component in the input of the CDA causes the gain equation to be

$$A_V = \frac{R_f}{R_i + r_d} \qquad (9.03)$$

where r_d is the dynamic resistance, $0.026/I_1$ Ω.

If R_B is made equal to $2R_f$, then this equation becomes

$$A_V = \frac{V^+ R_f}{V^+ R_i + 0.052 R_f} \qquad \text{(from 9.02 and 9.03)}$$

The input resistance of a noninverting CDA amplifier is just $R_i + r_d$. The dependence of gain and input resistance upon supply voltage can be made insignificant if we make R_i much greater than r_d. Because of the interdependence of A_V, R_i, R_f, and R_B, this condition limits the gain to values numerically much less than $20 \cdot V^+$. If having the circuit performance depend somewhat upon supply voltage does not matter in any given circuit, then this condition need not be adhered to.

In order for the diff amp in Fig. 9–5C to exhibit good common-mode rejection, r_d must be insignificant compared to R_i. This means that gains numerically greater than twice the value of the supply voltage must be avoided. Also, very good matching of R_{i_1} and R_{i_2} is essential. Even if all these conditions are met, this circuit is still limited in maximum CMRR because R_f and R_B cannot be made equal.

The 3900 is one of the most popular CDAs. Appendix C contains data sheets for the most popular CDA ICs. Included in these data sheets are many specific application circuits. Figure 9–6 shows a three-channel audio mixer circuit using the 3900. An unusual feature of this circuit is the use of the bias current at the noninverting input to enable or disable each channel, permitting any input to be disabled without inserting a switch into the signal path. This circuit would be useful only for fairly high-level sources, because the noise performance of the 3900 is not very impressive, and the necessity of large resistors in the circuit also increases the noise.

EXAMPLE

Problem

Determine the gain from each input and the low-frequency −3-dB point of the audio mixer shown in Fig. 9–6.

Solution

1. Each input stage is an inverting amplifier. Thus the gain is

$$A_V = \frac{R_f}{R_i} = \frac{1\ M\Omega}{100\ k\Omega} = 10$$

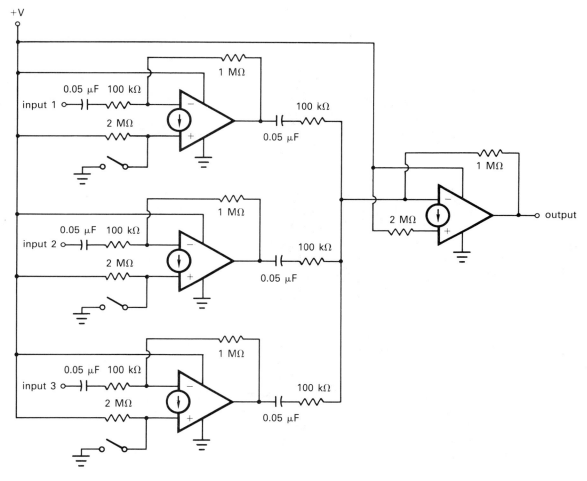

FIGURE 9–6: CDA Audio Mixer

2. The output amplifier is an inverting summer. The gain from each input of this summer is

$$A_V = \frac{R_\mathrm{f}}{R_\mathrm{i}} = \frac{1 \ \mathrm{M\Omega}}{100 \ \mathrm{k\Omega}} = 10$$

3. The total gain is $10 \cdot 10 = 100$.
4. The input resistance of each stage is equal to R_i. Thus the lower -3-dB frequency of each stage is given by

$$f_\mathrm{low} = \frac{1}{2\pi C R_\mathrm{i}} = \frac{1}{(2\pi)(0.05 \cdot 10^{-6} \ \mathrm{F})(10^5 \ \Omega)} = 32 \ \mathrm{Hz}$$

5. As discussed elsewhere in this book, if two stages have equal low -3-dB fre-

quencies, the overall -3-dB frequency when the stages are cascaded is

$$f_{\text{low,total}} = f_{\text{low}} \sqrt{2} = (32 \text{ Hz})(\sqrt{2}) = 45 \text{ Hz}$$

The data sheet for the LM3900 included in Appendix C is extraordinarily complete, and illustrates quite a few additional applications of this device.

Analog Multipliers

It was mentioned earlier in this book that amplification can be mathematically represented by multiplication. The input signal to an amplifier is multiplied by a fixed factor, the gain, to produce the output. There are a number of ICs designed as multipliers. These have the ability to multiply one voltage by another. In contrast to an amplifier, in which one of the factors is fixed, a multiplier can find the product of any two voltages within its input range.

Multipliers were first developed as part of analog computers used for military purposes and for circuit simulation. After monolithic multiplier ICs became available at a reasonably low price, many additional uses were found for them. There are two basic categories of analog multipliers: two-quadrant and four-quadrant. In order to discuss the difference between the two, we first need to define several terms. The two inputs to a multiplier are called V_X and V_Y. The output is called V_{OUT}; it is proportional to $V_X V_Y$. A two-quadrant multiplier responds to V_X voltages having either polarity, but only to positive V_Y voltages. Two-quadrant multipliers can perform very clean amplitude modulation, because mathematically, amplitude modulation is the multiplication of the carrier wave by the modulating signal.

Four-quadrant multipliers are more versatile. They will respond to either polarity of input signal at both the V_X and the V_Y inputs. Figure 9–7 shows transfer characteristics of both types of multiplier. The 1495 is probably the most commonly-used four-quadrant multiplier IC. Its data sheet is included in Appendix A. It is usually operated from a ± 15-V supply, and responds to input voltages in the range of ± 10 V. Naturally, the output voltage cannot be greater than the supply voltage, and in fact it is limited to ± 10 V, so the actual input-voltage range limitation must include the stipulation that the output must not exceed ± 10 V. To overcome this problem, the multiplier has provision for additionally multiplying the product of inputs by a *scale factor* K. Thus the equation for the output becomes

$$V_{\text{OUT}} = K V_X V_Y$$

The scale factor is chosen by means of several resistors and by the load resistance.

The 1495 operates as a transconductance device; that is, its output voltage depends directly upon its load resistance. The output is taken between pins 2 and 14, and the complete output equation is

$$I_{14} - I_2 = \frac{2 V_X V_Y}{R_X R_Y I_3}$$

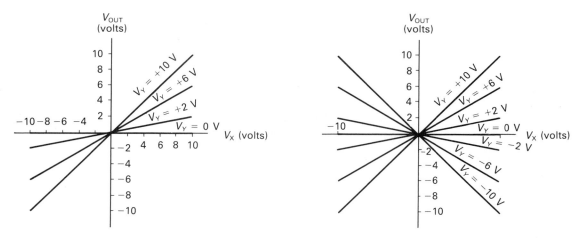

FIGURE 9–7A: Transfer Characteristic of Two-Quadrant Multiplier: $V_{OUT} = 1/10V_XV_Y$

FIGURE 9–7B: Transfer Characteristic of Four-Quadrant Multiplier: $V_{OUT} = 1/10V_XV_Y$

FIGURE 9–7: Multiplier Characteristics

where R_X is the resistance connected from pin 10 to pin 11, R_Y is the resistance connected from pin 5 to pin 6, and I_3 is the current drawn from pin 3. It can be recognized from this equation that the transconductance is given by:

$$g_m = \frac{2}{R_XR_YI_3}$$

Since the output voltage of a transconductance device is

$$V_{OUT} = V_{IN}g_mR_L$$

the output voltage of the 1495 can be found from

$$V_{OUT} = V_XV_Y\left(\frac{2R_L}{R_XR_YI_3}\right) \tag{9.04}$$

Thus the equation for scale factor is

$$K = \frac{2R_L}{R_XR_YI_3} \tag{9.05}$$

The output is accurate within about 2%, and the 1495 will drive a 50-Ω load with frequencies as high as 80 MHz.

The basic multiplier circuit is shown in Fig. 9–8A. The functions of resistors R_X, R_Y, and R_L have already been described. R_3 and R_{13} are used to establish the currents I_3 and I_{13}, according to the equations

$$R_3 = \frac{|V^-| - 0.7V}{I_3} - 500\ \Omega \tag{9.06}$$

$$R_{13} = \frac{|V^-| - 0.7\text{V}}{I_{13}} - 500 \ \Omega \tag{9.07}$$

Resistor R_1 sets the positive supply current and is chosen by the equation

$$R_1 = \frac{V^+ - V_1}{2I_3} \tag{9.08}$$

where V_1 is the voltage at pin 1. Usually, V_1 is chosen to be about two to four volts higher than the maximum expected input voltage.

Figure 9–7B shows the 1495 connected as a squaring circuit. This is basically a multiplier in which $V_X = V_Y$. This circuit can act as a frequency doubler, since the square of a sine wave contains a DC component and a sine wave at twice the original frequency. Figure 9–8C shows the concept behind a square-root circuit using an analog multiplier. Basically, it is a circuit in which the multiplier is connected in

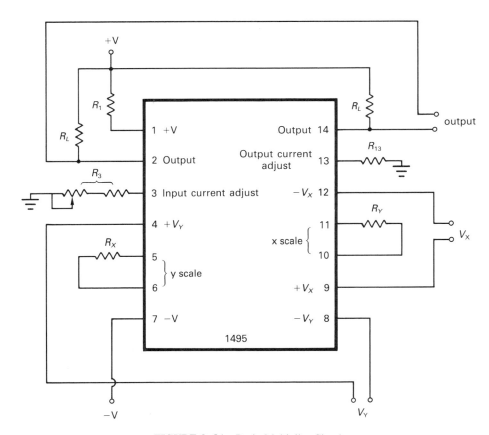

FIGURE 9–8A: Basic Multiplier Circuit

FIGURE 9–8: Applications of the Analog Multiplier

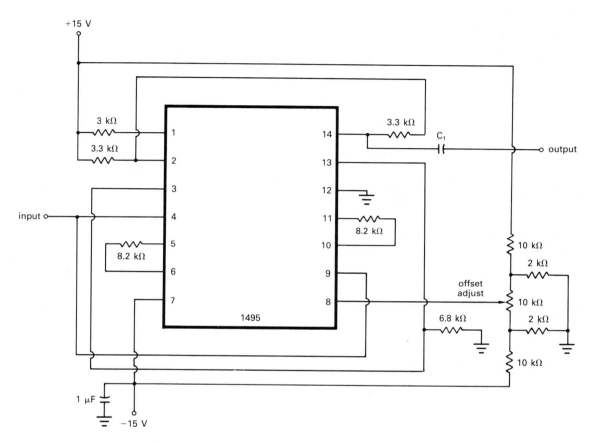

FIGURE 9–8B: Squaring (Frequency-Doubler) Circuit

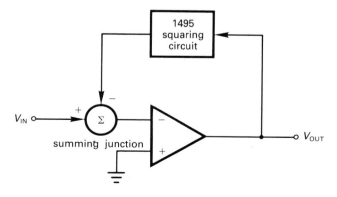

FIGURE 9–8C: Square-Root Circuit

the negative feedback loop of an op amp. The signal at the inverting input of the op amp is proportional to the square of the signal at the op amp's output. Therefore, in order for the signal to cancel V_{IN} at the zero-impedance node, the op amp's output voltage must be proportional to the square root of the input voltage.

Modulators and Demodulators

An analog multiplier IC can be used to perform amplitude modulation. The 1496 is a specialized form of multiplier especially designed to be used as a modulator or demodulator. Figure 9–9 shows the 1496 connected as a balanced modulator/demodulator. This sort of circuit is used in single-sideband communication transmitters and receivers to produce a DSSC (double-sideband suppressed carrier) signal. One sideband is then removed by filtering to leave the single-sideband (SSB) signal that is transmitted. Although such a function can be provided using individual op amps, the resulting circuit would be very complex. Other applications of the 1496 modulator/demodulator IC are in normal amplitude modulation, nonlinear mixing (heterodyning), and frequency doubling.

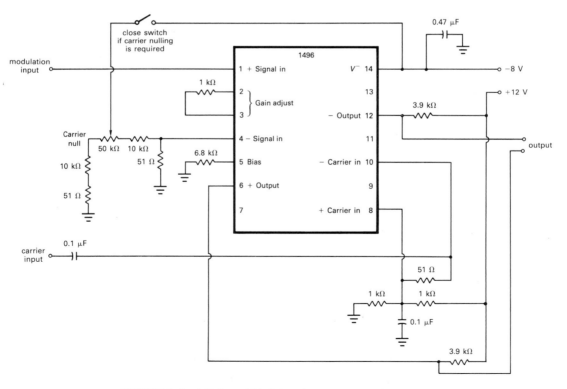

FIGURE 9–9: A Balanced Modulator/Demodulator Using the 1496

RMS Converters

In AC measurement applications, the value of an AC wave in which we are most often interested is the rms voltage. However, in the past, circuits that convert the rms value of AC input voltages into direct current to drive a meter have been very expensive. Also, their response time has been quite slow. Usually, the conversion was done by amplifying the AC input voltage, using it to heat a resistance wire, then measuring the increase in temperature of that wire. This procedure works, because the rms value of an AC wave is, by definition, its heating value. Because of the complexity, expense, and slowness of this approach, many AC measurement applications have made do with a second- or third-best approach: using rectifiers that respond to *approximately* the rms value, or using rectifiers that respond to the *average* value of the wave. Although the calibration of a meter can be compensated in order to make these approximations acceptable for sine-wave measurements, error is introduced when nonsinusoidal waves are measured. The greater the *crest factor* (V_P/V_{rms}) of a wave, the greater the error.

In 1977, Analog Devices introduced an analog IC that performs rms-to-DC conversion by analog-mathematical means. It applies the input wave to a squaring circuit, takes the average (or *mean*) of the output of the squarer, then extracts the square root of the result. The internal circuitry is very similar to that of the multipliers we have just discussed; in fact, this same function can be performed (with a great deal more trouble) by using two multipliers and an op amp. The AD536 performs true-rms-to-DC conversion with an accuracy of 0.5%. It operates from single or split supplies from 5 to 36 V. It can handle inputs having peak voltages in the range of 0 to ±20 V AC plus DC. For signals above 100 mV, the 3-dB measurement bandwidth is 100 kHz. In addition to the linear output, the AD536 provides a logarithmic output, allowing a decibel readout using a linear meter movement. Figure 9–10 shows the AD536 connected for rms-to-DC conversion with a dB output.

Phase-Locked Loops

The phase-locked loop (PLL) is a very versatile circuit that can be used for extremely linear FM modulation and demodulation, FSK generation and detection, frequency multiplication, precise motor-speed controls, and many other applications. Figure 9–11 shows a block diagram of a PLL. Its operation can best be described in three modes:

• Free-running—When the PLL is first powered up, there is no feedback signal at the input of the phase comparator. Therefore, the VCO operates at its *free-running* output frequency.

• Capture—As soon as an input frequency is applied, the phase detector produces a DC output proportional to the difference between the phase of the VCO output and the phase of the input signal. At first, these frequencies are not the same. The phase detector produces a positive output voltage if the input frequency is higher than the VCO frequency, and a negative output voltage if the input frequency is

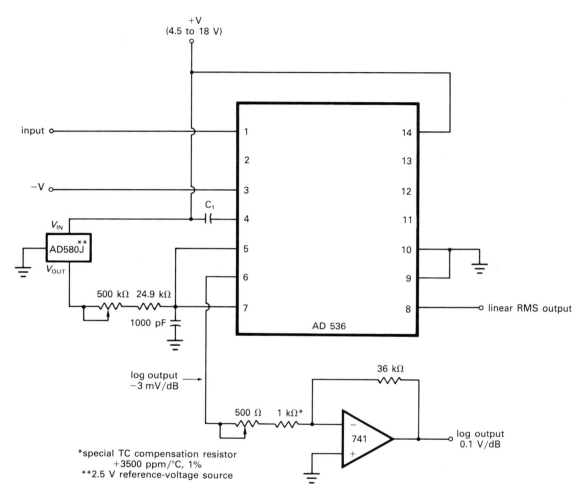

FIGURE 9–10: The AD536 RMS-to-DC Converter
(*Courtesy of Analog Devices, Inc.*)

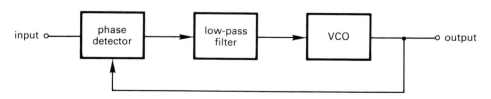

FIGURE 9–11: Operation of the Phase-Locked Loop

lower. The phase comparator's output voltage causes the VCO to adjust its output frequency to match the input frequency. Once the frequencies are matched, the phase detector continues to produce a small positive or negative output until the phases of the input and the VCO output are matched. In order to reduce *phase jitter,* or short-term fluctuations in phase produced by noise in the phase-detector output, a low-pass filter is inserted between the phase detector and the VCO. The characteristics of this filter also control the maximum rate of change of input frequency and phase that the PLL can track.

• Lock-in—Once the PLL has been captured by the input signal, the output of the VCO will remain phase-locked to the input over a certain range of input frequencies.

The PLL was invented in the 1930s, but the difficulty of building stable, linear VCOs made them too expensive and bulky for most applications. The introduction of the linear IC made PLLs practical for many circuits. More recently, the introduction of a number of PLL ICs has made the PLL easy to use and relatively inexpensive. The most common PLL ICs are the 561–565 family introduced by Signetics. Figure 9–12 shows the basic application circuit using a 565. We can learn quite a bit about the PLL by examining some of the most important specifications and design features of the NE565.

• Input level required for tracking—This is the minimum voltage that an input signal can have and still be trackable by the PLL. For the 565, it is 10 mV.
• Maximum center frequency—The center frequency is another name for the free-running frequency of the PLL. This frequency is chosen by the designer from the equation:

$$f_0 = \frac{1.2}{4RC_1} \tag{9.09}$$

where R and C_1 are as shown in Fig. 9–12.
The maximum center frequency that a designer should choose is about 300 kHz for the 565. (Notice that 500 kHz is the typical value. However, the guaranteed minimum is 300 kHz, and it is therefore somewhat chancy to design for a higher center frequency than this with a 565.) Some other PLLs in the 56X series have substantially higher maximum center frequencies.

• Triangle- and square-wave characteristics—The VCO of the 565 does not have a sine-wave output. Instead, triangle and square-wave outputs are provided. The important characteristics of the waveforms at these outputs is specified in the data sheet.
• Demodulated output characteristics—Since one of the most important applications of PLLs is in FM demodulation, the characteristics of the device are specified for this application. These include DC output voltage level, maximum AC output voltage swing, output voltage for ±10% frequency deviation at the input, harmonic distortion, output impedance, offset voltage, and AM rejection. This last characteristic has to do with noise performance. In an FM wave, the frequency changes with the instantaneous amplitude of the modulating signal. The amplitude of the output should be constant. Therefore, any amplitude variations (AM) that are present are

accidental. If these amplitude variations are converted into output signal, they will represent noise. Therefore, a high degree of AM rejection makes for a good S/N ratio at the output.

Besides the center frequency, there are two important design features of the 565 that are controlled by external conditions. The *capture range* is the range of frequencies within which the input must be located in order for it to capture the VCO. This is given by the equation:

$$f_C = \pm \sqrt{\frac{f_0}{2827 V_{CC} C_2}} \qquad (9.10)$$

where C_2 is as shown in Fig. 9–12, and V_{CC} is the total supply voltage from the most negative to the most positive point. The *lock-in range* is the range of frequencies through which the input can vary without the PLL losing phase-lock. This range is given by:

$$f_L = \frac{\pm 8 f_0}{V_{CC}} \qquad (9.11)$$

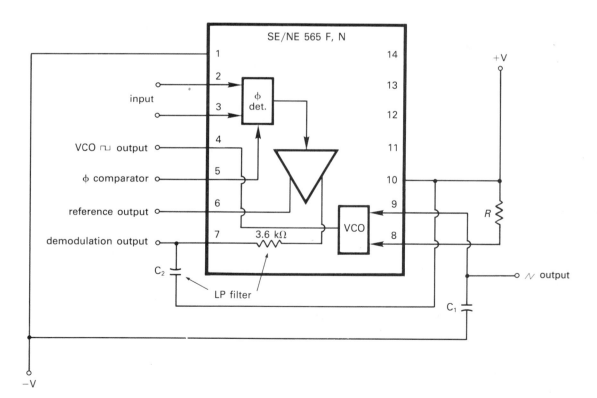

FIGURE 9–12: Basic 565 Application Circuit

Figure 9–13 shows two applications of the 565. Part A of the figure shows an FM demodulator circuit. The input frequency is applied to the phase detector. The VCO phase-locks with the input signal and follows its frequency. In order for this to occur, the phase detector must produce a signal that is proportional to the instantaneous frequency of the input signal. This output signal from the phase detector is the same as the signal with which the carrier was originally frequency modulated. In the circuit shown, R is made variable to provide the ability to tune the PLL's center frequency to the desired carrier frequency. The 0.001-μF capacitor connected between pins 7 and 8 is used to prevent parasitic oscillation.

EXAMPLE

Problem

Design an FM demodulator for a center frequency of 100 kHz, with a deviation of ±15 kHz. The circuit must avoid being captured by an 80-kHz signal.

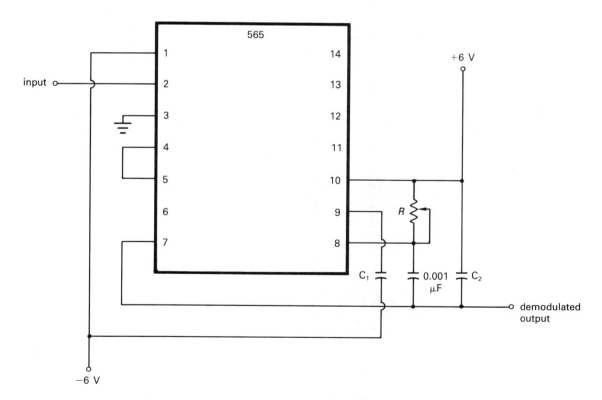

FIGURE 9–13A: FM Demodulator

FIGURE 9–13: Applications of the 565 Phase-Locked Loop

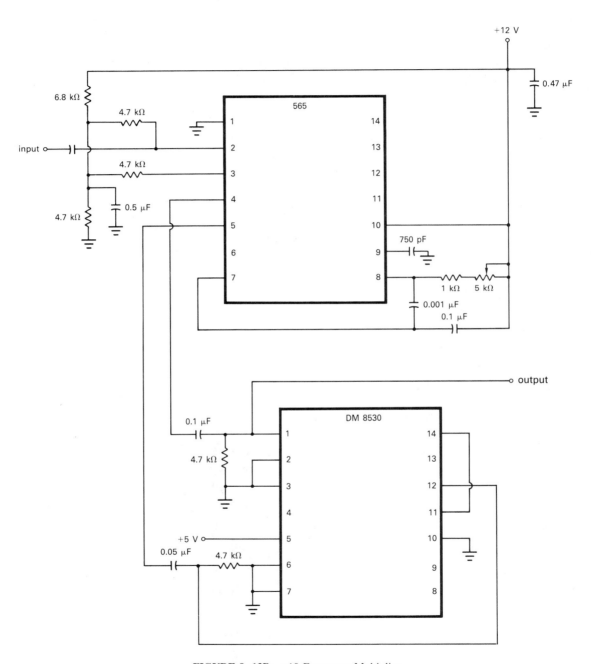

FIGURE 9–13B: ×10 Frequency Multiplier

Solution

1. The center frequency of the PLL is determined using equation 9.09:

$$f_0 = \frac{1.2}{4RC_1} \qquad (9.09)$$

We will choose a capacitor of 500 pF. Then we can solve for R:

$$R = \frac{1.2}{4f_0C_1}$$

$$\frac{1.2}{4(10^5 \text{ Hz})(5 \cdot 10^{-10} \text{ F})} = 6000 \ \Omega$$

2. The capture range must be at least ± 15 kHz, but less than ± 20 kHz, to exclude the 80-kHz signal. Let us choose ± 18 kHz. Then we can calculate the value of C_2 using equation 9.10:

$$f_C = \pm \sqrt{\frac{f_0}{2827V_{CC}C_2}} \qquad (9.10)$$

Solving for C_2:

$$f_C^2 = \frac{f_0}{2827V_{CC}C_2}$$

$$C_2 = \frac{f_0}{2827V_{CC}f_C^2} = \frac{100 \text{ kHz}}{2827(12 \text{ V})(18 \text{ kHz})^2} = 0.009 \ \mu\text{F}$$

Figure 9–13B shows a frequency multiplier using the 565. Actually, there are two methods of building a frequency multiplier using a PLL. One is to allow the PLL to phase-lock to a harmonic of the input frequency. Although it depends upon the harmonic content of the input wave, the maximum multiplication factor that can usually be achieved using this method is 5. The amplitude of harmonics above the fifth even in a square wave is likely to be too small to provide the required 10 mV at the input to the PLL. The other method is to use a digital frequency divider connected in the feedback loop of the PLL. This is the method shown in the figure. The free-running frequency of the PLL is set at the desired output frequency. The divider is chosen according to the required frequency-multiplication factor, 10 in this case. Then when the output is at the correct frequency, the signal from the divider to the PLL's phase detector will be the same as the input frequency. For example, if a 1-kHz input were to be multiplied to achieve a 19-kHz output, a divide-by-19 circuit would be inserted in the feedback loop of the PLL. Then if the output frequency were too high, the frequency-divided signal fed to the phase detector would be above the input frequency, and the output of the phase detector would go negative, decreasing the VCO frequency. Conversely, if the output frequency were too low, the output from the divider would be less than 1 kHz and the phase detector's positive output would cause the VCO to increase its output frequency. This type of circuit is more likely to be used with the 564 high-frequency PLL than with the 565, because the 564 has a maximum frequency of 60 MHz.

Compandors

In any communication circuit, noise is one of the limiting factors upon the performance of the system. In addition to using low-noise design techniques, a number of systems are used to reduce the *effect* of noise. One of the most common of these is *compandors*. A compandor is a system comprised of a *com*pressor and an ex*pan*dor. A compressor is a circuit that reduces the *dynamic range* of a signal, that is, the difference between the smallest signal voltage and the largest signal voltage. It does this by means of an amplifier whose gain is inversely proportional to the time-averaged amplitude of the input signal. In other words, it is an amplifier with a nonlinear transfer characteristic, but whose nonlinearity is only evident on very slowly varying signals. Thus, the waveshape of the input signal, which is a quickly changing voltage, is reproduced faithfully. However, the average amplitude varies much more slowly, and the gain is adjusted to keep the average *output* amplitude reasonably constant.

An expandor is a circuit that performs in exactly the opposite fashion from a compressor: It increases the dynamic range of a signal. Figure 9–14 illustrates the way in which a compandor can reduce the effect of noise in a communication system. Part A of the figure shows a noncompandored system. The average noise in the system is 10 mV$_{rms}$. The signal varies from 100 mV to 10 V. Thus the worst-case S/N ratio is 100 mV/10 mV = 10, or 20 dB. Part B of the figure shows a compandored system. A compressor is used at the input of the system to reduce the dynamic range of the signal. Now the signal fed into the communications system varies from 200 mV to 10 V. At the output of the system, an expandor is used to restore the original dynamic range of the signal. Thus at the output, the signal again varies from 100 mV to 10 V. However, within the communication system, where the large noise voltages exist, the minimum signal level is 200 mV, giving a S/N ratio of 200 mV/10 mV = 20, or 26 dB. Thus, although the actual noise level in the communication system remains the same, the *effect* of the noise is reduced by companding, providing a 6-dB increase in S/N ratio.

The amount of compansion used is expressed as the reduction/increase in dynamic range, in dB. The input signal has a dynamic range of 10 V/100 mV = 40 dB. The signal at the output of the compressor has a dynamic range of 10 V/200 mV = 34 dB. Thus the *compansion ratio* is 40 dB − 34 dB = 6 dB. In other words, the compansion ratio is numerically the same as the increase in S/N ratio.

Compandors can be built with discrete transistor circuits; however, these circuits have to be fairly complex to provide low-distortion performance. Using op amps greatly simplifies the design of compandors. However, unless the transfer characteristic of the compressor is exactly complementary to that of the expandor, the output signal from the communication system will be different from the input signal.

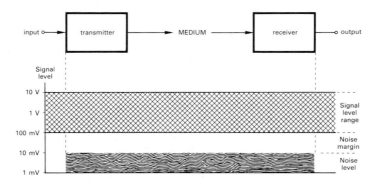

FIGURE 9–14A: Noncompandored System

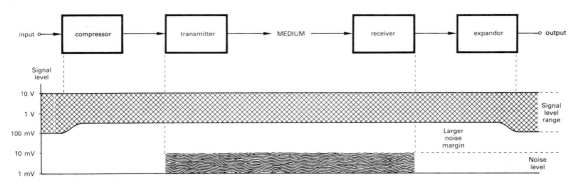

FIGURE 9–14B: Compandored System

FIGURE 9–14: The Use of Compandors to Reduce the Effect of Noise

A high degree of matching of transfer characteristics is difficult to obtain with op-amp circuits. The 570 and 571 compandor ICs introduced by Signetics provide a way of building compandors with excellent matching between the compressor and expandor sections while minimizing parts count, and hence manufacturing cost.

Figure 9–15A shows the NE570 connected as a compressor. For this circuit, the two R_{DC} resistors control the output DC bias:

$$V_{OUT,DC} = (1.8 \text{ V}) \frac{2R_{DC}}{30 \text{ k}\Omega}$$

Since C_{DC} acts as a bypass capacitor, and C_{f_1}, C_{f_2}, and C_{IN} are coupling capacitors, their reactances must be small at the lowest frequency of interest. The same values can be used for all of them:

$$C = \frac{1}{2\pi f_{low} \cdot 1 \text{ k}\Omega}$$

Figure 9–15B shows an expandor circuit using the 570. The capacitor values can be calculated from the previous formula. The 571 is essentially equivalent, and

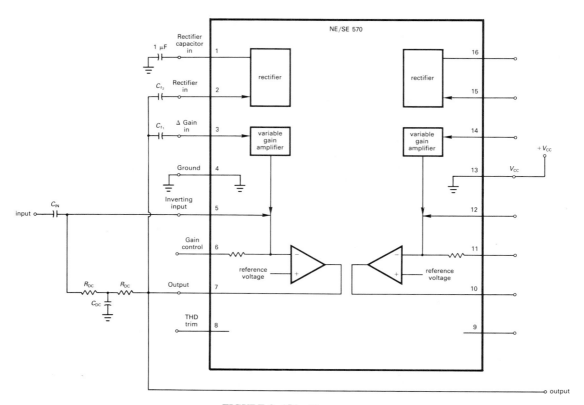

FIGURE 9–15A: Compressor

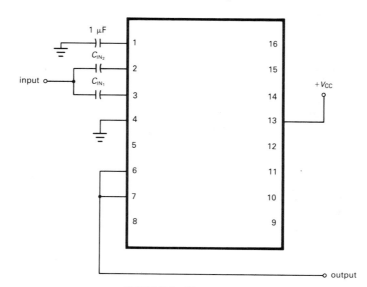

FIGURE 9–15B: Expandor

FIGURE 9–15: Applications of the NE570 Compandor

can be used interchangeably, so long as the more limited supply-voltage ratings are kept in mind. (The 570 can be supplied by voltages from 6 to 24 volts; the 571, from 6 to 18 volts.) The compansion ratio of these circuits is 6 dB.

SPECIALIZED CIRCUITS

By far most of the linear IC circuits that a technician is likely to encounter fall into the categories that have already been discussed in this book: amplifiers, filters, waveform generators, and so on. However, in some types of equipment, especially industrial and measuring instrumentation, highly specialized circuits are used. We will discuss these next.

Precision Rectifiers

Many electronic instruments require an AC voltage to be converted to a DC voltage. Of course this function is rectification, and simple diodes are used as rectifiers in power supplies. And in some cases, the rectification is a part of the rms-to-DC conversion described earlier in this chapter. But sometimes, neither of these fills the bill. Where the complexity and cost of true rms conversion are not justified, but where the 0.6-V turn-on voltage of a simple diode rectifier causes problems, a *precision rectifier* is used. This is a circuit that acts like an ideal diode: It conducts at *any* positive voltage, but blocks current when reverse biased.

Figure 9–16 shows a comparison of the transfer curve of a simple diode with that of a precision rectifier. Notice that the transfer curve of the diode becomes nonlinear at low signal voltages. This is because of the nonzero turn-on voltage. If you look closely at the face of a low-priced analog voltmeter, you will notice that there is a separate scale for the lowest AC voltage range. This scale is nonlinear at the lower end. In spite of the very-low-turn-on instrumentation rectifier diodes used, a nonlinear scale must be included to compensate for the nonlinear transfer char-

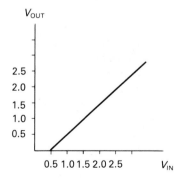

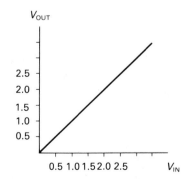

FIGURE 9–16A: Half-Wave Rectifier **FIGURE 9–16B:** Half-Wave Precision Rectifier

FIGURE 9–16: Transfer Curves for Diodes and Precision Rectifiers

acteristic. If we wished to measure AC voltages in the low-millivolt range, the problem would be even worse: They would not turn the rectifier on at all, and no measurement would be possible. In contrast, the transfer curve of the precision rectifier remains linear down to zero volts. This permits accurate rectification of extremely small AC voltages.

Figures 9–17A and B show circuits for half-wave and full-wave precision rectifiers. The precision rectifier is sometimes called an *absolute-value* circuit. As shown, the circuits produce a positive-voltage output. For a negative output, the diodes can be reversed. The elimination of the turn-on voltage can be explained as follows. When an input is applied to the op amp, the circuit has no negative feedback until the diode(s) turn on. Therefore, the output voltage rises quickly to the point at which the diodes turn on. Then the negative-feedback loop is closed, and the circuit acts as a normal unity-gain amplifier. This is exactly the same process as that discussed in Chapter 5 in connection with external booster transistors having no bias networks.

In the full-wave precision rectifier, the positive half-cycles produce no output from the left-hand op amp. Thus the summer is fed only a positive half-cycle from the input, and it produces a negative half-cycle. Negative half-cycles at the input produce positive half-cycles at the output of the left-hand op amp. The summer doubles the amplitude of these and adds the negative half-cycle from the input, producing an equivalent positive half-cycle input, resulting in another negative half-cycle output.

The circuits shown in Fig. 9–17 produce normal half-wave or full-wave-rectified output waves. If a DC meter movement is fed by these waveforms, the reading obtained will be half the average value (half-wave) or the full average value (full-wave) of the input wave. The addition of filter components provides other options. Adding a simple filter capacitor to the output converts the circuit into a peak detector. Then the output of the precision rectifier charges the capacitor to the peak input voltage. The capacitor discharges primarily through the load, and the time constant of the capacitor and the load resistance should be several times the period of the lowest frequency to be handled.

EXAMPLE

Problem

Choose a filter capacitor to be added to the circuit of Fig. 9–17A to turn it into a peak detector. The input signal will cover the frequency range from 300 to 3000 Hz. The circuit will feed another amplifier stage having a 10-kΩ input resistance.

Solution

1. The lowest frequency of interest is 300 Hz. The period of a 300-Hz wave is 1/300 Hz = 3.33 ms. We will make the time constant of the capacitor and the load resistor equal to 5 times this value:

$$\text{T.C.} = 5 \cdot 3.33 \text{ ms} = 16.7 \text{ ms}$$

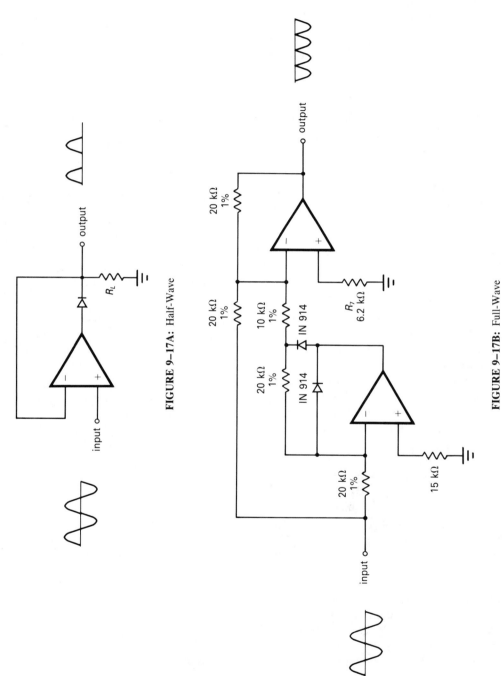

FIGURE 9–17A: Half-Wave

FIGURE 9–17B: Full-Wave

FIGURE 9–17: Precision Rectifiers

2. Since the load resistor is 10 kΩ, we can solve for the value of the capacitor:

$$\text{T.C.} = RC$$

$$C = \frac{T.C.}{R} = \frac{16.7 \text{ ms}}{10 \text{ k}\Omega} = 1.7 \text{ μF}$$

The addition of a resistor and a reference-voltage source as shown in Fig. 9–18A turns the half-wave precision rectifier into a clipper; that is, a circuit that clips off positive or negative peaks that exceed the reference voltage. As shown, the circuit is a positive-peak clipper. Reversing the diode will change it into a negative-peak clipper. The peak clamper circuit shown in Fig. 9–18B adds a DC level to the input wave. The precision rectifier charges the input capacitor to a voltage equal to the sum of the peak input voltage and V_{ref}. Notice that the output voltage is not rectified; it is only DC-level-shifted. The optional resistor R_B provides a discharge path for the capacitor to provide faster response to negative-going changes in input level.

The op amp chosen for use in any of these precision rectifier circuits must have a high slew rate, if operation at frequencies over 1 kHz is expected. This is because of the rapid change in output voltage necessary to eliminate the effects of turn-on voltage. As a minimum, the slew rate should be

$$\text{SR} = 0.000216 f_{\text{max}} \text{ V/μs} \qquad (9.12)$$

Logarithmic Amplifiers

In some measurement circuits, a DC voltage must be converted into a value proportional to the logarithm of that voltage. One example of such a circuit has already been discussed; the AD536 rms-to-DC converter IC contains internal log conversion to provide a dB output. Converting a DC voltage to its log value is the job of the *logarithmic amplifier*. Conversion in the reverse direction is performed by an *antilog* or *exponential* amplifier. The basic circuits of both of these devices are shown in Fig. 9–19A and B. In both cases, the key to their operation is the logarithmic relationship between the base-emitter voltage (V_{BE}) and the collector current (I_C) of a bipolar transistor. In its basic form, the log amplifier uses the op-amp output to control the V_{BE} of a transistor. The resulting collector-current variation directly affects the input signal to the op amp. In the antilog circuit, the input voltage controls the V_{BE} of the transistor. Figure 9–19C shows a basic practical log amplifier. The addition of the second amplifier and transistor provide compensation for the temperature effects that seriously impair the performance of the simple circuit shown in 9–19A, by balancing an undriven identical circuit against the circuit actually doing the conversion. Thus the summing amplifier subtracts the temperature effects that appear in A_2's output from the output signal of A_1. The output voltage of a log amplifier similar to the one shown in Fig. 9–19C would typically be measured in volts per decade change in input voltage. This value can be controlled by the sensitivity adjust potentiometer. In this circuit, R_3 should equal R_4, R_5 should

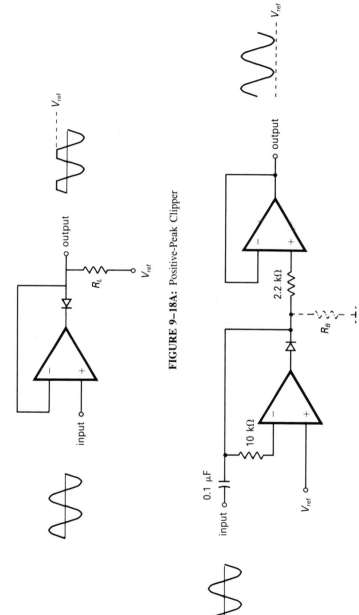

FIGURE 9–18A: Positive-Peak Clipper

FIGURE 9–18B: Clamper

FIGURE 9–18: Op-Amp Clipper and Clamper Circuits

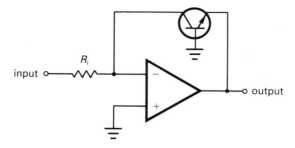

FIGURE 9–19A: Basic Logarithmic Amplifier

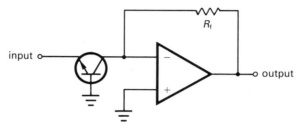

FIGURE 9–19B: Basic Antilogarithmic Amplifier

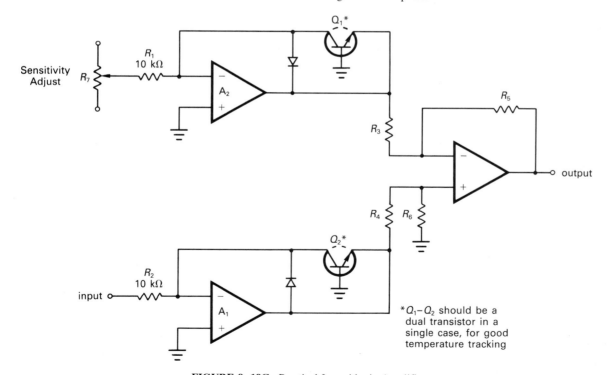

FIGURE 9–19C: Practical Logarithmic Amplifier

FIGURE 9–19: Logarithmic and Antilogarithmic Amplifiers

equal R_6, and the gain of the output amplifier is given by R_5/R_3. For bipolar or wide-range input signals, more complex circuits must be used.

Signal-Processing and Conversion Circuits

In many signal-processing applications, an analog waveform must be sampled at specific intervals, and then the sampled value must be held until a logic circuit is ready to read it. This is the job of a *sample-and-hold* circuit. An example of its use would be in a system in which the temperature of a process is monitored at periodic intervals by a microprocessor. The output of the temperature detector is applied to the sample-and-hold circuit. A multichannel A/D converter is used to feed the output of the sample-and-hold circuit, along with many other analog voltages, to the microprocessor. Most of the time, the microprocessor is examining inputs from the other circuits. During this time, the sample-and-hold circuit is in the sampling mode. Shortly before the microprocessor addresses the input that is fed by the sample-and-hold circuit, a control voltage is applied to that circuit, switching it to the hold mode. In this mode, the last output voltage is retained. Then when the A/D converter does address the temperature input, the output of the sample-and-hold circuit is a stable DC voltage that can be converted into a digital value. This also allows the sampling time to be much longer than the amount of time that the microprocessor allots for examining each input. The basic concept of the sample-and-hold circuit is shown in Fig. 9–20A. In the sampling mode, the electronic switch connects the input to the amplifier, and the ungrounded plate of the capacitor tracks the input voltage. The capacitor is chosen so as to have a sufficient reactance not to act as a short to ground at the highest signal frequency. Also, the sample-and-hold circuit must be fed from a low-impedance source to avoid having the source impedance and the capacitor act as a low-pass filter. In the holding mode, the input of the circuit is disconnected from the source, and the capacitor retains its last voltage. Naturally, the use of a low-input-current op amp is important. The one specified in the figure is an FET-input type. The sample-and-hold circuit can be combined with a precision rectifier and integrator circuit to make an average-and-hold circuit, for use when the value to be read from the output is to be the average value of the input wave.

Figure 9–20B shows a practical sample-and-hold circuit. In the sampling mode, amplifier A_1 and booster transistor Q_1 provide current to charge the capacitor. The 0 input to the TTL inverter produces a 1 output from the inverter, turning on transistor Q_3. This transistor and the 10-kΩ resistor provide a discharge path so that the voltage on the capacitor will not simply rise to the peak value and stay there, but will track the input voltage. In the holding mode, the inverter turns Q_3 off and the 1 control voltage turns Q_2 on, pulling the base of Q_1 negative. Thus Q_1 is turned off and prevented from passing signals to the capacitor. With Q_3 off, the capacitor can only discharge through the extremely-high-impedance path provided by the diode and the op-amp input. Thus it holds the voltage to which it has been charged.

In order to greatly simplify the design and construction of sample-and-hold circuits, a monolithic sample-and-hold amplifier such as the LF198 can be used. A

typical sample-and-hold circuit using the LF198 is shown in Fig. 9–20C. Figure
9–20D shows the LF198 used in an average-and-hold circuit. The averaging time is
selected by the choice of R_h and C_h. The product of these components should be
much larger than $1/2\pi f_{low}$, where f_{low} is the lowest frequency present in the input.

Two other important specialized op-amp circuits are current-to-voltage and voltage-to-current converters. These are used for a number of applications. One example

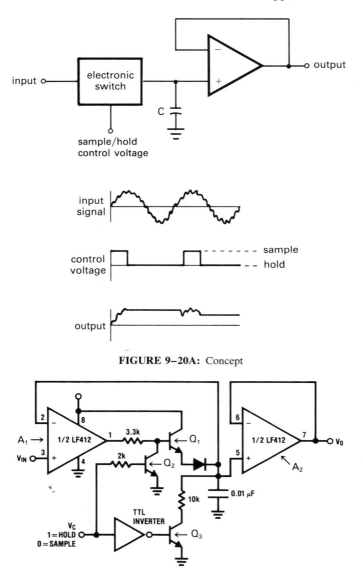

FIGURE 9–20A: Concept

FIGURE 9–20B: Practical Circuit *(Reprinted with permission of National Semiconductor Corp.)*

FIGURE 9–20: Sample-and-Hold Circuits

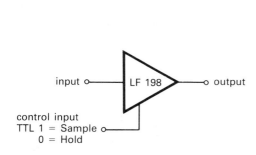

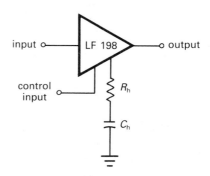

FIGURE 9–20C: LF198 Sample-and-Hold Application   **FIGURE 9–20D:** LF198 Average-and-Hold Application

is in industrial control systems. Many of these systems are very low-impedance systems in which the current is controlled in proportion to an input quantity such as temperature or liquid level. This 4–20-mA control system provides good immunity to induced noise. However, in order to interface such a system with many other types of electronic systems, the control current must be converted to or from a proportional control voltage. Figure 9–21 shows circuits for current-to-voltage and voltage-to-current converters. The current-to-voltage converter accepts an input directly at the op amp's inverting input. This is a zero-impedance point, so there is no input resistance to affect the value of current; it is controlled purely by the current source. In order to maintain the inverting input as a zero-impedance point, enough opposite-polarity current must be supplied from the op amp's output through R_f to cancel the input current. (Remember that ideally the op amp itself has zero input current.) This requires that the output voltage be:

$$V_{OUT} = I_{IN}R_f \tag{9.13}$$

EXAMPLE

Problem

Design a current-to-voltage converter to convert currents in the range of 4 to 20 mA into voltages from 0 to 10 V to be fed to an A/D converter.

Solution

1. We can solve for R_f, using the change in output voltage and input current in the equation:

$$R_f = \frac{\Delta V_{OUT}}{\Delta I_{IN}} = \frac{10\ V}{20\ mA - 4\ mA} = 625\ \Omega \qquad \text{(from 9.13)}$$

2. In order to make a 4-mA input give a 0-V output, we will need to bias the

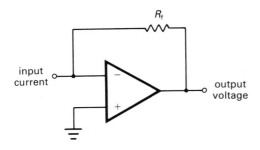

FIGURE 9–21A: Current-to-Voltage Converter

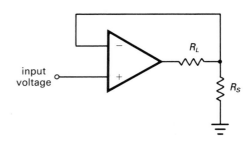

FIGURE 9–21B: Voltage-to-Current Converter

FIGURE 9–21: Current-to-Voltage and Voltage-to-Current Converters

noninverting input of the op amp negative by an amount

$$V_{\text{ref}} = 4 \text{ mA} \cdot 625 \text{ } \Omega = 2.5 \text{ V} \qquad \text{(from 9.13)}$$

The voltage-to-current converter includes the load resistance within the feedback loop. As usual in a negative-feedback op-amp circuit, the op amp attempts to keep the voltages at its inverting and noninverting inputs equal. The voltage at the inverting input is simply the load current multiplied by R_S:

$$V_{\text{inv}} = I_L R_S \qquad (9.14)$$

Since this must be numerically equal to the input voltage at the noninverting input,

$$V_{\text{IN}} = I_L R_S \qquad (9.15)$$

or

$$I_L = \frac{V_{\text{IN}}}{R_S} \qquad (9.16)$$

You will recognize this equation as having the same form as the output equation for a transconductance amplifier, and in fact we can identify the transconductance of this circuit as $1/R_S$. An OTA can be used as a voltage-to-current converter also.

The voltage at the output terminal of the op amp is equal to the algebraic sum of the input voltage and the product $I_L R_L$:

$$V_{\text{OUT}} = V_{\text{IN}} + I_L R_L \qquad (9.17)$$

EXAMPLE

Problem

Design a voltage-to-current converter for use in an electronic voltmeter. The circuit needs to provide a 1-mA output current to drive an analog meter movement with a full-scale input voltage of 100 mV. The meter resistance is 2 kΩ.

Solution

1. Solving for R_S, we have

$$R_S = \frac{V_{IN}}{I_L} = \frac{100 \text{ mV}}{1 \text{ mA}} = 100 \text{ } \Omega$$

2. In order to make sure that the op amp can provide enough output voltage to supply the required current, let us calculate the required output voltage for a 1-mA load current:

$$V_{OUT} = V_{IN} + I_L R_L = 0.1 \text{ V} + (1 \text{ mA} \cdot 2 \text{ k}\Omega) = 2.1 \text{ V} \qquad (9.17)$$

Even if we use a 124 op amp with a 5-V supply, we can easily handle this amount of output voltage.

A/D AND D/A CONVERTERS

The conversion of analog signals to digital words is quite important in all areas of computer-aided manufacturing and testing, as well as in the many digital measuring instruments available today. The conversion of digital words into analog signals is important in any device in which a computer controls an analog process. This section of the book deals with the operation of these devices. Since most IC A/D and D/A converters require a microprocessor for their proper operation, no details will be given concerning actual connection of the devices. Instead, general principles will be discussed.

Analog-to-Digital Conversion Principles

One form of A/D converter has already been discussed in this book: the flash converter (Chapter 2). As you remember, the flash converter is simply a stack of comparators arranged so that the number of "high" outputs at any given time corresponds to the analog input voltage. The output of a flash converter can be fed into a binary adder to make up a complete analog-to-binary converter. One of the important parameters of any A/D converter is its *resolution*. The resolution is the smallest change in input voltage that will cause a change in output voltage. For the examples of the flash converter we used, the resolution was 1 V. You may also remember that the main disadvantage of the flash converter is that numerous devices are required to implement a converter having fine resolution. However, for applications requiring the extreme speed that a flash converter offers, there is no other device that will work. Therefore, there are a number of companies who derive a sizeable portion of their income from the manufacture of flash converters.

Another form of A/D converter is illustrated in Fig. 9–22. This *single-slope* converter operates on a very simple principle. If a constant voltage is fed to the input of an integrator, a ramp voltage of constant slope will appear at the output. By

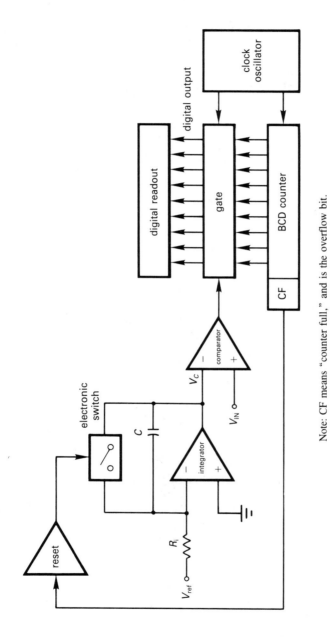

Note: CF means "counter full," and is the overflow bit.

FIGURE 9–22: Single-Slope A/D Converter

starting the integrator at a known voltage and applying a known voltage, we can closely predict the rate of change of the output voltage as well as the time required for the ramp to reach any given voltage. If this well-defined ramp is applied to the inverting input of a comparator, and the unknown input voltage is applied to the noninverting input, the output of the comparator will go negative as soon as the ramp voltage equals the input voltage. By using a binary counter fed by a clock generator, we can determine the amount of time required for the ramp to reach the input voltage. Since the starting voltage and rate of rise are known, the unknown voltage can be determined. For example, if the ramp increases at a rate of 10 mV/ms, the clock runs at a frequency of 1 kHz, and 50 clock pulses were required before the ramp voltage became equal to the unknown voltage, then the unknown voltage must have been (50 ms) (10 mV/ms) = 500 mV. This method of A/D conversion was popular in early digital voltmeters. It is subject to errors from the following sources:

1. Clock oscillator frequency drift
2. Reference voltage drift
3. Change in integrator capacitance with age
4. Comparator inaccuracy
5. AC noise in the unknown voltage

A better A/D converter is the *dual-slope* unit in Fig. 9–23. In this unit, the capacitor is initially charged to a known negative voltage by the voltage reference. Then switch S (actually an electronic switch) is changed to the other position and the integrator capacitor charges from the unknown voltage. When the voltage on the capacitor crosses the zero point, the comparator output goes positive, causing the clock signal to be fed to the counter. In other words, the counter starts timing. When the counter reaches its maximum count, it overflows, and the overflow bit causes switch S to change position again. Now the capacitor discharges into the reference source. When the capacitor voltage crosses the zero point in the negative direction, the comparator output becomes negative, disconnecting the clock signal from the counter. Since the counter began the discharge at the time when it overflowed, it started again with a count of zero at that time. Therefore, the count present when the comparator switches low again corresponds to the amount of time required for the capacitor to discharge to 0 V. Since the value of the resistor in series with the unknown voltage is known, and the amount of charging time is known, the voltage on the capacitor when the counter overflowed depends only upon the unknown voltage. And since the value of the reference voltage and its resistor are known, the discharge time depends upon the maximum voltage to which the capacitor was charged. Thus the count present when the comparator switches low corresponds to the unknown voltage. In this system, errors in the clock oscillator, capacitor, and comparator are present to an equal degree during both the charge and discharge portions of the cycle. Therefore, they cancel out. Also, it is possible to choose the charging time of the counter to be an exact number of periods of 60 Hz, so that there will be an equal number of positive and negative excursions of any 60-Hz noise present with the unknown voltage, nullifying the effect of that noise. The dual-slope converter

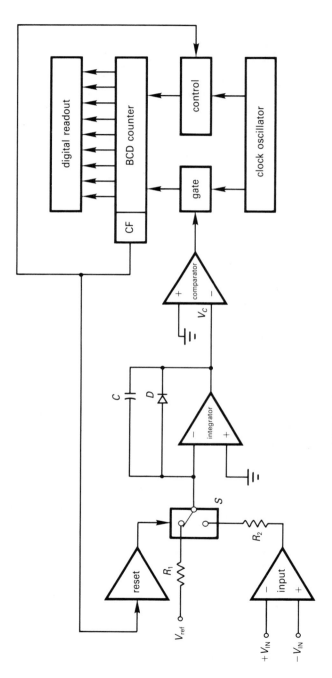

FIGURE 9–23: Dual-Slope A/D Converter

has been one of the most common A/D converters in better digital voltmeters for years.

Another type of A/D converter that has been mentioned earlier in this book is the VCO. If the frequency of a VCO is very linearly related to the control voltage, a frequency counter connected to the VCO output can provide the required binary conversion to make a complete A/D converter. A related A/D converter is used in a number of specialized ICs made for use in digital voltmeters. This is the *pulse-modulation converter* shown in Fig. 9–24. In order to understand its operation, first assume that the Q output of the D flip-flop is high. Then switch S_1 is closed, and capacitor C charges through resistor R. When V_C, the voltage on the capacitor, exceeds V_{IN}, the comparator output will switch low. This causes the flip-flop to change states at the rising edge of the next clock pulse, opening S_1 and closing S_2. The capacitor then discharges through R and R_s. When the voltage on the capacitor becomes less than V_{IN}, the comparator output goes high, S_1 closes, and the cycle begins again. The duty cycle of the rectangular wave at output Q therefore depends upon the input voltage, because a high voltage requires a longer time for V_C to charge to the input voltage. (This affects the frequency also, but the change in frequency is of no importance.) The counter counts clock pulses only when output Q is high. Therefore the average frequency fed to the counter is the product of the clock frequency and the duty cycle of the wave at Q. For example, if the duty cycle is 0.8 and the clock frequency is 200 kHz, then the frequency measured by the counter is 0.8 (200 kHz) = 160 kHz. Since the duty cycle is proportional to input voltage, the frequency is also proportional to input voltage.

The A/D converter type most commonly used in general-purpose microprocessor applications is the *successive-approximation converter* in Fig. 9–25. The heart of the device is the successive-approximation register (SAR). This device feeds binary numbers into a D/A converter, which then produces analog output voltages corresponding to the value of the binary number at its input. These voltages are compared with the input voltage by the comparator, which, in turn, controls the operation of the SAR. For example, if a certain A/D converter had an analog input voltage range of zero to 2.55 V, then since an 8-bit SAR has 256 states, each single-unit state change would correspond to 0.01 V at the output of the D/A converter. If an input voltage of 2.005 V were being measured, the typical measuring sequence would be as follows:

1. The SAR would apply 10000000_2 to the D/A converter. This is equivalent to 128_{10}, and is less than the input voltage, so the comparator output would remain high.
2. The SAR would apply 11000000_2 to the D/A converter which would then produce an output voltage of 1.92. Since this still is less than the input voltage, the comparator output would remain high.
3. The SAR would apply 11100000_2 to the D/A converter, producing an output of 2.24 V. This is higher than the input voltage, so the comparator output would go low.
4. The low comparator output would tell the SAR that a 1 in bit position 5 is invalid. It would then apply 11010000_2 to the D/A converter, whose output

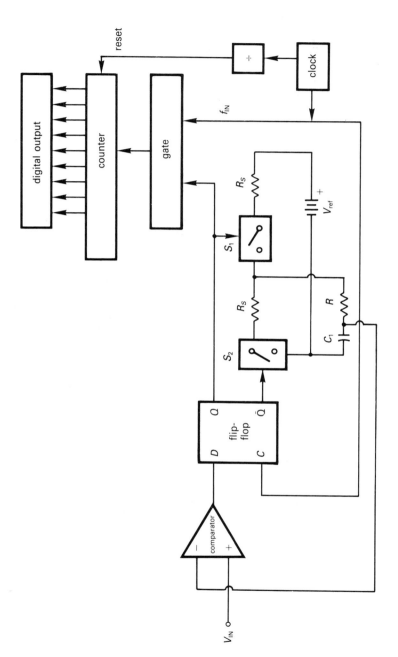

FIGURE 9–24: Pulse Modulation A/D Converter

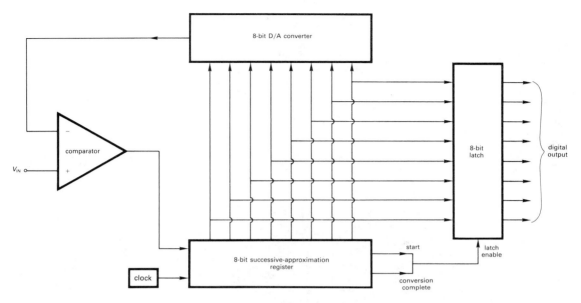

FIGURE 9–25: Successive-Approximation A/D Converter

would then be 2.08 V. This is also greater than the input voltage, so the comparator output remains low, telling the SAR that a 1 in bit position 4 is invalid.

5. The SAR applies 11001000_2 to the D/A converter, resulting in an output of 2 V. This is less than the input, so the 1 in position 3 is retained.

6. The SAR tries 11001100_2, then 11001010_2, then 11001001_2; all of these produce voltages greater than the input voltage, so the SAR registers 1's in positions 0, 1, and 2 as invalid. Once a 1 in position 0 has been tried, the SAR sends a "conversion complete" signal to the latch, and the valid bit pattern 11001000_2 is latched in and appears at the output.

This conversion sequence is similar to the single-slope conversion sequence, in that a series of reference voltages is generated, while comparing the reference voltage to the input voltage. In fact, it would be much simpler to just generate a digital "ramp" by beginning with 00000001_2 and counting up, feeding the counter output to a window comparator, and stopping at the matching input. However, to convert the value of 2.005 V that we used in the above example, 200 clock cycles would have been required. Using the scheme described above, the complete conversion was accomplished in 8 cycles. Thus the seemingly more complex plan is actually much faster. In fact, the successive-approximation converter is second only to the flash converter in speed of conversion.

Analog-to-Digital Converter ICs

An example of a common A/D converter IC is the ADC0802, whose data sheet is listed in Appendix A. This is a successive-approximation device designed for

A/D CONVERTER ICs

These two 12-bit A/D Converter ICs represent responses to very different needs. The hybrid circuit on the left is a multistage flash converter capable of 1 million conversions per second. The smaller monolithic circuit at right is a successive-approximation device that is much slower, but also much less expensive. (Courtesy of Analog Devices, Inc.)

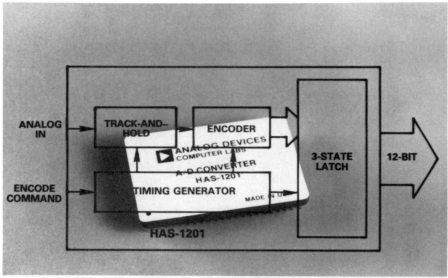

Analog Devices' HAS-1201 hybrid A/D converter includes an internal track-and-hold amplifier to simplify digitizing analog signals to 1MHz.

(continued)

(continued from page 456)

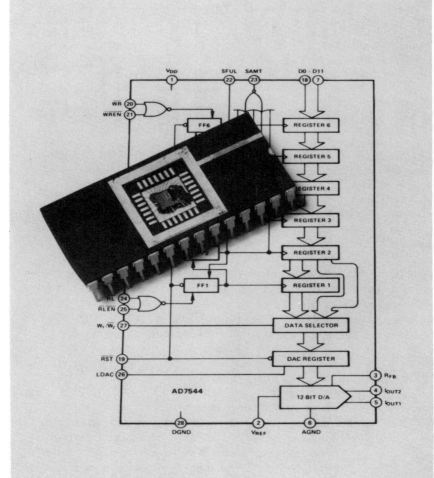

Analog Devices' new AD7544 is a 12-bit D/A converter with on-chip 12-bit wide 6-word FIFO memory.

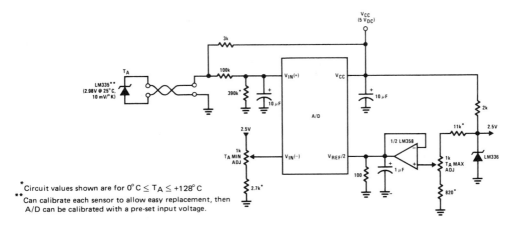

**Circuit values shown are for $0°C \leq T_A \leq +128°C$

**Can calibrate each sensor to allow easy replacement, then A/D can be calibrated with a pre-set input voltage.

FIGURE 9–26: Microprocessor-Interfaced Temperature-to-Digital Converter *(Reprinted with permission of National Semiconductor Corp.)*

interfacing with 8-bit microprocessors. Figure 9–26 shows a circuit using the ADC0802 as a microprocessor-interfaced temperature-to-digital converter. The temperature input is provided by an LM335 temperature sensor having a temperature coefficient of 10 mV/°K. It is fed a current through the 3-kΩ resistor. The resulting voltage is converted by the ADC0802. An adjustable reference voltage for calibration purposes is provided by a voltage divider fed by a Zener and buffered by an op amp. In order to prevent interaction of the analog and digital circuits, engineers provide separate analog and digital grounds on the ADC0802 and most other A/D ICs. Typically these grounds are separately decoupled and then joined only at the power supply.

Digital-to-Analog Converters

Most D/A converters are built using a resistor ladder circuit similar to the one shown in Fig. 9–27. Each input bit opens or closes a transistor switch, feeding a voltage to the corresponding resistor. Because the total effective resistance from each switch to the inverting input of the op amp is different, there is a different gain from each input of the amplifier. For example, if 5 V is applied whenever a switch is closed, then the output from the amplifier when bit 7 is a 1 (switch 7 closed) is

$$V_{OUT} = (5 \text{ V})\left(\frac{R_f}{R_i}\right) = (5 \text{ V})\left(\frac{20 \text{ k}\Omega}{20 \text{ k}\Omega}\right) = 5 \text{ V}.$$

For a 1 in bit position 6, the output equation is more complex. However, Thevenizing the circuit from each input and using the fact that the inverting input is a virtual ground, we find that a 1 in position 6 corresponds to a 2.5-V output; a 1 in position 5 corresponds to a 1.25-V output, etc. In other words, this so-called $R,2R$ network produces outputs that are related to the input bit position in a binary fashion. The result is that the output voltage from the op amp corresponds to the binary value of the input data.

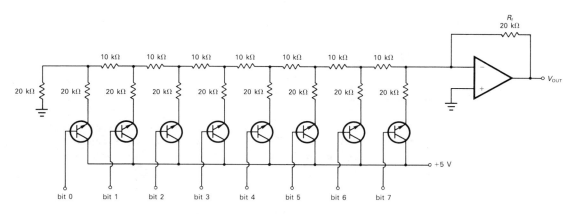

FIGURE 9–27: Ladder-Type D/A Converter

The DAC0832 is a common 8-bit D/A converter. It works very much as described above, except that it provides an output current, instead of an output voltage. As shown in Fig. 9–28, this current can be converted to a voltage in the desired range by using a current-to-voltage converter of the type discussed earlier in this chapter. The data sheet for the DAC0832 is included in Appendix A.

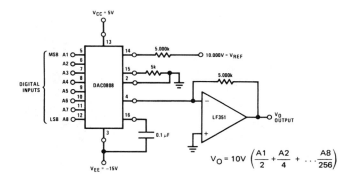

FIGURE 9–28: Typical Application of a Ladder-Type D/A Converter *(Reprinted with permission of National Semiconductor Corp.)*

DESIGN NOTES

Current-Differencing Amplifiers

Use the circuits of Fig. 9–29. Calculate as for a normal op amp, except that a bias resistor R_b must be used. The bias resistor must be twice the feedback resistor in value. Remember that the inputs and outputs will be referenced to half of the supply voltage, so capacitor coupling is necessary.

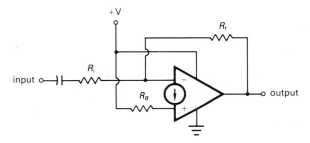

Inverting Amplifier

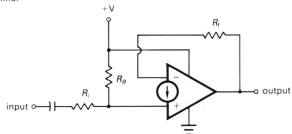

Noninverting amplifier

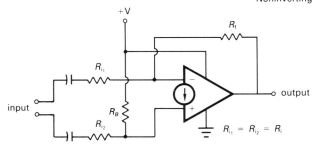

Differential Amplifier

$R_{i_1} = R_{i_2} = R_i$

FIGURE 9–29: CDA Applications

Design Notes

(continued)

(continued from page 460)

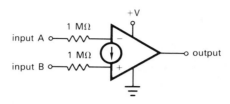

CDA Comparator

FIGURE 9–29 (continued): CDA Applications

Phase-Locked Loops

Use the circuit of Fig. 9–30.

1. Choose a capacitor for C_1.

2. Calculate R's value from

$$R = \frac{1.2}{4f_0 C_1} \qquad \text{(from 9.09)}$$

where f_0 is the free-running frequency.

3. Calculate C_2's value from

$$C_2 = \frac{\pm f_0}{2827\ V_{CC} f_c^2} \qquad \text{(from 9.10)}$$

where $\pm f_c$ is the capture range.

4. Choose the supply voltage between ± 5 V and ± 12 V from

$$V_{CC} = \pm 8 f_0 / f_L \qquad \text{(from 9.11)}$$

where $\pm f_L$ is the lock-in range.

Design
Notes

(continued from page 461)

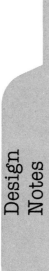

Design Notes

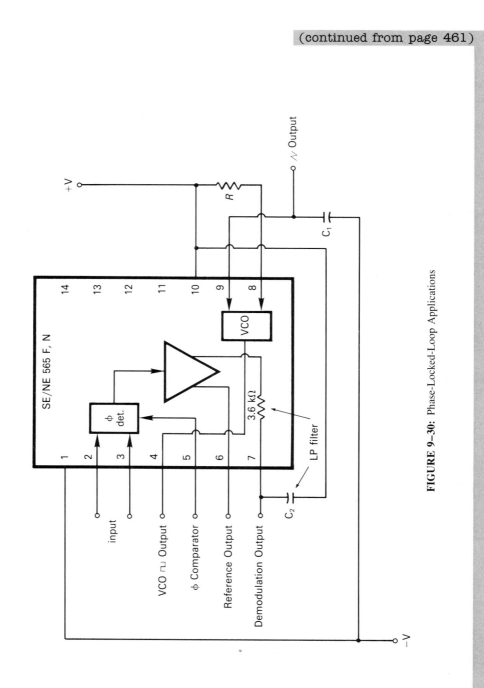

FIGURE 9–30: Phase-Locked-Loop Applications

(continued from page 462)

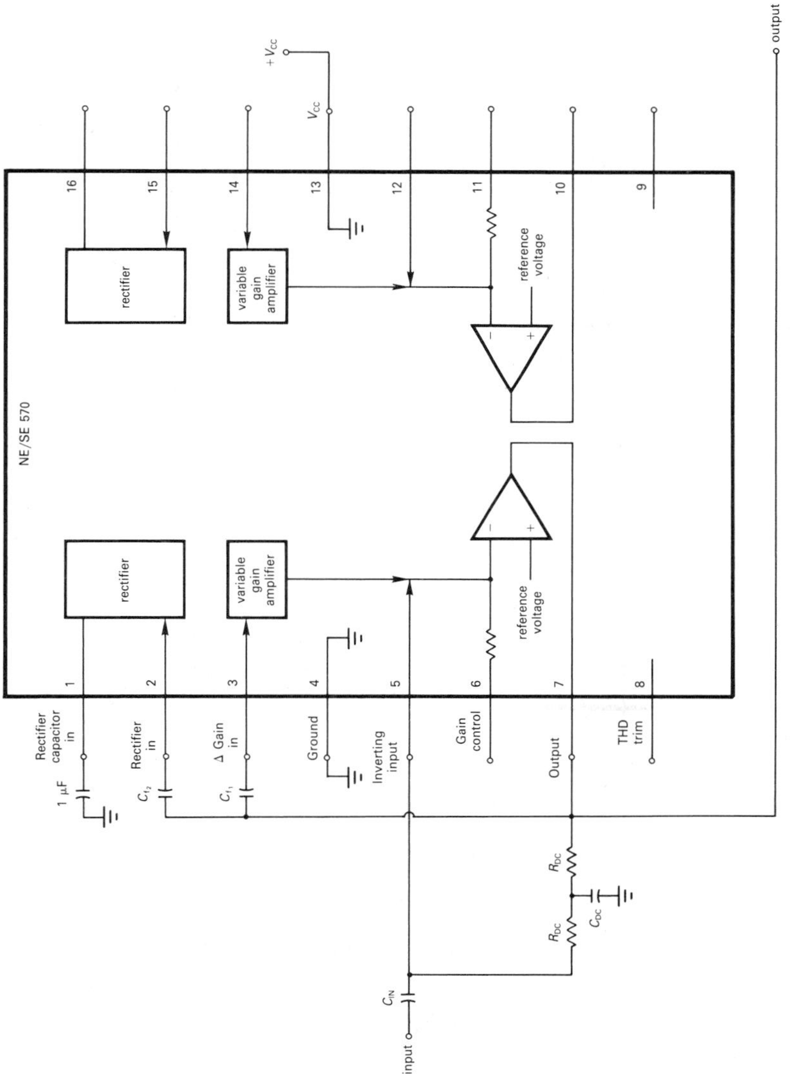

FIGURE 9–31A: Compressor

Design
Notes

(continued from page 463)

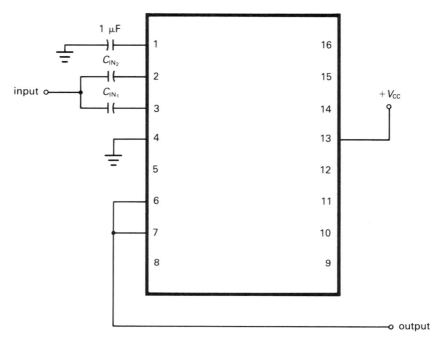

FIGURE 9–31B: Expandor

FIGURE 9–31: Compandor Applications

Compandors

Use the circuits of Fig. 9–31.

1. Calculate the value of all capacitors from

$$C = \frac{1}{2\pi f_{low} \cdot 1 \text{ k}\Omega}$$

where f_{low} is the lowest input frequency.

2. For the compressor, choose R_{DC} from

$$R_{DC} = \frac{30 \text{ k}\Omega \cdot V_{CC}}{3.6 \text{ V}}$$

Design
Notes

(continued from page 464)

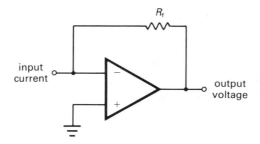

FIGURE 9–32: Current-to-Voltage Converter

Current-to-Voltage Converters

Use the circuit of Fig. 9–32. Calculate R_f from

$$R_f = \frac{\Delta V_{\text{OUT}}}{\Delta I_{\text{IN}}} \qquad \text{(from 9.13)}$$

where ΔV_{OUT} and ΔI_{IN} are the differences between the maximum and minimum desired values of V_{OUT} and I_{IN}, respectively.

Voltage-to-Current Converters

Use the circuit of Fig. 9–33.

1. Calculate the value of R_S from

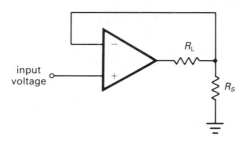

FIGURE 9–33: Voltage-to-Current Converter

Design
Notes

(continued from page 465)

$$R_S = \frac{\Delta V_{\text{IN}}}{\Delta I_L} \quad \text{(from 9.16)}$$

where ΔV_{IN} and ΔI_L represent the ranges of the input voltage and load current, respectively.

2. Determine the maximum V_{OUT} required from

$$V_{\text{OUT}} = V_{\text{IN,max}} + I_L R_L \quad \text{(from 9.17)}$$

Select a supply voltage sufficiently high that V_{SAT} is greater than this value of output voltage.

SUMMARY

Programmable amplifiers are op amps in which certain characteristics can be controlled by an external bias current.

Transconductance amplifiers are amplifiers whose output is represented by a current source. They have a gain that is expressed as a transconductance; that is, output current divided by input voltage.

Operational transconductance amplifiers are IC transconductance amplifiers in which some characteristics depend upon the value of an externally applied bias current.

Current-differencing amplifiers (CDAs) are amplifiers that respond to a difference in input current, rather than a difference in input voltage. They are usually operated from a unipolar supply.

Analog multipliers are circuits whose output voltage is equal to the product of their input voltages and an externally controllable scale factor. They can be used in amplitude modulators, squarers, square-root circuits, and in many other applications.

IC modulator/demodulators are specialized multipliers designed to perform all kinds of amplitude modulation.

IC rms converters provide conversion of AC voltage waves into their rms DC equivalent values. Some rms converters also have internal logarithmic conversion to provide a decibel output.

Phase-locked loops (PLLs) are circuits that provide extremely accurate FM modulation and demodulation and frequency multiplication.

Compandors are circuits that can be used to reduce (compress) or increase (expand) the dynamic range of a signal. They are used to reduce the effect of noise.

Precision rectifiers are circuits that provide rectification without the nonlinearity caused by diodes' turn-on voltages.

Clippers are circuits that clip waveforms above or below a certain voltage level.

Clampers are circuits that add a DC level to a signal.

Logarithmic amplifiers have an output that is proportional to the logarithm of the input voltage.

Sample-and-hold circuits can sample an input signal, then when a control voltage is changed, hold the latest sampled value.

Voltage-to-current converters provide controlled current sources that are proportional to an input voltage.

Current-to-voltage converters provide controlled voltage sources that are proportional to an input current.

Single-slope A/D converters are simple to build from separate components, but their conversion of A/D signals is not very accurate.

Dual-slope A/D converters can also be built relatively easily from separate components, and they have significantly better accuracy than single-slope converters.

VCOs and counters can be used to make simple A/D converters. The pulse-modulation A/D converter operates similarly and is available in IC form for use in digital voltmeters.

The successive-approximation A/D converter is the most common type for general use. It is available in a number of IC versions. It is second only to the flash converter in speed.

The $R,2R$ ladder-type D/A converter is the most popular type. It uses an op amp circuit with transistor switches corresponding to the data bit positions. The output voltage of the op amp is thus proportional to the binary value of the input data.

REVIEW QUESTIONS

1. Using an LM146, determine the current I_{SET} necessary to provide a GBW of 1 MHz.
2. At the value of I_{SET} determined in question 1, what is the:
   (a) power-supply current?
   (b) slew rate?
   (c) input bias current?
3. If the maximum modulating voltage in Fig. 9–3B is 10 V, and if the linearizing diodes were not biased by the 15-kΩ resistor, what would be the transconductance of the OTA?
4. If the differential input voltage in the question above were 5 mV, what would be the output voltage?
5. Design a differential amplifier using a dual potentiometer to provide variable gain and using a CDA as the active device. What is the maximum value the gain should have? What is the weakest point in this design as far as CMRR is concerned? (The answer to this last question is not in this chapter; it will require some thought.)
6. What value should the scale factor of a 1495 multiplier circuit have if the maximum input voltages are ±8 V? What components control the scale factor?
7. Discuss the effect of the "carrier null" potentiometer in Fig. 9–9, with respect to the output wave.

8. Design a PLL demodulator to demodulate a signal having a carrier frequency of 45 kHz, with ±4-kHz deviation.
9. Discuss the effect that using 12 dB of compansion in a communication circuit will have upon the S/N ratio, given in dB.
10. Design an AC average-responding electronic voltmeter using a full-wave precision rectifier and a voltage-to-current converter. The full-scale input voltage is to be 10 mV.
11. Discuss the difference between the performance of the circuit described in question 10 and that of a circuit using a true rms converter.
12. Describe the difference between clippers and clampers.
13. Compare the following types of A/D converters with respect to speed, accuracy, and ease of construction with separate components:
    (a) flash converter
    (b) single-slope converter
    (c) dual-slope converter
    (d) successive-approximation converter
14. What two kinds of A/D converters are most commonly employed in IC A/D converters?
15. Describe the operation of a ladder-type D/A converter.

LABORATORY EXPERIMENT—OPERATIONAL TRANSCONDUCTANCE AMPLIFIERS

Objective:

To investigate the use of OTAs as voltage-controlled amplifiers and to compare their operation with that of a multiplier.

Materials:

1 LM13600 OTA
1 1-kΩ potentiometer
3 30-kΩ resistors
1 13-kΩ resistor
1 5-kΩ resistor
2 10-kΩ potentiometers

Procedure:

1. Build the circuit shown in Fig. 9–3A. Use a ±15-V supply.
2. Apply a 1-V$_{P-P}$, 1-kHz sine wave at the input and adjust the 1-kΩ pot so that there is a 10-mV$_{P-P}$ input at the op amp.
3. Connect the terminals of the track of a 10-kΩ pot to the +15-V and −15-V points. Connect the wiper to the point marked *gain control*.
4. Vary the control voltage provided by the 10-kΩ pot in 1-V increments from −15 V to +15 V; measure the AC output voltage at each step.
5. Disconnect the sine-wave generator from your circuit's input. Connect a 10-kΩ pot between the supply terminals as before and use the wiper to feed the input of the amplifier. You will then have both pots connected to provide variable DC voltages.
6. By using the 10-kΩ and the 1-kΩ pots at the input, vary the input from −5 mV to +5 mV in 2-mV steps. At each step, measure the output voltage with the following values of control voltage: −10 V, −8 V, −6 V, −4 V, −2 V, 0 V, +2 V, +4 V, +6 V, +8 V, +10 V.

Analysis:

1. Using the data from step 4, above, make a graph of voltage gain versus control voltage.
2. Using the formulae in this chapter, convert the voltage gain to transconductance and make a graph of transconductance versus control current. To calculate the control current:

(continued)

(continued from page 469)

$$I_{ABC} = \frac{V_{control} - (-15\ V)}{R_{control}}$$

Compare your graph with the one given in the data sheet in Appendix A.

3. Using the data from step 6, make a graph similar to that in Fig. 9–7B. Calculate the scale factor that your circuit has when used as a multiplier.

LABORATORY EXPERIMENT—PHASE-LOCKED LOOP

Objective:

To examine the operation of a PLL and gain experience with the meaning of the capture range and lock-in range.

Materials:

1 LM 565 PLL
1 0.001-μF capacitor
1 500-pF capacitor
1 0.0082-μF capacitor
1 5600-Ω resistor

Procedure:

1. Using the circuit in Fig. 9–13A and the values given in the example on page 433, build an FM demodulator. (You can substitute the standard values 0.0082 μF for 0.009 μF and 5600 Ω for 6000 Ω.) Use a 10-V power supply.
2. Connect a sine-wave generator to the input. Using a 1-V_{P-P} signal, monitor the DC output voltage from the PLL as you increase the frequency slowly from 10 kHz. The output voltage should stay fairly constant at first, then start rising. Make a note of the low frequency at which the output voltage rises by 0.1 V. Continue adjusting until you find the frequency that produces the highest voltage. Note that voltage.
3. Adjust the sine-wave generator to 1 MHz. Slowly decrease the frequency and make a note of the high frequency at which the output DC voltage drops by 0.1 V. Continue adjusting until you find the frequency that produces the lowest voltage. Note that voltage.

(continued from page 470)

4. Adjust the sine-wave generator to 100 kHz. Now carefully adjust until you determine the frequency that produces an output voltage equal to the average of the highest and lowest voltages you measured. This average voltage should be very close to the voltages you measured above and below the frequencies at which the output voltage started changing.
5. Adjust the sine-wave generator slowly upward in frequency, noting the frequency at 0.2-V increments in the output voltage until the output voltage stops changing.
6. Return to the frequency you measured in step 4. Now slowly decrease the frequency of the generator, noting the frequency at 0.2-V increments until the output voltage stops changing.

Analysis:

1. From your data, determine the free-running frequency, the capture range, and the lock-in range of the PLL.
2. Plot the output voltage versus frequency from your measurements in steps 5 and 6. From your graph, determine the maximum frequency deviation for which the output voltage remains a linear function of the input frequency.
3. Determine the sensitivity of the PLL demodulator in volts per kilohertz.

appendix a
Specification Sheets

The following specification sheets are listed in alphanumerical order. They represent commonly used examples of each of the various types of linear integrated circuits that have been discussed in this book. For all design problems and for many troubleshooting tasks, a specification sheet on the particular IC used is quite helpful. In addition to the usual data, spec sheets often contain application diagrams using the particular IC. These diagrams offer clues to understanding the operation of many unusual circuits. Manufacturers of ICs often publish data books containing collections of these data sheets. These books range in price from free (for small paperbacks of short-form data sheets) to several hundred dollars per year for new data updating services. Below are listed the addresses for several of the more prominent IC manufacturers. If you are interested, you can write to these addresses to request further information and pricing for any data books in which you may be interested.

Analog Devices, Inc.
Two Technology Way
Norwood, MA 02062

DATEL, General Electric Co.
11 Cabot Blvd.
Mansfield, MA 02048

Exar Corp.
750 Palomar Ave.
Sunnyvale, CA 94088

Fairchild Semiconductor
10400 Ridgeview Ct.
Cupertino, CA 95014

Linear Technology Corp.
1630 McCarthy Blvd.
Milpitas, CA 95035

Motorola Semiconductor Products
P. O. Box 52073
Phoenix, AZ 85072

National Semiconductor Corp.
2900 Semiconductor Dr.
Santa Clara, CA 95051

NEC Electronics
401 Ellis Street
Mountain View, CA 94039

Panasonic Industrial Co.
Two Panasonic Way
Secaucus, NJ 07094

Precision Monolithic
1500 Space Park Dr.
Santa Clara, CA 95054

Raytheon Co., Semiconductor Div.
350 Ellis St.
Mountain View, CA 94039

RCA Solid State Div.
Rte. 202
Somerville, NJ 08876

Sanyo Semiconductor Corp.
7 Pearl Ct.
Allandale, NJ 07401

Signetics Div. U.S. Philips Corp.
811 East Arques Ave., P. O. Box 3409
Sunnyvale, CA 94088

Teledyne-Philbrick
40 Allied Dr.
Dedham, MA 02026

SGS Semiconductor Corp.
1000 E. Bell Rd.
Phoenix, AZ 85022

Sprague Electric Co.
92 Hayden Ave.
Lexington, MA 02173

Texas Instruments, Inc.
P. O. Box 660246
Dallas, Texas 75266

LH0004/LH0004C

![National Semiconductor logo] **National Semiconductor**

Operational Amplifiers/Buffers

LH0004/LH0004C High Voltage Operational Amplifier

General Description

The LH0004/LH0004C is a general purpose operational amplifier designed to operate from supply voltages up to ±40V. The device dissipates extremely low quiescent power, typically 8 mW at 25°C and V_S = ±40V. Additional features include:

- Capable of operation over the range of ±5V to ±40V
- Large output voltage typically ±35V for the LH0004 and ±33V for the LH0004C into a 2 KΩ load with ±40V supplies
- Low input offset current typically 20 nA for the LH0004 and 45 nA for the LH0004C
- Low input offset voltage typically 0.3 mV
- Frequency compensation with 2 small capacitors
- Low power consumption 8 mW at ±40V

The LH0004's high gain and wide range of operating voltages make it ideal for applications requiring large output swing and low power dissipation.

The LH0004 is specified for operation over the −55°C to +125°C military temperature range. The LH0004C is specified for operation over the 0°C to +85°C temperature range.

Applications

- Precision high voltage power supply
- Resolver excitation
- Wideband high voltage amplifier
- Transducer power supply

Schematic and Connection Diagrams

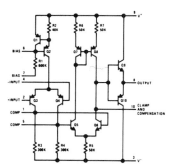

Note: Pin 7 must be grounded or connected to a voltage at least 5V more negative than the positive supply (Pin 9). Pin 7 may be connected to the negative supply; however, the standby current will be increased. A resistor may be inserted in series with Pin 7 to Pin 9. The value of the resistor should be a maximum of 100 KΩ per volt of potential between Pin 3 and Pin 9.

Order Number LH0004H or LH0004CH
See Package H10B

Typical Applications

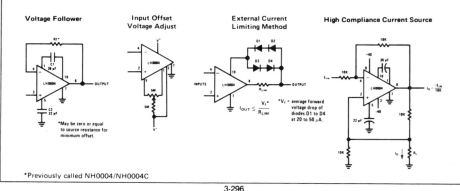

Previously called NH0004/NH0004C

3-296

Reprinted with Permission of National Semiconductor Corp.

Absolute Maximum Ratings

Supply Voltage, Continuous	±45V
Power Dissipation (See curve)	400 mW
Differential Input Voltage	±7V
Input Voltage	Equal to supply
Short Circuit Duration	3 sec
Operating Temperature Range LH0004	−55°C to +125°C
LH0004C	0°C to 85°C
Storage Temperature Range	−65°C to +150°C
Lead Temperature (Soldering, 10 sec)	300°C

Electrical Characteristics (Note 1)

PARAMETER	CONDITIONS	LH0004			LH0004C			UNITS
		MIN	TYP	MAX	MIN	TYP	MAX	
Input Offset Voltage	$R_S \leq 100\,\Omega$, $T_A = 25°C$		0.3	1.0		0.3	1.5	mV
	$R_S \leq 100\,\Omega$			2.0			3.0	mV
Input Bias Current	$T_A = 25°C$		20	100		30	120	nA
				300			300	nA
Input Offset Current	$T_A = 25°C$		3	20		10	45	nA
				100			150	nA
Positive Supply Current	$V_S = ±40V$, $T_A = 25°C$		110	150		110	150	μA
	$V_S = ±40V$			175			175	μA
Negative Supply Current	$V_S = ±40V$, $T_A = 25°C$		80	100		80	100	μA
	$V_S = ±40V$			135			135	μA
Voltage Gain	$V_S = ±40V$, $R_L = 100k$, $T_A = 25°C$ $V_{OUT} = ±30V$	30	60		30	60		V/mV
	$V_S = ±40V$, $R_L = 100k$ $V_{OUT} = ±30V$	10			10			V/mV
Output Voltage	$V_S = ±40V$, $R_L = 10k$	±30	±35		±30	±33		V
CMRR	$V_S = ±40V$, $R_S \leq 5k$ $V_{IN} = ±33V$	70	90		70	90		dB
PSRR	$V_S = ±40V$, $R_S \leq 5k$ $\Delta V = 20V$ to $40V$	70	90		70	90		dB
Average Temperature Coefficient Offset Voltage	$R_S \leq 100\,\Omega$		4.0			4.0		μV/°C
Average Temperature Coefficient of Offset Current			0.4			0.4		nA/°C
Equivalent Input Noise Voltage	$R_S = 100\,\Omega$, $V_S = ±40\,V$ $f = 500\,Hz$ to $5\,kHz$, $T_A = 25°C$		3.0			3.0		μVrms

Note 1: These specifications apply for $±5V \leq V_S \leq ±40V$, Pin 7 grounded, with capacitors C1 = 39 pF between Pin 1 and Pin 10, C2 = 22 pF between Pin 5 and ground, −55°C to +125°C for the LH0004, and 0°C to +85°C for the LH0004C unless otherwise specified.

3

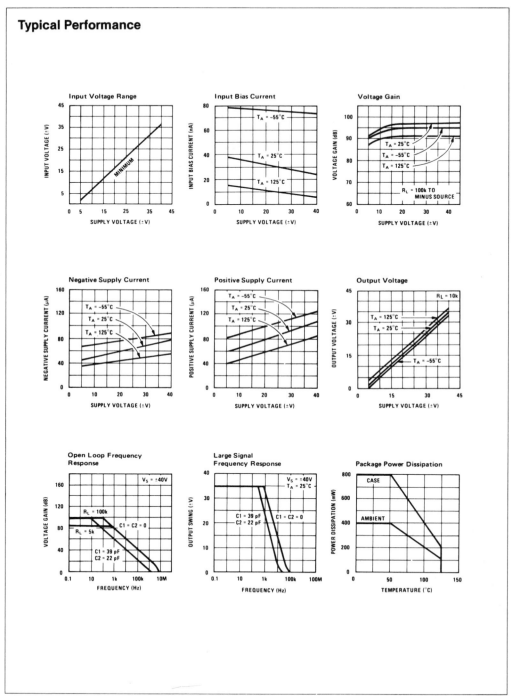

Reprinted with Permission of National Semiconductor Corp.

MF10

Industrial Blocks

MF10 Universal Monolithic Dual Switched Capacitor Filter

General Description

The MF10 consists of 2 independent and extremely easy to use, general purpose CMOS active filter building blocks. Each block, together with an external clock and 3 to 4 resistors, can produce various 2nd order functions. Each building block has 3 output pins. One of the outputs can be configured to perform either an allpass, highpass or a notch function; the remaining 2 output pins perform low-pass and bandpass functions. The center frequency of the lowpass and bandpass 2nd order functions can be either directly dependent on the clock frequency, or they can de-pend on both clock frequency and external resistor ratios. The center frequency of the notch and allpass functions is directly dependent on the clock frequency, while the highpass center frequency depends on both resistor ratio and clock. Up to 4th order functions can be performed by cascading the two 2nd order building blocks of the MF10; higher than 4th order functions can be obtained by cas-cading MF10 packages. Any of the classical filter config-urations (such as Butterworth, Bessel, Cauer and Chebyshev) can be formed.

Features

- Low cost
- 20-pin 0.3″ wide package
- Easy to use
- Clock to center frequency ratio accuracy = 0.6%
- Filter cutoff frequency stability directly dependent on external clock quality
- Low sensitivity to external component variation
- Separate highpass (or notch or allpass), bandpass, lowpass outputs
- $f_o \times Q$ range up to 200 kHz
- Operation up to 30 kHz

System Block Diagram

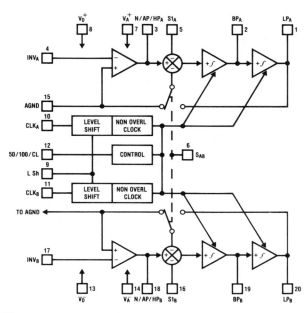

9-212

Reprinted with Permission of National Semiconductor Corp.

MF10

Absolute Maximum Ratings

Supply Voltage	7V
Power Dissipation	500 mW
Operating Temperature	0°C to 70°C
Storage Temperature	150°C
Lead Temperature (Soldering, 10 seconds)	300°C

Electrical Characteristics (Complete Filter) $V_S = \pm 5V$, $T_A = 25°C$

Parameter	Conditions	Min	Typ	Max	Units
Frequency Range	$f_o \times Q < 200$ kHz	20	30		kHz
Clock to Center Frequency Ratio, f_{CLK}/f_o					
MF10BN	Pin 12 High, Q = 10		$49.94 \pm 0.2\%$	$\pm 0.6\%$	
MF10CN	$f_o \times Q < 50$ kHz, Mode 1		$49.94 \pm 0.2\%$	$\pm 1.5\%$	
MF10BN	Pin 12 at Mid Supplies		$99.35 \pm 0.2\%$	$\pm 0.6\%$	
MF10CN	Q = 10, $f_o \times Q < 50$ kHz, Mode 1		$99.35 \pm 0.2\%$	$\pm 1.5\%$	
Q Accuracy (Q Deviation from an Ideal Continuous Filter)					
MF10BN	Pin 12 High, Mode 1		$\pm 2\%$	$\pm 4\%$	
MF10CN	$f_o \times Q < 100$ kHz, $f_o < 5$ kHz		$\pm 2\%$	$\pm 6\%$	
MF10BN	Pin 12 at Mid Supplies		$\pm 2\%$	$\pm 3\%$	
MF10CN	$f_o \times Q < 100$ kHz $f_o < 5$ kHz, Mode 1		$\pm 2\%$	$\pm 6\%$	
f_o Temperature Coefficient	Pin 12 High (~50:1)		± 10		ppm/°C
	Pin 12 Mid Supplies (~100:1) $f_o \times Q < 100$ kHz, Mode 1 External Clock Temperature Independent		± 100		ppm/°C
Q Temperature Coefficient	$f_o \times Q < 100$ kHz, Q Setting Resistors Temperature Independent		± 500		ppm/°C
DC Low Pass Gain Accuracy	Mode 1, R1 = R2 = 10k			± 2	%
Crosstalk			50		dB
Clock Feedthrough			10		mV
Maximum Clock Frequency		1	1.5		MHz
Power Supply Current			8	10	mA

9

Electrical Characteristics (Internal Op Amps) $T_A = 25°C$

Parameter	Conditions	Min	Typ	Max	Units
Supply Voltage		± 4	± 5		V
Voltage Swing (Pins 1, 2, 9, 20)	$V_S = \pm 5V$, $R_L = 5k$				
MF10BN		± 3.8	± 4		V
MF10CN		± 3.2	± 3.7		V
Voltage Swing (Pins 3 and 18)	$V_S = \pm 5V$, $R_L = 3.5k$				
MF10BN		± 3.8	± 4		V
MF10CN		± 3.2	± 3.7		V
Output Short Circuit Current	$V_S = \pm 5V$				
Source			3		mA
Sink			1.5		
Op Amp Gain BW Product			2.5		MHz
Op Amp Slew Rate			7		V/µs

Reprinted with Permission of National Semiconductor Corp.

MF10

Definition of Terms

f_{CLK}: the switched capacitor filter external clock frequency.

f_o: center of frequency of the second order function complex pole pair. f_o is measured at the bandpass output of each 1/2 MF10, and it is the frequency of the bandpass peak occurrence (*Figure 1*).

Q: quality factor of the 2nd order function complex pole pair. Q is also measured at the bandpass output of each 1/2 MF10 and it is the ratio of f_o over the -3 dB bandwidth of the 2nd order bandpass filter, *Figure 1*. The value of Q is not measured at the lowpass or highpass outputs of the filter, but its value relates to the possible amplitude peaking at the above outputs.

H_{OBP}: the gain in (V/V) of the bandpass output at $f = f_o$.

H_{OLP}: the gain in (V/V) of the lowpass output of each 1/2 MF10 at $f \rightarrow 0$ Hz, *Figure 2*.

H_{OHP}: the gain in (V/V) of the highpass output of each 1/2 MF10 as $f \rightarrow f_{CLK}/2$, *Figure 3*.

Q_z: the quality factor of the 2nd order function complex zero pair, if any. (Q_z is a parameter used when an allpass output is sought and unlike Q it cannot be directly measured).

f_z: the center frequency of the 2nd order function complex zero pair, if any. If f_z is different from f_o, and if the Q_z is quite high it can be observed as a notch frequency at the allpass output.

f_{notch}: the notch frequency observed at the notch output(s) of the MF10.

H_{ON_1}: the notch output gain as $f \rightarrow 0$ Hz.

H_{ON_2}: the notch output gain as $f \rightarrow f_{CLK}/2$.

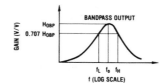

$$Q = \frac{f_o}{f_H - f_L} \ ; \ f_o = \sqrt{f_L f_H}$$

$$f_L = f_o \left(\frac{-1}{2Q} + \sqrt{\left(\frac{1}{2Q}\right)^2 + 1} \right)$$

$$f_H = f_o \left(\frac{1}{2Q} + \sqrt{\left(\frac{1}{2Q}\right)^2 + 1} \right)$$

FIGURE 1

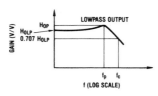

$$f_c = f_o \times \sqrt{\left(1 - \frac{1}{2Q^2}\right) + \sqrt{\left(1 - \frac{1}{2Q^2}\right)^2 + 1}}$$

$$f_p = f_o \sqrt{1 - \frac{1}{2Q^2}}$$

$$H_{OP} = H_{OLP} \times \frac{1}{\frac{1}{Q}\sqrt{1 - \frac{1}{4Q^2}}}$$

FIGURE 2

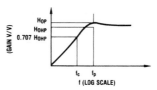

$$f_c = f_o \times \left[\sqrt{\left(1 - \frac{1}{2Q^2}\right) + \sqrt{\left(1 - \frac{1}{2Q^2}\right)^2 + 1}} \right]^{-1}$$

$$f_p = f_o \times \left[\sqrt{1 - \frac{1}{2Q^2}} \right]^{-1}$$

$$H_{OP} = H_{OHP} \times \frac{1}{\frac{1}{Q}\sqrt{1 - \frac{1}{4Q^2}}}$$

FIGURE 3

Reprinted with Permission of National Semiconductor Corp.

Connection Diagram

Dual-In-Line Package

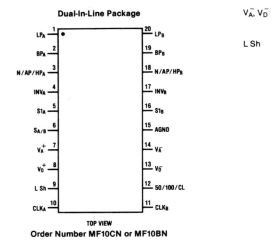

LP$_A$	1		20	LP$_B$
BP$_A$	2		19	BP$_B$
N/AP/HP$_A$	3		18	N/AP/HP$_B$
INV$_A$	4		17	INV$_B$
S1$_A$	5		16	S1$_B$
S$_{A/B}$	6		15	AGND
V$_A^+$	7		14	V$_A^-$
V$_D^+$	8		13	V$_D^-$
L Sh	9		12	50/100/CL
CLK$_A$	10		11	CLK$_B$

TOP VIEW

Order Number MF10CN or MF10BN

Pin Description

LP, BP, N/AP/HP — These are the lowpass, bandpass, notch or allpass or highpass outputs of each 2nd order section. The LP and BP outputs can sink typically 1 mA and source 3 mA. The N/AP/HP output can typically sink and source 1.5 mA and 3 mA, respectively.

INV — This is the inverting input of the summing op amp of each filter. The pin has static discharge protection.

S1 — S1 is a signal input pin used in the allpass filter configurations (see modes of operation 4 and 5). The pin should be driven with a source impedance of less than 1 kΩ.

S$_{A/B}$ — It activates a switch connecting one of the inputs of the filter's 2nd summer either to analog ground (S$_{A/B}$ low to V$_A^-$) or to the lowpass output of the circuit (S$_{A/B}$ high to V$_A^+$). This allows flexibility in the various modes of operation of the IC. S$_{A/B}$ is protected against static discharge.

V$_A^+$, V$_D^+$ — Analog positive supply and digital positive supply. These pins are internally connected through the IC substrate and therefore V$_A^+$ and V$_D^+$ should be derived from the same power supply source. They have been brought out separately so they can be bypassed by separate capacitors, if desired. They can be externally tied together and bypassed by a single capacitor.

V$_A^-$, V$_D^-$ — Analog and digital negative supply respectively. The same comments as for V$_A^+$ and V$_D^+$ apply here.

L Sh — Level shift pin; it accommodates various clock levels with dual or single supply operation. With dual ±5V supplies, the MF10 can be driven with CMOS clock levels (±5V) and the L Sh pin should be tied either to the system ground or to the negative supply pin. If the same supplies as above are used but T^{2}L clock levels, derived from 0V to 5V supply, are only available, the L Sh pin should be tied to the system ground. For single supply operation (0V and 10V) the V$_D^-$, V$_A^-$ pins should be connected to the system ground, the AGND pin should be biased at 5V and the L Sh pin should also be tied to the system ground. This will accommodate both CMOS and T^{2}L clock levels.

CLK (A or B) — Clock inputs for each switched capacitor filter building block. They should both be of the same level (T^{2}L or CMOS). The level shift (L Sh) pin description discusses how to accommodate their levels. The duty cycle of the clock should preferably be close to 50% especially when clock frequencies above 200 kHz are used. This allows the maximum time for the op amps to settle which yields optimum filter operation.

50/100/CL — By tying the pin high a 50:1 clock to filter center frequency operation is obtained. Tying the pin at mid supplies (i.e., analog ground with dual supplies) allows the filter to operate at a 100:1 clock to center frequency ratio. When the pin is tied low, a simple current limiting circuitry is triggered to limit the overall supply current down to about 2.5 mA. The filtering action is then aborted.

AGND — Analog ground pin; it should be connected to the system ground for dual supply operation or biased at mid supply for single supply operation. The positive inputs of the filter op amps are connected to the AGND pin so "clean" ground is mandatory. The AGND pin is protected against static discharge.

9

MF10

Modes of Operation

The MF10 is a switched capacitor (sampled data) filter. To fully describe its transfer functions, a time domain approach will be appropriate. Since this may appear cumbersome and, since the MF10 closely approximates continuous filters, the following discussion is based on the well known frequency domain. The following illustrations refer to 1/2 of the MF10; the other 1/2 is identical. Each MF10 can produce a full 2nd order function, so up to 4th order functions can be performed by using cascading techniques.

MODE 1: Notch 1, Bandpass, Lowpass Outputs: $f_{notch} = f_o$
(See *Figure 4*)

f_o = center frequency of the complex pole pair

$= \dfrac{f_{CLK}}{100}$ or $\dfrac{f_{CLK}}{50}$

f_{notch} = center frequency of the imaginary zero pair = f_o.

H_{OLP} = Lowpass gain (as f→0) = $-\dfrac{R2}{R1}$

H_{OBP} = Bandpass gain (at f = f_o) = $-\dfrac{R3}{R1}$

H_{ON} = Notch output gain as $\left.\begin{array}{l} f\to 0 - \dfrac{R2}{R1} \\[4pt] f\to f_{CLK}/2 \end{array}\right\}$

$Q \quad = \dfrac{f_o}{BW} = \dfrac{R3}{R2}$

= quality factor of the complex pole pair.

BW = the -3 dB bandwidth of the bandpass output.

Circuit dynamics:

$$H_{OLP} = \dfrac{H_{OBP}}{Q} \text{ or } H_{OBP} = H_{OLP} \times Q = H_{ON} \times Q.$$

$$H_{OLP\,(peak)} \cong Q \times H_{OLP} \text{ (for high Q's)}$$

The above expressions are important. They determine the swing at each output as a function of the desired Q of the 2nd order function.

MODE 1a: Non-Inverting BP, LP (See *Figure 5*)

$f_o \quad = \dfrac{f_{CLK}}{100}$ or $\dfrac{f_{CLK}}{50}$

$Q \quad = \dfrac{R3}{R2}$

$H_{OLP} = 1$; $H_{OLP\,(peak)} \cong Q \times H_{OLP}$ (for high Q's)

$H_{OPB_1} = -\dfrac{R3}{R2}$

$H_{OBP_2} = 1$ (non-inverting)

Circuit dynamics: $H_{OBP_1} = Q$

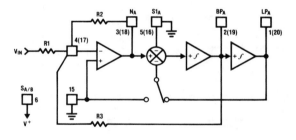

FIGURE 4. MODE 1

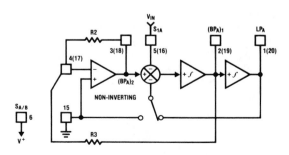

FIGURE 5. MODE 1a

9-216

Reprinted with Permission of National Semiconductor Corp.

MF10

Modes of Operation (Continued)

MODE 2: Notch 2, Bandpass, Lowpass: $f_{notch} < f_o$
(See *Figure 6*)

f_o = center frequency

$\quad = \dfrac{f_{CLK}}{100}\sqrt{\dfrac{R2}{R4}+1}$ or $\dfrac{f_{CLK}}{50}\sqrt{\dfrac{R2}{R4}+1}$

$f_{notch} = \dfrac{f_{CLK}}{100}$ or $\dfrac{f_{CLK}}{50}$

Q = quality factor of the complex pole pair

$\quad = \dfrac{\sqrt{R2/R4+1}}{R2/R3}$

H_{OLP} = Lowpass output gain (as $f \to 0$)

$\quad = -\dfrac{R2/R1}{R2/R4+1}$

H_{OBP} = Bandpass output gain (at $f = f_o$) $= -R3/R1$

H_{ON_1} = Notch output gain (as $f \to 0$)

$\quad = -\dfrac{R2/R1}{R2/R4+1}$

H_{ON_2} = Notch output gain $\left(\text{as } f \to \dfrac{f_{CLK}}{2}\right) = -R2/R1$

Filter dynamics: $H_{OBP} = Q\sqrt{H_{OLP}\,H_{ON_2}} = Q\,\sqrt{H_{ON_1}\,H_{ON_2}}$

MODE 3: Highpass, Bandpass, Lowpass Outputs
(See *Figure 7*)

$f_o \quad = \dfrac{f_{CLK}}{100} \times \sqrt{\dfrac{R2}{R4}}$ or $\dfrac{f_{CLK}}{50} \times \sqrt{\dfrac{R2}{R4}}$

Q = quality factor of the complex pole pair

$\quad = \sqrt{\dfrac{R2}{R4}} \times \dfrac{R3}{R2}$

H_{OHP} = Highpass gain $\left(\text{as } f \to \dfrac{f_{CLK}}{2}\right) = -\dfrac{R2}{R1}$

H_{OBP} = Bandpass gain (at $f = f_o$) $= -\dfrac{R3}{R1}$

H_{OLP} = Lowpass gain (as $f \to 0$) $= -\dfrac{R4}{R1}$

Circuit dynamics: $\dfrac{R2}{R4} = \dfrac{H_{OHP}}{H_{OLP}}$; $H_{OBP} = \sqrt{H_{OHP} \times H_{OLP}} \times Q$

$H_{OLP\,(peak)} \approx Q \times H_{OLP}$ (for high Q's)

$H_{OHP\,(peak)} \approx Q \times H_{OHP}$ (for high Q's)

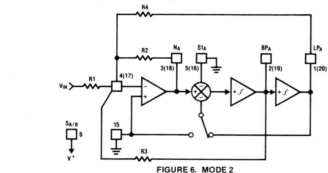

FIGURE 6. MODE 2

9

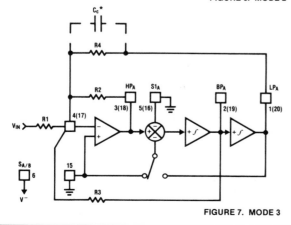

*In Mode 3, the feedback loop is closed around the input summing amplifier; the finite GBW product of this op amp causes a slight Q enhancement. If this is a problem, connect a small capacitor (10 pF–100 pF) across R4 to provide some phase lead.

FIGURE 7. MODE 3

Reprinted with Permission of National Semiconductor Corp.

MF10

Modes of Operation (Continued)

MODE 3a: HP, BP, LP and Notch with External Op Amp
(See *Figure 8*)

$$f_o = \frac{f_{CLK}}{100} \times \sqrt{\frac{R2}{R4}} \text{ or } \frac{f_{CLK}}{50} \times \sqrt{\frac{R2}{R4}}$$

$$Q = \sqrt{\frac{R2}{R4}} \times \frac{R3}{R2}$$

$$H_{OHP} = -\frac{R2}{R1}$$

$$H_{OBP} = -\frac{R3}{R1}$$

$$H_{OLP} = -\frac{R4}{R1}$$

$$f_n = \text{notch frequency} = \frac{f_{CLK}}{100} \sqrt{\frac{R_h}{R_l}} \text{ or } \frac{f_{CLK}}{50} \sqrt{\frac{R_h}{R_l}}$$

$$H_{on} = \text{gain of notch at } f = f_o = \left\| Q \left(\frac{R_g}{R_l} H_{OLP} - \frac{R_g}{R_h} H_{OHP} \right) \right\|$$

$$H_{n1} = \text{gain of notch (as } f \to 0) = \frac{R_g}{R_l} \times H_{OLP}$$

$$H_{n2} = \text{gain of notch } \left(\text{as } f \to \frac{f_{CLK}}{2} \right) = -\frac{R_g}{R_h} \times H_{OHP}$$

MODE 4: Allpass, Bandpass, Lowpass Outputs
(See *Figure 9*)

$$f_o = \text{center frequency}$$

$$= \frac{f_{CLK}}{100} \text{ or } \frac{f_{CLK}}{50},$$

$$f_z^* = \text{center frequency of the complex zero pair} \simeq f_o$$

$$Q = \frac{f_o}{BW} = \frac{R3}{R2},$$

$$Q_z = \text{quality factor of complex zero pair} = \frac{R3}{R1}$$

For AP output make R1 = R2

$$H_{OAP} = \text{Allpass gain} \left(\text{at } 0 < f < \frac{f_{CLK}}{2} \right) = -\frac{R2}{R1} = -1$$

$$H_{OLP} = \text{Lowpass gain (as } f \to 0)$$

$$= -\left(\frac{R2}{R1} + 1 \right) = -2$$

$$H_{OBP} = \text{Bandpass gain (at } f = f_o)$$

$$= -\frac{R3}{R2} \left(1 + \frac{R2}{R1} \right) = -2 \left(\frac{R3}{R2} \right)$$

Circuit dynamics: $H_{OBP} = (H_{OLP}) \times Q = (H_{OAP} + 1) Q$

*Due to the sampled data nature of the filter, a slight mismatch of f_z and f_o occurs causing a 0.4 dB peaking around f_o of the allpass filter amplitude response (which theoretically should be a straight line). If this is unacceptable, Mode 5 is recommended.

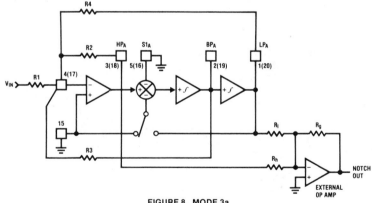

FIGURE 8. MODE 3a

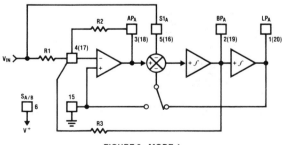

FIGURE 9. MODE 4

9-218

Reprinted with Permission of National Semiconductor Corp.

Modes of Operation (Continued)

MODE 5: Numerator Complex Zeros, BP, LP (See *Figure 10*)

$$f_o = \sqrt{1 + \frac{R2}{R4}} \times \frac{f_{CLK}}{100} \text{ or } \sqrt{1 + \frac{R2}{R4}} \times \frac{f_{CLK}}{50}$$

$$f_z = \sqrt{1 - \frac{R1}{R4}} \times \frac{f_{CLK}}{100} \text{ or } \sqrt{1 - \frac{R1}{R4}} \times \frac{f_{CLK}}{50}$$

$$Q = \sqrt{1 + R2/R4} \times \frac{R3}{R2}$$

$$Q_z = \sqrt{1 - R1/R4} \times \frac{R3}{R1}$$

$$H_{0z1} = \text{gain at C.z output (as } f \rightarrow 0 \text{ Hz)} = \frac{R2(R4 - R1)}{R1(R2 + R4)}$$

$$H_{0z2} = \text{gain at C.z output } \left(\text{as } f \rightarrow \frac{f_{CLK}}{2} \right) = \frac{R2}{R1}$$

$$H_{OBP} = \left(\frac{R2}{R1} + 1 \right) \times \frac{R3}{R2}$$

$$H_{OLP} = \left(\frac{R2 + R1}{R2 + R4} \right) \times \frac{R4}{R1}$$

MODE 6a: Single Pole, HP, LP Filter (See *Figure 11*)

$$f_c = \text{cutoff frequency of LP or HP output}$$

$$= \frac{R2}{R3} \frac{f_{CLK}}{100} \text{ or } \frac{R2}{R3} \frac{f_{CLK}}{50}$$

$$H_{OLP} = -\frac{R3}{R1}$$

$$H_{OHP} = -\frac{R2}{R1}$$

MODE 6b: Single Pole LP Filter (Inverting and Non-Inverting) (See *Figure 12*)

$$f_c = \text{cutoff frequency of LP outputs}$$

$$\cong \frac{R2}{R3} \frac{f_{CLK}}{100} \text{ or } \frac{R2}{R3} \frac{f_{CLK}}{50}$$

$$H_{OLP_1} = 1 \text{ (non-inverting)}$$

$$H_{OLP_2} = -\frac{R3}{R2}$$

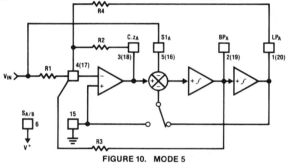

FIGURE 10.   MODE 5

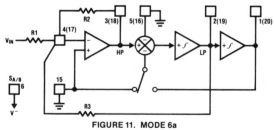

FIGURE 11.   MODE 6a

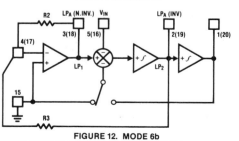

FIGURE 12.   MODE 6b

Reprinted with Permission of National Semiconductor Corp.

National Semiconductor

Operational Amplifiers/Buffers

LH0021/LH0021C 1.0 Amp Power Operational Amplifier
LH0041/LH0041C 0.2 Amp Power Operational Amplifier

General Description

The LH0021/LH0021C and LH0041/LH0041C are general purpose operational amplifiers capable of delivering large output currents not usually associated with conventional IC Op Amps. The LH0021 will provide output currents in excess of one ampere at voltage levels of ±12V; the LH0041 delivers currents of 200 mA at voltage levels closely approaching the available power supplies. In addition, both the inputs and outputs are protected against overload. The devices are compensated with a single external capacitor and are free of any unusual oscillation or latch-up problems.

Features

- Output current   1.0 Amp (LH0021)
                                     0.2 Amp (LH0041)
- Output voltage swing ±12V into 10Ω (LH0021)
                        ±14V into 100Ω (LH0041)
- Wide full power bandwidth   15 kHz
- Low standby power   100 mW at ±15V
- Low input offset
  voltage and current   1 mV and 20 nA

- High slew rate   3.0V/μs
- High open loop gain   100 dB

The excellent input characteristics and high output capability of the LH0021 make it an ideal choice for power applications such as DC servos, capstan drivers, deflection yoke drivers, and programmable power supplies.

The LH0041 is particularly suited for applications such as torque driver for inertial guidance systems, diddle yoke driver for alpha-numeric CRT displays, cable drivers, and programmable power supplies for automatic test equipment.

The LH0021 is supplied in a 8 pin TO-3 package rated at 20 watts with suitable heatsink. The LH0041 is supplied in both 12 pin TO-8 (2.5 watts with clip on heatsink) and a power 8 pin ceramic DIP (2 watts with suitable heatsink). The LH0021 and LH0041 are guaranteed over the temperature range of −55°C to +125°C while the LH0021C and LH0041C are guaranteed from −25°C to +85°C

Schematic and Connection Diagrams

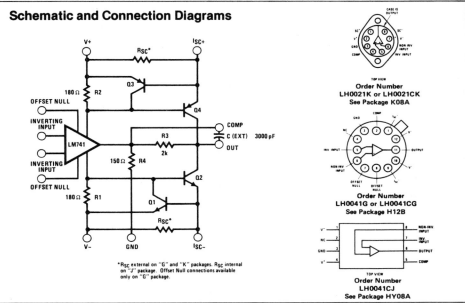

*R$_{SC}$ external on "G" and "K" packages. R$_{SC}$ internal on "J" package. Offset Null connections available only on "G" package.

Order Number
LH0021K or LH0021CK
See Package K08A

Order Number
LH0041G or LH0041CG
See Package H12B

Order Number
LH0041CJ
See Package HY08A

3-304

Reprinted with Permission of National Semiconductor Corp.

**LH0021/LH0021C,
LH0041/LH0041C**

Absolute Maximum Ratings

Supply Voltage	±18V
Power Dissipation	See curves
Differential Input Voltage	±30V
Input Voltage (Note 1)	±15V
Peak Output Current (Note 2) LH0021/LH0021C	2.0 Amps
LH0041/LH0041C	0.5 Amps
Output Short Circuit Duration (Note 3)	Continuous
Operating Temperature Range LH0021/LH0041	-55°C to $+125^\circ$C
LH0021C/LH0041C	-25°C to $+85^\circ$C
Storage Temperature Range	-65°C to $+150^\circ$C
Lead Temperature (Soldering, 10 sec)	300°C

3

DC Electrical Characteristics for LH0021/LH0021C (Note 4)

PARAMETER	CONDITIONS	LH0021 MIN	LH0021 TYP	LH0021 MAX	LH0021C MIN	LH0021C TYP	LH0021C MAX	UNITS
Input Offset Voltage	$R_S < 100\,\Omega$, $T_C = 25^\circ$C		1.0	3.0		3.0	6.0	mV
	$R_S < 100\,\Omega$			5.0			7.5	mV
Voltage Drift with Temperature	$R_S < 100\,\Omega$		3	25		5	30	μV/$^\circ$C
Offset Voltage Drift with Time			5			5		μV/week
Offset Voltage Change with Output Power			5	15		5	20	μV/watt
Input Offset Current	$T_C = 25^\circ$C		30	100		50	200	nA
				300			500	nA
Offset Current Drift with Temperature			0.1	1.0		0.2	1.0	nA/$^\circ$C
Offset Current Drift with Time			2			2		nA/week
Input Bias Current	$T_C = 25^\circ$C		100	300		200	500	nA
				1.0			1.0	μA
Input Resistance	$T_C = 25^\circ$C	0.3	1.0		0.3	1.0		MΩ
Input Capacitance			3			3		pF
Common Mode Rejection Ratio	$R_S < 100\,\Omega$, $\Delta V_{CM} = \pm 10$V	70	90		70	90		dB
Input Voltage Range	$V_S = \pm 15$V	±12			±12			V
Power Supply Rejection Ratio	$R_S < 100\,\Omega$, $\Delta V_S = \pm 10$V	80	96		70	90		dB
Voltage Gain	$V_S = \pm 15$V, $V_O = \pm 10$V $R_L = 1$ kΩ, $T_C = 25^\circ$C,	100	200		100	200		V/mV
	$V_S = \pm 15$V, $V_O = \pm 10$V $R_L = 100\,\Omega$,	25			20			V/mV
Output Voltage Swing	$V_S = \pm 15$V, $R_L = 100\,\Omega$	±13.5	14		±13	±14		V
	$V_S = \pm 15$V, $R_L = 100\,\Omega$, $T_C = 25^\circ$C	±11.0	±12		±10	±12		V
Output Short Circuit Current	$V_S = \pm 15$V, $T_C = 25^\circ$C, $R_{SC} = 0.5\,\Omega$	0.8	1.2	1.6	0.8	1.2	1.6	Amps
Power Supply Current	$V_S = \pm 15$V, $V_{OUT} = 0$		2.5	3.5		3.0	4.0	mA
Power Consumption	$V_S = \pm 15$V, $V_{OUT} = 0$		75	105		90	120	mW

AC Electrical Characteristics for LH0021/LH0021C ($T_A = 25^\circ$C, $V_S = \pm 15$V, $C_C = 3000$ pF)

PARAMETER	CONDITIONS	LH0021 MIN	LH0021 TYP	LH0021 MAX	LH0021C MIN	LH0021C TYP	LH0021C MAX	UNITS
Slew Rate	$A_V = +1$, $R_L = 100\,\Omega$	0.8	3.0		1.0	3.0		V/μs
Power Bandwidth	$R_L = 100\,\Omega$		20			20		kHz
Small Signal Transient Response			0.3	1.0		0.3	1.5	μs
Small Signal Overshoot			5	20		10	30	%
Settling Time (0.1%)	$\Delta V_{IN} = 10$V, $A_V = +1$		4			4		μs
Overload Recovery Time			3			3		μs
Harmonic Distortion	$f = 1$ kHz, $P_O = 0.5$W		0.2			0.2		%
Input Noise Voltage	$R_S = 50\,\Omega$, B.W. = 10 Hz to 10 kHz		5			5		μV rms
Input Noise Current	B.W. = 10 Hz to 10 kHz		0.05			0.05		nA rms

3-305

Reprinted with Permission of National Semiconductor Corp.

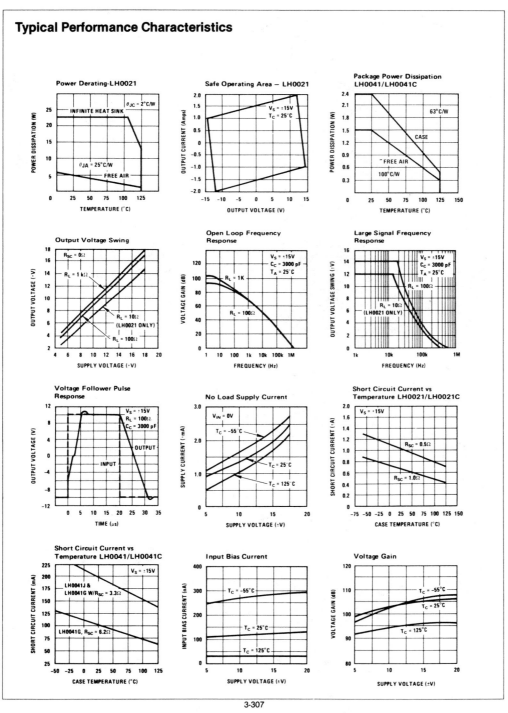

Typical Performance Characteristics

LH0021/LH0021C,
LH0041/LH0041C

3-307

Reprinted with Permission of National Semiconductor Corp.

Typical Performance Characteristics (Cont'd)

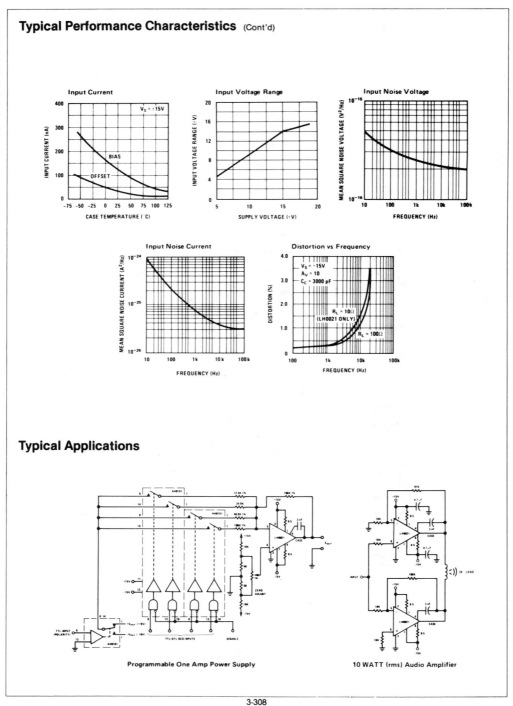

Typical Applications

Programmable One Amp Power Supply

10 WATT (rms) Audio Amplifier

Reprinted with Permission of National Semiconductor Corp.

National Semiconductor

Operational Amplifiers/Buffers

LM101A/LM201A/LM301A Operational Amplifiers

General Description

The LM101A series are general purpose operational amplifiers which feature improved performance over industry standards like the LM709. Advanced processing techniques make possible an order of magnitude reduction in input currents, and a redesign of the biasing circuitry reduces the temperature drift of input current. Improved specifications include:

- Offset voltage 3 mV maximum over temperature (LM101A/LM201A)
- Input current 100 nA maximum over temperature (LM101A/LM201A)
- Offset current 20 nA maximum over temperature (LM101A/LM201A)
- Guaranteed drift characteristics
- Offsets guaranteed over entire common mode and supply voltage ranges
- Slew rate of 10V/µs as a summing amplifier

This amplifier offers many features which make its application nearly foolproof: overload protection on the input and output, no latch-up when the common mode range is exceeded, freedom from oscillations and compensation with a single 30 pF capacitor. It has advantages over internally compensated amplifiers in that the frequency compensation can be tailored to the particular application. For example, in low frequency circuits it can be overcompensated for increased stability margin. Or the compensation can be optimized to give more than a factor of ten improvement in high frequency performance for most applications.

In addition, the device provides better accuracy and lower noise in high impedance circuitry. The low input currents also make it particularly well suited for long interval integrators or timers, sample and hold circuits and low frequency waveform generators. Further, replacing circuits where matched transistor pairs buffer the inputs of conventional IC op amps, it can give lower offset voltage and drift at a lower cost.

The LM101A is guaranteed over a temperature range of −55°C to +125°C, the LM201A from −25°C to +85°C, and the LM301A from 0°C to 70°C.

Schematic** and Connection Diagrams (Top Views)

Metal Can Package

Order Number LM101AH, LM201AH or LM301AH
See NS Package H08C

Dual-In-Line Package

Order Number LM101AJ, LM201AJ, LM301AJ
See NS Package J08A

Order Number LM301AN
See NS Package N08A

Dual-In-Line Package

Note: Pin 6 connected to bottom of package.

Order Number LM101AJ-14
LM201AJ-14 or LM301AJ-14
See NS Package J14A

**Pin connections shown are for metal can.

3-128

Reprinted with Permission of National Semiconductor Corp.

LM101A/LM201A/LM301A

Absolute Maximum Ratings

	LM101A/LM201A	LM301A
Supply Voltage	±22V	±18V
Power Dissipation (Note 1)	500 mW	500 mW
Differential Input Voltage	±30V	±30V
Input Voltage (Note 2)	±15V	±15V
Output Short Circuit Duration (Note 3)	Indefinite	Indefinite
Operating Temperature Range	$-55°$C to $+125°$C (LM101A)	$0°$C to $+70°$C
	$-25°$C to $+85°$C (LM201A)	
Storage Temperature Range	$-65°$C to $+150°$C	$-65°$C to $+150°$C
Lead Temperature (Soldering, 10 seconds)	$300°$C	$300°$C

Electrical Characteristics (Note 4)

PARAMETER	CONDITIONS	LM101A/LM201A			LM301A			UNITS
		MIN	TYP	MAX	MIN	TYP	MAX	
Input Offset Voltage LM101A, LM201A, LM301A	$T_A = 25°$C, $R_S \leq 50$ kΩ		0.7	2.0		2.0	7.5	mV
Input Offset Current	$T_A = 25°$C		1.5	10		3.0	50	nA
Input Bias Current	$T_A = 25°$C		30	75		70	250	nA
Input Resistance	$T_A = 25°$C	1.5	4.0		0.5	2.0		MΩ
Supply Current	$T_A = 25°$C							
	$V_S = ±20$V		1.8	3.0				mA
	$V_S = ±15$V					1.8	3.0	mA
Large Signal Voltage Gain	$T_A = 25°$C, $V_S = ±15$V $V_{OUT} = ±10$V, $R_L \geq 2$ kΩ	50	160		25	160		V/mV
Input Offset Voltage	$R_S \leq 50$ kΩ			3.0			10	mV
	$R_S \leq 10$ kΩ							mV
Average Temperature Coefficient of Input Offset Voltage	$R_S \leq 50$ kΩ		3.0	15		6.0	30	μV/$°$C
	$R_S \leq 10$ kΩ							μV/$°$C
Input Offset Current				20			70	nA
	$T_A = T_{MAX}$							nA
	$T_A = T_{MIN}$							nA
Average Temperature Coefficient of Input Offset Current	$25°$C $\leq T_A \leq T_{MAX}$		0.01	0.1		0.01	0.3	nA/$°$C
	$T_{MIN} \leq T_A \leq 25°$C		0.02	0.2		0.02	0.6	nA/$°$C
Input Bias Current				0.1			0.3	μA
Supply Current	$T_A = T_{MAX}$, $V_S = ±20$V		1.2	2.5				mA
Large Signal Voltage Gain	$V_S = ±15$V, $V_{OUT} = ±10$V, $R_L \geq 2$k	25			15			V/mV
Output Voltage Swing	$V_S = ±15$V							
	$R_L = 10$ kΩ	±12	±14		±12	±14		V
	$R_L = 2$ kΩ	±10	±13		±10	±13		V
Input Voltage Range	$V_S = ±20$V	±15						V
	$V_S = ±15$V		+15, -13		±12	+15, -13		V
Common-Mode Rejection Ratio	$R_S \leq 50$ kΩ	80	96		70	90		dB
	$R_S \leq 10$ kΩ							dB
Supply Voltage Rejection Ratio	$R_S \leq 50$ kΩ	80	96		70	96		dB
	$R_S \leq 10$ kΩ							dB

Note 1: The maximum junction temperature of the LM101A is $150°$C, and that of the LM201A/LM301A is $100°$C. For operating at elevated temperatures, devices in the TO-5 package must be derated based on a thermal resistance of $150°$C/W, junction to ambient, or $45°$C/W, junction to case. The thermal resistance of the dual-in-line package is $187°$C/W, junction to ambient.

Note 2: For supply voltages less than $±15$V, the absolute maximum input voltage is equal to the supply voltage.

Note 3: Continuous short circuit is allowed for case temperatures to $125°$C and ambient temperatures to $75°$C for LM101A/LM201A, and $70°$C and $55°$C respectively for LM301A.

Note 4: Unless otherwise specified, these specifications apply for C1 = 30 pF, $±5$V $\leq V_S \leq ±20$V and $-55°$C $\leq T_A \leq +125°$C (LM101A), $±5$V $\leq V_S \leq ±20$V and $-25°$C $\leq T_A \leq +85°$C (LM201A), $±5$V $\leq V_S \leq ±15$V and $0°$C $\leq T_A \leq +70°$C (LM301A).

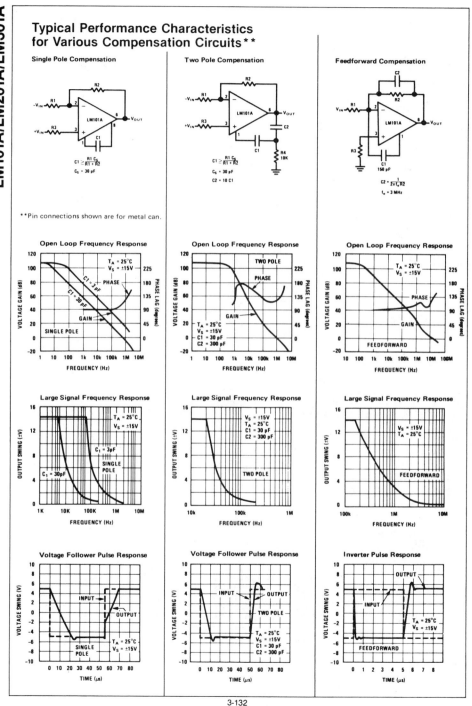

LM101A/LM201A/LM301A

Typical Performance Characteristics
for Various Compensation Circuits**

Single Pole Compensation

Two Pole Compensation

Feedforward Compensation

**Pin connections shown are for metal can.

Reprinted with Permission of National Semiconductor Corp.

National Semiconductor

Voltage Regulators

LM117/LM217/LM317 3-Terminal Adjustable Regulator

General Description

The LM117/LM217/LM317 are adjustable 3-terminal positive voltage regulators capable of supplying in excess of 1.5A over a 1.2V to 37V output range. They are exceptionally easy to use and require only two external resistors to set the output voltage. Further, both line and load regulation are better than standard fixed regulators. Also, the LM117 is packaged in standard transistor packages which are easily mounted and handled.

In addition to higher performance than fixed regulators, the LM117 series offers full overload protection available only in IC's. Included on the chip are current limit, thermal overload protection and safe area protection. All overload protection circuitry remains fully functional even if the adjustment terminal is disconnected.

Features

- Adjustable output down to 1.2V
- Guaranteed 1.5A output current
- Line regulation typically 0.01%/V
- Load regulation typically 0.1%
- Current limit constant with temperature
- **100% electrical burn-in**
- Eliminates the need to stock many voltages
- Standard 3-lead transistor package
- 80 dB ripple rejection

Normally, no capacitors are needed unless the device is situated far from the input filter capacitors in which case an input bypass is needed. An optional output capacitor can be added to improve transient response. The adjustment terminal can be bypassed to achieve very high ripple rejections ratios which are difficult to achieve with standard 3-terminal regulators.

Besides replacing fixed regulators, the LM117 is useful in a wide variety of other applications. Since the regulator is "floating" and sees only the input-to-output differential voltage, supplies of several hundred volts can be regulated as long as the maximum input to output differential is not exceeded.

Also, it makes an especially simple adjustable switching regulator, a programmable output regulator, or by connecting a fixed resistor between the adjustment and output, the LM117 can be used as a precision current regulator. Supplies with electronic shutdown can be achieved by clamping the adjustment terminal to ground which programs the output to 1.2V where most loads draw little current.

The LM117K, LM217K and LM317K are packaged in standard TO-3 transistor packages while the LM117H, LM217H and LM317H are packaged in a solid Kovar base TO-39 transistor package. The LM117 is rated for operation from $-55°C$ to $+150°C$, the LM217 from $-25°C$ to $+150°C$ and the LM317 from $0°C$ to $+125°C$. The LM317T and LM317MP, rated for operation over a $0°C$ to $+125°C$ range, are available in a TO-220 plastic package and a TO-202 package, respectively.

For applications requiring greater output current in excess of 3A and 5A, see LM150 series and LM138 series data sheets, respectively. For the negative complement, see LM137 series data sheet.

LM117 Series Packages and Power Capability

DEVICE	PACKAGE	RATED POWER DISSIPATION	DESIGN LOAD CURRENT
LM117	TO-3	20W	1.5A
LM217	TO-39	2W	0.5A
LM317			
LM317T	TO-220	15W	1.5A
LM317M	TO-202	7.5W	0.5A
LM317LZ	TO-92	0.6W	0.1A

Typical Applications

1.2V–25V Adjustable Regulator

Digitally Selected Outputs

5V Logic Regulator with Electronic Shutdown*

†Optional—improves transient response. Output capacitors in the range of 1 μF to 1000 μF of aluminum or tantalum electrolytic are commonly used to provide improved output impedance and rejection of transients.

*Needed if device is far from filter capacitors.

$$^{††}V_{OUT} = 1.25V \left(1 + \frac{R2}{R1}\right)$$

*Sets maximum V_{OUT}

* Min output ≈ 1.2V

1-23

LM117/LM217/LM317

Absolute Maximum Ratings

Power Dissipation	Internally limited
Input—Output Voltage Differential	40V
Operating Junction Temperature Range	
LM117	-55°C to $+150^\circ$C
LM217	-25°C to $+150^\circ$C
LM317	0°C to $+125^\circ$C
Storage Temperature	-65°C to $+150^\circ$C
Lead Temperature (Soldering, 10 seconds)	300°C

Preconditioning

Burn-In in Thermal Limit   **100% All Devices**

Electrical Characteristics (Note 1)

PARAMETER	CONDITIONS	LM117/217			LM317			UNITS
		MIN	TYP	MAX	MIN	TYP	MAX	
Line Regulation	$T_A = 25^\circ$C, $3V \leq V_{IN} - V_{OUT} \leq 40V$ (Note 2)		0.01	0.02		0.01	0.04	%/V
Load Regulation	$T_A = 25^\circ$C, 10 mA $\leq I_{OUT} \leq I_{MAX}$							
	$V_{OUT} \leq 5V$, (Note 2)		5	15		5	25	mV
	$V_{OUT} \geq 5V$, (Note 2)		0.1	0.3		0.1	0.5	%
Thermal Regulation	$T_A = 25^\circ$C, 20 ms Pulse		0.03	0.07		0.04	0.07	%/W
Adjustment Pin Current			50	100		50	100	μA
Adjustment Pin Current Change	10 mA $\leq I_L \leq I_{MAX}$ $3V \leq (V_{IN}-V_{OUT}) \leq 40V$		0.2	5		0.2	5	μA
Reference Voltage	$3V \leq (V_{IN}-V_{OUT}) \leq 40V$, (Note 3) 10 mA $\leq I_{OUT} \leq I_{MAX}$, $P \leq P_{MAX}$	1.20	1.25	1.30	1.20	1.25	1.30	V
Line Regulation	$3V \leq V_{IN} - V_{OUT} \leq 40V$, (Note 2)		0.02	0.05		0.02	0.07	%/V
Load Regulation	10 mA $\leq I_{OUT} \leq I_{MAX}$, (Note 2)							
	$V_{OUT} \leq 5V$		20	50		20	70	mV
	$V_{OUT} \geq 5V$		0.3	1		0.3	1.5	%
Temperature Stability	$T_{MIN} \leq T_j \leq T_{MAX}$		1			1		%
Minimum Load Current	$V_{IN}-V_{OUT} = 40V$		3.5	5		3.5	10	mA
Current Limit	$V_{IN}-V_{OUT} \leq 15V$							
	K and T Package	1.5	2.2		1.5	2.2		A
	H and P Package	0.5	0.8		0.5	0.8		A
	$V_{IN}-V_{OUT} = 40V$, $T_j = +25^\circ$C							
	K and T Package	0.30	0.4		0.15	0.4		A
	H and P Package	0.15	0.07		0.075	0.07		A
RMS Output Noise, % of V_{OUT}	$T_A = 25^\circ$C, 10 Hz $\leq f \leq 10$ kHz		0.003			0.003		%
Ripple Rejection Ratio	$V_{OUT} = 10V$, $f = 120$ Hz		65			65		dB
	$C_{ADJ} = 10\mu$F	66	80		66	80		dB
Long-Term Stability	$T_A = 125^\circ$C		0.3	1		0.3	1	%
Thermal Resistance, Junction to Case	H Package		12	15		12	15	$^\circ$C/W
	K Package		2.3	3		2.3	3	$^\circ$C/W
	T Package		4			4		$^\circ$C/W
	P Package					12		$^\circ$C/W

Note 1: Unless otherwise specified, these specifications apply -55°C $\leq T_j \leq +150^\circ$C for the LM117, -25°C $\leq T_j \leq +150^\circ$C for the LM217, and 0°C $\leq T_j \leq +125^\circ$C for the LM317; $V_{IN} - V_{OUT} = 5V$; and $I_{OUT} = 0.1A$ for the TO-39 and TO-202 packages and $I_{OUT} = 0.5A$ for the TO-3 and TO-220 packages. Although power dissipation is internally limited, these specifications are applicable for power dissipations of 2W for the TO-39 and TO-202, and 20W for the TO-3 and TO-220. I_{MAX} is 1.5A for the TO-3 and TO-220 packages and 0.5A for the TO-39 and TO-202 packages.

Note 2: Regulation is measured at constant junction temperature, using pulse testing with a low duty cycle. Changes in output voltage due to heating effects are covered under the specification for thermal regulation.

Note 3: Selected devices with tightened tolerance reference voltage available.

1-24

Reprinted with Permission of National Semiconductor Corp.

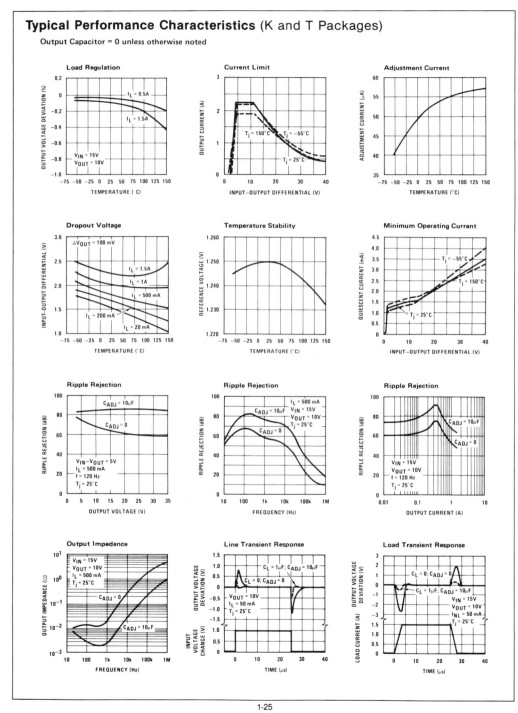

Typical Performance Characteristics (K and T Packages)

Output Capacitor = 0 unless otherwise noted

LM117/LM217/LM317

1-25

Reprinted with Permission of National Semiconductor Corp.

LM117/LM217/LM317

Application Hints

In operation, the LM117 develops a nominal 1.25V reference voltage, V_{REF}, between the output and adjustment terminal. The reference voltage is impressed across program resistor R1 and, since the voltage is constant, a constant current I_1 then flows through the output set resistor R2, giving an output voltage of

$$V_{OUT} = V_{REF}\left(1 + \frac{R2}{R1}\right) + I_{ADJ}R2$$

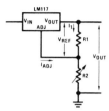

FIGURE 1.

Since the 100µA current from the adjustment terminal represents an error term, the LM117 was designed to minimize I_{ADJ} and make it very constant with line and load changes. To do this, all quiescent operating current is returned to the output establishing a minimum load current requirement. If there is insufficient load on the output, the output will rise.

External Capacitors

An input bypass capacitor is recommended. A 0.1µF disc or 1µF solid tantalum on the input is suitable input bypassing for almost all applications. The device is more sensitive to the absence of input bypassing when adjustment or output capacitors are used but the above values will eliminate the possibility of problems.

The adjustment terminal can be bypassed to ground on the LM117 to improve ripple rejection. This bypass capacitor prevents ripple from being amplified as the output voltage is increased. With a 10µF bypass capacitor 80 dB ripple rejection is obtainable at any output level. Increases over 10µF do not appreciably improve the ripple rejection at frequencies above 120 Hz. If the bypass capacitor is used, it is sometimes necessary to include protection diodes to prevent the capacitor from discharging through internal low current paths and damaging the device.

In general, the best type of capacitors to use are solid tantalum. Solid tantalum capacitors have low impedance even at high frequencies. Depending upon capacitor construction, it takes about 25µF in aluminum electrolytic to equal 1µF solid tantalum at high frequencies. Ceramic capacitors are also good at high frequencies; but some types have a large decrease in capacitance at frequencies around 0.5 MHz. For this reason, 0.01µF disc may seem to work better than a 0.1µF disc as a bypass.

Although the LM117 is stable with no output capacitors, like any feedback circuit, certain values of external capacitance can cause excessive ringing. This occurs with values between 500 pF and 5000 pF. A 1µF solid tantalum (or 25µF aluminum electrolytic) on the output swamps this effect and insures stability.

Load Regulation

The LM117 is capable of providing extremely good load regulation but a few precautions are needed to obtain maximum performance. The current set resistor connected between the adjustment terminal and the output terminal (usually 240Ω) should be tied directly to the output of the regulator rather than near the load. This eliminates line drops from appearing effectvely in series with the reference and degrading regulation. For example, a 15V regulator with 0.05Ω resistance between the regulator and load will have a load regulation due to line resistance of 0.05Ω x I_L. If the set resistor is connected near the load the effective line resistance will be 0.05Ω (1 + R2/R1) or in this case, 11.5 times worse.

Figure 2 shows the effect of resistance between the regulator and 240Ω set resistor.

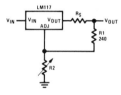

FIGURE 2. Regulator with Line Resistance in Output Lead

With the TO-3 package, it is easy to minimize the resistance from the case to the set resistor, by using two separate leads to the case. However, with the TO-5 package, care should be taken to minimize the wire length of the output lead. The ground of R2 can be returned near the ground of the load to provide remote ground sensing and improve load regulation.

Protection Diodes

When external capacitors are used with *any* IC regulator it is sometimes necessary to add protection diodes to prevent the capacitors from discharging through low current points into the regulator. Most 10µF capacitors have low enough internal series resistance to deliver 20A spikes when shorted. Although the surge is short, there is enough energy to damage parts of the IC.

When an output capacitor is connected to a regulator and the input is shorted, the output capacitor will discharge into the output of the regulator. The discharge

Reprinted with Permission of National Semiconductor Corp.

Application Hints (cont'd.)

current depends on the value of the capacitor, the output voltage of the regulator, and the rate of decrease of V_{IN}. In the LM117, this discharge path is through a large junction that is able to sustain 15A surge with no problem. This is not true of other types of positive regulators. For output capacitors of 25μF or less, there is no need to use diodes.

The bypass capacitor on the adjustment terminal can discharge through a low current junction. Discharge

occurs when *either* the input or output is shorted. Internal to the LM117 is a 50Ω resistor which limits the peak discharge current. No protection is needed for output voltages of 25V or less and 10μF capacitance. *Figure 3* shows an LM117 with protection diodes included for use with outputs greater than 25V and high values of output capacitance.

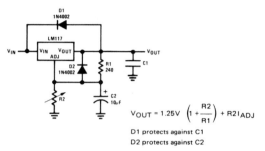

$$V_{OUT} = 1.25V \left(1 + \frac{R2}{R1}\right) + R2 I_{ADJ}$$

D1 protects against C1
D2 protects against C2

FIGURE 3. Regulator with Protection Diodes

Connection Diagrams

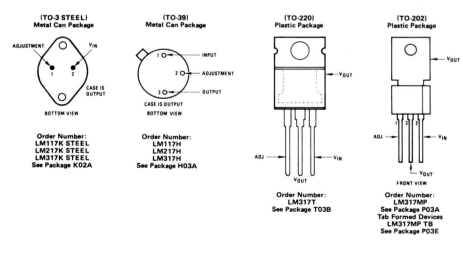

(TO-3 STEEL) Metal Can Package	(TO-39) Metal Can Package	(TO-220) Plastic Package	(TO-202) Plastic Package
Order Number: LM117K STEEL LM217K STEEL LM317K STEEL See Package K02A	Order Number: LM117H LM217H LM317H See Package H03A	Order Number: LM317T See Package T03B	Order Number: LM317MP See Package P03A Tab Formed Devices LM317MP TB See Package P03E

Reprinted with Permission of National Semiconductor Corp.

National Semiconductor

Operational Amplifiers/Buffers

LM118/LM218/LM318 Operational Amplifiers

General Description

The LM118 series are precision high speed operational amplifiers designed for applications requiring wide bandwidth and high slew rate. They feature a factor of ten increase in speed over general purpose devices without sacrificing DC performance.

Features

- 15 MHz small signal bandwidth
- Guaranteed 50V/μs slew rate
- Maximum bias current of 250 nA
- Operates from supplies of ±5V to ±20V
- Internal frequency compensation
- Input and output overload protected
- Pin compatible with general purpose op amps

The LM118 series has internal unity gain frequency compensation. This considerably simplifies its application since no external components are necessary for operation. However, unlike most internally compensated amplifiers, external frequency compensation may be added for optimum performance For inverting applications, feedforward compensation will boost the slew rate to over 150V/μs and almost double the bandwidth. Overcompensation can be used with the amplifier for greater stability when maximum bandwidth is not needed. Further, a single capacitor can be added to reduce the 0.1% settling time to under 1 μs.

The high speed and fast settling time of these op amps make them useful in A/D converters, oscillators, active filters, sample and hold circuits, or general purpose amplifiers. These devices are easy to apply and offer an order of magnitude better AC performance than industry standards such as the LM709.

The LM218 is identical to the LM118 except that the LM218 has its performance specified over a −25°C to +85°C temperature range. The LM318 is specified from 0°C to +70°C.

Schematic and Connection Diagrams

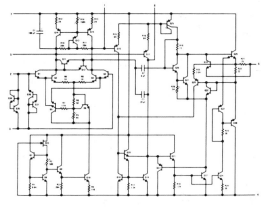

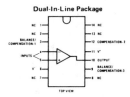

Dual-In-Line Package

Order Number LM118J, LM218J
or LM318J
See NS Package J14A

Metal Can Package*

*Pin connections shown on schematic diagram
and typical applications are for TO-5 package.

Order Number LM118H, LM218H
or LM318H
See NS Package H08C

Dual-In-Line Package

Order Number LM118J-8,
LM218J-8 or LM318J-8
See NS Package J08A
Order Number LM318N
See NS Package N08B

LM118/LM218/LM318

Absolute Maximum Ratings

Supply Voltage	±20V
Power Dissipation (Note 1)	500 mW
Differential Input Current (Note 2)	±10 mA
Input Voltage (Note 3)	±15V
Output Short-Circuit Duration	Indefinite
Operating Temperature Range	
LM118	−55°C to +125°C
LM218	−25°C to +85°C
LM318	0°C to +70°C
Storage Temperature Range	−65°C to +150°C
Lead Temperature (Soldering, 10 seconds)	300°C

Electrical Characteristics (Note 4)

PARAMETER	CONDITIONS	LM118/LM218			LM318			UNITS
		MIN	TYP	MAX	MIN	TYP	MAX	
Input Offset Voltage	$T_A = 25°C$		2	4		4	10	mV
Input Offset Current	$T_A = 25°C$		6	50		30	200	nA
Input Bias Current	$T_A = 25°C$		120	250		150	500	nA
Input Resistance	$T_A = 25°C$	1	3		0.5	3		MΩ
Supply Current	$T_A = 25°C$		5	8		5	10	mA
Large Signal Voltage Gain	$T_A = 25°C$, $V_S = ±15V$ $V_{OUT} = ±10V$, $R_L \geq 2 k\Omega$	50	200		25	200		V/mV
Slew Rate	$T_A = 25°C$, $V_S = ±15V$, $A_v = 1$	50	70		50	70		V/μs
Small Signal Bandwidth	$T_A = 25°C$, $V_S = ±15V$		15			15		MHz
Input Offset Voltage				6			15	mV
Input Offset Current				100			300	nA
Input Bias Current				500			750	nA
Supply Current	$T_A = 125°C$		4.5	7				mA
Large Signal Voltage Gain	$V_S = ±15V$, $V_{OUT} = ±10V$ $R_L \geq 2 k\Omega$	25			20			V/mV
Output Voltage Swing	$V_S = ±15V$, $R_L = 2 k\Omega$	±12	±13		±12	±13		V
Input Voltage Range	$V_S = ±15V$	±11.5			±11.5			V
Common-Mode Rejection Ratio		80	100		70	100		dB
Supply Voltage Rejection Ratio		70	80		65	80		dB

Note 1: The maximum junction temperature of the LM118 is 150°C, the LM218 is 110°C, and the LM318 is 110°C. For operating at elevated temperatures, devices in the TO-5 package must be derated based on a thermal resistance of 150°C/W, junction to ambient, or 45°C/W, junction to case. The thermal resistance of the dual-in-line package is 100°C/W, junction to ambient.

Note 2: The inputs are shunted with back-to-back diodes for overvoltage protection. Therefore, excessive current will flow if a differential input voltage in excess of 1V is applied between the inputs unless some limiting resistance is used.

Note 3: For supply voltages less than ±15V, the absolute maximum input voltage is equal to the supply voltage.

Note 4: These specifications apply for $±5V \leq V_S \leq ±20V$ and $−55°C \leq T_A \leq +125°C$,(LM118),$−25°C \leq T_A \leq +85°C$ (LM218), and $0°C \leq T_A \leq +70°C$ (LM318). Also, power supplies must be bypassed with 0.1μF disc capacitors.

3-166

Reprinted with Permission of National Semiconductor Corp.

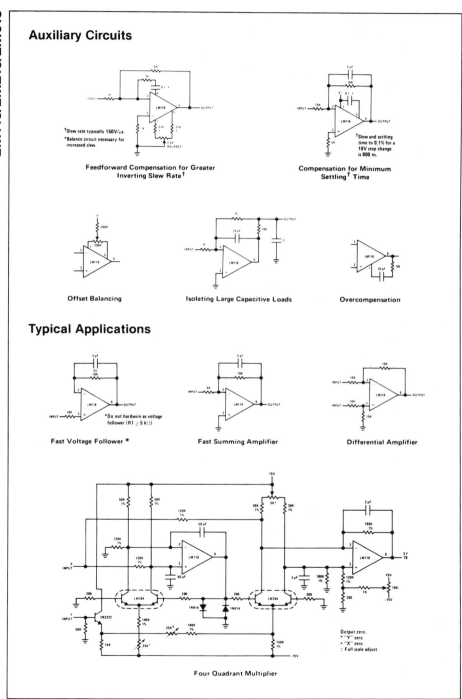

Reprinted with Permission of National Semiconductor Corp.

LM124/LM224/LM324, LM124A/
LM224A/LM324A, LM2902

▶◀ National
Semiconductor

Operational Amplifiers/Buffers

LM124/LM224/LM324, LM124A/LM224A/LM324A, LM2902
Low Power Quad Operational Amplifiers

General Description

The LM124 series consists of four independent, high gain, internally frequency compensated operational amplifiers which were designed specifically to operate from a single power supply over a wide range of voltages. Operation from split power supplies is also possible and the low power supply current drain is independent of the magnitude of the power supply voltage.

Application areas include transducer amplifiers, dc gain blocks and all the conventional op amp circuits which now can be more easily implemented in single power supply systems. For example, the LM124 series can be directly operated off of the standard +5 V_{DC} power supply voltage which is used in digital systems and will easily provide the required interface electronics without requiring the additional ±15 V_{DC} power supplies.

Unique Characteristics

- In the linear mode the input common-mode voltage range includes ground and the output voltage can also swing to ground, even though operated from only a single power supply voltage.

- The unity gain cross frequency is temperature compensated.

- The input bias current is also temperature compensated.

Advantages

- Eliminates need for dual supplies
- Four internally compensated op amps in a single package
- Allows directly sensing near GND and V_{OUT} also goes to GND
- Compatible with all forms of logic
- Power drain suitable for battery operation

Features

- Internally frequency compensated for unity gain
- Large dc voltage gain   100 dB
- Wide bandwidth (unity gain)   1 MHz
  (temperature compensated)
- Wide power supply range:
  Single supply   3 V_{DC} to 30 V_{DC}
  or dual supplies   ±1.5 V_{DC} to ±15 V_{DC}
- Very low supply current drain (800μA) — essentially independent of supply voltage (1 mW/op amp at +5 V_{DC})
- Low input biasing current   45 nA_{DC}
  (temperature compensated)
- Low input offset voltage   2 mV_{DC}
  and offset current   5 nA_{DC}
- Input common-mode voltage range includes ground
- Differential input voltage range equal to the power supply voltage
- Large output voltage   0 V_{DC} to V^+ − 1.5 V_{DC}
  swing

Connection Diagram

Dual-In-Line Package

OUTPUT 4   INPUT 4⁻   INPUT 4⁺   GND   INPUT 3⁺   INPUT 3⁻   OUTPUT 3

| 14 | 13 | 12 | 11 | 10 | 9 | 8 |

| 1 | 2 | 3 | 4 | 5 | 6 | 7 |

OUTPUT 1   INPUT 1⁻   INPUT 1⁺   V⁺   INPUT 2⁺   INPUT 2⁻   OUTPUT 2

TOP VIEW

Order Number LM124J, LM124AJ,
LM224J, LM224AJ, LM324J,
LM324AJ or LM2902J
See NS Package J14A

Order Number LM324N, LM324AN
or LM2902N
See NS Package N14A

Schematic Diagram (Each Amplifier)

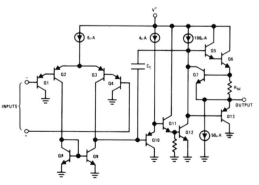

3-172

Reprinted with Permission of National Semiconductor Corp.

**LM124/LM224/LM324, LM124A/
LM224A/LM324A, LM2902**

3

Absolute Maximum Ratings

	LM124/LM224/LM324 LM124A/LM224A/LM324A	LM2902
Supply Voltage, V+	32 VDC or ±16 VDC	26 VDC or ±13 VDC
Differential Input Voltage	32 VDC	26 VDC
Input Voltage	−0.3 VDC to +26 VDC	−0.3 VDC to +26 VDC
Power Dissipation (Note 1)		
Molded DIP	570 mW	570 mW
Cavity DIP	900 mW	
Flat Pack	800 mW	
Output Short-Circuit to GND (One Amplifier) (Note 2) V+ ≤ 15 VDC and TA = 25°C	Continuous	Continuous
Input Current (VIN < −0.3 VDC) (Note 3)		50 mA
Operating Temperature Range		−40°C to +85°C
LM324/LM324A	0°C to +70°C	
LM224/LM224A	−25°C to +85°C	
LM124/LM124A	−55°C to +125°C	
Storage Temperature Range	−65°C to +150°C	−65°C to +150°C
Lead Temperature (Soldering, 10 seconds)	300°C	300°C

Electrical Characteristics (V+ = +5.0 VDC, Note 4)

PARAMETER	CONDITIONS	LM124A MIN	TYP	MAX	LM224A MIN	TYP	MAX	LM324A MIN	TYP	MAX	LM124/LM224 MIN	TYP	MAX	LM324 LM124A/LM224A/LM324A MIN	TYP	MAX	LM2902 MIN	TYP	MAX	UNITS
Input Offset Voltage	TA = 25°C, (Note 5)		1	2		1	3		2	3		±2	±5		±2	±7		±2	±7	mVDC
Input Bias Current (Note 6)	IIN(+) or IIN(−), TA = 25°C		20	50		40	80		45	100		45	150		45	250		45	250	nADC
Input Offset Current	IIN(+) − IIN(−), TA = 25°C		2	10		2	15		5	30		±3	±30		±5	±50		±5	±50	nADC
Input Common-Mode Voltage Range (Note 7)	V+ = 30 VDC, TA = 25°C	0		V+−1.5	0		V+−1.5	0		V+−1.5	0		V+−1.5	0		V+−1.5	0		V+−1.5	VDC
Supply Current	RL = ∞, VCC = 30V, (LM2902 VCC = 26V) RL = ∞ On All Op Amps Over Full Temperature Range		1.5	3		1.5	3		1.5	3		1.5	3		1.5	3		1.5	3	mADC
			0.7	1.2		0.7	1.2		0.7	1.2		0.7	1.2		0.7	1.2		0.7	1.2	mADC
Large Signal Voltage Gain	V+ = 15 VDC (For Large VO Swing) RL ≥ 2 kΩ, TA = 25°C	50	100		50	100		25	100		50	100		25	100			100		V/mV
Output Voltage Swing	RL = 2 kΩ, TA = 25°C (LM2902 RL ≥ 10 kΩ)	0		V+−1.5	0		V+−1.5	0		V+−1.5	0		V+−1.5	0		V+−1.5	0		V+−1.5	VDC
Common-Mode Rejection Ratio	DC, TA = 25°C	70	85		70	85		65	85		70	85		65	70		50	70		dB
Power Supply Rejection Ratio	DC, TA = 25°C	65	100		65	100		65	100		65	100		65	100		50	100		dB
Amplifier-to-Amplifier Coupling (Note 8)	f = 1 kHz to 20 kHz, TA = 25°C (Input Referred)		−120			−120			−120			−120			−120			−120		dB
Output Current Source	VIN+ = 1 VDC, VIN− = 0 VDC, V+ = 15 VDC, TA = 25°C	20	40		20	40		20	40		20	40		20	40		20	40		mADC
Sink	VIN− = 1 VDC, VIN+ = 0 VDC, V+ = 15 VDC, TA = 25°C	10	20		10	20		10	20		10	20		10	20		10	20		mADC
	VIN− = 1 VDC, VO = 200 mVDC	12	50		12	50		12	50		12	50		12	50					µADC
Short Circuit to Ground	TA = 25°C, (Note 2)		40	60		40	60		40	60		40	60		40	60		40	60	mADC

3-173

Reprinted with Permission of National Semiconductor Corp.

LM124/LM224/LM324, LM124A/LM224A/LM324A, LM2902

Electrical Characteristics (Continued)

PARAMETER	CONDITIONS	LM124A			LM224A			LM324A			LM124/LM224			LM324			LM2902			UNITS
		MIN	TYP	MAX	MIN	TYP	MAX	MIN	TYP	MAX	MIN	TYP	MAX	MIN	TYP	MAX	MIN	TYP	MAX	
Input Offset Voltage	(Note 5)			4			4			5			±7			±9			±10	mVDC
Input Offset Voltage Drift	$R_S = 0\,\Omega$		7	20		7	20		7	30		7			7			7		µV/°C
Input Offset Current	$I_{IN(+)} - I_{IN(-)}$			30			30			75			±100			±150			±200	nADC
Input Offset Current Drift			10	200		10	200		10	300		10			10			10		pADC/°C
Input Bias Current	$I_{IN(+)}$ or $I_{IN(-)}$		40	100		40	100		40	200		40	300		40	500		40	500	nADC
Input Common-Mode Voltage Range (Note 7)	$V^+ = 30\ V_{DC}$	0		$V^+{-}2$	0		$V^+{-}2$	0		$V^+{-}2$	0		$V^+{-}2$	0		$V^+{-}2$	0		$V^+{-}2$	VDC
Large Signal Voltage Gain	$V^+ = +15\ V_{DC}$ (For Large V_O Swing) $R_L \geq 2\ k\Omega$	25			25			15			25			15			15			V/mV
Output Voltage Swing V_{OH}	$V^+ = +30\ V_{DC}$, $R_L = 2\ k\Omega$	26			26			26			26			26			22			VDC
	$R_L \geq 10\ k\Omega$	27	28		27	28		27	28		27	28		27	28		23	24		VDC
V_{OL}	$V^+ = 5\ V_{DC}$, $R_L \leq 10\ k\Omega$		5	20		5	20		5	20		5	20		5	20		5	100	mVDC
Output Current Source	$V_{IN}^+ = +1\ V_{DC}$, $V_{IN}^- = 0\ V_{DC}$, $V^+ = 15\ V_{DC}$	10	20		10	20		10	20		10	20		10	20		10	20		mADC
Sink	$V_{IN}^- = +1\ V_{DC}$, $V_{IN}^+ = 0\ V_{DC}$, $V^+ = 15\ V_{DC}$	10	15		5	8		5	8		5	8		5	8		5	8		mADC
Differential Input Voltage	(Note 7)			32			32			32			32			32			26	VDC

Note 1: For operating at high temperatures, the LM324/LM324A, LM2902 must be derated based on a +125°C maximum junction temperature and a thermal resistance of 175°C/W which applies for the device soldered in a printed circuit board, operating in a still air ambient. The LM224/LM224A and LM124/LM124A can be derated based on a +150°C maximum junction temperature. The dissipation is the total of all four amplifiers—use external resistors, where possible, to allow the amplifier to saturate or to reduce the power which is dissipated in the integrated circuit.

Note 2: Short circuits from the output to V^+ can cause excessive heating and eventual destruction. The maximum output current is approximately 40 mA independent of the magnitude of V^+. At values of supply voltage in excess of +15 V_{DC}, continuous short-circuits can exceed the power dissipation ratings and cause eventual destruction. Destructive dissipation can result from simultaneous shorts on all amplifiers.

Note 3: This input current will only exist when the voltage at any of the input leads is driven negative. It is due to the collector-base junction of the input PNP transistors becoming forward biased and thereby acting as input diode clamps. In addition to this diode action, there is also lateral NPN parasitic transistor action on the IC chip. This transistor action can cause the output voltages of the op amps to go to the V^+ voltage level (or to ground for a large overdrive) for the time duration that an input is driven negative. This is not destructive and normal output states will re-establish when the input voltage, which was negative, again returns to a value greater than $-0.3\ V_{DC}$ (at 25°C).

Note 4: These specifications apply for $V^+ = +5\ V_{DC}$ and $-55^\circ C \leq T_A \leq +125^\circ C$, unless otherwise stated. With the LM224/LM224A, all temperature specifications are limited to $-25^\circ C \leq T_A \leq +85^\circ C$, the LM324/LM324A temperature specifications are limited to $0^\circ C \leq T_A \leq +70^\circ C$, and the LM2902 specifications are limited to $-40^\circ C \leq T_A \leq +85^\circ C$.

Note 5: $V_O \cong 1.4\ V_{DC}$. $R_S = 0\,\Omega$ with V^+ from 5 V_{DC} to 30 V_{DC}; and over the full input common-mode range (0 V_{DC} to $V^+ - 1.5\ V_{DC}$).

Note 6: The direction of the input current is out of the IC due to the PNP input stage. This current is essentially constant, independent of the state of the output so no loading change exists on the input lines.

Note 7: The input common-mode voltage of either input signal voltage should not be allowed to go negative by more than 0.3V (at 25°C). The upper end of the common-mode voltage range is $V^+ - 1.5V$, but either or both inputs can go to +32 V_{DC} without damage (+26 V_{DC} for LM2902).

Note 8: Due to proximity of external components, insure that coupling is not originating via stray capacitance between these external parts. This typically can be detected as this type of capacitive increases at higher frequencies.

Reprinted with Permission of National Semiconductor Corp.

LM381/LM381A

National Semiconductor

Audio/Radio Circuits

LM381/LM381A Low Noise Dual Preamplifier

General Description

The LM381/LM381A is a dual preamplifier for the amplication of low level signals in applications requiring optimum noise performance. Each of the two amplifiers is completely independent, with individual internal power supply decoupler-regulator, providing 120 dB supply rejection and 60 dB channel separation. Other outstanding features include high gain (112 dB), large output voltage swing (V_{CC} −2V) p-p, and wide power bandwidth (75 kHz, 20V_{P-P}). The LM381/LM381A operates from a single supply across the wide range of 9 to 40V.

Either differential input or single ended input configurations may be selected. The amplifier is internally compensated with the provision for additional external compensation for narrow band

applications. For additional information see AN-64, AN-104.

Features

- Low Noise − .5 µV total input noise
- High Gain − 112 dB open loop
- Single Supply Operation
- Wide supply range 9–40V
- Power supply rejection 120 dB
- Large output voltage swing (V_{CC} −2V)$_{p-p}$
- Wide bandwidth 15 MHz unity gain
- Power bandwidth 75 kHz, 20 V_{p-p}
- Internally compensated
- Short circuit protected

Schematic and Connection Diagrams

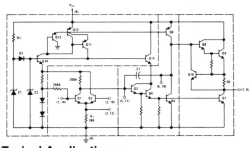

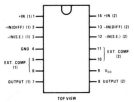

Dual-In-Line Package

TOP VIEW

**Order Number LM381N or LM381AN
See NS Package N14A**

Typical Applications

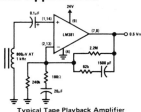

Typical Tape Playback Amplifier

Typical Magnetic Phono Preamp

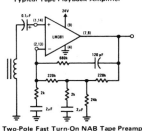

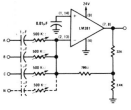

Two-Pole Fast Turn-On NAB Tape Preamp

Audio Mixer

10-26

Reprinted with Permission of National Semiconductor Corp.

Absolute Maximum Ratings

Supply Voltage	+40V
Power Dissipation (Note 1)	715 mW
Operating Temperature Range	0°C to 70°C
Storage Temperature Range	–65°C to +150°C
Lead Temperature (Soldering, 10 sec)	300°C

Electrical Characteristics T_A = 25°C, V_{CC} = 14V, unless otherwise stated.

PARAMETER	CONDITIONS	MIN	TYP	MAX	UNITS
Voltage Gain	Open Loop (Differential Input), f = 100 Hz		160,000		V/V
	Open Loop (Single Ended), f = 100 Hz		320,000		V/V
Supply Current	V_{CC} 9 to 40V, R_L = ∞		10		mA
Input Resistance					
(Positive Input)			100		kΩ
(Negative Input)			200		kΩ
Input Current					
(Negative Input)			0.5		μA
Output Resistance	Open Loop		150		Ω
Output Current	Source		8		mA
	Sink		2		mA
Output Voltage Swing	Peak-to-Peak		$V_{CC} - 2$		V
Unity Gain Bandwidth			15		MHz
Power Bandwidth	20 $V_{p\text{-}p}$ (V_{CC} = 24V)		75		kHz
Maximum Input Voltage	Linear Operation			300	mVrms
Supply Rejection Ratio	f = 1 kHz		120		dB
Channel Separation	f = 1 kHz		60		dB
Total Harmonic Distortion	60 dB Gain, f = 1 kHz		0.1		%
Total Equivalent Input Noise	R_S = 600Ω, 10 – 10,000 Hz (Single Ended Input, Flat Gain Circuit, A_V = 1000)				
LM381A			0.5	0.7	μVrms
LM381			0.5	1.0	μVrms

Note 1: For operation in ambient temperatures above 25°C, the device must be derated based on a 150°C maximum junction temperature and a thermal resistance of 175°C/W junction to ambient.

Typical Applications (Continued)

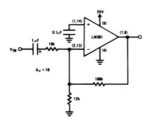

Ultra-Low Distortion Amplifier
(A_V = 10, THD < 0.05%, V_{OUT} = 3 V_{RMS})

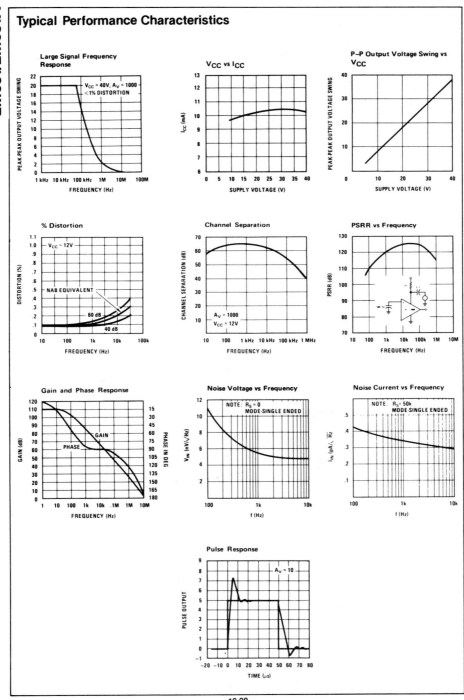

Reprinted with Permission of National Semiconductor Corp.

LM386

Audio/Radio Circuits

LM386 Low Voltage Audio Power Amplifier

General Description

The LM386 is a power amplifier designed for use in low voltage consumer applications. The gain is internally set to 20 to keep external part count low, but the addition of an external resistor and capacitor between pins 1 and 8 will increase the gain to any value up to 200.

The inputs are ground referenced while the output is automatically biased to one half the supply voltage. The quiescent power drain is only 24 milliwatts when operating from a 6 volt supply, making the LM386 ideal for battery operation.

Features

- Battery operation
- Minimum external parts
- Wide supply voltage range   4V−12V or 5V−18V
- Low quiescent current drain   4 mA

- Voltage gains from 20 to 200
- Ground referenced input
- Self-centering output quiescent voltage
- Low distortion
- Eight pin dual-in-line package

Applications

- AM-FM radio amplifiers
- Portable tape player amplifiers
- Intercoms
- TV sound systems
- Line drivers
- Ultrasonic drivers
- Small servo drivers
- Power converters

Equivalent Schematic and Connection Diagrams

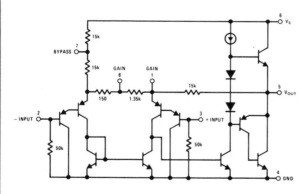

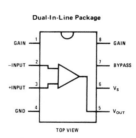

Typical Applications

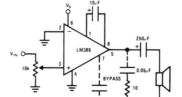

10-40

Reprinted with Permission of National Semiconductor Corp.

LM386

Absolute Maximum Ratings

Supply Voltage (LM386N)	15V	Storage Temperature	$-65°C$ to $+150°C$
Supply Voltage (LM386N-4)	22V	Operating Temperature	$0°C$ to $+70°C$
Package Dissipation (Note 1) (LM386N-4)	1.25W	Junction Temperature	$+150°C$
Package Dissipation (Note 2) (LM386)	660 mW	Lead Temperature (Soldering, 10 seconds)	$+300°C$
Input Voltage	±0.4V		

Electrical Characteristics $T_A = 25°C$

PARAMETER	CONDITIONS	MIN	TYP	MAX	UNITS
Operating Supply Voltage (V_S)					
LM386		4		12	V
LM386N-4		5		18	V
Quiescent Current (I_Q)	$V_S = 6V$, $V_{IN} = 0$		4	8	mA
Output Power (P_{OUT})					
LM386N-1	$V_S = 6V$, $R_L = 8Ω$, THD = 10%	250	325		mW
LM386N-3	$V_S = 9V$, $R_L = 8Ω$, THD = 10%	500	700		mW
LM386N-4	$V_S = 16V$, $R_L = 32Ω$, THD = 10%	700	1000		mW
Voltage Gain (A_V)	$V_S = 6V$, f = 1 kHz		26		dB
	$10\mu F$ from Pin 1 to 8		46		dB
Bandwidth (BW)	$V_S = 6V$, Pins 1 and 8 Open		300		kHz
Total Harmonic Distortion (THD)	$V_S = 6V$, $R_L = 8Ω$, $P_{OUT} = 125$ mW f = 1 kHz, Pins 1 and 8 Open		0.2		%
Power Supply Rejection Ratio (PSRR)	$V_S = 6V$, f = 1 kHz, $C_{BYPASS} = 10\mu F$ Pins 1 and 8 Open, Referred to Output		50		dB
Input Resistance (R_{IN})			50		kΩ
Input Bias Current (I_{BIAS})	$V_S = 6V$, Pins 2 and 3 Open		250		nA

Note 1: For operation in ambient temperatures above $25°C$, the device must be derated based on a $150°C$ maximum junction temperature and a thermal resistance of $100°C/W$ junction to ambient.

Note 2: For operation in ambient temperatures above $25°C$, the device must be derated based on a $150°C$ maximum junction temperature and a thermal resistance of $187°C$ junction to ambient.

Application Hints

GAIN CONTROL

To make the LM386 a more versatile amplifier, two pins (1 and 8) are provided for gain control. With pins 1 and 8 open the 1.35 kΩ resistor sets the gain at 20 (26 dB). If a capacitor is put from pin 1 to 8, bypassing the 1.35 kΩ resistor, the gain will go up to 200 (46 dB). If a resistor is placed in series with the capacitor, the gain can be set to any value from 20 to 200. Gain control can also be done by capacitively coupling a resistor (or FET) from pin 1 to ground.

Additional external components can be placed in parallel with the internal feedback resistors to tailor the gain and frequency response for individual applications. For example, we can compensate poor speaker bass response by frequency shaping the feedback path. This is done with a series RC from pin 1 to 5 (paralleling the internal 15 kΩ resistor). For 6 dB effective bass boost: R ≅ 15 kΩ, the lowest value for good stable operation is R = 10 kΩ if pin 8 is open. If pins 1 and 8 are bypassed then R as low as 2 kΩ can be used. This restriction is because the amplifier is only compensated for closed-loop gains greater than 9.

INPUT BIASING

The schematic shows that both inputs are biased to ground with a 50 kΩ resistor. The base current of the input transistors is about 250 nA, so the inputs are at about 12.5 mV when left open. If the dc source resistance driving the LM386 is higher than 250 kΩ it will contribute very little additional offset (about 2.5 mV at the input, 50 mV at the output). If the dc source resistance is less than 10 kΩ, then shorting the unused input to ground will keep the offset low (about 2.5 mV at the input, 50 mV at the output). For dc source resistances between these values we can eliminate excess offset by putting a resistor from the unused input to ground, equal in value to the dc source resistance. Of course all offset problems are eliminated if the input is capacitively coupled.

When using the LM386 with higher gains (bypassing the 1.35 kΩ resistor between pins 1 and 8) it is necessary to bypass the unused input, preventing degradation of gain and possible instabilities. This is done with a $0.1\mu F$ capacitor or a short to ground depending on the dc source resistance on the driven input.

10

Reprinted with Permission of National Semiconductor Corp.

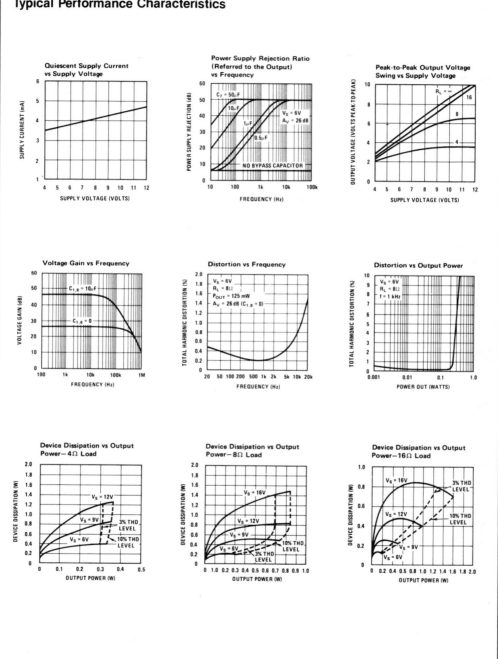

Typical Performance Characteristics

LM386

Reprinted with Permission of National Semiconductor Corp.

National Semiconductor

Operational Amplifiers/Buffers

BI-FET II™ Technology

LF411A/LF411 Low Offset, Low Drift JFET Input Operational Amplifier

General Description

These devices are low cost, high speed, JFET input operational amplifiers with very low input offset voltage and guaranteed input offset voltage drift. They require low supply current yet maintain a large gain bandwidth product and fast slew rate. In addition, well matched high voltage JFET input devices provide very low input bias and offset currents. The LF411 is pin compatible with the standard LM741 allowing designers to immediately upgrade the overall performance of existing designs.

These amplifiers may be used in applications such as high speed integrators, fast D/A converters, sample and hold circuits and many other circuits requiring low input offset voltage and drift, low input bias current, high input impedance, high slew rate and wide bandwidth.

Features

- Internally trimmed offset voltage   0.5 mV (max)
- Input offset voltage drift $10\,\mu V/°C$ (max)
- Low input bias current   50 pA
- Low input noise current $0.01\,pA/\sqrt{Hz}$
- Wide gain bandwidth   3 MHz (min)
- High slew rate $10V/\mu s$ (min)
- Low supply current   1.8 mA
- High input impedance $10^{12}\Omega$
- Low total harmonic distortion $A_V = 10$, $<0.02\%$
  $R_L = 10k$, $V_O = 20$ Vp-p, BW = 20 Hz–20 kHz
- Low 1/f noise corner   50 Hz
- Fast settling time to 0.01% $2\,\mu s$

3

Typical Connection

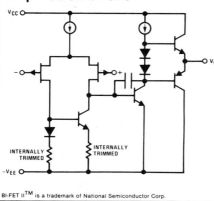

Simplified Schematic

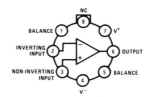

Ordering Information

LF411XYZ

X indicates electrical grade

Y indicates temperature range
"M" for military,
"C" for commercial

Z indicates package type
"H" or "N"

Connection Diagrams

**LF411AMH/LF411MH, LF411ACH/LF411CH
Metal Can Package**

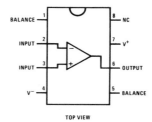

TOP VIEW

Note: Pin 4 connected to case.

**Order Number LF411AMH, LF411MH, LF411ACH
or LF411CH
See NS Package H08B**

**LF411ACN, LF411CN
Dual-In-Line Package**

TOP VIEW

**Order Number LF411ACN or LF411CN
See NS Package N08A**

BI-FET II™ is a trademark of National Semiconductor Corp.

3-53

Reprinted with Permission of National Semiconductor Corp.

LF411A/LF411

Absolute Maximum Ratings

	LF411A	LF411			H Package	N Package
Supply Voltage	± 22V	± 18V		Power Dissipation (Note 2)	670 mW	500 mW
Differential Input Voltage	± 38V	± 30V		T_j max	150°C	115°C
Input Voltage Range (Note 1)	± 19V	± 15V		θ_{jA}	150°C/W	160°C/W
Output Short Circuit Duration	Continuous	Continuous		Operating Temperature Range	(Note 3)	(Note 3)
				Storage Temperature Range	$-65°C \leq T_A \leq 150°C$	$-65°C \leq T_A \leq 150°C$
				Lead Temperature (Soldering, 10 seconds)	300°C	300°C

DC Electrical Characteristics (Note 4)

Symbol	Parameter	Conditions		LF411A			LF411			Units
				Min	Typ	Max	Min	Typ	Max	
V_{OS}	Input Offset Voltage	$R_S = 10$ kΩ, $T_A = 25°C$			0.3	0.5		0.8	2.0	mV
$\Delta V_{OS}/\Delta T$	Average TC of Input Offset Voltage	$R_S = 10$ kΩ (Note 5)			7	10		7	20 (Note 5)	$\mu V/°C$
I_{OS}	Input Offset Current	$V_S = \pm 15V$ Notes 4 and 6	$T_j = 25°C$		25	100		25	100	pA
			$T_j = 70°C$			2			2	nA
			$T_j = 125°C$			25			25	nA
I_B	Input Bias Current	$V_S = \pm 15V$ Notes 4 and 6	$T_j = 25°C$		50	200		50	200	pA
			$T_j = 70°C$			4			4	nA
			$T_j = 125°C$			50			50	nA
R_{IN}	Input Resistance	$T_j = 25°C$			10^{12}			10^{12}		Ω
A_{VOL}	Large Signal Voltage Gain	$V_S = \pm 15V$, $V_O = \pm 10V$, $R_L = 2k$, $T_A = 25°C$		50	200		25	200		V/mV
		Over Temperature		25	200		15	200		V/mV
V_O	Output Voltage Swing	$V_S = \pm 15V$, $R_L = 10k$		± 12	± 13.5		± 12	± 13.5		V
V_{CM}	Input Common-Mode Voltage Range			± 16	+ 19.5		± 11	+ 14.5		V
					− 16.5			− 11.5		V
CMRR	Common-Mode Rejection Ratio	$R_S \leq 10k$		80	100		70	100		dB
PSRR	Supply Voltage Rejection Ratio	(Note 7)		80	100		70	100		dB
I_S	Supply Current				1.8	2.8		1.8	3.4	mA

AC Electrical Characteristics (Note 4)

Symbol	Parameter	Conditions	LF411A			LF411			Units
			Min	Typ	Max	Min	Typ	Max	
SR	Slew Rate	$V_S = \pm 15V$, $T_A = 25°C$	10	15		8	15		V/μs
GBW	Gain-Bandwidth Product	$V_S = \pm 15V$, $T_A = 25°C$	3	4		2.7	4		MHz
e_n	Equivalent Input Noise Voltage	$T_A = 25°C$, $R_S = 100\Omega$, $f = 1$ kHz		25			25		nV/$\sqrt{Hz}$
i_n	Equivalent Input Noise Current	$T_A = 25°C$, $f = 1$ kHz		0.01			0.01		pA/$\sqrt{Hz}$

3-54

Reprinted with Permission of National Semiconductor Corp.

FAIRCHILD
A Schlumberger Company

µA709
High Performance
Operational Amplifier

Linear Division Operational Amplifiers

Description

The µA709 is a monolithic high gain operational amplifier constructed using the Fairchild Planar Epitaxial process. It features low offset, high input impedance, large input common mode range, high output swing under load, and low power consumption. The device displays exceptional temperature stability and will operate over a wide range of supply voltages with little performance degradation. The amplifier is intended for use in DC servo systems, high impedance analog computers, low level instrumentation applications, and for the generation of special linear and nonlinear transfer functions.

Connection Diagram
8-Lead DIP and SO-8 Package
(Top View)

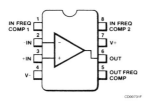

Order Information

Device Code	Package Code	Package Description
µA709TC	9T	Molded DIP
µA709SC	KC	Molded Surface Mount

Connection Diagram
8-Lead Metal Package
(Top View)

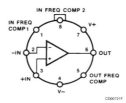

Lead 4 connected to case

Order Information

Device Code	Package Code	Package Description
µA709AHM	5W	Metal
µA709HM	5W	Metal
µA709HC	5W	Metal

Connection Diagram
14-Lead DIP
(Top View)

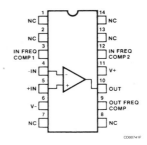

Order Information

Device Code	Package Code	Package Description
µA709PC	9A	Molded DIP

7-58

Copyright Fairchild Semiconductor Corporation. Used by Permission.

μA709

Absolute Maximum Ratings

Storage Temperature Range
Metal Can   −65°C to +175°C
Molded DIP and SO-8   −65°C to +150°C
Operating Temperature Range
Extended (μA709AM, μA709M)   −55°C to +125°C
Commercial (μA709C)   0°C to +70°C
Lead Temperature
Metal Can (soldering, 60 s)   300°C
Molded DIP and SO-8
   (soldering, 10s)   265°C

Internal Power Dissipation[1, 2]
8L-Metal Can   1.00 W
8L-Molded DIP   0.93 W
SO-8   0.81 W
14L-Molded DIP   1.04 W
Supply Voltage   ± 18 V
Differential Input Voltage   ± 5.0 V
Input Voltage   ± 10 V
Output Short Circuit Duration   5.0 s

Notes
1. $T_{J\ Max}$ = 150°C for the Molded DIP and SO-8, and 175°C for the Metal Can.
2. Ratings apply to ambient temperature at 25°C. Above this temperature, derate the 8L-Metal Can at 6.7 mW/°C, the 8L-Molded DIP at 7.5 mW/°C, the SO-8 at 6.5 mW/°C, and the 14L-Molded DIP at 8.3 mW/°C.

Equivalent Circuit

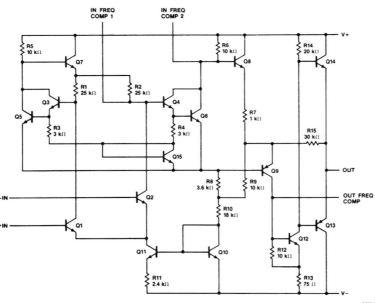

μA709

μA709A and μA709
Electrical Characteristics $T_A = 25°C$, ± 9.0 V $\leqslant V_{CC} \leqslant \pm 15$ V, unless otherwise specified.

Symbol	Characteristic		Condition	μA709A			μA709			Unit
				Min	Typ	Max	Min	Typ	Max	
V_{IO}	Input Offset Voltage		$R_S \leqslant 10$ kΩ		0.6	2.0		1.0	5.0	mV
I_{IO}	Input Offset Current				10	50		50	200	nA
I_{IB}	Input Bias Current				100	200		200	500	nA
Z_I	Input Impedance			350	700		150	400		kΩ
I_{CC}	Supply Current		$V_{CC} = \pm 15$ V		2.5	3.6		2.7	5.5	mA
P_c	Power Consumption		$V_{CC} = \pm 15$ V		75	108		80	165	mW
TR	Transient Response	Rise time	$V_{CC} = \pm 15$ V $V_I = 20$ mV $R_L = 2.0$ kΩ C1 = 5.0 nF $A_V = 1.0$		0.3	1.5		0.3	1.0	μs
		Overshoot	R2 = 50 Ω $C_L \leqslant 100$ pF R1 = 1.5 kΩ C2 = 200 pF $A_V = 1.0$		10	30		10	30	%

The following specifications apply over the range of −55°C to +125°C for the μA709A and μA709.

Symbol	Characteristic	Condition	μA709A			μA709			Unit
			Min	Typ	Max	Min	Typ	Max	
V_{IO}	Input Offset Voltage	$R_S \leqslant 10$ kΩ			3.0			6.0	mV
$\Delta V_{IO}/\Delta T$	Input Offset Voltage Temperature Sensitivity	$R_S = 50$ Ω		1.8	10		3.0		μV/°C
		$R_S \leqslant 10$ kΩ		4.8	25		6.0		
I_{IO}	Input Offset Current	$T_A = +125°C$		3.5	50		20	200	nA
		$T_A = -55°C$		40	250		100	500	
$\Delta I_{IO}/\Delta T$	Input Offset Current Temperature Sensitivity	$T_A = +25°C$ to +125°C		0.08	0.5				nA/°C
		$T_A = +25°C$ to −55°C		0.45	2.8				
I_{IB}	Input Bias Current	$T_A = -55°C$		300	600		500	1500	nA
$\Delta I_{IB}/\Delta T$	Input Bias Current Temperature Sensitivity	$T_A = +125°C$		2.1	3.0				nA/°C
		$T_A = -55°C$		2.7	4.5				
Z_I	Input Impedance	$T_A = -55°C$	85	170		40	100		kΩ
CMR	Common Mode Rejection	$R_S \leqslant 10$ kΩ	80	110		70	90		db
V_{IR}	Input Voltage Range	$V_{CC} = \pm 15$ V	± 8.0	± 10		± 8.0	± 10		V
PSRR	Power Supply Rejection Ratio	$R_S \leqslant 10$ kΩ		40	100		50	150	μV/V
A_{VS}	Large Signal Voltage Gain	$V_{CC} = \pm 15$ V $R_L \geqslant 2.0$ kΩ $V_O = \pm 10$ V	25		70	25	45	70	V/mV
V_{OP}	Output Voltage Swing	$V_{CC} = \pm 15$ V $R_L = 10$ kΩ	± 12	± 14		± 12	± 14		V
		$V_{CC} = \pm 15$ V $R_L = 2.0$ kΩ	± 10	± 13		± 10	± 13		

μA709

7

μA709A and μA709 (Cont.)
Electrical Characteristics $T_A = 25°C$, ± 9.0 V $\leqslant V_{CC} \leqslant \pm 15$ V, unless otherwise specified.

Symbol	Characteristic	Condition	μA709A			μA709			Unit
			Min	Typ	Max	Min	Typ	Max	
I_{CC}	Supply Current	$T_A = \pm 125°C$		2.1	3.0				mA
		$T_A = -55°C$		2.7	4.5				

μA709C
Electrical Characteristics $T_A = 25°C$, $V_{CC} = \pm 15$ V, unless otherwise specified.

Symbol	Characteristic		Condition	μA709C			Unit
				Min	Typ	Max	
V_{IO}	Input Offset Voltage		$R_S \leqslant 10$ kΩ		2.0	7.5	mV
I_{IO}	Input Offset Current				100	500	nA
I_{IB}	Input Bias Current				300	1500	nA
Z_I	Input Impedance			50	250		kΩ
I_{CC}	Supply Current		$V_{CC} = \pm 15$ V		2.7	6.66	mA
P_c	Power Consumption		$V_{CC} = \pm 15$ V		80	200	mW
CMR	Common Mode Rejection		$R_S \leqslant 10$ kΩ	65	90		dB
V_{IR}	Input Voltage Range		$V_{CC} = \pm 15$ V	± 8.0	± 10		V
PSRR	Power Supply Rejection Ratio		$R_S \leqslant 10$ kΩ		50	200	μV/V
TR	Transient Response	Rise time	$V_{CC} = \pm 15$ V $V_I = 20$ mV $R_L = 2.0$ kΩ $C1 = 5.0$ nF $A_V = 1.0$		0.3		μs
		Overshoot	R2 = 50 Ω $C_L = 100$ pF R1 = 1.5 kΩ C2 = 200 pF $A_V = 1.0$		10		%

The following specifications apply over the range of 0°C to +70°C.

V_{IO}	Input Offset Voltage		$R_S \leqslant 10$ kΩ			10.0	mV
I_{IO}	Input Offset Current		$T_A = 0°C$			750	nA
I_{IB}	Input Bias Current		$T_A = 0°C$			2000	nA
Z_I	Input Impedance		$T_A = 0°C$	35	80		kΩ
A_{VS}	Large Signal Voltage Gain		$V_{CC} = \pm 15$ V $R_L \geqslant 2.0$ kΩ $V_O = \pm 10$ V	15	45		V/mV
V_{OP}	Output Voltage Swing		$V_{CC} = \pm 15$ V $R_L = 10$ kΩ	± 12	± 14		V
			$V_{CC} = \pm 15$ V $R_L = 2.0$ kΩ	± 10	± 13		V

μA709

Typical Performance Curves for μA709 and μA709C (Cont.)

**Voltage Gain vs
Supply Voltage (μA709C)**

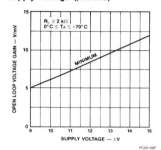

PC05100F

**Voltage Gain vs
Supply Voltage (μA709)**

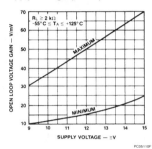

PC05110F

**Input Common Mode Voltage
Range vs Supply Voltage**

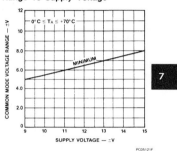

PC05121F

7

Frequency Compensation Curves For All Types

**Open Loop Frequency
Response For Various Values
Of Compensation**

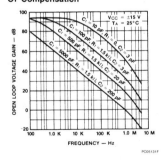

PC05131F

**Frequency Response For
Various Closed Loop Gains**

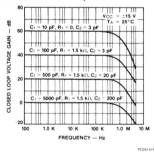

PC05141F

**Output Voltage Swing vs
Frequency For Various
Values Of Compensation**

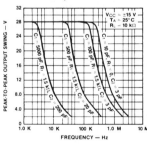

PC05151F

µA723
Precision Voltage Regulator

Linear Division Voltage Regulators

Description

The µA723 is a monolithic voltage regulator constructed using the Fairchild Planar Epitaxial process. The device consists of a temperature compensated reference amplifier, error amplifier, power series pass transistor and current-limit circuitry. Additional NPN or PNP pass elements may be used when output currents exceeding 150 mA are required. Provisions are made for adjustable current-limiting and remote shutdown. In addition to the above, the device features low standby current drain, low temperature drift and high ripple rejection. The µA723 is intended for use with positive or negative supplies as a series, shunt, switching or floating regulator. Applications include laboratory power supplies, isolation regulators for low level data amplifiers, logic card regulators, small instrument power supplies, airborne systems and other power supplies for digital and linear circuits.

- **Positive Or Negative Supply Operation**
- **Series, Shunt, Switching Or Floating Operation**
- **0.01% Line And Load Regulation**
- **Output Voltage Adjustable From 2 V To 37 V**
- **Output Current To 150 mA Without External Pass Transistor**

Absolute Maximum Ratings

Storage Temperature Range	
Ceramic DIP/Metal Can	−65°C to +175°C
Molded DIP/SO Package	−55°C to +150°C
Operating Temperature Range	
Extended (µA723M)	−55°C to +125°C
Commercial (µA723C)	0°C to +70°C
Lead Temperature	
Ceramic DIP/Metal Can	
(soldering, 60 s)	300°C
Molded DIP/SO-14 (soldering, 10 s)	265°C
Internal Power Dissipation[1,2]	
10L-Metal Can	1.07 W
14L-Ceramic DIP	1.36 W
14L-Molded DIP	1.04 W
SO-14	0.93 W
Pulse Voltage from V+ to V−,	
(50 ms) (µA723M)	50 V
Continuous Voltage from V+ to V−	40 V
Input/Output Voltage Differential	40 V
Differential Input Voltage	±5.0 V
Voltage Between Non-Inverting	
Input and V−	8.0 V
Current from V_Z	25 mA
Current from V_{REF}	15 mA

Notes

1. $T_{J\ Max} = 150°C$ for the Molded DIP, and 175°C for the Metal Can and Ceramic DIP.
2. Ratings supply to ambient temperature at 25°C. Above this temperature, derate the 10L-Metal Can at 7.1 mW/°C, the 14L-Ceramic DIP at 9.1 mW/°C, the 14L-Molded DIP at 8.3 mW/°C, and the SO-14 at 7.5 mW/°C.

Connection Diagram
10-Lead Metal Package
(Top View)

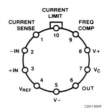

Lead 5 connected to case.

Order Information

Device Code	Package Code	Package Description
µA723HM	5X	Metal
µA723HC	5X	Metal

Connection Diagram
14-Lead DIP and SO-14 Package
(Top View)

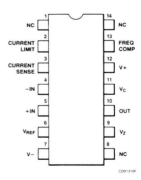

Order Information

Device Code	Package Code	Package Description
µA723DM	6A	Ceramic DIP
µA723DC	6A	Ceramic DIP
µA723PC	9A	Molded DIP
µA723SC	KD	Molded Surface Mount

6

μA723

Block Diagram

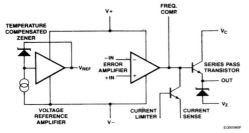

Equivalent Circuit

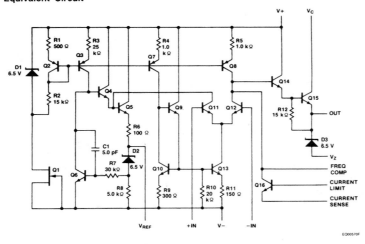

μA723

μA723C
Electrical Characteristics $T_A = 25°C$, $V_I = V+ = V_C = 12$ V, $V- = 0$, $V_O = 5$ V, $I_L = 1$ mA, $R_{SC} = 0$, $C1 = 100$ pF, $C_{REF} = 0$, unless otherwise specified.

Symbol	Characteristic[1]	Condition	Min	Typ	Max	Unit
$V_{R\ LINE}$	Line Regulation	$V_I = 12$ V to $V_I = 15$ V		0.01	0.1	%V_O
		$V_I = 12$ V to $V_I = 40$ V		0.1	0.5	
		$0°C \leqslant T_A \leqslant 70°C$, $V_I = 12$ V to $V_I = 15$ V			0.3	
$V_{R\ LOAD}$	Load Regulation	$I_L = 1.0$ mA to $I_L = 50$ mA		0.03	0.2	%V_O
		$0°C \leqslant T_A \leqslant 70°C$, $I_L = 1.0$ mA to $I_L = 50$ mA			0.6	
$\Delta V_I/\Delta V_O$	Ripple Rejection	$f = 50$ Hz to 10 kHz		74		dB
		$f = 50$ Hz to 10 kHz, $C_{REF} = 5$ μF		86		
$\Delta V_O/\Delta T$	Average Temperature Coefficient of Output Voltage	$0°C \leqslant T_A \leqslant 70°C$		0.003	0.015	%/°C
I_{OS}	Output Short Circuit Current	$R_{SC} = 10$ Ω, $V_O = 0$		65		mA
V_{REF}	Reference Voltage	$I_{REF} = 0.1$ mA	6.80	7.15	7.50	V
V_{REF}(Load)	Reference Voltage Change With Load	$I_{REF} = 0.1$ mA to 5 mA			20	mV
N_O	Noise	BW = 100 Hz to 10 kHz, $C_{REF} = 0$		20		μV_{rms}
		BW = 100 Hz to 10 kHz, $C_{REF} = 5$ μF		2.0		
S	Long Term Stability	$T_J = T_{J\ Max}$ | $T_A = 25°C$ For End Point Measurement		0.1		%/1000 hrs
I_{SCD}	Standby Current Drain	$I_L = 0$, $V_I = 30$ V		2.3	4.0	mA
V_{IR}	Input Voltage Range		9.5		40	V
V_{OR}	Output Voltage Range		2.0		37	V
$V_I - V_O$	Input/Output Voltage Differential		3.0		38	V

Note
1. Divider impedance as seen by error amplifier $\leqslant 10$ kΩ connected as shown in *Figure 1*. Line and load regulation specifications are given for the condition of constant chip temperature. Temperature drifts must be taken into account separately for high dissipation conditions.

A Schlumberger Company

µA741
Operational Amplifier

Linear Division Operational Amplifiers

Description

The µA741 is a high performance monolithic operational amplifier constructed using the Fairchild Planar Epitaxial process. It is intended for a wide range of analog applications. High common mode voltage range and absence of latch up tendencies make the µA741 ideal for use as a voltage follower. The high gain and wide range of operating voltage provide superior performance in integrator, summing amplifier, and general feedback applications.

- **No Frequency Compensation Required**
- **Short Circuit Protection**
- **Offset Voltage Null Capability**
- **Large Common Mode And Differential Voltage Ranges**
- **Low Power Consumption**
- **No Latch Up**

Absolute Maximum Ratings

Storage Temperature Range	
Metal Can and Ceramic DIP	−65°C to +175°C
Molded DIP and SO-8	−65°C to +150°C
Operating Temperature Range	
Extended (µA741AM, µA741M)	−55°C to +125°C
Commercial (µA741EC, µA741C)	0°C to +70°C
Lead Temperature	
Metal Can and Ceramic DIP	
(soldering, 60 s)	300°C
Molded DIP and SO-8	
(soldering, 10 s)	265°C
Internal Power Dissipation[1, 2]	
8L-Metal Can	1.00 W
8L-Molded DIP	0.93 W
8L-Ceramic DIP	1.30 W
SO-8	0.81 W
Supply Voltage	
µA741A, µA741, µA741E	± 22 V
µA741C	± 18 V
Differential Input Voltage	± 30 V
Input Voltage[3]	± 15 V
Output Short Circuit Duration[4]	Indefinite

Notes

1. $T_{J\ Max}$ = 150°C for the Molded DIP and SO-8, and 175°C for the Metal Can and Ceramic DIP.
2. Ratings apply to ambient temperature at 25°C. Above this temperature, derate the 8L-Metal Can at 6.7 mW/°C, the 8L-Molded DIP at 7.5 mW/°C, the 8L-Ceramic DIP at 8.7 mW/°C, and the SO-8 at 6.5 mW/°C.
3. For supply voltages less than ± 15 V, the absolute maximum input voltage is equal to the supply voltage.
4. Short circuit may be be to ground or either supply. Rating applies to 125°C case temperature or 75°C ambient temperature.

Connection Diagram
8-Lead Metal Package
(Top View)

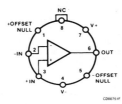

Lead 4 connected to case.

Order Information

Device Code	Package Code	Package Description
µA741HM	5W	Metal
µA741HC	5W	Metal
µA741AHM	5W	Metal
µA741EHC	5W	Metal

Connection Diagram
8-Lead DIP and SO-8 Package
(Top View)

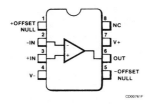

Order Information

Device Code	Package Code	Package Description
µA741RM	6T	Ceramic DIP
µA741RC	6T	Ceramic DIP
µA741SC	KC	Molded Surface Mount
µA741TC	9T	Molded DIP
µA741ARM	6T	Ceramic DIP
µA741ERC	6T	Ceramic DIP
µA741ETC	9T	Molded DIP

μA741

μA741 and μA741C

Electrical Characteristics $T_A = 25°C$, $V_{CC} = \pm 15$ V, unless otherwise specified.

Symbol	Characteristic		Condition	μA741			μA741C			Unit
				Min	Typ	Max	Min	Typ	Max	
V_{IO}	Input Offset Voltage		$R_S \leqslant 10$ kΩ		1.0	5.0		2.0	6.0	mV
$V_{IO\ adj}$	Input Offset Voltage Adjustment Range				± 15			± 15		mV
I_{IO}	Input Offset Current				20	200		20	200	nA
I_{IB}	Input Bias Current				80	500		80	500	nA
Z_I	Input Impedance			0.3	2.0		0.3	2.0		MΩ
I_{CC}	Supply Current				1.7	2.8		1.7	2.8	mA
P_c	Power Consumption				50	85		50	85	mW
CMR	Common Mode Rejection			70			70	90		dB
V_{IR}	Input Voltage Range			± 12	± 13		± 12	± 13		V
PSRR	Power Supply Rejection Ratio				30	150				μV/V
			$V_{CC} = \pm 5.0$ V to ± 18 V					30	150	
I_{OS}	Output Short Circuit Current				25			25		mA
A_{VS}	Large Signal Voltage Gain		$R_L \geqslant 2.0$ kΩ, $V_O = \pm 10$ V	50	200		20	200		V/mV
V_{OP}	Output Voltage Swing		$R_L = 10$ kΩ	± 12			± 12	± 14		V
			$R_L = 2.0$ kΩ	± 10			± 10	± 13		
TR	Transient Response	Rise time	$V_I = 20$ mV, $R_L = 2.0$ kΩ, $C_L = 100$ pF, $A_V = 1.0$		0.3			0.3		μs
		Overshoot			5.0			5.0		%
BW	Bandwidth				1.0			1.0		MHz
SR	Slew Rate		$R_L \geqslant 2.0$ kΩ, $A_V = 1.0$		0.5			0.5		V/μs

Copyright Fairchild Semiconductor Corporation. Used by Permission.

μA741

Typical Performance Curves (Cont.)

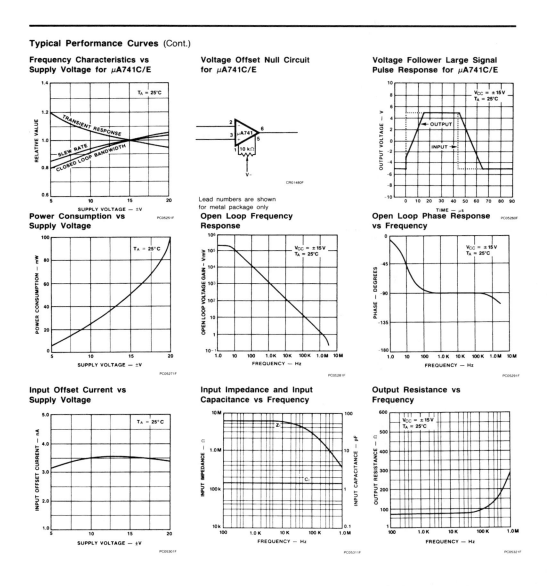

μA741

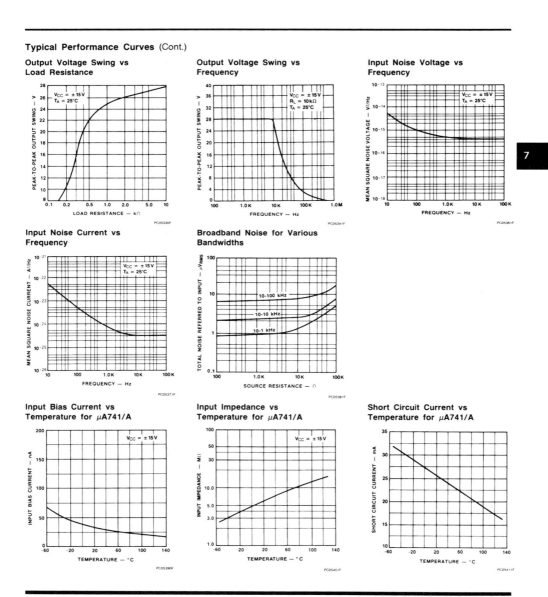

Typical Performance Curves (Cont.)

ADC0801, ADC0802, ADC0803, ADC0804, ADC0805

![National Semiconductor logo]

A to D, D to A

ADC0801, ADC0802, ADC0803, ADC0804, ADC0805 8-Bit μP Compatible A/D Converters

General Description

The ADC0801, ADC0802, ADC0803, ADC0804 and ADC0805 are CMOS 8-bit successive approximation A/D converters which use a differential potentiometric ladder—similar to the 256R products. These converters are designed to allow operation with the NSC800 and INS8080A derivative control bus, and TRI-STATE® output latches directly drive the data bus. These A/Ds appear like memory locations or I/O ports to the micro-processor and no interfacing logic is needed.

A new differential analog voltage input allows increasing the common-mode rejection and offsetting the analog zero input voltage value. In addition, the voltage refer-ence input can be adjusted to allow encoding any smaller analog voltage span to the full 8 bits of resolution.

Features

- Compatible with 8080 μP derivatives—no inter-facing logic needed — access time — 135 ns
- Easy interface to all microprocessors, or operates "stand alone"

- Differential analog voltage inputs
- Logic inputs and outputs meet both MOS and T^{2}L voltage level specifications
- Works with 2.5V (LM336) voltage reference
- On-chip clock generator
- 0V to 5V analog input voltage range with single 5V supply
- No zero adjust required
- 0.3″ standard width 20-pin DIP package
- Operates ratiometrically or with 5 V_{DC}, 2.5 V_{DC}, or analog span adjusted voltage reference

Key Specifications

- Resolution   8 bits
- Total error   ±1/4 LSB, ±1/2 LSB and ±1 LSB
- Conversion time   100 μs

Typical Applications

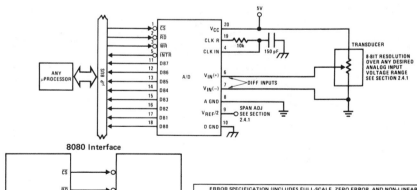

8080 Interface

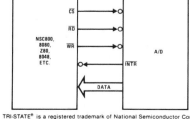

ERROR SPECIFICATION (INCLUDES FULL-SCALE, ZERO ERROR, AND NON-LINEARITY)			
PART NUMBER	FULL-SCALE ADJUSTED	V$_{REF}$/2 = 2.500 V$_{DC}$ (NO ADJUSTMENTS)	V$_{REF}$/2 = NO CONNECTION (NO ADJUSTMENTS)
ADC0801	±1/4 LSB		
ADC0802		±1/2 LSB	
ADC0803	±1/2 LSB		
ADC0804		±1 LSB	
ADC0805			±1 LSB

TRI-STATE® is a registered trademark of National Semiconductor Corp.

Reprinted with Permission of National Semiconductor Corp.

ADC0801, ADC0802, ADC0803, ADC0804, ADC0805

Absolute Maximum Ratings (Notes 1 and 2)

Supply Voltage (V_{CC}) (Note 3)	6.5V
Voltage	
Logic Control Inputs	−0.3V to +18V
At Other Input and Outputs	−0.3V to (V_{CC} + 0.3V)
Storage Temperature Range	−65°C to +150°C
Package Dissipation at T_A = 25°C	875 mW
Lead Temperature (Soldering, 10 seconds)	300°C

Operating Ratings (Notes 1 and 2)

Temperature Range	$T_{MIN} \leq T_A \leq T_{MAX}$
ADC0801/02LD	−55°C $\leq T_A \leq$ +125°C
ADC0801/02/03/04LCD	−40°C $\leq T_A \leq$ +85°C
ADC0801/02/03/05LCN	−40°C $\leq T_A \leq$ +85°C
ADC0804LCN	0°C $\leq T_A \leq$ +70°C
Range of V_{CC}	4.5 V_{DC} to 6.3 V_{DC}

Electrical Characteristics

The following specifications apply for V_{CC} = 5 V_{DC}, $T_{MIN} \leq T_A \leq T_{MAX}$ and f_{CLK} = 640 kHz unless otherwise specified.

PARAMETER	CONDITIONS	MIN	TYP	MAX	UNITS
ADC0801:					
Total Adjusted Error	With Full-Scale Adj.			±1/4	LSB
(Note 8)	(See Section 2.5.2)				
ADC0802:					
Total Unadjusted Error	V_{REF}/2 = 2.500 V_{DC}			±1/2	LSB
(Note 8)					
ADC0803:					
Total Adjusted Error	With Full-Scale Adj.			±1/2	LSB
(Note 8)	(See Section 2.5.2)				
ADC0804:					
Total Unadjusted Error	V_{REF}/2 = 2.500 V_{DC}			±1	LSB
(Note 8)					
ADC0805:					
Total Unadjusted Error	V_{REF}/2 − No Connection			±1	LSB
(Note 8)					
V_{REF}/2 Input Resistance (Pin 9)	ADC0801/02/03/05	2.5	8.0		kΩ
	ADC0804 (Note 9)	1.0	1.3		kΩ
Analog Input Voltage Range	(Note 4) V(+) or V(−)	Gnd−0.05		V_{CC}+0.05	V_{DC}
DC Common-Mode Error	Over Analog Input Voltage Range		±1/16	±1/8	LSB
Power Supply Sensitivity	V_{CC} = 5 V_{DC} ±10% Over Allowed V_{IN}(+) and V_{IN}(−) Voltage Range (Note 4)		±1/16	±1/8	LSB

AC Electrical Characteristics

The following specifications apply for V_{CC} = 5 V_{DC} and T_A = 25°C unless otherwise specified.

PARAMETER		CONDITIONS	MIN	TYP	MAX	UNITS
T_C	Conversion Time	f_{CLK} = 640 kHz (Note 6)	103		114	µs
T_C	Conversion Time	(Note 5, 6)	66		73	1/f_{CLK}
f_{CLK}	Clock Frequency	V_{CC} = 5V, (Note 5)	100	640	1460	kHz
	Clock Duty Cycle	(Note 5)	40		60	%
CR	Conversion Rate In Free-Running Mode	$\overline{INTR}$ tied to $\overline{WR}$ with $\overline{CS}$ = 0 V_{DC}, f_{CLK} = 640 kHz			8770	conv/s
$t_W(\overline{WR})L$	Width of $\overline{WR}$ Input (Start Pulse Width)	$\overline{CS}$ = 0 V_{DC} (Note 7)	100			ns
t_{ACC}	Access Time (Delay from Falling Edge of $\overline{RD}$ to Output Data Valid)	C_L = 100 pF		135	200	ns
t_{1H}, t_{0H}	TRI-STATE Control (Delay from Rising Edge of $\overline{RD}$ to Hi-Z State)	C_L = 10 pF, R_L = 10k (See TRI-STATE Test Circuits)		125	200	ns
t_{WI}, t_{RI}	Delay from Falling Edge of $\overline{WR}$ or $\overline{RD}$ to Reset of $\overline{INTR}$			300	450	ns
C_{IN}	Input Capacitance of Logic Control Inputs			5	7.5	pF
C_{OUT}	TRI-STATE Output Capacitance (Data Buffers)			5	7.5	pF

Reprinted with Permission of National Semiconductor Corp.

ADC0801, ADC0802, ADC0803, ADC0804, ADC0805

Electrical Characteristics

The following specifications apply for V_{CC} = 5 V_{DC} and $T_{MIN} \leq T_A \leq T_{MAX}$, unless otherwise specified.

PARAMETER		CONDITIONS	MIN	TYP	MAX	UNITS
CONTROL INPUTS [Note: CLK IN (Pin 4) is the input of a Schmitt trigger circuit and is therefore specified separately]						
V_{IN} (1)	Logical "1" Input Voltage (Except Pin 4 CLK IN)	V_{CC} = 5.25 V_{DC}	2.0		15	V_{DC}
V_{IN} (0)	Logical "0" Input Voltage (Except Pin 4 CLK IN)	V_{CC} = 4.75 V_{DC}			0.8	V_{DC}
I_{IN} (1)	Logical "1" Input Current (All Inputs)	V_{IN} = 5 V_{DC}		0.005	1	μA_{DC}
I_{IN} (0)	Logical "0" Input Current (All Inputs)	V_{IN} = 0 V_{DC}	−1	−0.005		μA_{DC}
CLOCK IN AND CLOCK R						
V_{T+}	CLK IN (Pin 4) Positive Going Threshold Voltage		2.7	3.1	3.5	V_{DC}
V_{T-}	CLK IN (Pin 4) Negative Going Threshold Voltage		1.5	1.8	2.1	V_{DC}
V_H	CLK IN (Pin 4) Hysteresis $(V_{T+}) - (V_{T-})$		0.6	1.3	2.0	V_{DC}
V_{OUT} (0)	Logical "0" CLK R Output Voltage	I_O = 360 μA V_{CC} = 4.75 V_{DC}			0.4	V_{DC}
V_{OUT} (1)	Logical "1" CLK R Output Voltage	I_O = −360 μA V_{CC} = 4.75 V_{DC}	2.4			V_{DC}
DATA OUTPUTS AND $\overline{INTR}$						
V_{OUT}(0)	Logical "0" Output Voltage Data Outputs	I_{OUT} = 1.6 mA, V_{CC} = 4.75 V_{DC}			0.4	V_{DC}
	$\overline{INTR}$ Output	I_{OUT} = 1.0 mA, V_{CC} = 4.75 V_{DC}			0.4	V_{DC}
V_{OUT} (1)	Logical "1" Output Voltage	I_O = −360 μA, V_{CC} = 4.75 V_{DC}	2.4			V_{DC}
V_{OUT} (1)	Logical "1" Output Voltage	I_O = −10 μA, V_{CC} = 4.75 V_{DC}	4.5			V_{DC}
I_{OUT}	TRI-STATE Disabled Output Leakage (All Data Buffers)	V_{OUT} = 0 V_{DC}	−3			μA_{DC}
		V_{OUT} = 5 V_{DC}			3	μA_{DC}
I_{SOURCE}		V_{OUT} Short to Gnd, T_A = 25°C	4.5	6		mA_{DC}
I_{SINK}		V_{OUT} Short to V_{CC}, T_A = 25°C	9.0	16		mA_{DC}
POWER SUPPLY						
I_{CC}	Supply Current (Includes Ladder Current)	f_{CLK} = 640 kHz, $V_{REF}/2$ = NC, T_A = 25°C and $\overline{CS}$ = "1"				
		ADC0801/02/03/05		1.1	1.8	mA
		ADC0804 (Note 9)		1.9	2.5	mA

Note 1: Absolute maximum ratings are those values beyond which the life of the device may be impaired.

Note 2: All voltages are measured with respect to Gnd, unless otherwise specified. The separate A Gnd point should always be wired to the D Gnd.

Note 3: A zener diode exists, internally, from V_{CC} to Gnd and has a typical breakdown voltage of 7 V_{DC}.

Note 4: For $V_{IN}(-) \geq V_{IN}(+)$ the digital output code will be 0000 0000. Two on-chip diodes are tied to each analog input (see block diagram) which will forward conduct for analog input voltages one diode drop below ground or one diode drop greater than the V_{CC} supply. Be careful, during testing at low V_{CC} levels (4.5V), as high level analog inputs (5V) can cause this input diode to conduct—especially at elevated temperatures, and cause errors for analog inputs near full-scale. The spec allows 50 mV forward bias of either diode. This means that as long as the analog V_{IN} does not exceed the supply voltage by more than 50 mV, the output code will be correct. To achieve an absolute 0 V_{DC} to 5 V_{DC} input voltage range will therefore require a minimum supply voltage of 4.950 V_{DC} over temperature variations, initial tolerance and loading.

Note 5: Accuracy is guaranteed at f_{CLK} = 640 kHz. At higher clock frequencies accuracy can degrade. For lower clock frequencies, the duty cycle limits can be extended so long as the minimum clock high time interval or minimum clock low time interval is no less than 275 ns.

Note 6: With an asynchronous start pulse, up to 8 clock periods may be required before the internal clock phases are proper to start the conversion process. The start request is latched, see *Figure 2* and section 2.0.

Note 7: The $\overline{CS}$ input is assumed to bracket the $\overline{WR}$ strobe input and therefore timing is dependent on the $\overline{WR}$ pulse width. An arbitrarily wide pulse width will hold the converter in a reset mode and the start of conversion is initiated by the low to high transition of the $\overline{WR}$ pulse (see timing diagrams).

Note 8: None of these A/Ds requires a zero adjust (see section 2.5.1). To obtain zero code at other analog input voltages see section 2.5 and *Figure 5*.

Note 9: For ADC0804LCD typical value of $V_{REF}/2$ input resistance is 8 kΩ and of I_{CC} is 1.1 mA.

Reprinted with Permission of National Semiconductor Corp.

ADC0801, ADC0802, ADC0803, ADC0804, ADC0805

Typical Performance Characteristics

Logic Input Threshold Voltage vs. Supply Voltage

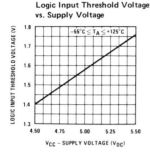

Delay From Falling Edge of RD to Output Data Valid vs. Load Capacitance

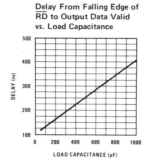

CLK IN Schmitt Trip Levels vs. Supply Voltage

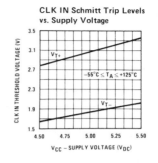

f_{CLK} vs. Clock Capacitor

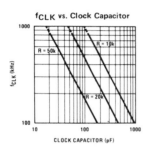

Full-Scale Error vs Conversion Time

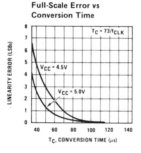

Effect of Unadjusted Offset Error vs. $V_{REF}/2$ Voltage

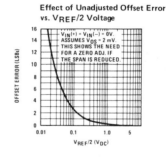

Output Current vs Temperature

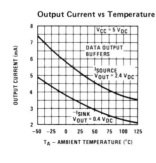

Power Supply Current vs Temperature (Note 9)

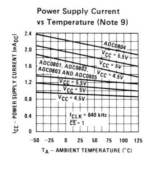

Linearity Error at Low $V_{REF}/2$ Voltages

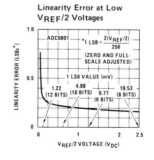

8

8-31

Reprinted with Permission of National Semiconductor Corp.

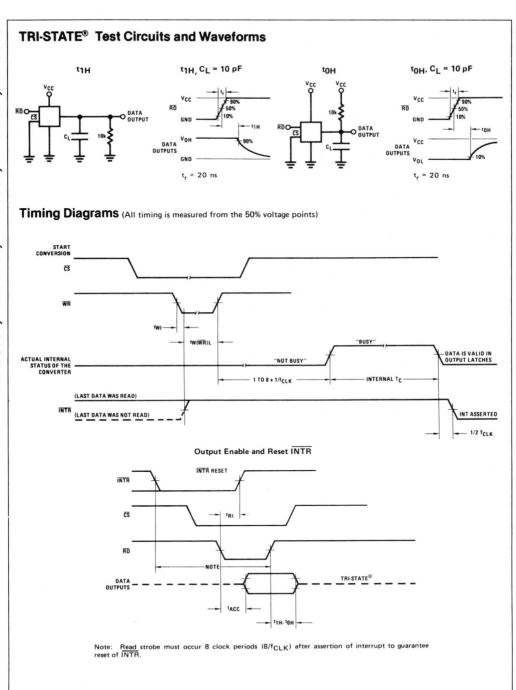

ADC0801, ADC0802, ADC0803, ADC0804, ADC0805

TRI-STATE® Test Circuits and Waveforms

t_{1H}

t_{1H}, C_L = 10 pF

t_r = 20 ns

t_{0H}

t_{0H}, C_L = 10 pF

t_r = 20 ns

Timing Diagrams (All timing is measured from the 50% voltage points)

Output Enable and Reset INTR

Note: Read strobe must occur 8 clock periods (8/f_{CLK}) after assertion of interrupt to guarantee reset of INTR.

8-32

Reprinted with Permission of National Semiconductor Corp.

A to D, D to A

National Semiconductor

MICRO-DAC™ DAC0830/0831/0832
8-Bit µP Compatible, Double-Buffered D to A Converters

General Description

The DAC0830 is an advanced CMOS/Si-Cr 8-bit multiplying DAC designed to interface directly with the 8080, 8048, 8085, Z-80, and other popular microprocessors. A deposited silicon-chromium R-2R resistor ladder network divides the reference current and provides the circuit with excellent temperature tracking characteristics (0.05% of Full Scale Range maximum linearity error over temperature). The circuit uses CMOS current switches and control logic to achieve low power consumption and low output leakage current errors. Special circuitry provides TTL logic input voltage level compatibility.

Double buffering allows these DACs to output a voltage corresponding to one digital word while holding the next digital word. This permits the simultaneous updating of any number of DACs.

The DAC0830 series are the 8-bit members of a family of microprocessor-compatible DAC's (MICRO-DAC's™). For applications demanding higher resolution, the DAC1000 series (10-bits) and the DAC1208 and DAC1230 (12-bits) are available alternatives.

Micro-Dac is a trademark of National Semiconductor Corp.

Features

- Double-buffered, single-buffered or flow-through digital data inputs
- Easy interchange and pin-compatible with 12-bit DAC1230 series
- Direct interface to all popular microprocessors
- Linearity specified with zero and full scale adjust only—NOT BEST STRAIGHT LINE FIT.
- Works with ±10V reference-full 4-quadrant multiplication
- Can be used in the voltage switching mode
- Logic inputs which meet TTL voltage level specs (1.4V logic threshold)
- Operates "STAND ALONE" (without µP) if desired

Key Specifications

- Current settling time   1 µs
- Resolution   8-bits
- Linearity   8, 9, or 10 bits
  (guaranteed over temp.)
- Gain Tempco   0.0002% FS/°C
- Low power dissipation   20 mW
- Single power supply   5 to 15 V$_{DC}$

Typical Application

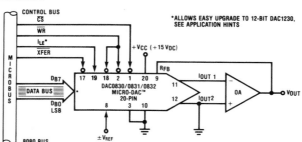

Pin Configuration Top View

$\overline{CS}$	1	20 — V$_{CC}$
$\overline{WR}_1$	2	19 — I$_{LE}$ (BYTE1/$\overline{BYTE2}$)†
AGND	3	18 — $\overline{WR}_2$
DI$_3$	4	17 — $\overline{XFER}$
DI$_2$	5	16 — DI$_4$
DI$_1$	6	15 — DI$_5$
DI$_0$ (LSB)	7	14 — DI$_6$
V$_{REF}$	8	13 — DI$_7$ (MSB)
R$_{fb}$	9	12 — I$_{OUT2}$
DGND	10	11 — I$_{OUT1}$

DAC0830
DAC0831
DAC0832

†THIS IS NECESSARY FOR THE 12-BIT DAC1230 SERIES TO PERMIT INTERCHANGING FROM AN 8-BIT TO A 12-BIT DAC WITH NO PC BOARD CHANGES AND NO SOFTWARE CHANGES, SEE APPLICATIONS SECTION.

8-133

8

Reprinted with Permission of National Semiconductor Corp.

DAC0830/DAC0831/DAC0832

Absolute Maximum Ratings (Notes 1 and 2)

Supply Voltage (V_{CC})	17 V_{DC}
Voltage at any digital input	V_{CC} to GND
Voltage at V_{REF} input	±25V
Storage temperature range	−65°C to +150°C
Package dissipation at $T_A = 25$°C (Note 3)	500 mW
DC voltage applied to I_{OUT1} or I_{OUT2} (Note 4)	−100 mV to V_{CC}
Lead temperature (soldering, 10 seconds)	300°C

Operating Ratings

Temperature Range

Part numbers with 'LCN' suffix	0°C to 70°C
Part numbers with 'LCD' suffix	−40°C to +85°C
Part numbers with 'LD' Suffix	−55°C to +125°C
Voltage at any digital input	V_{CC} TO GND

General Electrical Characteristics $T_A = 25$°C, $V_{REF} = 10.000$ V_{DC} unless otherwise noted

Parameter	Conditions	See Note	$V_{CC} = 12V_{DC} \pm 5\%$ to $15V_{DC} \pm 5\%$			$V_{CC} = 5V_{DC} \pm 5\%$			Units
			Min.	Typ.	Max.	Min.	Typ.	Max.	
Resolution			8	8	8	8	8	8	bits
Linearity Error	Zero and full scale adjusted	4,7							
	$T_{MIN} < T_A < T_{MAX}$	6							
	$-10V \leqslant V_{REF} \leqslant +10V$	5							
	DAC0830				0.05			0.05	% of FSR
	DAC0831				0.1			0.1	% of FSR
	DAC0832				0.2			0.2	% of FSR
Differential Nonlinearity	Zero and full scale adjusted	4,7							
	$T_{MIN} < T_A < T_{MAX}$	6							
	$-10V \leqslant V_{REF} \leqslant +10V$	5							
	DAC0830				0.1			0.1	% of FSR
	DAC0831				0.2			0.2	% of FSR
	DAC0832				0.4			0.4	% of FSR
Monotonicity	$T_{MIN} < T_A < T_{MAX}$	4,6							
	$-10V \leqslant V_{REF} \leqslant +10V$	5	8	8	8	8	8	8	bits
Gain Error	Using internal R_{fb}								
	$-10V \leqslant V_{REF} \leqslant +10V$	5	−1.0	±0.2	1.0	−1.0	±0.2	1.0	% of FS
Gain Error Tempco	$T_{MIN} < T_A < T_{MAX}$	6							
	Using internal R_{fb}	10		0.0002	0.0006		0.0002	0.0006	% of FS/°C
Power Supply Rejection	All digital inputs latched high								
	$V_{CC} = 14.5V$ to $15.5V$			0.0002					% FSR/V
	11.5V to 12.5V			0.0006					% FSR/V
	4.5V to 5.5V						0.0130		%FSR/V
Reference Input Resistance			10	15	20	10	15	20	kΩ
Output Feedthrough Error	$V_{REF} = 20V_{P-P}$, $f = 100$ kHz All data inputs latched low								
	D Package	9		3			3		mV_{P-P}
	N Package			3			3		mV_{P-P}
Output Capacitance I_{OUT1} I_{OUT2}	All data inputs latched low			70 200			70 200		pF pF
I_{OUT1} I_{OUT2}	All data inputs latched high			200 70			200 70		pF pF
Supply Current Drain	$T_{MIN} \leqslant T_A \leqslant T_{MAX}$	6		1.2	2.0		1.2	2.0	mA

8-134

Reprinted with Permission of National Semiconductor Corp.

General Electrical Characteristics $T_A = 25°C$, $V_{REF} = 10.000 V_{DC}$ unless otherwise noted

Parameter		Conditions	See Note	$V_{CC} = 12 V_{DC} \pm 5\%$ to $15 V_{DC} \pm 5\%$			$V_{CC} = 5 V_{DC} \pm 5\%$			Units
				Min.	Typ.	Max.	Min.	Typ.	Max.	
Output Leakage Current	I_{OUT1}	$T_{MIN} \leq T_A \leq T_{MAX}$ All data inputs latched low	6 11			100			100	nA
	I_{OUT2}	All data inputs latched high				100			100	nA
Digital Input Voltages		$T_{MIN} \leq T_A \leq T_{MAX}$ Low Level	6							
		LD suffix				0.8			0.6	V_{DC}
		Parts with LCD or LCN suffix				0.8			0.8	V_{DC}
		High Level-All Parts		2.0			2.0			V_{DC}
Digital Input Currents		$T_{MIN} \leq T_A \leq T_{MAX}$	6							
		Digital inputs < 0.8V			-50	-200		-50	-200	μA_{DC}
		Digital inputs > 2.0V			0.1	$+10$		0.1	$+10$	μA_{DC}
Current Settling Time	t_S	$V_{IL} = 0V$, $V_{IH} = 5V$			1.0			1.0		μs
Write and XFER Pulse Width	t_W	$V_{IL} = 0V$, $V_{IH} = 5V$, $T_A = 25°C$	8	320	60		320	250		ns
		$T_{MIN} \leq T_A \leq T_{MAX}$	10	320	100		500	350		ns
Data Set Up Time	t_{DS}	$V_{IL} = 0V$, $V_{IH} = 5V$, $T_A = 25°C$	10	320	60		320	250		ns
		$T_{MIN} \leq T_A \leq T_{MAX}$		320	100		500	350		ns
Data Hold Time	t_{DH}	$V_{IL} = 0V$, $V_{IH} = 5V$ $T_A = 25°C$	10	90	50		300	200		ns
		$T_{MIN} \leq T_A \leq T_{MAX}$		90	60		350	260		ns
Control Set Up Time	t_{CS}	$V_{IL} = 0V$, $V_{IL} = 5V$, $T_A = 25°C$	10	320	60		320	250		ns
		$T_{MIN} \leq T_A \leq T_{MAX}$		320	100		500	350		ns
Control Hold Time	t_{CH}	$V_{IL} = 0V$, $V_{IH} = 5V$, $T_A = 25°C$	10	10			10			ns
		$T_{MIN} \leq T_A \leq T_{MAX}$		10			10			ns

Note 1: *"Absolute Maximum Ratings"* are those values beyond which the safety of the device cannot be guaranteed. These specifications are not meant to imply that the devices should be operated at these *"Absolute Maximum"* limits.

Note 2: All voltages are measured with respect to GND, unless otherwise specified.

Note 3: This 500 mW specification applies for all packages. The low intrinsic power dissipation of this part (and the fact that there is no way to significantly modify the power dissipation) removes concern for heat sinking.

Note 4: For current switching applications, both I_{OUT1} and I_{OUT2} must go to ground or the "Virtual Ground" of an operational amplifier. The linearity error is degraded by approximately $V_{OS} \div V_{REF}$. For example, if $V_{REF} = 10V$ then a 1 mV offset, V_{OS}, on I_{OUT1} or I_{OUT2} will introduce an additional 0.01% linearity error.

Note 5: Guaranteed at $V_{REF} = \pm 10 V_{DC}$ and $V_{REF} = \pm 1 V_{DC}$.

Note 6: $T_{MIN} = 0°C$ and $T_{MAX} = 70°C$ for "LCN" suffix parts.
$T_{MIN} = -40°C$ and $T_{MAX} = 85°C$ for "LCD" suffix parts.
$T_{MIN} = -55°C$ and $T_{MAX} = 125°C$ for "LD" suffix parts.

Note 7: The unit "FSR" stands for "Full Scale Range." "Linearity Error" and "Power Supply Rejection" specs are based on this unit to eliminate dependence on a particular V_{REF} value and to indicate the true performance of the part. The "Linearity Error" specification of the DAC0830 is "0.05% of FSR (MAX)." This guarantees that after performing a zero and full scale adjustment (See Sections 2.5 and 2.6), the plot of the 256 analog voltage outputs will each be within 0.05% $\times V_{REF}$ of a straight line which passes through zero and full scale.

Note 8: This specification implies that all parts are guaranteed to operate with a write pulse or transfer pulse width (t_W) of 320 ns. A typical part will operate with t_W of only 100 ns. The entire write pulse must occur within the valid data interval for the specified t_W, t_{DS}, t_{DH}, and t_S to apply.

Note 9: To achieve this low feedthrough in the D package, the user must ground the metal lid. If the lid is left floating, the feedthrough is typically 6 mV.

Note 10: Guaranteed by design but not tested.

Note 11: A 100 nA leakage current with $R_{fb} = 20k$ and $V_{REF} = 10V$ corresponds to a zero error of $(100 \times 10^{-9} \times 20 \times 10^3) \times 100/10$ which is 0.02% of FS.

8

Reprinted with Permission of National Semiconductor Corp.

DAC0830/DAC0831/DAC0832

Switching Waveforms:

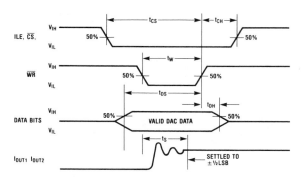

Definition of Package Pinouts

Control Signals (All control signals level actuated)

$\overline{CS}$: **Chip Select** (active low). The $\overline{CS}$ in combination with ILE will enable $\overline{WR_1}$.

ILE: Input Latch Enable (active high). The ILE in combination with $\overline{CS}$ enables $\overline{WR_1}$.

$\overline{WR_1}$: **Write 1.** The active low $\overline{WR_1}$ is used to load the digital input data bits (DI) into the input latch. The data in the input latch is latched when $\overline{WR_1}$ is high. To update the input latch — $\overline{CS}$ and $\overline{WR_1}$ must be low while ILE is high.

$\overline{WR_2}$: **Write 2** (active low). This signal, in combination with $\overline{XFER}$, causes the 8-bit data which is available in the input latch to transfer to the DAC register.

$\overline{XFER}$: **Transfer control signal** (active low). The $\overline{XFER}$ will enable $\overline{WR_2}$.

Other Pin Functions

DI_0-DI_7: **Digital Inputs.** DI_0 is the least significant bit (LSB) and DI_7 is the most significant bit (MSB).

I_{OUT1}: **DAC Current Output 1.** I_{OUT1} is a maximum for a digital code of all 1's in the DAC register, and is zero for all 0's in DAC register.

I_{OUT2}: **DAC Current Output 2.** I_{OUT2} is a constant minus I_{OUT1}, or $I_{OUT1} + I_{OUT2} =$ constant (I full scale for a fixed reference voltage).

R_{fb}: **Feedback Resistor.** The feedback resistor is provided on the IC chip for use as the shunt feedback resistor for the external op amp which is used to provide an output voltage for the DAC. This on-chip resistor should always be used (not an external resistor) since it matches the resistors which are used in the on-chip R-2R ladder and tracks these resistors over temperature.

V_{REF}: **Reference Voltage Input.** This input connects an external precision voltage source to the internal R-2R ladder. V_{REF} can be selected over the range of $+10$ to $-10V$. This is also the analog voltage input for a 4-quadrant multiplying DAC application.

V_{CC}: **Digital Supply Voltage.** This is the power supply pin for the part. V_{CC} can be from $+5$ to $+15V_{DC}$. Operation is optimum for $+15V_{DC}$.

AGND: Analog Ground. This is the ground for the analog circuitry. This pin must always be connected to the digital ground potential.

DGND: Digital Ground. This is the ground for the digital logic.

8-136

Reprinted with Permission of National Semiconductor Corp.

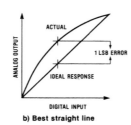

a) End point test after zero and fs adj.

b) Best straight line

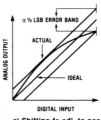

c) Shifting fs adj. to pass best straight line test

Definition of Terms

Resolution: Resolution is directly related to the number of switches or bits within the DAC. For example, the DAC0830 has 2^8 or 256 steps and therefore has 8-bit resolution.

Linearity Error: Linearity Error is the maximum deviation from a *straight line passing through the endpoints of the DAC transfer characteristic.* It is measured after adjusting for zero and full-scale. Linearity error is a parameter intrinsic to the device and cannot be externally adjusted.

National's linearity "end point test" (a) and the "best straight line" test (b,c) used by other suppliers are illustrated above. The "end point test" greatly simplifies the adjustment procedure by eliminating the need for multiple iterations of checking the linearity and then adjusting full scale until the linearity is met. The "end point test" guarantees that linearity is met after a single full scale adjust. (One adjustment vs. multiple iterations of the adjustment.) The "end point test" uses a standard zero and F.S. adjustment procedure and is a much more stringent test for DAC linearity.

Power Supply Sensitivity: Power supply sensitivity is a measure of the effect of power supply changes on the DAC full-scale output.

Settling Time: Settling time is the time required from a code transition until the DAC output reaches within $\pm \frac{1}{2}$ LSB of the final output value. Full-scale settling time requires a zero to full-scale or full-scale to zero output change.

Full-Scale Error: Full scale error is a measure of the output error between an ideal DAC and the actual device output. Ideally, for the DAC0830 series, full-scale is $V_{REF} - 1$ LSB. For $V_{REF} = 10V$ and unipolar operation, $V_{FULL\text{-}SCALE} = 10.0000V - 39 \, mV = 9.961V$. Full-scale error is adjustable to zero.

Differential Nonlinearity: The difference between any two consecutive codes in the transfer curve from the theoretical 1 LSB is differential nonlinearity.

Monotonic: If the output of a DAC increases for increasing digital input code, then the DAC is monotonic. An 8-bit DAC which is monotonic to 8 bits simply means that increasing digital input codes will produce an increasing analog output.

8

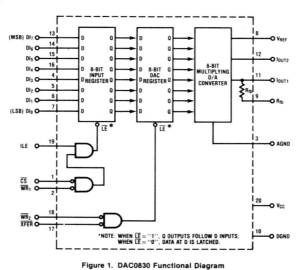

Figure 1. DAC0830 Functional Diagram

8-137

DAC0830/DAC0831/DAC0832

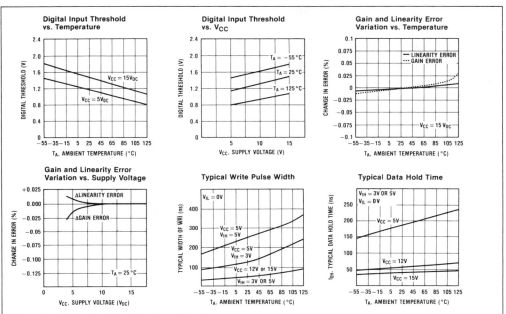

Digital Input Threshold vs. Temperature

Digital Input Threshold vs. V_{CC}

Gain and Linearity Error Variation vs. Temperature

Gain and Linearity Error Variation vs. Supply Voltage

Typical Write Pulse Width

Typical Data Hold Time

DAC0830 Series Application Hints

These DAC's are the industry's first microprocessor compatible, double-buffered 8-bit multiplying D to A converters. Double-buffering allows the utmost application flexibility from a digital control point of view. This 20-pin device is also pin for pin compatible (with one exception) with the DAC1230, a 12-bit MICRO-DAC™. In the event that a system's analog output resolution and accuracy must be upgraded, substituting the DAC1230 can be easily accomplished. By tying address bit A_0 to the ILE pin, a two-byte μP write instruction (double precision) which automatically increments the address for the second byte write (starting with A_0 = "1") can be used. This allows either an 8-bit or the 12-bit part to be used with no hardware or software changes. For the simplest 8-bit application, this pin should be tied to V_{CC} (also see other uses in section 1.1).

Analog signal control versatility is provided by a precision R-2R ladder network which allows full 4-quadrant multiplication of a wide range bipolar reference voltage by an applied digital word.

1.0 Digital Considerations

A most unique characteristic of these DAC's is that the 8-bit digital input byte is double-buffered. This means that the data must transfer through two independently controlled 8-bit latching registers before being applied to the R-2R ladder network to change the analog output. The addition of a second register allows two useful control features. First, any DAC in a system can simultaneously hold the current DAC data in one register (DAC register) and the next data word in the second register (input register) to allow fast updating of the DAC output on demand. Second, and probably more important, double-

buffering allows any number of DAC's in a system to be updated to their new analog output levels simultaneously via a common strobe signal.

The timing requirements and logic level convention of the register control signals have been designed to minimize or eliminate external interfacing logic when applied to most popular microprocessors and development systems. It is easy to think of these converters as 8-bit "write only" memory locations that provide an analog output quantity. All inputs to these DAC's meet TTL voltage level specs and can also be driven directly with high voltage CMOS logic in non-microprocessor based systems. To prevent damage to the chip from static discharge, all unused digital inputs should be tied to V_{CC} or ground. If any of the digital inputs are inadvertently left floating, the DAC interprets the pin as a logic "1".

1.1 Double-Buffered Operation

Updating the analog output of these DAC's in a double-buffered manner is basically a two step or double write operation. In a microprocessor system two unique system addresses must be decoded, one for the input latch controlled by the $\overline{CS}$ pin and a second for the DAC latch which is controlled by the $\overline{XFER}$ line. If more than one DAC is being driven, Figure 2, the $\overline{CS}$ line of each DAC would typically be decoded individually, but all of the converters could share a common $\overline{XFER}$ address to allow simultaneous updating of any number of DAC's. The timing for this operation is shown, Figure 3.

It is important to note that the analog outputs that will change after a simultaneous transfer are those from the DAC's whose input register had been modified prior to the $\overline{XFER}$ command.

Reprinted with Permission of National Semiconductor Corp.

Voltage Comparators

LM1514/LM1414 Dual Differential Voltage Comparator

General Description

The LM1514/LM1414 is a dual differential voltage comparator intended for applications requiring high accuracy and fast response times. The device is constructed on a single monolithic silicon chip.

The LM1514/LM1414 is useful as a variable threshold Schmitt trigger, a pulse height discriminator, a voltage comparator in high-speed A-D converters, a memory sense amplifier or a high noise immunity line receiver. The output of the comparator is compatible with all integrated logic forms. The LM1514/LM1414 meet or exceed the specifications for the MC1514/MC1414 and are pin-for-pin replacements. The LM1514 is available in the ceramic dual-in-line package. The LM1414 is available in either the ceramic or molded dual-in-line package.

The LM1514 is specified for operation over the −55°C to +125°C military temperature range. The LM1414 is specified for operation over the 0°C to +70°C temperature range.

Features

- Two totally separate comparators per package
- Independent strobe capability
- High speed 30 ns typ
- Low input offset voltage and current
- High output sink current over temperature
- Output compatible with TTL/DTL logic
- Molded or ceramic dual-in-line package

Schematic and Connection Diagrams

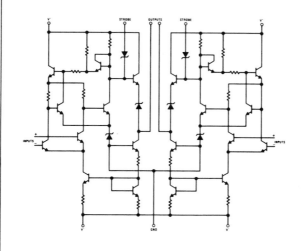

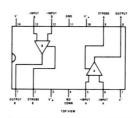

Dual-In-Line Package

Order Number LM1414J or LM1514J
See NS Package J14A
Order Number LM1414N
See NS Package N14A

5-62

Reprinted with Permission of National Semiconductor Corp.

Absolute Maximum Ratings (Note 1)

Positive Supply Voltage	+14.0V
Negative Supply Voltage	−7.0V
Peak Output Current	10 mA
Differential Input Voltage	±5.0V
Input Voltage	±7.0V
Power Dissipation (Note 2)	600 mW
Operating Temperature Range LM1514	−55°C to +125°C
LM1414	0°C to +70°C
Storage Temperature Range	−65°C to +150°C
Lead Temperature (Soldering, 10 seconds)	300°C

Electrical Characteristics for T_A = 25°C, V^+ = +12V, V^- = −6V, unless otherwise specified

PARAMETER	CONDITIONS	LM1514 MIN	LM1514 TYP	LM1514 MAX	LM1414 MIN	LM1414 TYP	LM1414 MAX	UNITS
Input Offset Voltage	$R_S \leq 200\Omega$, V_{CM} = 0V, V_{OUT} = 1.4V		0.6	2.0		1.0	5.0	mV
Input Offset Current	V_{CM} = 0V, V_{OUT} = 1.4V		0.8	3.0		1.2	5.0	μA
Input Bias Current				20			25	μA
Voltage Gain		1250			1000			
Output Resistance			200			200		Ω
Differential Input Voltage Range		±5.0			±5.0			V
Input Voltage Range	V^- = −7.0V	±5.0			±5.0			V
Common Mode Rejection Ratio	$R_S \leq 200\Omega$, V^- = −7.0V	80	100		70	100		dB
Positive Output Voltage	$V_{IN} \geq 7.0$ mV, $0 \leq I_{OUT} \leq$ −5.0 mA	2.5	3.2	4.0	2.5	3.2	4.0	V
Negative Output Voltage	$V_{IN} \leq$ −7.0 mV	−1.0	−0.5	0	−1.0	−0.5	0	V
Strobed Output Voltage	$V_{STROBE} \leq 0.3V$	−1.0	−0.5	0	−1.0	−0.5	0	V
Strobe "0" Current	V_{STROBE} = 100 mV		−1.2	−2.5		−1.2	−2.5	mA
Positive Supply Current	$V_{IN} \leq$ −7 mV			18			18	mA
Negative Supply Current	$V_{IN} \leq$ −7 mV			−14			−14	mA
Power Consumption			180	300		180	300	mW
Response Time	(Note 3)		30			30		ns

LM1514/LM1414: The following apply for $T_L \leq T_A < T_H$ (Note 4) unless otherwise specified

PARAMETER	CONDITIONS	LM1514 MIN	LM1514 TYP	LM1514 MAX	LM1414 MIN	LM1414 TYP	LM1414 MAX	UNITS
Input Offset Voltage	$R_S \leq 200\Omega$, V_{OUT} = 1.8V for T_A = T_L			3.0			6.5	mV
	V_{CM} = 0V, V_{OUT} = 1.0V for T_A = T_H			3.0			6.5	mV
Input Bias Current				45			40	μA
Temperature Coefficient of Input Offset Voltage			3.0			5.0		μV/°C
Input Offset Current	V_{CM} = 0V, V_{OUT} = 1.8V, T_A = T_L			7.0			7.5	μA
	V_{CM} = 0V, V_{OUT} = 1.0V, T_A = T_H			3.0			7.5	μA
Voltage Gain		1000			800			
Output Sink Current	$V_{IN} \leq$ −9.0 mV, $V_{OUT} \geq$ 0V	2.8	4.0		1.6	2.5		mA

Note 1: Voltage values are with respect to network ground terminal. Positive current is defined as current into the referenced pin.

Note 2: LM1514 ceramic package: The maximum junction temperature is +150°C, for operating at elevated temperatures, devices must be derated linearly at 12.5 mW/°C. LM1414 ceramic package: The maximum junction temperature is +95°C for operating at elevated temperatures, devices must be derated linearly at 12.5 mW/°C. LM1414 molded package: The maximum junction temperature is +115°C, for operating at elevated temperatures, devices must be derated linearly at 6.7 mW/°C.

Note 3: The response time specified (see definitions) for a 100 mV input step with 5 mV overdrive.

Note 4: For LM1514, T_L = −55°C, T_H = +125°C. For LM1414, T_L = 0°C, T_H = +70°C.

5

Reprinted with Permission of National Semiconductor Corp.

MC1595L
MC1495L

Specifications and Applications Information

WIDEBAND MONOLITHIC
FOUR-QUADRANT MULTIPLIER

. . . designed for uses where the output is a linear product of two input voltages. Maximum versatility is assured by allowing the user to select the level shift method. Typical applications include: multiply, divide*, square root*, mean square*, phase detector, frequency doubler, balanced modulator/demodulator, electronic gain control.

*When used with an operational amplifier.

- Wide Bandwidth
- Excellent Linearity — 1% max Error on X-Input, 2% max Error on Y-Input — MC1595L
- Excellent Linearity — 2% max Error on X-Input, 4% max Error on Y-Input — MC1495L
- Adjustable Scale Factor, K
- Excellent Temperature Stability
- Wide Input Voltage Range — ± 10 Volts
- ± 15 Volt Operation

LINEAR FOUR-QUADRANT MULTIPLIER

SILICON MONOLITHIC INTEGRATED CIRCUIT

(top view)

CERAMIC PACKAGE
CASE 632
TO-116

FIGURE 1 — FOUR-QUADRANT MULTIPLIER TRANSFER CHARACTERISTIC

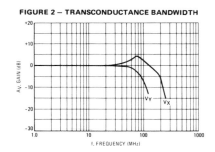

FIGURE 2 — TRANSCONDUCTANCE BANDWIDTH

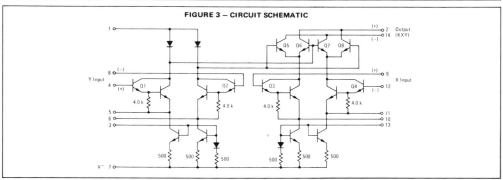

FIGURE 3 — CIRCUIT SCHEMATIC

Copyright by Motorola, Inc. Used by Permission.

MC1595L ● MC1495L

ELECTRICAL CHARACTERISTICS (V^+ = +32V, V^- = –15 V, T_A = +25°C, I_3 = I_{13} = 1 mA, R_X = R_Y = 15 kΩ, R_L = 11 kΩ unless otherwise noted)

Characteristic	Figure	Symbol	Min	Typ	Max	Unit
Linearity: Output Error in Percent of Full Scale:	5					%
T_A = +25°C						
–10 < V_X < +10 (V_Y = ±10 V) MC1495		E_{RX}	–	± 1.0	± 2.0	
MC1595			–	± 0.5	± 1.0	
–10 < V_Y < +10 (V_X = ±10 V) MC1495		E_{RY}	–	± 2.0	± 4.0	
MC1595			–	± 1.0	± 2.0	
T_A = 0 to +70°C						
–10 < V_X < +10 (V_Y = ±10 V)		E_{RX}	–	± 1.5	–	
–10 < V_Y < +10 (V_X = ±10 V)		E_{RY}	–	± 3.0	–	
T_A = –55°C to +125°C MC1595						
–10 < V_X < +10 (V_Y = ±10 V)		E_{RX}	–	+ 0.75	–	
–10 < V_Y < +10 (V_X = ±10 V)		E_{RY}	–	± 1.50	–	
Squaring Mode Error: Accuracy in Percent of Full Scale After Offset and Scale Factor Adjustment	5	E_{SQ}				%
T_A = +25°C MC1495			–	+ 0.75	–	
MC1595			–	+ 0.5	–	
T_A = 0 to +70°C MC1495			–	+ 1.0		
T_A = –55°C to +125°C MC1595			–	+ 0.75		
Scale Factor (Adjustable) $(K = \dfrac{2R_L}{I_3 R_X R_Y})$	–	K		0.1		
Input Resistance MC1495	7	R_{INX}		20	–	MegOhms
(f = 20 Hz) MC1595				35	–	
MC1495		R_{INY}		20		
MC1595				35		
Differential Output Resistance (f = 20 Hz)	8	R_O		300		k Ohms
Input Bias Current $I_{bx} = \dfrac{(I_9 + I_{12})}{2}$, $I_{by} = \dfrac{(I_4 + I_8)}{2}$ MC1495	6	I_{bx}		2.0	12	μA
MC1595				2.0	8.0	
MC1495		I_{by}		2.0	12	
MC1595			–	2.0	8.0	
Input Offset Current $|I_9 - I_{12}|$ MC1495	6	$|I_{iox}|$	–	0.4	2.0	μA
MC1595				0.2	1.0	
$|I_4 - I_8|$ MC1495		$|I_{ioy}|$		0.4	2.0	
MC1595				0.2	1.0	
Average Temperature Coefficient of Input Offset Current	6	$|TC_{Iio}|$				nA/°C
(T_A = 0 to +70°C) MC1495				2.0		
(T_A = –55°C to +125°C) MC1595			–	2.0		
Output Offset Current $|I_{14} - I_2|$ MC1495	6	$|I_{oo}|$		20	100	μA
MC1595				10	50	
Average Temperature Coefficient of Output Offset Current	6	$|TC_{Ioo}|$				nA/°C
(T_A = 0 to +70°C) MC1495				20		
(T_A = –55°C to +125°C) MC1595				20		
Frequency Response						
3.0 dB Bandwidth, R_L = 11 kΩ	9,10	BW$_{3dB}$		3.0		MHz
3.0 dB Bandwidth, R_L = 50 Ω (Transconductance Bandwidth)		^{T}BW3 dB	–	80	–	MHz
3° Relative Phase Shift Between V_X and V_Y		f_ϕ		750		kHz
1% Absolute Error Due to Input-Output Phase Shift		f_{ii}		30		kHz
Common Mode Input Swing (Either Input) MC1495	11	CMV	+10.5	+12		Vdc
MC1595			±11.5	+13		
Common Mode Gain (Either Input) MC1495	11	A_{CM}	–40	–50		dB
MC1595			–50	–60		
Common Mode Quiescent Output Voltage	12	V_{o1}		21		Vdc
		V_{o2}		21		
Differential Output Voltage Swing Capability	9	V_O	–	+14		V peak
Power Supply Sensitivity	12	S^+	–	5.0		mV/V
		S^-		10		
Power Supply Current	12	I_7		6.0	7.0	mA
DC Power Dissipation	12	P_D		135	170	mW

MOTOROLA *Semiconductor Products Inc.*

Copyright by Motorola, Inc. Used by Permission.

MC1595L ● MC1495L

MAXIMUM RATINGS (T_A = +25°C unless otherwise noted)

Rating	Symbol	Value	Unit
Applied Voltage (V_2-V_1, $V_{14}-V_1$, V_1-V_9, V_1-V_{12}, V_1-V_4, V_1-V_8, $V_{12}-V_7$, V_9-V_7, V_8-V_7, V_4-V_7)	$\triangle V$	30	Vdc
Differential Input Signal	$V_{12}-V_9$ V_4-V_8	$\pm(6+I_{13}R_X)$ $\pm(6+I_3R_Y)$	Vdc Vdc
Maximum Bias Current	I_3 I_{13}	10 10	mA
Power Dissipation (Package Limitation) Ceramic Package Derate above T_A = +25°C	P_D	750 5.0	mW mW/°C
Operating Temperature Range MC1495 MC1595	T_A	0 to +70 –55 to +125	°C °C
Storage Temperature Range	T_{stg}	–65 to +150	°C

TEST CIRCUITS

FIGURE 4 – LINEARITY (USING NULL TECHNIQUE)

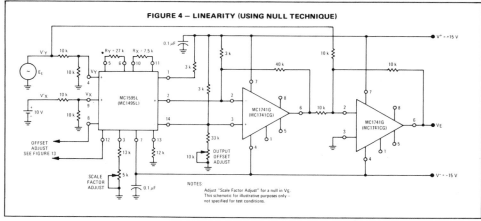

NOTES:
Adjust "Scale Factor Adjust" for a null in V_E.
This schematic for illustrative purposes only –
not specified for test conditions.

FIGURE 5 – LINEARITY (USING X-Y PLOTTER TECHNIQUE)

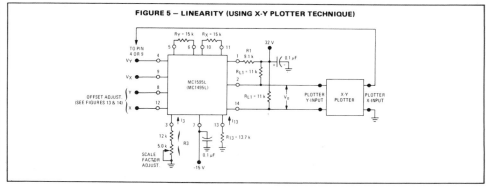

Ⓜ **MOTOROLA** *Semiconductor Products Inc.*

LM2005 20 Watt Automotive Power Amplifier

PRELIMINARY
May 1984

LM2005 20-Watt Automotive Power Amplifier

General Description

The LM2005 is a dual high power amplifier, designed to deliver optimum performance and reliability for automotive applications. High current capability (3.5A) enables the device to deliver 10W/channel into 2Ω (LM2005S), or 20W bridged monaural (LM2005M) into 4Ω, with low distortion.

Features

- Wide supply range (8V–18V)
- Externally programmable gain
- With or without bootstrap
- Low distortion
- Low noise

- High peak current capability
- $P_O = 20W$ bridge
- High voltage protection
- AC and DC output short circuit protection to ground or across load
- Thermal protection
- Inductive load protection
- Accidental open ground protection
- Immunity to 40V power supply transients
- 3°C/W device dissipation
- Pin for pin compatible with TDA2005

Connection Diagram

Plastic Package

TAB CONNECTED
TO PIN 6

Pin	
11	BOOTSTRAP 1
10	OUTPUT 1
9	+V_S
8	OUTPUT 2
7	BOOTSTRAP 2
6	GND
5	INPUT +2
4	INPUT −2
3	BYPASS
2	INPUT −1
1	INPUT +1

TOP VIEW

TL/H/5129–1

Typical Application

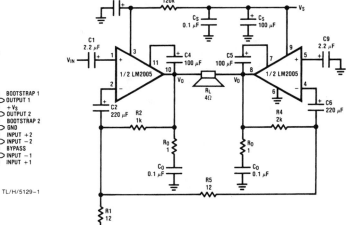

TL/H/5129–2

FIGURE 1. 20W Bridge Amplifier Application and Test Circuit

Reprinted with Permission of National Semiconductor Corp.

Absolute Maximum Ratings

Operating Supply Voltage	18V
DC Supply Voltage (Note 1)	28V
Peak Supply Voltage (50 ms)	40V
Output Current	
Repetitive (Note 2)	3.5A
Non-Repetitive	4.5A

Power Dissipation	30W
Operating Temperature	−40°C to +85°C
Storage Temperature	−60°C to +150°C
Lead Temp. (Soldering, 10 seconds)	300°C

Electrical Characteristics

$V_S = 14.4V$, $R_L = 2\Omega$ dual, $R_L = 4\Omega$ bridge, $T_{TAB} = 25°C$, frequency = 1 kHz unless otherwise specified

Parameter	Conditions	Min	Typ	Max	Units
Supply Voltage Range		8		18	V
Quiescent Supply Current	$P_O = 0W$, Dual Mode		70	120	mA
DC Output Level (Pins 8 and 10)		6.6	7.2	7.8	V
Output V_{OS} (Between Pins 8 and 10)	LM2005M only			150	mV
Output Power	THD = 10%				
	$R_L = 4\Omega$ Dual	6	6.5		W/Ch
	2Ω Dual	9	10		W/Ch
	4Ω Bridge	18	20		W
	1.6Ω Dual	10	11		W/Ch
	3.2Ω Bridge	20	22		W
Distortion	$R_L = 4\Omega$, $P_O = 2W$ Dual		0.2	1	%
	$R_L = 4\Omega$, $P_O = 4W$ Bridge		0.3	1	%
	$R_L = 1.6\Omega$, $P_O = 4W$ Dual		0.3	1	%
	$R_L = 3.2\Omega$, $P_O = 8W$ Bridge		0.3	1	%
Power Supply Rejection Ratio (Output Referred)	$R_S = 0\Omega$, f = 100 Hz				
	Dual	35	45		dB
	Bridge	45	55		dB
Noise (Note 3)	Equivalent Input Noise $R_S = 0\Omega$, BW = 20-20 kHz		1.5	5	μV
Channel Separation	Output Referred $V_O = 4$ Vrms, LM2005S only		60		dB
Input Impedance	Pins 5 and 1 (Non-Inverting)	70	200		$k\Omega$
Voltage Gain (Open Loop)			90		dB
Voltage Gain (Closed Loop)		48	50	51	dB
Low Frequency Roll Off	−3 dB				
	Dual			50	Hz
	Bridge			40	Hz
High Frequency Roll Off	−3 dB				
	Dual	15			kHz
	Bridge	20			kHz

Note 1: Internal voltage limit.
Note 2: Internal current limit.
Note 3: Not production tested. Not used to calculate AQL.

2

Reprinted with Permission of National Semiconductor Corp.

Typical Performance Characteristics

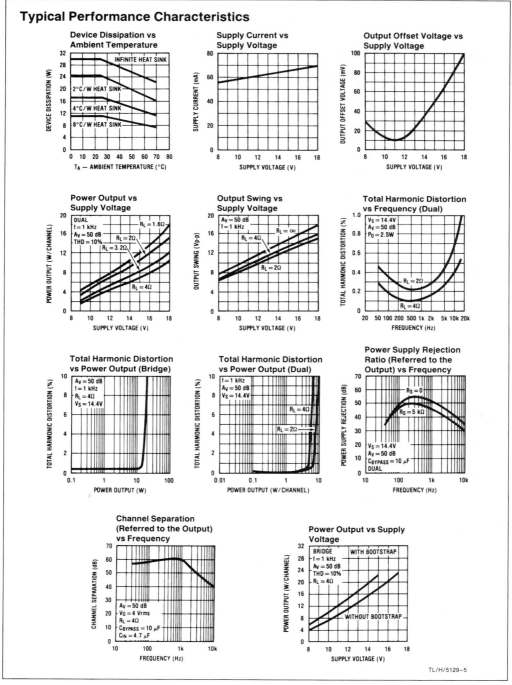

TL/H/5129–5

Reprinted with Permission of National Semiconductor Corp.

 **EXAR**   **XR-2206**

Monolithic Function Generator

GENERAL DESCRIPTION

The XR-2206 is a monolithic function generator integrated circuit capable of producing high quality sine,
square, triangle, ramp, and pulse waveforms of high-stability
and accuracy. The output waveforms can be both amplitude
and frequency modulated by an external voltage. Frequency
of operation can be selected externally over a range of 0.01
Hz to more than 1 MHz.

The circuit is ideally suited for communications, instrumentation, and function generator applications requiring
sinusoidal tone, AM, FM, or FSK generation. It has a typical
drift specification of 20 ppm/°C. The oscillator frequency
can be linearly swept over a 2000:1 frequency range, with
an external control voltage, having a very small affect on
distortion.

FEATURES

Low-Sine Wave Distortion	.5%, Typical
Excellent Temperature Stability	20 ppm/°C, Typical
Wide Sweep Range	2000:1, Typical
Low-Supply Sensitivity	0.01%V, Typical
Linear Amplitude Modulation	
TTL Compatible FSK Controls	
Wide Supply Range	10V to 26V
Adjustable Duty Cycle	1% to 99%

APPLICATIONS

Waveform Generation
Sweep Generation
AM/FM Generation
V/F Conversion
FSK Generation
Phase-Locked Loops (VCO)

ABSOLUTE MAXIMUM RATINGS

Power Supply	26V
Power Dissipation	750 mW
Derate Above 25°C	5 mW/°C
Total Timing Current	6 mA
Storage Temperature	−65°C to +150°C

FUNCTIONAL BLOCK DIAGRAM

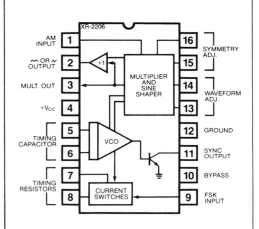

ORDERING INFORMATION

Part Number	Package	Operating Temperature
XR-2206M	Ceramic	−55°C to +125°C
XR-2206N	Ceramic	0°C to +70°C
XR-2206P	Plastic	0°C to +70°C
XR-2206CN	Ceramic	0°C to +70°C
XR-2206CP	Plastic	0°C to +70°C

SYSTEM DESCRIPTION

The XR-2206 is comprised of four functional blocks; a
voltage-controlled oscillator (VCO), an analog multiplier
and sine-shaper; a unity gain buffer amplifier; and a set
of current switches.

The VCO actually produces an output frequency porpor-
tional to an input current, which is produced by a resistor
from the timing terminals to ground. The current switches
route one of the timing pins current to the VCO controlled
by an FSK input pin, to produce an output frequency. With
two timing pins, two discrete output frequencies can be
independently produced for FSK Generation Applications.

 EXAR Integrated Systems, Inc., 750 Palomar Avenue, Sunnyvale, CA 94086 • (408) 732-7970 • TWX 910-339-9233

Reprinted Courtesy of Exar Corporation.

XR-2206

ELECTRICAL CHARACTERISTICS

Test Conditions: Test Circuit of Figure 1, V^+ = 12V, T_A = 25°, C = 0.01 μF, R_1 = 100 kΩ, R_2 = 10 kΩ, R_3 = 25 kΩ unless otherwise specified. S_1 open for triangle, closed for sine wave.

PARAMETER	XR-2206M			XR-2206C			UNIT	CONDITIONS
	MIN.	TYP.	MAX.	MIN.	TYP.	MAX.		
GENERAL CHARACTERISTCS								
Single Supply Voltage	10		26	10		26	V	
Split-Supply Voltage	±5		±13	±5		±13	V	
Supply Current		12	17		14	20	mA	$R_1 \geqslant 10$ kΩ
OSCILLATOR SECTION								
Max. Operating Frequency	0.5	1		0.5	1		MHz	C = 1000 pF, R_1 = 1 kΩ
Lowest Practical Frequency		0.01			0.01		Hz	C = 50 μF, R_1 = 2 MΩ
Frequency Accuracy		±1	±4		±2		% of f_o	$f_o = 1/R_1 C$
Temperature Stability		±10	±50		±20		ppm/°C	0°C $\leq T_A \leq$ 75°C,
								$R_1 = R_2 = 20$ kΩ
Supply Sensitivity		0.01	0.1		0.01		%/V	V_{LOW} = 10V, V_{HIGH} = 20V,
								$R_1 = R_2 = 20$ kΩ
Sweep Range	1000:1	2000:1			2000:1		$f_H : f_L$	f_H @ R_1 = 1 kΩ
								f_L @ R_1 = 2 MΩ
Sweep Linearity								
10:1 Sweep		2			2		%	f_L = 1 kHz, f_H = 10 kHz
1000:1 Sweep		8			8		%	f_L = 100 Hz, f_H = 100 kHz
FM Distortion		0.1			0.1		%	±10% Deviation
Recommended Timing								
Components								
Timing Capacitor: C	0.001		100	0.001		100	μF	See Figure 4.
Timing Resistors: R_1 & R_2	1		2000	1		2000	kΩ	
Triangle Sine Wave Output								See Note 1, Figure 2.
Triangle Amplitude		160			160		mV/kΩ	Figure 1, S_1 Open
Sine Wave Amplitude	40	60	80		60		mV/kΩ	Figure 1, S_1 Closed
Max. Output Swing		6			6		V p-p	
Output Impedance		600			600		Ω	
Triangle Linearity		1			1		%	
Amplitude Stability		0.5			0.5		dB	For 1000:1 Sweep
Sine Wave Amplitude Stability		4800			4800		ppm/°C	See Note 2.
Sine Wave Distortion								
Without Adjustment		2.5			2.5		%	R_1 = 30 kΩ
With Adjustment		0.4	1.0		0.5	1.5	%	See Figures 6 and 7.
Amplitude Modulation								
Input Impedance	50	100		50	100		kΩ	
Modulation Range		100			100		%	
Carrier Suppression		55			55		dB	
Linearity		2			2		%	For 95% modulation
Square-Wave Output								
Amplitude		12			12		V p-p	Measured at Pin 11.
Rise Time		250			250		nsec	C_L = 10 pF
Fall Time		50			50		nsec	C_L = 10 pF
Saturation Voltage		0.2	0.4		0.2	0.6	V	I_L = 2 mA
Leakage Current		0.1	20		0.1	100	μA	V_{11} = 26V
FSK Keying Level (Pin 9)	0.8	1.4	2.4	0.8	1.4	2.4	V	See section on circuit controls
Reference Bypass Voltage	2.9	3.1	3.3	2.5	3	3.5	V	Measured at Pin 10.

Note 1: Output amplitude is directly proportional to the resistance, R_3, on Pin 3. See Figure 2.
Note 2: For maximum amplitude stability, R_3 should be a positive temperature coefficient resistor.

Reprinted Courtesy of Exar Corporation.

XR-2206

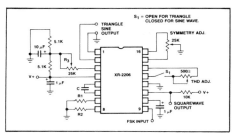

Figure 1: Basic Test Circuit.

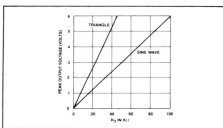

Figure 2: Output Amplitude as a Function of the Resistor, R_3, at Pin 3.

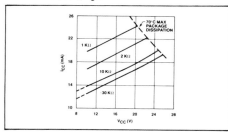

Figure 3: Supply Current versus Supply Voltage, Timing, R.

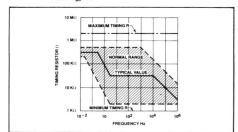

Figure 4: R versus Oscillation Frequency.

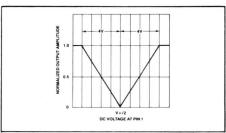

Figure 5: Normalized Output Amplitude versus DC Bias at AM Input (Pin 1).

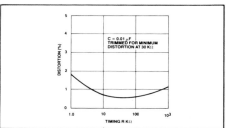

Figure 6: Trimmed Distortion versus Timing Resistor.

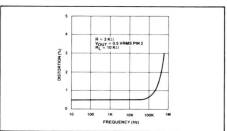

Figure 7: Sine Wave Distortion versus Operating Frequency with Timing Capacitors Varied.

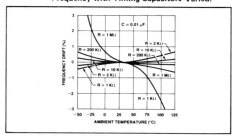

Figure 8: Frequency Drift versus Temperature.

3

XR-2206

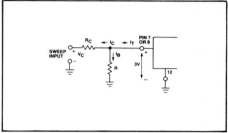

Figure 9: Circuit Connection for Frequency Sweep.

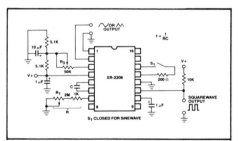

Figure 10: Circuit for Sine Wave Generation without External Adjustment. (See Figure 2 for Choice of R_3.)

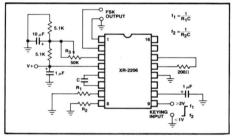

Figure 12: Sinusoidal FSK Generator.

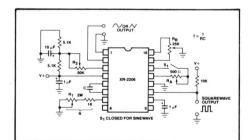

Figure 11: Circuit for Sine Wave Generation with Minimum Harmonic Distortion. (R_3 Determines Output Swing — See Figure 2.)

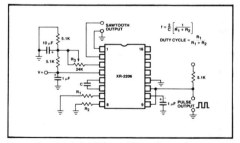

Figure 13: Circuit for Pulse and Ramp Generation.

4

XR-2206

Frequency-Shift Keying:

The XR-2206 can be operated with two separate timing resistors, R_1 and R_2, connected to the timing Pin 7 and 8, respectively, as shown in Figure 12. Depending on the polarity of the logic signal at Pin 9, either one or the other of these timing resistors is activated. If Pin 9 is open-circuited or connected to a bias voltage $\geqslant 2V$, only R_1 is activated. Similarly, if the voltage level at Pin 9 is $\leqslant 1V$, only R_2 is activated. Thus, the output frequency can be keyed between two levels, f_1 and f_2, as:

$$f_1 = 1/R_1 C \text{ and } f_2 = 1/R_2 C$$

For split-supply operation, the keying voltage at Pin 9 is referenced to V^-.

Output DC Level Control:

The dc level at the output (Pin 2) is approximately the same as the dc bias at Pin 3. In Figures 10, 11 and 12, Pin 3 is biased midway between V^+ and ground, to give an output dc level of $\approx V^+/2$.

APPLICATIONS INFORMATION

Sine Wave Generation

Without External Adjustment:

Figure 10 shows the circuit connection for generating a sinusoidal output from the XR-2206. The potentiometer, R_1 at Pin 7, provides the desired frequency tuning. The maximum output swing is greater than $V^+/2$, and the typical distortion (THD) is $<2.5\%$. If lower sine wave distortion is desired, additional adjustments can be provided as described in the following section.

The circuit of Figure 10 can be converted to split-supply operation, simply by replacing all ground connections with V^-. For split-supply operation, R_3 can be directly connected to ground.

With External Adjustment:

The harmonic content of sinusoidal output can be reduced to $\approx 0.5\%$ by additional adjustments as shown in Figure 11. The potentiometer, R_A, adjusts the sine-shaping resistor, and R_B provides the fine adjustment for the waveform symmetry. The adjustment procedure is as follows:

1. Set R_B at midpoint, and adjust R_A for minimum distortion.

2. With R_A set as above, adjust R_B to further reduce distortion.

Triangle Wave Generation

The circuits of Figures 10 and 11 can be converted to triangle wave generation, by simply open-circuiting Pin 13 and 14 (i.e., S_1 open). Amplitude of the triangle is approximately twice the sine wave output.

FSK Generation

Figure 12 shows the circuit connection for sinusoidal FSK signal operation. Mark and space frequencies can be independently adjusted, by the choice of timing resistors, R_1 and R_2; the output is phase-continuous during transitions. The keying signal is applied to Pin 9. The circuit can be converted to split-supply operation by simply replacing ground with V^-.

Pulse and Ramp Generation

Figure 13 shows the circuit for pulse and ramp waveform generation. In this mode of operation, the FSK keying terminal (Pin 9) is shorted to the square-wave output (Pin 11), and the circuit automatically frequency-shift keys itself between two separate frequencies during the positive-going and negative-going output waveforms. The pulse width and duty cycle can be adjusted from 1% to 99%, by the choice of R_1 and R_2. The values of R_1 and R_2 should be in the range of 1 kΩ to 2 MΩ.

Reprinted Courtesy of Exar Corporation.

XR-2206

PRINCIPLES OF OPERATION

Description of Controls

Frequency of Operation:

The frequency of oscillation, f_0, is determined by the external timing capacitor, C, across Pin 5 and 6, and by the timing resistor, R, connected to either Pin 7 or 8. The frequency is given as:

$$f_0 = \frac{1}{RC} \text{ Hz}$$

and can be adjusted by varying either R or C. The recommended values of R, for a given frequency range, are shown in Figure 4. Temperature stability is optimum for $4 \text{ k}\Omega < R < 200 \text{ k}\Omega$. Recommended values of C are from 1000 pF to 100 μF.

Frequency Sweep and Modulation:

Frequency of oscillation is proportional to the total timing current, I_T, drawn from Pin 7 or 8:

$$f = \frac{320 I_T \text{ (mA)}}{C \text{ } (\mu F)} \text{ Hz}$$

Timing terminals (Pin 7 or 8) are low-impedance points, and are internally biased at +3V, with respect to Pin 12. Frequency varies linearly with I_T, over a wide range of current values, from 1 μA to 3 mA. The frequency can be controlled by applying a control voltage, V_C, to the activated timing pin as shown in Figure 9. The frequency of oscillation is related to V_C as:

$$f = \frac{1}{RC} \left[1 + \frac{R}{R_C} \left(1 - \frac{V_C}{3} \right) \right] \text{ Hz}$$

where V_C is in volts. The voltage-to-frequency conversion gain, K, is given as:

$$K = \partial f / \partial V_C = - \frac{0.32}{R_C C} \text{ Hz/V}$$

CAUTION: For safe operation of the circuit, I_T should be limited to $\leqslant 3$ mA.

Output Amplitude:

Maximum output amplitude is inversely proportional to the external resistor, R_3, connected to Pin 3 (see Figure 2). For sine wave output, amplitude is approximately 60 mV peak per kΩ of R_3; for triangle, the peak amplitude is approximately 160 mV peak per kΩ of R_3. Thus, for example, $R_3 = 50$ kΩ would produce approximately ± 3V sinusoidal output amplitude.

Amplitude Modulation:

Output amplitude can be modulated by applying a dc bias and a modulating signal to Pin 1. The internal impedance at Pin 1 is approximately 100 kΩ. Output amplitude varies linearly with the applied voltage at Pin 1, for values of dc bias at this pin, within ± 4 volts of $V^+/2$ as shown in Figure 5. As this bias level approaches $V^+/2$, the phase of the output signal is reversed, and the amplitude goes through zero. This property is suitable for phase-shift keying and suppressed-carrier AM generation. Total dynamic range of amplitude modulation is approximately 55 dB.

CAUTION: AM control must be used in conjunction with a well-regulated supply, since the output amplitude now becomes a function of V^+.

EQUIVALENT SCHEMATIC DIAGRAM

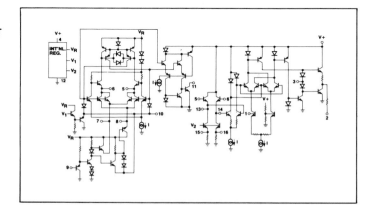

6

Reprinted Courtesy of Exar Corporation.

PRODUCT SPECIFICATIONS   **LINEAR INTEGRATED CIRCUITS**

Raytheon
General Purpose
Quad 741 Operational Amplifier   **RC4136**

Features

- Unity gain bandwidth — 3MHz
- Short circuit protection
- No frequency compensation required
- No latch-up
- Large common mode and differential voltage ranges
- Low power consumption
- Parameter tracking over temperature range
- Gain and phase match between amplifiers

Description

The 4136 is made up of four 741 type independent high gain operational amplifiers internally compensated and constructed on a single silicon chip using the planar epitaxial process.

This amplifier meets or exceeds all specifications for 741 type amplifiers. Excellent channel separation allows the use of the 4136 quad amplifier in all 741 operational amplifier applications providing the highest possible packaging density.

The specially designed low noise input transistors allow the 4136 to be used in low noise signal processing applications such as audio preamplifiers and signal conditioners.

Mask Pattern

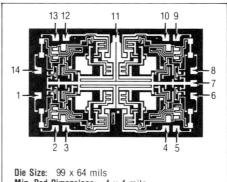

Die Size: 99 x 64 mils
Min. Pad Dimensions: 4 x 4 mils

Schematic Diagram (1/4 Shown)

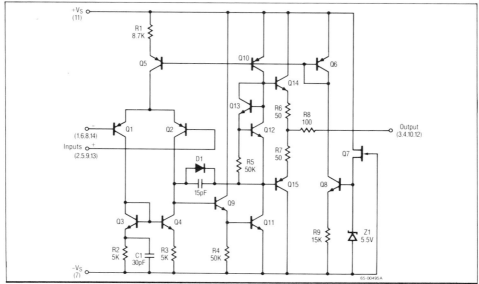

RAYTHEON COMPANY • Semiconductor Division • 350 Ellis Street • Mountain View, CA 94039-7016
Printed in U.S.A.   65-1139A June 1984

Courtesy of Raytheon Company.

RC4136

General Purpose
Quad 741 Operational Amplifier

Connection Information

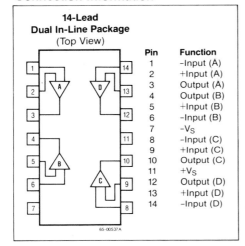

14-Lead
Dual In-Line Package
(Top View)

Pin	Function
1	–Input (A)
2	+Input (A)
3	Output (A)
4	Output (B)
5	+Input (B)
6	–Input (B)
7	–V_S
8	–Input (C)
9	+Input (C)
10	Output (C)
11	+V_S
12	Output (D)
13	+Input (D)
14	–Input (D)

65-00537A

Absolute Maximum Ratings

Supply Voltage
   RM4136 .... ±22V
   RC4136, RV4136 .... ±18V
Input Voltage[1] .... ±15V
Differential Input Voltage 30V
Output Short Circuit Duration[2] ...... Indefinite
Storage Temperature
   Range .... –65°C to +150°C
Operating Temperature Range
   RM4136 .... –55°C to +125°C
   RC4136 .... 0°C to +70°C
   RV4136 .... –40°C to +85°C
Lead Soldering Temperature
   (60 Sec) .... +300°C

Notes: 1. For supply voltages less than ±15V, the absolute maximum input voltage is equal to the supply voltage.
      2. Short circuit may be to ground, typically 45mA.

Thermal Characteristics

	14-Lead Plastic DIP	14-Lead Ceramic DIP
Max. Junction Temp.	125°C	175°C
Max. P_D T_A < 50°C	468mW	1042mW
Therm. Res. θ_{JC}	—	60°C/W
Therm. Res. θ_{JA}	160°C/W	120°C/W
For T_A > 50°C Derate at	6.25mW per °C	8.33mW per °C

Ordering Information

Part Number	Package	Operating Temperature Range
RC4136DB	Plastic	0°C to +70°C
RC4136DC	Ceramic	0°C to +70°C
RV4136DB	Plastic	–40°C to +85°C
RV4136DC	Ceramic	–40°C to +85°C
RM4136DC	Ceramic	–55°C to +125°C
RM4136DC/883B*	Ceramic	–55°C to +125°C

*MIL-STD-883, Level B Processing

2

Raytheon

Courtesy of Raytheon Company.

General Purpose
Quad 741 Operational Amplifier   RC4136

Electrical Characteristics ($V_S = \pm15V$ and $T_A = +25°C$)

Parameters	Test Conditions	RM4136 Min	RM4136 Typ	RM4136 Max	RC/RV4136 Min	RC/RV4136 Typ	RC/RV4136 Max	Units
Input Offset Voltage	$R_S \leq 10k\Omega$		0.5	5.0		0.5	6.0	mV
Input Offset Current			5.0	200		5.0	200	nA
Input Bias Current			40	500		40	500	nA
Input Resistance		0.3	5.0		0.3	5.0		$M\Omega$
Large Signal Voltage Gain	$R_L \geq 2k\Omega$, $V_{OUT} = \pm10V$	50	300		20	300		V/mV
Output Voltage Swing	$R_L \geq 10k\Omega$	±12	±14		±12	±14		V
	$R_L \geq 2k\Omega$	±10	±13		±10	±13		
Input Voltage Range		±12	±14		±12	±14		V
Common Mode Rejection Ratio	$R_S \leq 10k\Omega$	70	100		70	100		dB
Power Supply Rejection Ratio	$R_S \leq 10k\Omega$	76	100		76	100		dB
Power Consumption	$R_L = \infty$, All Outputs		210	340		210	340	mW
Transient Response Rise Time	$V_{IN} = 20mV$, $R_L = 2k\Omega$		0.13			0.13		μS
Overshoot	$C_L \leq 100pF$		5.0			5.0		%
Unity Gain Bandwidth			3.0			3.0		MHz
Slew Rate	$R_L \geq 2k\Omega$		1.5			1.0		$V/\mu S$
Channel Separation	$f = 1.0kHz$, $R_S = 1k\Omega$		90			90		dB
The following specification apply for $-55°C \leq T_A \leq +125°C$ for RM4136; $0°C \leq T_A \leq +70°C$ for RC4136; $-40°C \leq T_A \leq +85°C$ for RV4136, $V_S = \pm15V$								
Input Offset Voltage	$R_S \leq 10k\Omega$			6.0			7.5	mV
Input Offset Current RM/RC4136				500			300	nA
RV4136							500	
Input Bias Current RM/RC4136				1500			800	nA
RV4136							1500	
Large Signal Voltage Gain	$R_L \geq 2k\Omega$, $V_{OUT} = \pm10V$	25			15			V/mV
Output Voltage Swing	$R_L \geq 2k\Omega$	±10			±10			V
Power Consumption			240	400		240	400	mW

Raytheon   3

Courtesy of Raytheon Company.

RC4136

General Purpose
Quad 741 Operational Amplifier

Electrical Characteristics Comparison ($V_S = \pm15V$ and $T_A = +25°C$)

Parameter	RC4136 (Typ)	RC741 (Typ)	LM324 (Typ)	Units
Input Offset Voltage	0.5	2.0	2.0	mV
Input Offset Current	5.0	10	5.0	nA
Input Bias Current	40	80	55	nA
Input Resistance	5.0	2.0		MΩ
Large Signal Voltage Gain ($R_L = 2k\Omega$)	300	200	100	V/mV
Output Voltage Swing ($R_L = 2k\Omega$)	±13V	±13V	$\|+V_S - 1.2V\|$ to $-V_S$	V
Input Voltage Range	±14V	±13V	$\|+V_S - 1.5V\|$ to $-V_S$	V
Common Mode Rejection Ratio	100	90	85	dB
Power Supply Rejection Ratio	100	90	100	dB
Transient Response Rise Time	0.13	0.3		μS
Overshoot	5.0	5.0		%
Unity Gain Bandwidth	3.0	0.8	0.8	MHz
Slew Rate	1.0	0.5	0.5	V/μS
Input Noise Voltage Density (f = 1kHz)	10	22.5		nV/√Hz
Short Circuit Current	±45	±25		mA

Typical Performance Characteristics

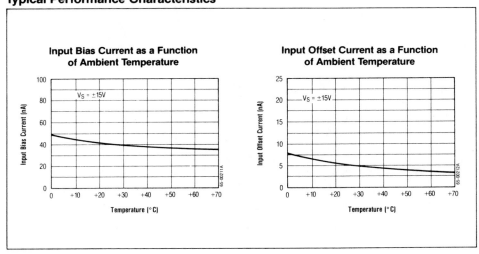

4

Raytheon

Courtesy of Raytheon Company.

RC4136

General Purpose
Quad 741 Operational Amplifier

Typical Performance Characteristics (Continued)

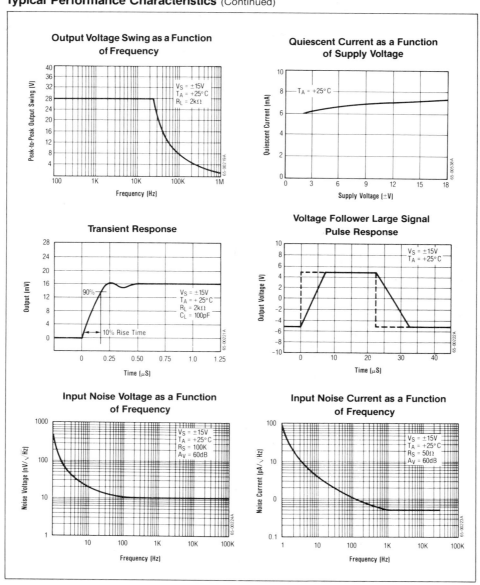

Raytheon

Courtesy of Raytheon Company.

General Purpose
Quad 741 Operational Amplifier   RC4136

Typical Performance Characteristics (Continued)

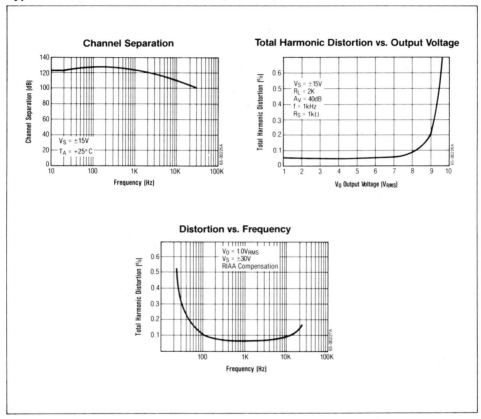

Courtesy of Raytheon Company.

XR-4195

±15V Dual-Tracking Voltage Regulators

GENERAL DESCRIPTION

The XR-4195 is a dual-polarity tracking regulator designed to provide balanced positive and negative 15V output voltages at currents of up to 100mA.

The device is ideal for local "on-card" regulation, which eliminates the distribution problems associated with single-point regulation. Intended for ease of application, the XR-4195 requires only two external components for operation.

FEATURES

Direct Replacement for RM/RC 4195
±15V Operational Amplifier Power
Thermal Shutdown at T_i = +175°C
Output Currents to 100mA
As a Single Output Regulator, it may be
  used with up to +50V Output
Available in 8-Pin Plastic Mini-DIP
Low External Parts Count

AVAILABLE TYPES

Part Number	Package	Operating Temperature
XR-4195CP	DIP	0°C to +70°C

ABSOLUTE MAXIMUM RATINGS

Input Voltage ±V to Ground	±30V
Power Dissipation at T_A = 25°C	600mW
Load Current	100mA
Operating Junction Temperature Range	0°C to +125°C
Storage Temperature Range	−65°C to +150°C

SIMPLIFIED SCHEMATIC DIAGRAM

FUNCTIONAL BLOCK DIAGRAM

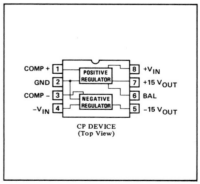

EXAR INTEGRATED SYSTEMS, INC.
750 Palomar Ave., P.O. Box 62229, Sunnyvale, CA 94088
(408) 732-7970   TWX 910-339-9233

© EXAR INTEGRATED SYSTEMS, INC.   ■ Printed in U.S.A.

Reprinted Courtesy of Exar Corporation.

ELECTRICAL CHARACTERISTICS

Test Conditions: (I_L = 1mA, V_{CC} = ±20V, C_L = 10μF unless otherwise specified)

CHARACTERISTICS	XR-4195CP MIN	XR-4195CP TYP	XR-4195CP MAX	UNITS	CONDITIONS
Line Regulation		2	20	mV	V_{IN} = ±18 to ±30V
Load Regulation		5	30	mV	I_L = 1 to 100 mA
Output Voltage Temperature Stability		0.005	0.015	%/°C	
Standby Current Drain		±1.5	±3.0	mA	V_{IN} = ±30V, I_L = 0mA
Input Voltage Range	18		30	V	
Output Voltage	14.5	15	15.5	V	T_j = +25°C
Output Voltage Tracking		±50	±300	mV	
Ripple Rejection		75		dB	f = 120Hz, T_j = +25°C
Input-Output Voltage Differential	3			V	I_L = 50mA
Short-Circuit Current		220		mA	T_j = +25°C
Output Noise Voltage		60		μV RMS	T_j = +25°C, f = 100Hz to 100kHz
Internal Thermal Shutdown		175		°C	

THERMAL CHARACTERISTICS

CHARACTERISTICS	XR-4195CP MIN	XR-4195CP TYP	XR-4195CP MAX	CONDITIONS
Power Dissipation			0.6W	T_A = 25°C T_C = 25°C
Thermal Resistance		210°C/W		$\theta_{J\text{-}C}$ $\theta_{J\text{-}A}$

TYPICAL APPLICATIONS

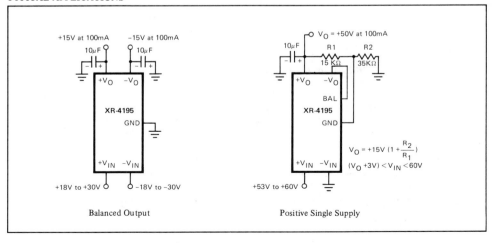

Balanced Output

Positive Single Supply

$V_O = +15V \left(1 + \dfrac{R_2}{R_1}\right)$

$(V_O +3V) < V_{IN} < 60V$

Reprinted Courtesy of Exar Corporation.

SE5534, SE5534A, NE5534, NE5534A
LOW-NOISE OPERATIONAL AMPLIFIERS

D2532, JULY 1979—REVISED AUGUST 1985

- Equivalent Input Noise Voltage
  $3.5 \, \text{nV}/\sqrt{\text{Hz}}$ Typ

- Unity-Gain Bandwidth . . . . . . 10 MHz Typ

- Common-Mode Rejection Ratio
  100 dB Typ

- High DC Voltage Gain . . . . 100 V/mV Typ

- Peak-to-Peak Output Voltage Swing
  32 V Typ with $V_{CC \pm} = \pm 18$ V and
  $R_L = 600 \, \Omega$

- High Slew Rate . . . . 13 V/μs Typ

- Wide Supply Voltage Range
  ± 3 V to ± 20 V

- Low Harmonic Distortion

- Designed to be Interchangeable with Signetics
  SE5534, SE5534A, NE5534, and NE5534A

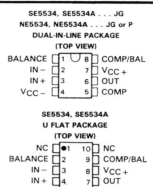

symbol

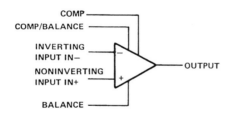

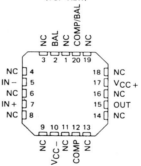

NC—No internal connection

SE5534A FROM TI NOT RECOMMENDED FOR NEW DESIGNS

description

The SE5534, SE5534A, NE5534, and NE5534A are monolithic high-performance operational amplifiers combining excellent dc and ac characteristics. Some of the features include very low noise, high output drive capability, high unity-gain and maximum-output-swing bandwidths, low distortion, and high slew rate.

These operational amplifiers are internally compensated for a gain equal to or greater than three. Optimization of the frequency response for various applications can be obtained by use of an external compensation capacitor between COMP and COMP/BAL. The devices feature input-protection diodes, output short-circuit protection, and offset-voltage nulling capability.

The SE5534A and NE5534A have guaranteed maximums on equivalent input noise voltage.

The SE5534 and SE5534A are characterized for operation over the full military temperature range of $-55\,°C$ to $125\,°C$; the NE5534 and NE5534A are characterized for operation from $0\,°C$ to $70\,°C$.

TEXAS INSTRUMENTS
POST OFFICE BOX 225012 • DALLAS, TEXAS 75265

Courtesy of Texas Instruments Incorporated.

SE5534, SE5534A, NE5534, NE5534A
LOW-NOISE OPERATIONAL AMPLIFIERS

schematic

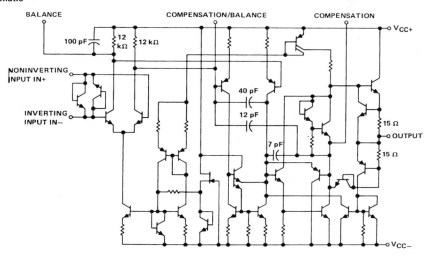

All component values shown are nominal.

absolute maximum ratings over operating free-air temperature range (unless otherwise noted)

Supply voltage, V_{CC+} (see Note 1)	22 V
Supply voltage, V_{CC-} (see Note 1)	−22 V
Input voltage either input (see Notes 1 and 2)	V_{CC+}
Input current (see Note 3)	± 10 mA
Duration of output short-circuit (see Note 4)	unlimited
Continuous total power dissipation at (or below) 25 °C free-air temperature (see Note 5)	
FK package (see Note 6)	1375 mW
SE5534, SE5534A in JG package	1050 mW
NE5534, NE5534A in JG package	825 mW
P package	725 mW
U package	675 mW
Operating free-air temperature range: SE5534, SE5534A	−55 °C to 125 °C
NE5534, NE5534A	0 °C to 70 °C
Storage temperature range	−65 °C to 150 °C
Lead temperature 1,6 mm (1/16 inch) from case for 60 seconds: FK, JG, or U package	300 °C
Lead temperature 1,6 mm (1/16 inch) from case for 10 seconds: P package	260 °C

NOTES: 1. All voltage values, except differential voltages, are with respect to the midpoint between V_{CC+} and V_{CC-}.
     2. The magnitude of the input voltage must never exceed the magnitude of the supply voltage.
     3. Excessive current will flow if a differential input voltage in excess of approximately 0.6 V is applied between the inputs unless some limiting resistance is used.
     4. The output may be shorted to ground or either power supply. Temperature and/or supply voltages must be limited to ensure the maximum dissipation rating is not exceeded.
     5. For operation above 25 °C free-air temperature, refer to the Dissipation Derating Curves, Section 2. In the JG package, SE5534 and SE5534A chips are alloy mounted; NE5534 and NE5534A chips are glass mounted.
     6. For the FK package, power rating and derating factor will vary with actual mounting technique used. The values stated here are believed to be conservative.

TEXAS
INSTRUMENTS
POST OFFICE BOX 225012 • DALLAS, TEXAS 75265

Courtesy of Texas Instruments Incorporated.

SE5534, SE5534A, NE5534, NE5534A
LOW-NOISE OPERATIONAL AMPLIFIERS

electrical characteristics, $V_{CC\pm} = \pm 15$ V, $T_A = 25°C$ (unless otherwise noted)

PARAMETER		TEST CONDITIONS[†]		SE5534, SE5534A MIN	TYP	MAX	NE5534, NE5534A MIN	TYP	MAX	UNIT
V_{IO}	Input offset voltage	$V_O = 0$, $R_S = 50$ Ω	$T_A = 25°C$		0.5	2		0.5	4	mV
			T_A = full range			3			5	
I_{IO}	Input offset current	$V_O = 0$	$T_A = 25°C$		10	200		20	300	nA
			T_A = full range			500			400	
I_{IB}	Input bias current	$V_O = 0$	$T_A = 25°C$		400	800		500	1500	nA
			T_A = full range			1500			2000	
V_{ICR}	Common-mode input voltage range			±12	±13		±12	±13		V
V_{OPP}	Maximum peak-to-peak output voltage swing	$R_L \geq 600$ Ω	$V_{CC\pm} = \pm 15$ V	24	26		24	26		V
			$V_{CC\pm} = \pm 18$ V	30	32		30	32		
A_{VD}	Large-signal differential voltage amplification	$V_O = \pm 10$ V, $R_L \geq 600$ Ω	$T_A = 25°C$	50	100		25	100		V/mV
			T_A = full range	25			15			
A_{vd}	Small-signal differential voltage amplification	$f = 10$ kHz	$C_C = 0$		6			6		V/mV
			$C_C = 22$ pF		2.2			2.2		
B_{OM}	Maximum-output-swing bandwidth	$V_O = \pm 10$ V, $C_C = 0$			200			200		kHz
		$V_O = \pm 10$ V, $C_C = 22$ pF			95			95		
		$V_{CC\pm} = \pm 18$ V, $V_O = \pm 14$ V, $R_L = 600$ Ω, $C_C = 22$ pF			70			70		
B_1	Unity-gain bandwidth	$C_C = 22$ pF,	$C_L = 100$ pF		10			10		MHz
r_i	Input resistance			50	100		30	100		kΩ
z_o	Output impedance	$A_{VD} = 30$ dB, $R_L = 600$ Ω, $C_C = 22$ pF, $f = 10$ kHz			0.3			0.3		Ω
CMRR	Common-mode rejection ratio	$V_O = 0$, $R_S = 50$ Ω	$V_{IC} = V_{ICR}$ min.	80	100		70	100		dB
k_{SVR}	Supply voltage rejection ratio ($\Delta V_{CC}/\Delta V_{IO}$)	$V_{CC\pm} = \pm 9$ V to ± 15 V, $V_O = 0$, $R_S = 50$ Ω		86	100		80	100		dB
I_{OS}	Output short-circuit current				38			38		mA
I_{CC}	Supply current	No load, $V_O = 0$	$T_A = 25°C$		4	6.5		4	8	mA
			T_A = full range		9					

[†]All characteristics are measured under open-loop conditions with zero common-mode input voltage unless otherwise specified. Full range for $T_A = -55°C$ to 125°C for SE5534 and SE5534A and 0°C to 70°C for NE5534 and NE5534A.

operating characteristics, $V_{CC\pm} = \pm 15$ V, $T_A = 25°C$

PARAMETER		TEST CONDITIONS	SE5534, NE5534 MIN	TYP	MAX	SE5534A, NE5534A MIN	TYP	MAX	UNIT
SR	Slew rate at unity gain	$C_C = 0$		13			13		V/μs
		$C_C = 22$ pF		6			6		
t_r	Rise time	$V_I = 50$ mV, $A_{VD} = 1$, $R_L = 600$ Ω, $C_C = 22$ pF, $C_L = 100$ pF		20			20		ns
	Overshoot factor			20%			20%		
t_r	Rise time	$V_I = 50$ mV, $A_{VD} = 1$, $R_L = 600$ Ω, $C_C = 47$ pF, $C_L = 500$ pF		50			50		ns
	overshoot factor			35%			35%		
V_n	Equivalent input noise voltage	$f = 30$ Hz		7			5.5	7	nV/√Hz
		$f = 1$ kHz		4			3.5	4.5	
I_n	Equivalent input noise current	$f = 30$ Hz		2.5			1.5		pA/√Hz
		$f = 1$ kHz		0.6			0.4		
F	Average noise figure	$R_S = 5$ kΩ, $f = 10$ Hz to 20 kHz					0.9		dB

Courtesy of Texas Instruments Incorporated.

SE5534, SE5534A, NE5534, NE5534A
LOW-NOISE OPERATIONAL AMPLIFIERS

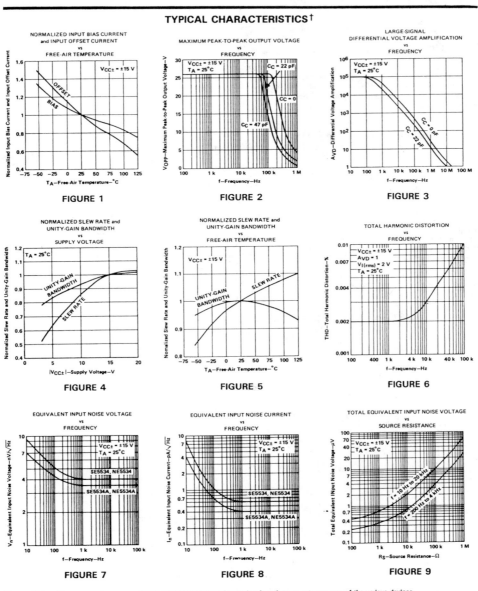

TYPICAL CHARACTERISTICS†

FIGURE 1

FIGURE 2

FIGURE 3

FIGURE 4

FIGURE 5

FIGURE 6

FIGURE 7

FIGURE 8

FIGURE 9

†Data at high and low temperatures are applicable only within the rated operating free-air temperature ranges of the various devices.

TEXAS
INSTRUMENTS
POST OFFICE BOX 225012 ● DALLAS, TEXAS 75265

Courtesy of Texas Instruments Incorporated.

LM78XX Series Voltage Regulators

Voltage Regulators

General Description

The LM78XX series of three terminal regulators is available with several fixed output voltages making them useful in a wide range of applications. One of these is local on card regulation, eliminating the distribution problems associated with single point regulation. The voltages available allow these regulators to be used in logic systems, instrumentation, HiFi, and other solid state electronic equipment. Although designed primarily as fixed voltage regulators these devices can be used with external components to obtain adjustable voltages and currents.

The LM78XX series is available in an aluminum TO-3 package which will allow over 1.0A load current if adequate heat sinking is provided. Current limiting is included to limit the peak output current to a safe value. Safe area protection for the output transistor is provided to limit internal power dissipation. If internal power dissipation becomes too high for the heat sinking provided, the thermal shutdown circuit takes over preventing the IC from overheating.

Considerable effort was expended to make the LM78XX series of regulators easy to use and minimize the number of external components. It is not necessary to bypass the output, although this does improve transient response. Input bypassing is needed only if the regulator is located far from the filter capacitor of the power supply.

For output voltage other than 5V, 12V and 15V the LM117 series provides an output voltage range from 1.2V to 57V.

Features

- Output current in excess of 1A
- Internal thermal overload protection
- No external components required
- Output transistor safe area protection
- Internal short circuit current limit
- Available in the aluminum TO-3 package

Voltage Range

LM7805C	5V
LM7812C	12V
LM7815C	15V

Schematic and Connection Diagrams

Metal Can Package
TO-3 (K)
Aluminum

OUTPUT — GND

INPUT

BOTTOM VIEW

Order Numbers
LM7805CK
LM7812CK
LM7815CK
See Package KC02A

Plastic Package
TO-220 (T)

GND

OUTPUT
GND
INPUT

TOP VIEW

Order Numbers:
LM7805CT
LM7812CT
LM7815CT
See Package T03B

1-181

Reprinted with Permission of National Semiconductor Corp.

LM78XX Series

Absolute Maximum Ratings

Input Voltage (V_O = 5V, 12V and 15V)	35V
Internal Power Dissipation (Note 1)	Internally Limited
Operating Temperature Range (T_A)	0°C to +70°C
Maximum Junction Temperature	
(K Package)	150°C
(T Package)	125°C
Storage Temperature Range	−65°C to +150°C
Lead Temperature (Soldering, 10 seconds)	
TO-3 Package K	300°C
TO-220 Package T	230°C

Electrical Characteristics LM78XXC (Note 2) 0°C ≤ Tj ≤ 125°C unless otherwise noted.

OUTPUT VOLTAGE			5V			12V			15V			
INPUT VOLTAGE (unless otherwise noted)			10V			19V			23V			UNITS
PARAMETER		CONDITIONS	MIN	TYP	MAX	MIN	TYP	MAX	MIN	TYP	MAX	
V_O	Output Voltage	T_j = 25°C, 5 mA ≤ I_O ≤ 1A	4.8	5	5.2	11.5	12	12.5	14.4	15	15.6	V
		P_D ≤ 15W, 5 mA ≤ I_O ≤ 1A	4.75		5.25	11.4		12.6	14.25		15.75	V
		V_{MIN} ≤ V_{IN} ≤ V_{MAX}	(7 ≤ V_{IN} ≤ 20)			(14.5 ≤ V_{IN} ≤ 30)			(17.5 ≤ V_{IN} ≤ 30)			V
ΔV_O	Line Regulation	I_O = 500 mA — T_j = 25°C		3	50		4	120		4	150	mV
		ΔV_{IN}	(7 ≤ V_{IN} ≤ 25)			(14.5 ≤ V_{IN} ≤ 30)			(17.5 ≤ V_{IN} ≤ 30)			V
		0°C ≤ T_j ≤ +125°C			50			120			150	mV
		ΔV_{IN}	(8 ≤ V_{IN} ≤ 20)			(15 ≤ V_{IN} ≤ 27)			(18.5 ≤ V_{IN} ≤ 30)			V
		I_O ≤ 1A — T_j = 25°C			50			120			150	mV
		ΔV_{IN}	(7.3 ≤ V_{IN} ≤ 20)			(14.6 ≤ V_{IN} ≤ 27)			(17.7 ≤ V_{IN} ≤ 30)			V
		0° ≤ T_j ≤ +125°C			25			60			75	mV
		ΔV_{IN}	(8 ≤ IN ≤ 12)			(16 ≤ V_{IN} ≤ 22)			(20 ≤ V_{IN} ≤ 26)			V
ΔV_O	Load Regulation	T_j = 25°C, 5 mA ≤ I_O ≤ 1.5A		10	50		12	120		12	150	mV
		250 mA ≤ I_O ≤ 750 mA			25			60			75	mV
		5 mA ≤ I_O ≤ 1A, 0°C ≤ T_j ≤ +125°C			50			120			150	mV
I_Q	Quiescent Current	I_O ≤ 1A — T_j = 25°C			8			8			8	mA
		0°C ≤ T_j ≤ +125°C			8.5			8.5			8.5	mA
ΔI_Q	Quiescent Current Change	5 mA ≤ I_O ≤ 1A			0.5			0.5			0.5	mA
		T_j = 25°C, I_O ≤ 1A			1.0			1.0			1.0	mA
		V_{MIN} ≤ V_{IN} ≤ V_{MAX}	(7.5 ≤ V_{IN} ≤ 20)			(14.8 ≤ V_{IN} ≤ 27)			(17.9 ≤ V_{IN} ≤ 30)			V
		I_O ≤ 500 mA, 0°C ≤ T_j ≤ +125°C			1.0			1.0			1.0	mA
		V_{MIN} ≤ V_{IN} ≤ V_{MAX}	(7 ≤ V_{IN} ≤ 25)			(14.5 ≤ V_{IN} ≤ 30)			(17.5 ≤ V_{IN} ≤ 30)			V
V_N	Output Noise Voltage	T_A = 25°C, 10 Hz ≤ f ≤ 100 kHz		40			75			90		μV
$\dfrac{\Delta V_{IN}}{\Delta V_{OUT}}$ Ripple Rejection		f = 120 Hz { I_O ≤ 1A, T_j = 25°C or I_O ≤ 500 mA	62	80		55	72		54	70		dB
		0°C ≤ T_j ≤ +125°C	62			55			54			dB
		V_{MIN} ≤ V_{IN} ≤ V_{MAX}	(8 ≤ V_{IN} ≤ 18)			(15 ≤ V_{IN} ≤ 25)			(18.5 ≤ V_{IN} ≤ 28.5)			V
R_O	Dropout Voltage	T_j = 25°C, I_{OUT} = 1A		2.0			2.0			2.0		V
	Output Resistance	f = 1 kHz		8			18			19		mΩ
	Short-Circuit Current	T_j = 25°C		2.1			1.5			1.2		A
	Peak Output Current	T_j = 25°C		2.4			2.4			2.4		A
	Average TC of V_{OUT}	0°C ≤ T_j ≤ +125°C, I_O = 5 mA		0.6			1.5			1.8		mV/°C
V_{IN}	Input Voltage Required to Maintain Line Regulation	T_j = 25°C, I_O ≤ 1A	7.3			14.6			17.7			V

NOTE 1: Thermal resistance of the TO-3 package (K, KC) is typically 4°C/W junction to case and 35°C/W case to ambient. Thermal resistance of the TO-220 package (T) is typically 4°C/W junction to case and 50°C/W case to ambient.

NOTE 2: All characteristics are measured with capacitor across the inut of 0.22 μF, and a capacitor across the output of 0.1 μF. All characteristics except noise voltage and ripple rejection ratio are measured using pulse techniques (t_w ≤ 10 ms, duty cycle ≤ 5%). Output voltage changes due to changes in internal temperature must be taken into account separately.

Reprinted with Permission of National Semiconductor Corp.

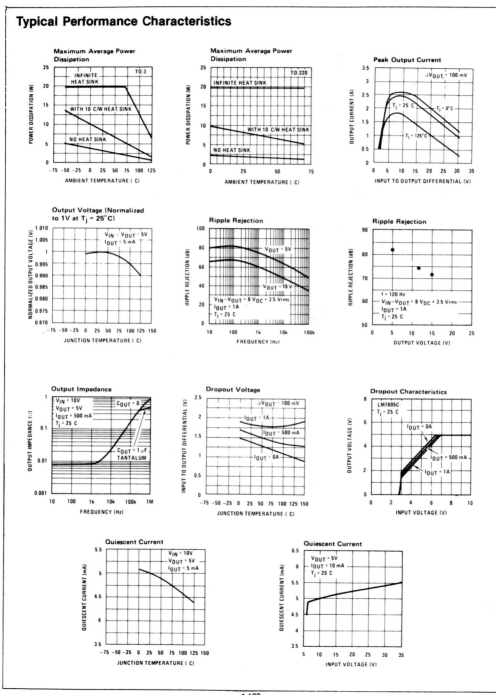

Reprinted with Permission of National Semiconductor Corp.

 National Semiconductor

Voltage Regulators

LM79XX Series 3-Terminal Negative Regulators

General Description

The LM79XX series of 3-terminal regulators is available with fixed output voltages of −5V, −12V, and −15V. These devices need only one external component—a compensation capacitor at the output. The LM79XX series is packaged in the TO-220 power package and is capable of supplying 1.5A of output current.

These regulators employ internal current limiting safe area protection and thermal shutdown for protection against virtually all overload conditions.

Low ground pin current of the LM79XX series allows output voltage to be easily boosted above the preset value with a resistor divider. The low quiescent current

drain of these devices with a specified maximum change with line and load ensures good regulation in the voltage boosted mode.

For applications requiring other voltages, see LM137 data sheet.

Features

- Thermal, short circuit and safe area protection
- High ripple rejection
- 1.5A output current
- 4% preset output voltage

Typical Applications

±15V, 1 Amp Tracking Regulators

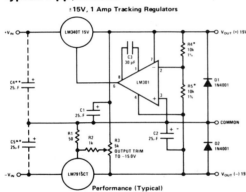

Variable Output

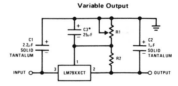

*Improves transient response and ripple rejection. Do not increase beyond 50μF.

$$V_{OUT} = V_{SET}\left(\frac{R1 + R2}{R2}\right)$$

Select R2 as follows

LM7905CT	300Ω
LM7912CT	750Ω
LM7915CT	1k

Performance (Typical)

	(−15)	(+15)
Load Regulation at ΔI_L = 1A	40 mV	2 mV
Output Ripple, C_{IN} = 3000μF, I_L = 1A	100μVrms	100μVrms
Temperature Stability	50 mV	50 mV
Output Noise 10 Hz ≤ f ≤ 10 kHz	150μVrms	150μVrms

*Resistor tolerance of R4 and R5 determine matching of (+) and (−) outputs
**Necessary only if raw supply filter capacitors are more than 3″ from regulators

Fixed Regulator

*Required if regulator is separated from filter capacitor by more than 3″. For value given, capacitor must be solid tantalum. 25μF aluminum electrolytic may be substituted.

†Required for stability. For value given, capacitor must be solid tantalum. 25μF aluminum electrolytic may be substituted. Values given may be increased without limit.

For output capacitance in excess of 100μF, a high current diode from input to output (1N4001, etc.) will protect the regulator from momentary input shorts.

Dual Trimmed Supply

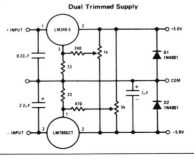

Reprinted with Permission of National Semiconductor Corp.

LM79XX Series

Absolute Maximum Ratings

Input Voltage
  (V_O = 5V)   −35V
  (V_O = 12V and 15V)   −40V
Input-Output Differential
  (V_O = 5V)   25V
  (V_O = 12V and 15V)   30V
Power Dissipation   Internally Limited
Operating Junction Temperature Range $0°C$ to +125$°C$
Storage Temperature Range   −65$°C$ to +150$°C$
Lead Temperature (Soldering, 10 seconds)   230$°C$

Electrical Characteristics Conditions unless otherwise noted: I_{OUT} = 500 mA, C_{IN} = 2.2μF, C_{OUT} = 1μF, $0°C \leq T_J \leq +125°C$, Power Dissipation $\leq$ 15W.

PART NUMBER			LM7905C			UNITS
OUTPUT VOLTAGE			5V			
INPUT VOLTAGE (unless otherwise specified)			−10V			
PARAMETER		CONDITIONS	MIN	TYP	MAX	
V_O	Output Voltage	T_J = 25$°C$	−4.8	−5.0	−5.2	V
		5 mA $\leq I_{OUT} \leq$ 1A,	−4.75		−5.25	V
		P $\leq$ 15W	($-20 \leq V_{IN} \leq -7$)			V
ΔV_O	Line Regulation	T_J = 25$°C$, (Note 2)		8	50	mV
			($-25 \leq V_{IN} \leq -7$)			V
				2	15	mV
			($-12 \leq V_{IN} \leq -8$)			V
ΔV_O	Load Regulation	T_J = 25$°C$, (Note 2)				mV
		5 mA $\leq I_{OUT} \leq$ 1.5A		15	100	mV
		250 mA $\leq I_{OUT} \leq$ 750 mA		5	50	mV
I_Q	Quiescent Current	T_J = 25$°C$		1	2	mA
ΔI_Q	Quiescent Current	With Line			0.5	mA
	Change		($-25 \leq V_{IN} \leq -7$)			V
		With Load, 5 mA $\leq I_{OUT} \leq$ 1A			0.5	mA
V_n	Output Noise Voltage	T_A = 25$°C$, 10 Hz $\leq$ f $\leq$ 100 Hz		125		μV
	Ripple Rejection	f = 120 Hz	54	66		dB
			($-18 \leq V_{IN} \leq -8$)			V
	Dropout Voltage	T_J = 25$°C$, I_{OUT} = 1A		1.1		V
I_{OMAX}	Peak Output Current	T_J = 25$°C$		2.2		A
	Average Temperature Coefficient of Output Voltage	I_{OUT} = 5 mA, 0 C $\leq T_J \leq$ 100 C		0.4		mV/C

Reprinted with Permission of National Semiconductor Corp.

LM79XX Series

1

Electrical Characteristics (Continued) Conditions unless otherwise noted: I_{OUT} = 500 mA, C_{IN} = 2.2µF, C_{OUT} = 1µF, 0°C $\leq$ T$_J$ $\leq$ +125°C, Power Dissipation = 1.5W.

PART NUMBER		LM7912C			LM7915C			UNITS
OUTPUT VOLTAGE		12V			15V			
INPUT VOLTAGE (unless otherwise specified)		−19V			−23V			
PARAMETER	CONDITIONS	MIN	TYP	MAX	MIN	TYP	MAX	
V_O Output Voltage	T$_J$ = 25°C	−11.5	−12.0	−12.5	−14.4	−15.0	−15.6	V
	5 mA $\leq$ I_{OUT} $\leq$ 1A,	−11.4		−12.6	−14.25		−15.75	V
	P $\leq$ 15W	(−27 $\leq$ V$_{IN}$ $\leq$ −14.5)			(−30 $\leq$ V$_{IN}$ $\leq$ −17.5)			V
ΔV_O Line Regulation	T$_J$ = 25°C, (Note 2)		5	80		5	100	mV
		(−30 $\leq$ V$_{IN}$ $\leq$ −14.5)			(−30 $\leq$ V$_{IN}$ $\leq$ −17.5)			V
			3	30		3	50	mV
		(−22 $\leq$ V$_{IN}$ $\leq$ −16)			(−26 $\leq$ V$_{IN}$ $\leq$ −20)			V
ΔV_O Load Regulation	T$_J$ = 25°C, (Note 2)		15	200		15	200	mV
	5 mA $\leq$ I_{OUT} $\leq$ 1.5A		15	200		15	200	mV
	250 mA $\leq$ I_{OUT} $\leq$ 750 mA		5	75		5	75	mV
I_Q Quiescent Current	T$_J$ = 25°C		1.5	3		1.5	3	mA
ΔI_Q Quiescent Current Change	With Line			0.5			0.5	mA
		(−30 $\leq$ V$_{IN}$ $\leq$ −14.5)			(−30 $\leq$ V$_{IN}$ $\leq$ −17.5)			V
	With Load, 5 mA $\leq$ I_{OUT} $\leq$ 1A			0.5			0.5	mA
V_n Output Noise Voltage	T$_A$ = 25°C, 10 Hz $\leq$ f $\leq$ 100 Hz		300			375		µV
Ripple Rejection	f = 120 Hz	54	70		54	70		dB
		(−25 $\leq$ V$_{IN}$ $\leq$ −15)			(−30 $\leq$ V$_{IN}$ $\leq$ −17.5)			V
Dropout Voltage	T$_J$ = 25°C, I_{OUT} = 1A		1.1			1.1		V
I_{OMAX} Peak Output Current	T$_J$ = 25°C		2.2			2.2		A
Average Temperature Coefficient of Output Voltage	I_{OUT} = 5 mA, 0°C $\leq$ T$_J$ $\leq$ 100°C		−0.8			−1.0		mV/°C

Note 1: For calculations of junction temperature rise due to power dissipation, thermal resistance junction to ambient (θ_{JA}) is 50°C/W (no heat sink) and 5°C/W (infinite heat sink).

Note 2: Regulation is measured at a constant junction temperature by pulse testing with a low duty cycle. Changes in output voltage due to heating effects must be taken into account.

Reprinted with Permission of National Semiconductor Corp.

LM79XX Series

Typical Applications (Continued)

High Stability 1 Amp Regulator

Load and line regulation < 0.01% temperature stability ≤ 0.2%

† Determines Zener current

†† Solid tantalum

*Select resistors to set output voltage. 2 ppm/°C tracking suggested

Preventing Positive Regulator Latch-Up

Current Source

R1 and D1 allow the positive regulator to "start-up" when $+V_{IN}$ is delayed relative to $-V_{IN}$ and a heavy load is drawn between the outputs. Without R1 and D1, most three-terminal regulators will not start with heavy (0.1A–1A) load current flowing to the negative regulator, even though the positive output is clamped by D2.

*R2 is optional. Ground pin current from the positive regulator flowing through R1 will increase $+V_{OUT} \approx 60$ mV if R2 is omitted.

$$*I_{OUT} = 1 \text{ mA} + \frac{5V}{R1}$$

Light Controllers Using Silicon Photo Cells

*Lamp brightness increases until $i_l = i_Q$ (≈ 1 mA) + 5V/R1.

† Necessary only if raw supply filter capacitor is more than 2" from LM7905CT

*Lamp brightness increases until $i_l = 5V/R1$ (i_l can be set as low as 1μA)

† Necessary only if raw supply filter capacitor is more than 2" from LM7905CT

Connection Diagrams

TO-3 Package

Order Numbers:
LM7905CK
LM7912CK
LM7915CK
See NS Package KC02A

TO-220 Package

Order Numbers:
LM7905CT
LM7912CT
LM7915CT
See NS Package T03B

1-196

Reprinted with Permission of National Semiconductor Corp.

Audio/Radio Circuits

LM13600/LM13600A/LM11600A Dual Operational Transconductance Amplifiers With Linearizing Diodes and Buffers

(sidebar) LM13600/LM13600A/LM11600A

General Description

The LM13600 series consists of two current controlled transconductance amplifiers each with differential inputs and a push pull output. The two amplifiers share common supplies but otherwise operate independently. Linearizing diodes are provided at the inputs to reduce distortion and allow higher input levels. The results is a 10 dB signal-to-noise improvement referenced to 0.5 percent THD. Controlled impedance buffers are provided which are especially designed to complement the dynamic range of the amplifiers.

Features

- gm adjustable over 6 decades

- Excellent gm linearity
- Excellent matching between amplifiers
- Linearizing diodes
- Controlled impedance buffers
- High output signal to noise ratio
- Wide supply range ± 2V to ± 22V.

Applications

- Current controlled amplifiers
- Current controlled impedances
- Current controlled filters
- Current controlled oscillators
- Multiplexers
- Timers
- Sample and hold circuits

Schematic and Connection Diagrams

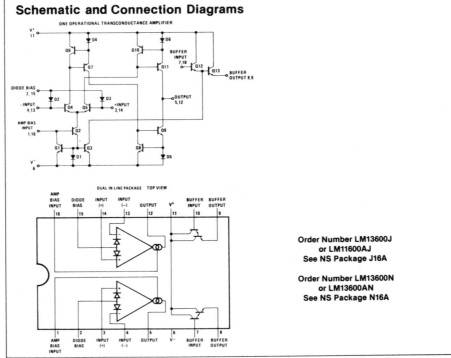

Order Number LM13600J
or LM11600AJ
See NS Package J16A

Order Number LM13600N
or LM13600AN
See NS Package N16A

10-242

Reprinted with Permission of National Semiconductor Corp.

Absolute Maximum Ratings

Supply Voltage (Note 1)
LM13600   36 V_{DC} or ± 18 V
LM13600A, LM11600A   44 V_{DC} or ± 22 V
Power Dissipation (Note 2) T_A = 25°C
   LM13600N, LM13600AN   570 mW
   LM13600J, LM11600AJ   600mW
Differential Input Voltage   ± 5 V
Diode Bias Current (I_D)   2 mA
Amplifier Bias Current (I_{ABC})   2 mA
Output Short Circuit Duration   Indefinite
Buffer Output Current (Note 3)   20 mA
Operating Temperature Range
   LM13600N, LM13600AN   0° C to + 70° C
   LM13600J, LM11600AJ   -55° C to + 125° C
DC Input Voltage   + V_S to -V_S
Storage Temperature Range   -65° C to + 150° C
Lead Temperature (Soldering, 10 seconds)   300° C

Electrical Characteristics (Note 4)

Parameters	Conditions	LM13600			LM13600A LM11600A			Units
		Min	Typ	Max	Min	Typ	Max	
Input Offset Voltage (V_{OS})			0.4	4		0.4	1	mV
	Over Specified Temperature Range						2	mV
	I_{ABC} 5 μA		0.3	4		0.3	1	mV
V_{OS} Including Diodes	Diode Bias Current (I_D) = 500 μA		0.5	5		0.5	2	mV
Input Offset Change	5 μA ≤ I_{ABC} ≤ 500 μA		0.1	3		0.1	1	mV
Input Offset Current			0.1	0.6		0.1	0.6	μA
Input Bias Current			0.4	5		0.4	5	μA
	Over Specified Temperature Range		1	8		1	7	μA
Forward Transconductance(gm)		6700	9600	13000	7700	9600	12000	μmho
	Over specified Temp Range	5400			4000			μmho
gm Tracking			0.3			0.3		dB
Peak Output Current	R_L = 0, I_{ABC} = 5 μA		5		3	5	7	μA
	R_L = 0, I_{ABC} = 500 μA	350	500	650	350	500	650	μA
	R_L = 0, Over Specified Temp Range	300			300			μA
Peak Output Voltage								
Positive	R_L = ∞, 5 μA ≤ I_{ABC}≤ 500 μA	+ 12	+ 14.2		+ 12	+ 14.2		V
Negative	R_L = ∞, 5 μA ≤ I_{ABC}≤ 500 μA	− 12	− 14.4		− 12	− 14.4		V
Supply Current	I_{ABC}=500μA, Both Channels		2.6			2.6		mA
V_{OS} Sensitivity								
Positive	$\triangle V_{OS}/\triangle$ V +		20	150		20	150	μV/V
Negative	$\triangle V_{OS}/\triangle$ V –		20	150		20	150	μV/V
CMRR		80	110		80	110		dB
Common Mode Range		± 12	± 13.5		± 12	± 13.5		V
Crosstalk	Referred to Input (Note 5) 20 Hz < f < 20 KHz		100			100		dB
Diff.Input Current	I_{ABC} = 0, Input = ± 4 V		0.02	100		0.02	10	nA
Leakage Current	I_{ABC} = 0 (Refer To Test Circuit)		0.2	100		0.2	5	nA
Input Resistance		10	26		10	26		KΩ
Open Loop Bandwith			2			2		MHz
Slew Rate	Unity Gain Compensated		50			50		V/μSec
Buff. Input Current	(Note 5, Except I_{ABC} = 0 μA)		0.2	0.4		0.2	0.4	μA
Peak Buffer Output Voltage	(Note 5)	10			10			V

Note 1. For selections to a supply voltage above ± 22V, contact factory.
Note 2. For operating at high temperatures, the device must be derated based on a 150° C maximum junction temperature and a thermal resistance of 175° C/W which applies for the device soldered in a printed circuit board, operating in still air.
Note 3. Buffer output current should be limited so as to not exceed package dissipation.
Note 4. These specifications apply for V_S = ± 15 V, T_A = 25° C, amplifier bias current (I_{ABC}) = 500μA, pins 2 and 15 open unless otherwise specified. The inputs to the buffers are grounded and outputs are open.
Note 5. These specifications apply for V_S = ± 15V, I_{ABC} = 500 μA, R_{OUT} = 5 KΩ connected from the buffer output to – V_S and the input of the buffer is connected to the transconductance amplifier output.

10

Reprinted with Permission of National Semiconductor Corp.

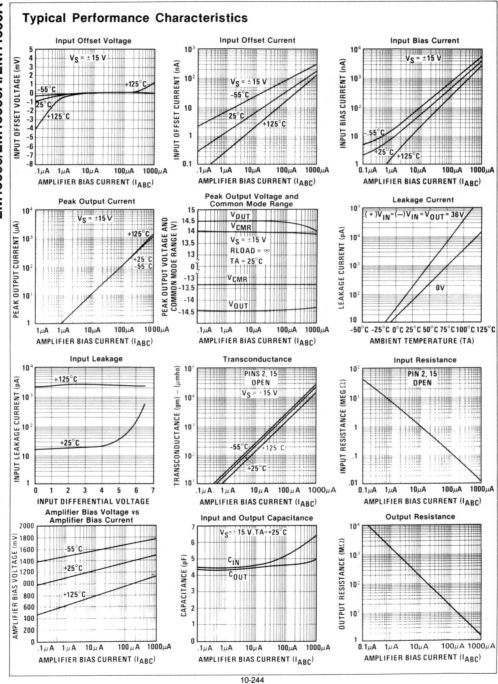

Reprinted with Permission of National Semiconductor Corp.

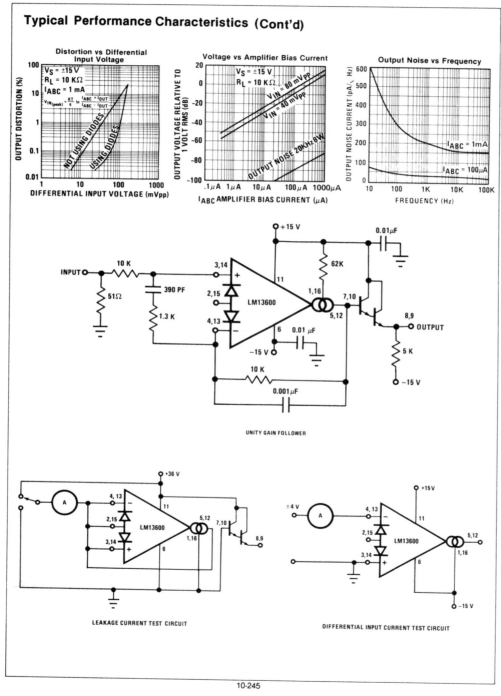

Reprinted with Permission of National Semiconductor Corp.

TIP31, TIP31A, TIP31B, TIP31C,
TIP31D, TIP31E, TIP31F
N-P-N SILICON POWER TRANSISTORS
DECEMBER 1970 – REVISED OCTOBER 1984

- **40 W at 25°C Case Temperature**
- **3 A Continuous Collector Current**
- **5 A Peak Collector Current**
- **Minimum f_T of 3 MHz at 10 V, 0.5 mA**
- **Customer-Specified Selections Available**

device schematic

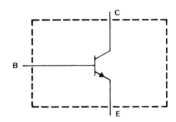

TO-220AB PACKAGE

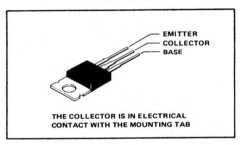

EMITTER
COLLECTOR
BASE

**THE COLLECTOR IS IN ELECTRICAL
CONTACT WITH THE MOUNTING TAB**

absolute maximum ratings at 25°C case temperature (unless otherwise noted)

	TIP31	TIP31A	TIP31B	TIP31C
Collector-base voltage	80 V	100 V	120 V	140 V
Collector-emitter voltage (I_B = 0)	40 V	60 V	80 V	100 V
Emitter-base voltage	5 V			
Continuous collector current	3 A			
Peak collector current (see Note 1)	5 A			
Continuous base current	1 A			
Safe operating area at 25°C case temperature	See Figure 4			
Continuous device dissipation at (or below) 25°C case temperature (see Note 2)	40 W			
Continuous device dissipation at (or below) 25°C free-air temperature (see Note 3)	2 W			
Unclamped inductive load energy (see Note 4)	32 mJ			
Operating collector junction and storage temperature range	− 65°C to 150°C			
Lead temperature 3,2 mm (0.125 inch) from case for 10 seconds	250°C			

NOTES: 1. This value applies for t_w ⩽ 0.3 ms, duty cycle ⩽ 10%.
2. Derate linearly to 150°C case temperature at the rate of 0.32 W/°C.
3. Derate linearly to 150°C free-air temperature at the rate of 16 mW/°C.
4. This rating is based on the capability of the transistor to operate safely in the circuit in Figure 2.

5

TIP Devices

TEXAS
INSTRUMENTS
POST OFFICE BOX 225012 • DALLAS, TEXAS 75265

Courtesy of Texas Instruments Incorporated.

TIP31, TIP31A, TIP31B, TIP31C,
TIP31D, TIP31E, TIP31F
N-P-N SILICON POWER TRANSISTORS

absolute maximum ratings at 25°C case temperature (unless otherwise noted)

	TIP31D	TIP31E	TIP31F
Collector-base voltage	160 V	180 V	200 V
Collector-emitter voltage ($I_B = 0$)	120 V	140 V	160 V
Emitter-base voltage	5 V		
Continuous collector current	3 A		
Peak collector current (see Note 1)	5 A		
Continuous base current	1 A		
Safe operating area at 25°C case temperature	See Figure 4		
Continuous device dissipation at (or below) 25°C case temperature (see Note 2)	40 W		
Continuous device dissipation at (or below) 25°C free-air temperature (see Note 3)	2 W		
Unclamped inductive load energy (see Note 4)	32 mJ		
Operating collector junction and storage temperature range	−65°C to 150°C		
Lead temperature 3,2 mm (0.125 inch) from case for 10 seconds	250°C		

NOTES: 1. This value applies for $t_w \leqslant 0.3$ ms, duty cycle $\leqslant 10\%$.
2. Derate linearly to 150°C case temperature at the rate of 0.32 W/°C.
3. Derate linearly to 150°C free-air temperature at the rate of 16 mW/°C.
4. This rating is based on the capability of the transistor to operate safely in the circuit in Figure 2.

electrical characteristics at 25°C case temperature (unless otherwise noted)

PARAMETER	TEST CONDITIONS	TIP31			TIP31A			TIP31B			TIP31C			UNIT
		MIN	TYP	MAX	MIN	TYP	MAX	MIN	TYP	MAX	MIN	TYP	MAX	
$V_{(BR)CEO}$	$I_C = 30$ mA, $I_B = 0$, See Note 5	40			60			80			100			V
I_{CEO}	$V_{CE} = 30$ V, $I_B = 0$			0.3			0.3							mA
	$V_{CE} = 60$ V, $I_B = 0$									0.3			0.3	
I_{CES}	$V_{CE} = 80$ V, $V_{BE} = 0$			0.2										mA
	$V_{CE} = 100$ V, $V_{BE} = 0$						0.2							
	$V_{CE} = 120$ V, $V_{BE} = 0$									0.2				
	$V_{CE} = 140$ V, $V_{BE} = 0$												0.2	
I_{EBO}	$V_{EB} = 5$ V, $I_C = 0$			1			1			1			1	mA
h_{FE}	$V_{CE} = 4$ V, $I_C = 1$ A, See Notes 5 and 6	25			25			25			25			
	$V_{CE} = 4$ V, $I_C = 3$ A, See Notes 5 and 6	10		50	10		50	10		50	10		50	
V_{BE}	$V_{CE} = 4$ V, $I_C = 3$ A, See Notes 5 and 6			1.8			1.8			1.8			1.8	V
$V_{CE(sat)}$	$I_B = 375$ mA, $I_C = 3$ A, See Notes 5 and 6			1.2			1.2			1.2			1.2	V
h_{fe}	$V_{CE} = 10$ V, $I_C = 0.5$ A, f = 1 kHz	20			20			20			20			
h_{fe}	$V_{CE} = 10$ V, $I_C = 0.5$ A, f = 1 MHz	3			3			3			3			

NOTES: 5. These parameters must be measured using pulse techniques, $t_w = 300\,\mu s$, duty cycle $\leqslant 2\%$.
6. These parameters are measured with voltage-sensing contacts separate from the current-carrying contacts.

TEXAS
INSTRUMENTS
POST OFFICE BOX 225012 • DALLAS, TEXAS 75265

Courtesy of Texas Instruments Incorporated.

TIP31, TIP31A, TIP31B, TIP31C,
TIP31D, TIP31E, TIP31F
N-P-N SILICON POWER TRANSISTORS

electrical characteristics at 25°C case temperature (unless otherwise noted)

PARAMETER	TEST CONDITIONS	TIP31D			TIP31E			TIP31F			UNIT
		MIN	TYP	MAX	MIN	TYP	MAX	MIN	TYP	MAX	
$V_{(BR)CEO}$	$I_C = 30$ mA, $I_B = 0$, See Note 5	120			140			160			V
I_{CEO}	$V_{CE} = 90$ V, $I_B = 0$			0.3			0.3			0.3	mA
I_{CES}	$V_{CE} = 160$ V, $V_{BE} = 0$			0.2							mA
	$V_{CE} = 180$ V, $V_{BE} = 0$						0.2				
	$V_{CE} = 200$ V, $V_{BE} = 0$									0.2	
I_{EBO}	$V_{EB} = 5$ V, $I_C = 0$			1			1			1	mA
h_{FE}	$V_{CE} = 4$ V, $I_C = 1$ A, See Notes 5 and 6	25			25			25			
	$V_{CE} = 4$ V, $I_C = 3$ A, See Notes 5 and 6	5			5			5			
V_{BE}	$V_{CE} = 4$ V, $I_C = 3$ A, See Notes 5 and 6			1.8			1.8			1.8	V
$V_{CE(sat)}$	$I_B = 750$ mA, $I_C = 3$ A, See Notes 5 and 6			2.5			2.5			2.5	V
h_{fe}	$V_{CE} = 10$ V, $I_C = 0.5$ A, f = 1 kHz	20			20			20			
h_{fe}	$V_{CE} = 10$ V, $I_C = 0.5$ A, f = 1 MHz	3			3			3			

NOTES: 5. These parameters must be measured using pulse techniques, $t_w = 300\,\mu s$, duty cycle ≤ 2%.
6. These parameters are measured using voltage-sensing contacts separate from the current-carrying contacts.

thermal characteristics

PARAMETER		MIN	TYP	MAX	UNIT
$R_{\theta JC}$				3.125	°C/W
$R_{\theta JA}$				62.5	

resistive-load switching characteristic at 25°C case temperature (unless otherwise noted)

PARAMETER	TEST CONDITIONS†			MIN	TYP	MAX	UNIT
t_{on}	$I_C = 1$ A,	$I_{B1} = 0.1$ A,	$I_{B2} = -0.1$ A,			0.5	μs
t_{off}	$V_{BE(off)} = -4.3$ V, $R_L = 30\,\Omega$,		See Figure 1			2	

† Voltage and current values shown are nominal; exact values vary slightly with transistor parameters.

5

TIP Devices

TEXAS
INSTRUMENTS
POST OFFICE BOX 225012 • DALLAS, TEXAS 75265

Courtesy of Texas Instruments Incorporated.

TIP32, TIP32A, TIP32B, TIP32C,
TIP32D, TIP32E, TIP32F
P-N-P SILICON POWER TRANSISTORS

JULY 1968 – REVISED OCTOBER 1984

- Designed for Complementary Use With TIP31 Series
- 40 W at 25°C Case Temperature
- 3 A Continuous Collector Current
- 5 A Peak Collector Current
- Minimum f_T of 3 MHz at 10 V, 0.5 A
- Customer-Specified Selections Available

device schematic

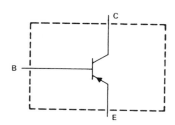

TO-220AB PACKAGE

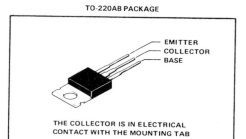

EMITTER
COLLECTOR
BASE

THE COLLECTOR IS IN ELECTRICAL
CONTACT WITH THE MOUNTING TAB

absolute maximum ratings at 25°C case temperature (unless otherwise noted)

	TIP32	TIP32A	TIP32B	TIP32C
Collector-base voltage	– 80 V	– 100 V	– 120 V	– 140 V
Collector-emitter voltage ($I_B = 0$)	– 40 V	– 60 V	– 80 V	– 100 V
Emitter-base voltage	– 5 V			
Continuous collector current	– 3 A			
Peak collector current (see Note 1)	– 5 A			
Continuous base current	– 1 A			
Safe operating areas at 25°C case temperature	See Figure 4			
Continuous device dissipation at 25°C case temperature (see Note 2)	40 W			
Continuous device dissipation at (or below) 25°C free-air temperature (see Note 3)	2 W			
Unclamped inductive load energy (see Note 4)	32 mJ			
Operating collector junction and storage temperature range	– 65°C to 150°C			
Lead temperature 3,2 mm (0.125 inch) from case for 10 seconds	250°C			

NOTES: 1. This value applies for $t_w \leqslant 0.3$ms, duty cycle $\leqslant 10\%$.
2. Derate linearly to 150°C case temperature at the rate of 0.32 W/°C.
3. Derate linearly to 150°C free-air temperature at the rate of 16 mW/°C.
4. This rating is based on the capability of the transistor to operate safely in the circuit of Figure 2.

5

TIP Devices

TIP32, TIP32A, TIP32B, TIP32C, TIP32D, TIP32E, TIP32F
P-N-P SILICON POWER TRANSISTORS

absolute maximum ratings at 25°C case temperature (unless otherwise noted)

	TIP32D	TIP32E	TIP32F
Collector-base voltage	– 160 V	– 180 V	– 200 V
Collector-emitter voltage (I_B = 0)	– 120 V	– 140 V	– 160 V
Emitter-base voltage		– 5 V	
Continuous collector current		– 3 A	
Peak collector current (see Note 1)		– 5 A	
Continuous base current		– 1 A	
Safe operating area at 25°C case temperature		See Figure 4	
Continuous device dissipation at 25°C case temperature (see Note 2)		40 W	
Continuous device dissipation at (or below) 25°C free-air temperature (see Note 3)		2 W	
Unclamped inductive load energy (see Note 4)		32 mJ	
Operating collector junction and storage temperature range		– 65°C to 150°C	
Lead temperature 3,2 mm (0.125 inch) from case for 10 seconds		250°C	

NOTES: 1. This value applies for t_w ⩽ 0.3 ms, duty cycle ⩽ 10%.
2. Derate linearly to 150°C case temperature at the rate of 0.32 W/°C.
3. Derate linearly to 150°C free-air temperature at the rate of 16 mW/°C.
4. This rating is based on the capability of the transistor to operate safely in the circuit in Figure 2.

electrical characteristics at 25°C case temperature (unless otherwise noted)

PARAMETER	TEST CONDITIONS	TIP32 MIN TYP MAX	TIP32A MIN TYP MAX	TIP32B MIN TYP MAX	TIP32C MIN TYP MAX	UNIT
$V_{(BR)CEO}$	I_C = – 30 mA, I_B = 0, See Note 5	– 40	– 60	– 80	– 100	V
I_{CEO}	V_{CE} = – 30 V, I_B = 0	– 0.3	– 0.3			mA
	V_{CE} = – 60 V, I_B = 0			– 0.3	– 0.3	
I_{CES}	V_{CE} = – 80 V, V_{BE} = 0	– 0.2				mA
	V_{CE} = – 100 V, V_{BE} = 0		– 0.2			
	V_{CE} = – 120 V, V_{BE} = 0			– 0.2		
	V_{CE} = – 140 V, V_{BE} = 0				– 0.2	
I_{EBO}	V_{EB} = – 5 V, I_C = 0	– 1	– 1	– 1	– 1	mA
h_{FE}	V_{CE} = – 4 V, I_C = – 1 A, See Notes 5 and 6	25	25	25	25	
	V_{CE} = – 4 V, I_C = – 3 A, See Notes 5 and 6	10 50	10 50	10 50	10 50	
V_{BE}	V_{CE} = – 4 V, I_C = – 3 A, See Notes 5 and 6	– 1.8	– 1.8	– 1.8	– 1.8	V
$V_{CE(sat)}$	I_B = – 0.375 A, I_C = – 3 A, See Notes 5 and 6	– 1.2	– 1.2	– 1.2	– 1.2	V
h_{fe}	V_{CE} = – 10 V, I_C = – 0.5 A, f = 1 MHz	20	20	20	20	
$|h_{fe}|$	V_{CE} = – 10 V, I_C = – 0.5 A, f = 1 MHz	3	3	3	3	

NOTES: 5. These parameters must be measured using pulse techniques, t_w = 300 µs, duty cycle ⩽ 2%.
6. These parameters are measured with voltage-sensing contacts separate from the current-carrying contacts.

5

TIP Devices

TEXAS
INSTRUMENTS

POST OFFICE BOX 225012 • DALLAS, TEXAS 75265

Courtesy of Texas Instruments Incorporated.

TIP32, TIP32A, TIP32B, TIP32C,
TIP32D, TIP32E, TIP32F
P-N-P SILICON POWER TRANSISTORS

electrical characteristics at 25°C case temperature (unless otherwise noted)

PARAMETER	TEST CONDITIONS	TIP32D MIN TYP MAX	TIP32E MIN TYP MAX	TIP32F MIN TYP MAX	UNIT
$V_{(BR)CEO}$	$I_C = -30$ mA, $I_B = 0$, See Note 5	-120	-140	-160	V
I_{CEO}	$V_{CE} = -90$ V, $I_B = 0$	-0.3	-0.3	-0.3	mA
I_{CES}	$V_{CE} = -160$ V, $V_{BE} = 0$	-0.2			mA
	$V_{CE} = -180$ V, $V_{BE} = 0$		-0.2		
	$V_{CE} = -200$ V, $V_{BE} = 0$			-0.2	
I_{EBO}	$V_{EB} = -5$ V, $I_C = 0$	-1	-1	-1	mA
h_{FE}	$V_{CE} = -4$ V, $I_C = -1$ A, See Notes 5 and 6	25	25	25	
	$V_{CE} = -4$ V, $I_C = -3$ A, See Notes 5 and 6	5	5	5	
V_{BE}	$V_{CE} = -4$ V, $I_C = -3$ A, See Notes 5 and 6	-1.8	-1.8	-1.8	V
$V_{CE(sat)}$	$I_B = -750$ mA, $I_C = -3$ A, See Notes 5 and 6	-2.5	-2.5	-2.5	V
h_{fe}	$V_{CE} = -10$ V, $I_C = -0.5$ A, $f = 1$ MHz	20	20	20	
$|h_{fe}|$	$V_{CE} = -10$ V, $I_C = -0.5$ A, $f = 1$ MHz	3	3	3	

NOTES: 5. These parameters must be measured using pulse techniques, $t_w = 300\,\mu s$, duty cycle $\leqslant 2\%$.
6. These parameters are measured with voltage-sensing contacts separate from the current-carrying contacts.

thermal characteristics

PARAMETER	MIN TYP MAX	UNIT
$R_{\theta JC}$	3.125	°C/W
$R_{\theta JA}$	62.5	

resistive-load switching characteristic at 25°C case temperature (unless otherwise noted)

PARAMETER	TEST CONDITIONS†	MIN TYP MAX	UNIT
t_{on}	$I_C = -1$ A, $I_{B1} = -0.1$ A, $I_{B2} = 0.1$ A,	0.3	μs
t_{off}	$V_{BE(off)} = 4.3$ V, $R_L = 30\,\Omega$, See Figure 1	1	

† Voltage and current values shown are nominal; exact values vary slightly with transistor parameters.

5

TIP Devices

TEXAS
INSTRUMENTS
POST OFFICE BOX 225012 • DALLAS, TEXAS 75265

appendix b
Decibel Calculations

Early telephone engineers discovered very quickly that they had to work with an enormous range of voltages—from microvolts to tens of volts—because of the tremendous range of sensitivity of the human ear. At the threshold of hearing, the sound pressure is so small that it causes a peak-to-peak eardrum motion of less than the diameter of a hydrogen molecule. Yet the sound pressure that can be endured without immediate damage is about ten million times as great as the pressure at the threshold of hearing. Let us put these figures into a perspective that is more familiar to the electronics student. The output voltage of a common high-impedance dynamic PA microphone is about one millivolt at normal conversation levels. At the threshold of hearing, the output would be about 250 nanovolts. At the level at which human hearing would be immediately damaged, the microphone's output would be roughly two volts.

To simplify the handling of this large range of voltage magnitudes (without pocket calculators, you remember!), a logarithmic means of expressing voltage ratios was devised. In fact, the response of humans to light and sound is logarithmic, so this system had the added advantage of assigning numbers to voltage and power levels and ratios that corresponded with human perception. What does it mean to talk of a logarithmic response to a variable? First, let us review what a logarithm is. The logarithm of number A is simply the power to which the number ten must be raised in order to obtain the same value as the number A. In other words, $\log_{10}(A) = B$ means that $10^B = A$. For example, the logarithm of 2 is 0.303. This means that $10^{0.303} = 2$. The logarithmic system that we have just described is the *base-10* or *common* log system. There is also a log system based upon the exponential function e; this is called the *natural* log system.

The logarithmic system that we call the *decibel* system is founded upon the logarithm of power ratios. If it is desired to logarithmically express the ratio of two power levels P_1 and P_2, we can write:

$$\text{logarithmic level} = \log_{10}(P_1/P_2)$$

This logarithmic level is expressed in *bels*, named after Alexander Graham Bell. It turns out that the bel is an impractically large unit, so we commonly use units of decibels: a decibel is one-tenth of a bel, or there are ten dB in a bel. Thus:

$$\text{power ratio in dB} = 10\log_{10}(P_1/P_2) \tag{B.01}$$

EXAMPLE

Problem

An amplifier has an input signal power of 20 μW and an output power of 1 mW. Express the power gain in dB.

Solution

$$A_{P\,dB} = 10\log_{10}(P_{OUT}/P_{IN}) \tag{B.01}$$
$$= 10\log_{10}(1\text{ mW}/20\ \mu\text{W}) = 10\log_{10}(50) = 17\text{ dB}$$

The power gain is 17 dB.

It is also possible to express voltage or current ratios in dB. In order to simplify calculations of gains and losses, it was decided that for any circuit, the voltage gain in dB, the current gain in dB, and the power gain in dB should all be equal. Therefore it is necessary to multiply the logarithm of a current or voltage ratio by 20 rather than 10 to obtain the dB value:

$$A_{V\,dB} = 20\log_{10}(V_{OUT}/V_{IN}) \tag{B.02}$$

and

$$A_{I\,dB} = 20\log_{10}(I_{OUT}/I_{IN}) \tag{B.03}$$

EXAMPLE

Problem

An amplifier has a signal input current of 10 μA, a signal input voltage of 6 mV, and an output signal current and voltage of 1 mA and 0.6 V, respectively. Verify that the power gain in dB is the same as $A_{I\,dB}$ and $A_{V\,dB}$.

Solution

$$A_I = I_{OUT}/I_{IN} = 1\text{ mA}/10\ \mu\text{A} = 100$$
$$A_{I\,dB} = 20\log_{10}(100) = 40\text{ dB} \quad \text{(from B.03)}$$
$$A_V = V_{OUT}/V_{IN} = 0.6\text{ V}/6\text{ mV} = 100$$
$$A_{V\,dB} = 20\log_{10}(100) = 40\text{ dB} \quad \text{(from B.02)}$$
$$A_P = P_{OUT}/P_{IN} = (1\text{ mA} \cdot 0.6\text{ V})/(10\ \mu\text{A} \cdot 6\text{ mV}) = 0.6\text{ mW}/60\text{ nW} = 10{,}000$$
$$A_{P\,dB} = 10\log_{10}(10{,}000) = 40\text{ dB} \quad \text{(from B.01)}$$

Thus the power gain in dB does equal both the voltage gain and the current gain in dB.

In the above example, the deck was stacked, in that the input and output impedances of the amplifier were the same. (You can verify this for yourself.) If they had not been the same, the gains in dB would not have been equal. This brings us to one of those few glaring inconsistencies between theory and practice in the field of electronics. In order to be strictly and theoretically correct, we should add an impedance correction factor to the equations for voltage and current gain in dB:

$$A_{V\,dB} = 20\log_{10}(V_{OUT}/V_{IN})(Z_{IN}/Z_{OUT})$$
$$A_{I\,dB} = 20\log_{10}(I_{OUT}/I_{IN})(Z_{OUT}/Z_{IN})$$

However, in practice, these impedance corrections are almost never used. Therefore, current and voltage ratios are almost always expressed in dB as indicated in equations B.02 and B.03, and these values will not be equal to each other, or to the power ratio, unless the input and output impedances happen to be equal.

It is possible to express actual voltages and power levels (not just ratios of two levels) in dB fashion, provided that a fixed reference voltage or power is used. The most common way of representing power levels in dB is to use one milliwatt as the reference value. The result is then expressed in dBm (decibels referred to one milliwatt). Voltages are sometimes expressed in dBV (decibels referred to one volt). Thus:

$$P_{dBm} = 10\log_{10}(P/1\text{ mW}) \tag{B.04}$$
$$V_{dBV} = 20\log_{10}(V/1\text{ V}) \tag{B.05}$$

EXAMPLE

Problem

Express the following in dBm or dBV, as appropriate: 14 μW, 1 mW, 22 mW, 1 W, 5 mV, 1 V, 27 V.

Solution

$10\log_{10}(14\text{ μW}/1\text{ mW}) = 10\log_{10}(0.014) = -18.54\text{ dBm}$
$10\log_{10}(1\text{ mW}/1\text{ mW}) = 10\log_{10}(1) = 0\text{ dBm}$
$10\log_{10}(22\text{ mW}/1\text{ mW}) = 13.42\text{ dBm}$
$10\log_{10}(1\text{ W}/1\text{ mW}) = 30\text{ dBm}$
$20\log_{10}(5\text{ mV}/1\text{ V}) = 20\log_{10}(0.005) = -46\text{ dBV}$
$20\log_{10}(1\text{ V}/1\text{ V}) = 0\text{ dBV}$
$20\log_{10}(27\text{ V}/1\text{ V}) = 28.63\text{ dBV}$

Notice in the above examples that zero dB represents a ratio of unity. Thus A_V = 0 and $A_{V dB}$ = 0 dB do not mean the same thing. A numerical voltage gain of zero means that the output voltage is zero; whereas, a gain of zero dB means that the output voltage is the same as the input voltage.

When two or more amplifiers or attenuators are connected in tandem, the total numerical gain must be found by multiplying the individual gains. If the gains are expressed in dB, however, the total dB gain is found by adding the individual dB gains. This is a logical consequence of the dB value being related to an exponent: $X^A \cdot X^B = X^{(A + B)}$. Thus if an amplifier having a voltage gain of 30, an attenuator having a gain of 0.044, and another amplifier having a gain of 86 are cascaded, the resulting gain is $30 \cdot 0.044 \cdot 86 = 113.5$. A voltage gain of 30 is 29.5 dB; a gain of 0.044 is −27.13 dB; and a gain of 86 is 38.69 dB. Thus the total gain in dB is 29.5 dB + (−27.13 dB) + 38.69 dB = 41.06 dB. Sure enough, the dB value corresponding to a numerical gain of 113.5 is 41.1 dB. (We did some rounding of the individual values, or the dB gains would have matched exactly.)

Finding the ratio of current, voltage, or power levels from the dB value is simply a matter of reversing the equations:

$$\text{Power ratio} = \text{antilog(ratio in dB}/10) \qquad \text{(B.06)}$$

$$\text{Voltage ratio} = \text{antilog(ratio in dB}/20) \qquad \text{(B.07)}$$

$$\text{Current ratio} = \text{antilog(ratio in dB}/20) \qquad \text{(B.08)}$$

It should be mentioned here that antilog(x) can also be indicated as $\log^{-1}(x)$ or as 10^x.

EXAMPLE

Problem

Find the numerical gains of amplifiers having the following dB gains:

$$A_{P dB} = 35 \text{ dB} \qquad A_{V dB} = 22 \text{ dB} \qquad A_{I dB} = -18 \text{ dB}$$

Solution

$$A_P = \text{antilog(35 dB}/10) = 3162$$
$$A_V = \text{antilog(22}/20) = 12.6$$
$$A_I = \text{antilog(}-18/20) = 0.126$$

There are certain values of dB gains that are worth memorizing:

dB VALUE	VOLTAGE OR CURRENT RATIO	POWER RATIO
−60 dB	0.001	0.000001
−40 dB	0.01	0.0001
−30 dB	0.0316	0.001
−20 dB	0.1	0.01
−10 dB	0.316 (roughly $\frac{1}{3}$)	0.1
−6 dB	0.5	0.25
−3 dB	0.707 (or $1/\sqrt{2}$)	0.5
0 dB	1.0	1.0
3 dB	1.414 (or $\sqrt{2}$)	2.0
6 dB	2.0	4.0
10 dB	3.16 (roughly 3)	10.0
20 dB	10.0	100.0
30 dB	31.62	1,000.0
40 dB	100	10,000.0
60 dB	1,000	1,000,000.0

Using only these values, it is possible to rapidly approximate the conversion of virtually any number to or from dB without the use of a calculator. For example, to convert a power ratio of 53 dB into a numerical gain, just notice that 53 dB = 40 dB + 10 dB + 3 dB. Thus the numerical gain is $10,000 \cdot 10 \cdot 2 = 200,000$. (The actual value is 199,526.) Working in the other direction, a numerical voltage gain of 60 becomes $10 \cdot 3 \cdot 2$. Thus the dB value is roughly 20 dB + 10 dB + 6 dB = 36 dB. (The actual value is 35.56 dB.)

appendix c

CDA Applications

Current-differencing amplifiers were discussed in Chapter 9, and the differences between their application and that of common op amps was pointed out. However, because of the popularity of CDAs among many experimenters, this appendix has been included. It consists of the full data sheets of two CDAs manufactured by National Semiconductor, at whose lab Thomas M. Frederiksen designed the 3900. The data sheets show many applications for CDAs. As you can see, these application circuits are just the common op amp circuits modified for the particular biasing and input requirements of the CDA, as discussed in Chapter 9.

![National Semiconductor]

Operational Amplifiers/Buffers

LM159/LM359 Dual, High Speed, Programmable, Current Mode (Norton) Amplifiers

General Description

The LM159/LM359 consists of two current differencing (Norton) input amplifiers. Design emphasis has been placed on obtaining high frequency performance and providing user programmable amplifier operating characteristics. Each amplifier is broadbanded to provide a high gain bandwidth product, fast slew rate and stable operation for an inverting closed loop gain of 10 or greater. Pins for additional external frequency compensation are provided. The amplifiers are designed to operate from a single supply and can accommodate input common-mode voltages greater than the supply.

Applications

- General purpose video amplifiers
- High frequency, high Q active filters
- Photo-diode amplifiers
- Wide frequency range waveform generation circuits
- All LM3900 AC applications work to much higher frequencies

Features

- User programmable gain bandwidth product, slew rate, input bias current, output stage biasing current and total device power dissipation

- High gain bandwidth product ($I_{SET} = 0.5$ mA)
  400 MHz for $A_V = 10$ to 100
  30 MHz for $A_V = 1$

- High slew rate ($I_{SET} = 0.5$ mA)
  60 V/μs for $A_V = 10$ to 100
  30 V/μs for $A_V = 1$

- Current differencing inputs allow high common-mode input voltages

- Operates from a single 5V to 22V supply

- Large inverting amplifier output swing, 2 mV to $V_{CC} - 2V$

- Low spot noise, 6 nV/$\sqrt{Hz}$, for f>1 kHz

Typical Application

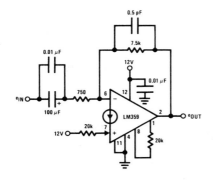

- $A_V = 20$ dB
- -3 dB bandwidth = 2.5 Hz to 25 MHz
- Differential phase error<1° at 3.58 MHz
- Differential gain error <0.5% at 3.58 MHz

Connection Diagram

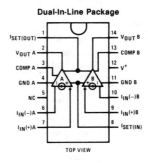

Dual-In-Line Package

TOP VIEW

Order Number LM159J or LM359J
See NS Package J14A
Order Number LM359N
See NS Package N14A

3-226

Reprinted with Permission of National Semiconductor Corp.

Absolute Maximum Ratings

Supply Voltage	22 V$_{DC}$	Input Currents, I$_{IN}$(+) or I$_{IN}$(−)	10 mA$_{DC}$
	± 11 V$_{DC}$	Set Currents, I$_{SET(IN)}$ or I$_{SET(OUT)}$	2 mA$_{DC}$
Power Dissipation (Note 1)		Operating Temperature Range	
J Package	1W	LM159	− 55 °C to + 125 °C
N Package	750 mW	LM359	0 °C to 70 °C
Maximum T$_j$		Storage Temperature Range	− 65 °C to + 150 °C
J Package	150 °C	Lead Temperature (Soldering, 10 seconds)	300 °C
N Package	125 °C		
θjA			
J Package	100 °C/W		
N Package	160 °C/W		

Electrical Characteristics I$_{SET(IN)}$ = I$_{SET(OUT)}$ = 0.5 mA, V$_{supply}$ = 12V, T$_A$ = 25 °C unless otherwise noted.

Parameter	Conditions	LM159			LM359			Units
		Min	Typ	Max	Min	Typ	Max	
Open Loop Voltage Gain	V$_{supply}$ = 12V, R$_L$ = 1k, f = 100 Hz	66	72		62	72		dB
	T$_A$ = 125 °C	62	68			68		dB
Bandwidth								
Unity Gain	R$_{IN}$ = 1 kΩ, C$_{comp}$ = 10 pF	20	30		15	30		MHz
Gain Bandwidth Product Gain of 10 to 100	R$_{IN}$ = 50Ω to 200Ω	300	400		200	400		MHz
Slew Rate								
Unity Gain	R$_{IN}$ = 1 kΩ, C$_{comp}$ = 10 pF		30			30		V/μs
Gain of 10 to 100	R$_{IN}$<200Ω		60			60		V/μs
Amplifier to Amplifier Coupling	f = 100 Hz to 100 kHz, R$_L$ = 1k		−80			−80		dB
Mirror Gain (Note 2)	@2 mA I$_{IN}$(+), I$_{SET}$ = 5 μA, T$_A$ = 25 °C	0.95	1.0	1.05	0.9	1.0	1.1	μA/μA
	@0.2 mA I$_{IN}$(+), I$_{SET}$ = 5 μA Over Temp	0.95	1.0	1.05	0.9	1.0	1.1	μA/μA
	@20 μA I$_{IN}$(+), I$_{SET}$ = 5 μA Over Temp	0.95	1.0	1.05	0.9	1.0	1.1	μA/μA
ΔMirror Gain (Note 2)	@20 μA to 0.2 mA I$_{IN}$(+) Over Temp, I$_{SET}$ = 5 μA		1	5		3	5	%
Input Bias Current	Inverting Input, T$_A$ = 25 °C		8	15		8	15	μA
	Over Temp			30			30	μA
Input Resistance (βre)	Inverting Input		2.5			2.5		kΩ
Output Resistance	I$_{OUT}$ = 15 mA rms, f = 1 MHz		3.5			3.5		Ω
Output Voltage Swing	R$_L$ = 600Ω							
V$_{OUT}$ High	I$_{IN}$(−) & I$_{IN}$(+) Grounded	9.5	10.3		9.5	10.3		V
V$_{OUT}$ Low	I$_{IN}$(−) = 100 μA, I$_{IN}$(+) = 0		2	50		2	50	mV
Output Currents								
Source	I$_{IN}$(−) & I$_{IN}$(+) Grounded, R$_L$ = 100Ω	20	40		16	40		mA
Sink (Linear Region)	V$_{comp}$ − 0.5V = V$_{OUT}$ = 1V, I$_{IN}$(+) = 0		4.7			4.7		mA
Sink (Overdriven)	I$_{IN}$(−) = 100 μA, I$_{IN}$(+) = 0, V$_{OUT}$ Force = 1V	2	3		1.5	3		mA
Supply Current	Non-Inverting Input Grounded, R$_L$ = ∞		18.5	20		18.5	22	mA
Power Supply Rejection (Note 3)	f = 120 Hz, I$_{IN}$(+) Grounded	40	50		40	50		dB

Note 1: See Maximum Power Dissipation graph.

Note 2: Mirror gain is the current gain of the current mirror which is used as the non-inverting input. $\left(A_I = \dfrac{I_{IN}(-)}{I_{IN}(+)} \right)$ ΔMirror Gain is the % change in A$_I$ for two different mirror currents at any given temperature.

Note 3: See Supply Rejection graphs.

Typical Performance Characteristics

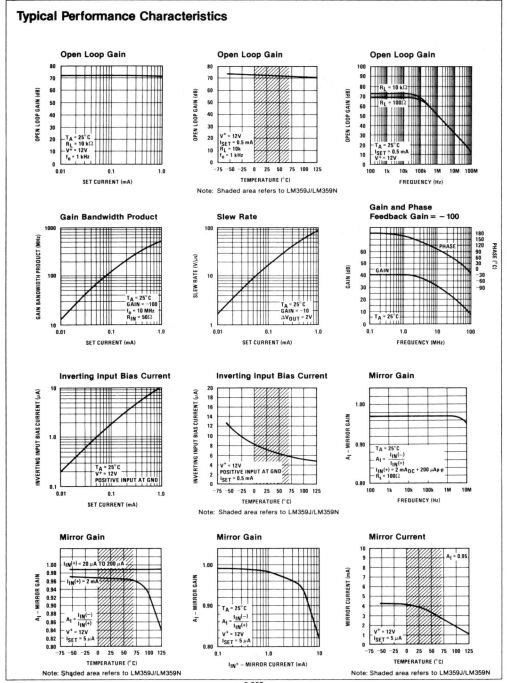

Note: Shaded area refers to LM359J/LM359N

Note: Shaded area refers to LM359J/LM359N

Note: Shaded area refers to LM359J/LM359N

Note: Shaded area refers to LM359J/LM359N

3-229

Reprinted with Permission of National Semiconductor Corp.

LM159/LM359

Typical Performance Characteristics (Continued)

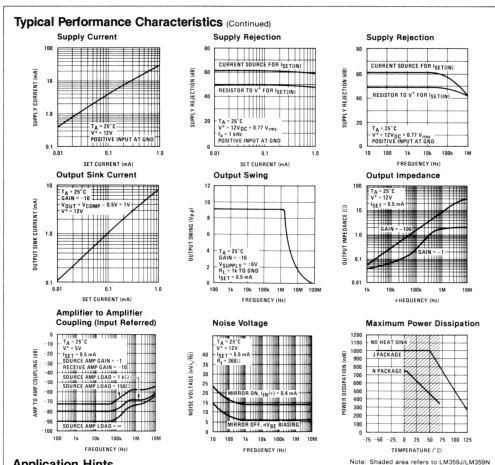

Application Hints

The LM159/LM359 consists of two wide bandwidth, decompensated current differencing (Norton) amplifiers. Although similar in operation to the original LM3900, design emphasis for these amplifiers has been placed on obtaining much higher frequency performance as illustrated in *Figure 1*.

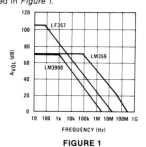

FIGURE 1

This significant improvement in frequency response is the result of using a common-emitter/common-base (cascode) gain stage which is typical in many discrete and integrated video and RF circuit designs. Another versatile aspect of these amplifiers is the ability to externally program many internal amplifier parameters to suit the requirements of a wide variety of applications in which this type of amplifier can be used.

DC BIASING

The LM359 is intended for single supply voltage operation which requires DC biasing of the output. The current mirror circuitry which provides the non-inverting input for the amplifier also facilitates DC biasing the output. The basic operation of this current mirror is that *the current (both AC and DC) flowing into the non-inverting input will force an equal amount of current to flow into the inverting input*. The mirror gain (A_I) specification is the measure of how closely these two currents match. For more details see National Application Note AN-72.

Note: Shaded area refers to LM359J/LM359N

Reprinted with Permission of National Semiconductor Corp.

Application Hints (Continued)

DC biasing of the output is accomplished by establishing a reference DC current into the (+) input, $I_{IN}(+)$, and requiring the output to provide the (−) input current. This forces the output DC level to be whatever value necessary (within the output voltage swing of the amplifier) to provide this DC reference current, *Figure 2*.

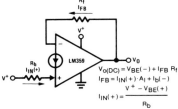

$$V_{o(DC)} = V_{BE}(-) + I_{FB} \cdot R_f$$
$$I_{FB} = I_{IN}(+) \cdot A_I + I_b(-)$$
$$I_{IN}(+) = \frac{V^+ - V_{BE}(+)}{R_b}$$

$I_b(-)$ is the inverting input bias current

FIGURE 2

The DC input voltage at each input is a transistor V_{BE} ($\cong 0.6\ V_{DC}$) and must be considered for DC biasing. For most applications, the supply voltage, V^+, is suitable and convenient for establishing $I_{IN}(+)$. The inverting input bias current, $I_b(-)$, is a direct function of the programmable input stage current (see current programmability section) and to obtain predictable output DC biasing set $I_{IN}(+) \geq 10 I_b(-)$.

The following figures illustrate typical biasing schemes for AC amplifiers using the LM359:

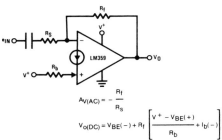

$$A_{V(AC)} = -\frac{R_f}{R_s}$$
$$V_{o(DC)} = V_{BE}(-) + R_f \left[\frac{V^+ - V_{BE}(+)}{R_b} + I_b(-) \right]$$

FIGURE 3. Biasing an Inverting AC Amplifier

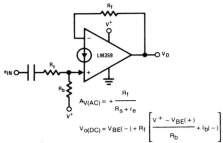

$$A_{V(AC)} = +\frac{R_f}{R_s + r_e}$$
$$V_{o(DC)} = V_{BE}(-) + R_f \left[\frac{V^+ - V_{BE}(+)}{R_b} + I_b(-) \right]$$

FIGURE 4. Biasing a Non-Inverting AC Amplifier

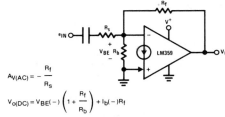

$$A_{V(AC)} = -\frac{R_f}{R_s}$$
$$V_{o(DC)} = V_{BE}(-) \left(1 + \frac{R_f}{R_b}\right) + I_b(-) R_f$$

FIGURE 5. nV$_{BE}$ Biasing

The nV$_{BE}$ biasing configuration is most useful for low noise applications where a reduced input impedance can be accommodated (see typical applications section).

OPERATING CURRENT PROGRAMMABILITY (I$_{SET}$)

The input bias current, slew rate, gain bandwidth product, output drive capability and total device power consumption of both amplifiers can be simultaneously controlled and optimized via the two programming pins $I_{SET(OUT)}$ and $I_{SET(IN)}$.

I$_{SET(OUT)}$

The output set current ($I_{SET(OUT)}$) is equal to the amount of current sourced from pin 1 and establishes the class A biasing current for the Darlington emitter follower output stage. Using a single resistor from pin 1 to ground, as shown in *Figure 6*, this current is equal to:

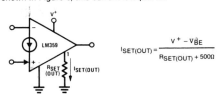

$$I_{SET(OUT)} = \frac{V^+ - V_{BE}}{R_{SET(OUT)} + 500\Omega}$$

FIGURE 6. Establishing the Output Set Current

The output set current can be adjusted to optimize the amount of current the output of the amplifier can sink to drive load capacitance and for loads connected to V^+. *The maximum output sinking current is approximately 10 times $I_{SET(OUT)}$.* This set current is best used to reduce the total device supply current if the amplifiers are not required to drive small load impedances.

I$_{SET(IN)}$

The input set current $I_{SET(IN)}$ is equal to the current flowing into pin 8. A resistor from pin 8 to V^+ sets this current to be:

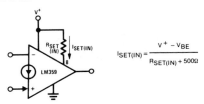

$$I_{SET(IN)} = \frac{V^+ - V_{BE}}{R_{SET(IN)} + 500\Omega}$$

FIGURE 7. Establishing the Input Set Current

Application Hints (Continued)

$I_{SET(IN)}$ is most significant in controlling the AC characteristics of the LM359 as it directly sets the total input stage current of the amplifiers which determines the maximum slew rate, the frequency of the open loop dominant pole, the input resistance of the (−) input and the biasing current $I_b(-)$. All of these parameters are significant in wide band amplifier design. The input stage current is approximately 3 times $I_{SET(IN)}$ and by using this relationship the following first order approximations for these AC parameters are:

$$S_{r(MAX)} = \text{max slew rate} \cong \frac{3I_{SET(IN)}(10^{-6})}{C_{comp}} \text{ (V/}\mu\text{s)}$$

$$\text{frequency of} \atop \text{dominant pole} \cong \frac{3I_{SET(IN)}}{2\pi\, C_{comp}\, A_{VOL}\, (0.026\ V)} \text{ (Hz)}$$

$$\text{input resistance} = \beta re \cong \frac{150\ (0.026\ V)}{3I_{SET(IN)}} \text{ (}\Omega\text{)}$$

where C_{comp} is the total capacitance from the compensation pin (pin 3 or pin 13) to ground, A_{VOL} is the low frequency open loop voltage gain in V/V and an ambient temperature of 25°C is assumed (KT/q = 26 mV and $\beta_{typ} = 150$). $I_{SET(IN)}$ also controls the DC input bias current by the expression:

$$I_b(-) = \frac{3I_{SET}}{\beta} \cong \frac{I_{SET}}{50} \text{ for NPN } \beta = 150$$

which is important for DC biasing considerations.

The total device supply current (for both amplifiers) is also a direct function of the set currents and can be approximated by:

$$I_{supply} \cong 27 \times I_{SET(OUT)} + 11 \times I_{SET(IN)}$$

with each set current programmed by individual resistors.

PROGRAMMING WITH A SINGLE RESISTOR

Operating current programming may also be accomplished using only one resistor by letting $I_{SET(IN)}$ equal $I_{SET(OUT)}$. The programming current is now referred to as I_{SET} and it is created by connecting a resistor from pin 1 to pin 8 (Figure 8).

$$I_{SET} = \frac{V^+ - 2V_{BE}}{R_{SET} + 1\ k\Omega} \text{ where } V_{BE} \cong 0.6V$$

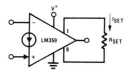

$I_{SET(IN)} = I_{SET(OUT)} = I_{SET}$

FIGURE 8. Single Resistor Programming of I_{SET}

This configuration does not affect any of the internal set current dependent parameters differently than previously discussed except the total supply current which is now equal to:

$$I_{supply} \cong 37 \times I_{SET}$$

Care must be taken when using resistors to program the set current to prevent significantly increasing the supply voltage above the value used to determine the set current. This would cause an increase in total supply current due to the resulting increase in set current and the maximum device power dissipation could be exceeded. The set resistor value(s) should be adjusted for the new supply voltage.

One method to avoid this is to use an adjustable current source which has voltage compliance to generate the set current as shown in Figure 9.

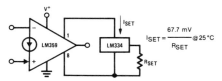

FIGURE 9. Current Source Programming of I_{SET}

This circuit allows I_{SET} to remain constant over the entire supply voltage range of the LM359 which also improves power supply ripple rejection as illustrated in the Typical Performance Characteristics. It should be noted, however, that the current through the LM334 as shown will change linearly with temperature but this can be compensated for (see LM334 data sheet).

Pin 1 must never be shorted to ground or pin 8 never shorted to V + without limiting the current to 2 mA or less to prevent catastrophic device failure.

CONSIDERATIONS FOR HIGH FREQUENCY OPERATION

The LM359 is intended for use in relatively high frequency applications and many factors external to the amplifier itself must be considered. Minimization of stray capacitances and their effect on circuit operation are the primary requirements. The following list contains some general guidelines to help accomplish this end:

1. Keep the leads of all external components as short as possible.
2. Place components conducting signal current from the output of an amplifier away from that amplifier's non-inverting input.
3. Use reasonably low value resistances for gain setting and biasing.
4. Use of a ground plane is helpful in providing a shielding effect between the inputs and from input to output. Avoid using vector boards.
5. Use a single-point ground and single-point supply distribution to minimize crosstalk. Always connect the two grounds (one from each amplifier) together.

Reprinted with Permission of National Semiconductor Corp.

Application Hints (Continued)

6. Avoid use of long wires (> 2") but if necessary, use shielded wire.

7. Bypass the supply close to the device with a low inductance, low value capacitor (typically a .01 μF ceramic) to create a good high frequency ground. If long supply leads are unavoidable, a small resistor (~10Ω) in series with the bypass capacitor may be needed and using shielded wire for the supply leads is also recommended.

COMPENSATION

The LM359 is internally compensated for stability with closed loop inverting gains of 10 or more. For an inverting gain of less than 10 and all non-inverting amplifiers (the amplifier always has 100% negative current feedback regardless of the gain in the non-inverting configuration) some external frequency compensation is required because the stray capacitance to ground from the (−) input and the feedback resistor add additional lagging phase within the feedback loop. The value of the input capacitance will typically be in the range of 6 pF to 10 pF for a reasonably constructed circuit board. When using a feedback resistance of 30 kΩ or less, the best method of compensation, without sacrificing slew rate, is to add a lead capacitor in parallel with the feedback resistor with a value on the order of 1 pF to 5 pF as shown in *Figure 10*.

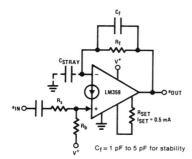

$C_f = 1$ pF to 5 pF for stability

FIGURE 10. Best Method of Compensation

Another method of compensation is to increase the effective value of the internal compensation capacitor by adding capacitance from the COMP pin of an amplifier to ground. An external 20 pF capacitor will generally compensate for all gain settings but will also reduce the gain bandwidth product and the slew rate. These same results can also be obtained by reducing $I_{SET(IN)}$ if the full capabilities of the amplifier are not required. This method is termed over-compensation.

Another area of concern from a stability standpoint is that of capacitive loading. The amplifier will generally drive capacitive loads up to 100 pF without oscillation problems. Any larger C loads can be isolated from the output as shown in *Figure 11*. Over-compensation of the amplifier can also be used if the corresponding reduction of the GBW product can be afforded.

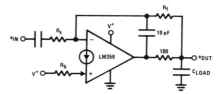

FIGURE 11. Isolating Large Capacitive Loads

In most applications using the LM359, the input signal will be AC coupled so as not to affect the DC biasing of the amplifier. This gives rise to another subtlety of high frequency circuits which is the effective series inductance (ESL) of the coupling capacitor which creates an increase in the impedance of the capacitor at high frequencies and can cause an unexpected gain reduction. Low ESL capacitors like solid tantalum for large values of C and ceramic for smaller values are recommended. A parallel combination of the two types is even better for gain accuracy over a wide frequency range.

AMPLIFIER DESIGN EXAMPLES

The ability of the LM359 to provide gain at frequencies higher than most monolithic amplifiers can provide makes it most useful as a basic broadband amplification stage. The design of standard inverting and non-inverting amplifiers, though different than standard op amp design due to the current differencing inputs, also entail subtle design differences between the two types of amplifiers. These differences will be best illustrated by design examples. For these examples a practical video amplifier with a passband of 8 Hz to 10 MHz and a gain of 20 dB will be used. It will be assumed that the input will come from a 75Ω source and proper signal termination will be considered. The supply voltage is 12 V_{DC} and single resistor programming of the operating current, I_{SET}, will be used for simplicity.

AN INVERTING VIDEO AMPLIFIER

1. Basic circuit configuration:

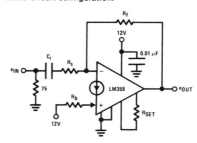

2. Determine the required I_{SET} from the characteristic curves for gain bandwidth product.

$$GBW_{MIN} = 10 \times 10 \text{ MHz} = 100 \text{ MHz}$$

For a flat response to 10 MHz a closed loop response to two octaves above 10 MHz (40 MHz) will be sufficient.

Application Hints (Continued)

Actual GBW = 10×40 MHz = 400 MHz

I_{SET} required = 0.5 mA

$$R_{SET} = \frac{V^+ - 2V_{BE}}{I_{SET}} - 1\,k\Omega = \frac{10.8V}{0.5\,mA} - 1\,k\Omega = 20.6\,k\Omega$$

3. Determine maximum value for R_f to provide stable DC biasing

$$I_{f(MIN)} \geqslant 10 \times \frac{3I_{SET}}{\beta} = 100\,\mu A \text{ minimum DC feedback current}$$

Optimum output DC level for maximum symmetrical swing without clipping is:

$$V_{oDC(opt)} = \frac{V_{o(MAX)} - V_{o(MIN)}}{2} + V_{o(MIN)}$$

$$\approx \frac{(V^+ - 3V_{BE}) - 2\,mV}{2}$$

$$V_{oDC(opt)} \cong \frac{12 - 1.8V}{2} = \frac{10.2V}{2} = 5.1\,V_{DC}$$

$R_{f(MAX)}$ can now be found:

$$R_{f(MAX)} = \frac{V_{oDC(opt)} - V_{BE}^{(-)}}{I_{f(MIN)}} = \frac{5.1V - 0.6}{100\,\mu A} = 45\,k\Omega$$

This value should not be exceeded for predictable DC biasing.

4. Select R_s to be large enough so as not to appreciably load the input termination resistance:

$$R_s \geqslant 750\Omega \quad \text{Let } R_s = 750\Omega$$

5. Select R_f for appropriate gain:

$$A_V = -\frac{R_f}{R_s} \text{ so; } R_f = 10R_s = 7.5\,k\Omega$$

7.5 kΩ is less than the calculated $R_{f(MAX)}$ so DC predictability is insured.

6. Since $R_f = 7.5k$, for the output to be biased to 5.1 V_{DC}, the reference current $I_{IN}(+)$ must be:

$$I_{IN}(+) = \frac{5.1V - V_{BE}(-)}{R_f} = \frac{5.1V - .6V}{7.5\,k\Omega} = 600\,\mu A$$

Now R_b can be found by:

$$R_b = \frac{V^+ - V_{BE}(+)}{I_{IN}(+)} = \frac{12 - 0.6}{600\,\mu A} = 19\,k\Omega$$

7. Select C_i to provide the proper gain for the 8 Hz minimum input frequency:

$$C_i \geqslant \frac{1}{2\pi\,R_s\,(f_{low})} = \frac{1}{2\pi\,(750\Omega)\,(8\,Hz)} = 26\,\mu F$$

A larger value of C_i will allow a flat frequency response down to 8 Hz and a 0.01 µF ceramic capacitor in parallel with C_i will maintain high frequency gain accuracy.

8. Test for peaking of the frequency response and add a feedback "lead" capacitor to compensate if necessary.

Final Circuit Using Standard 5% Tolerance Resistor Values:

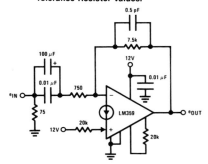

Circuit Performance:

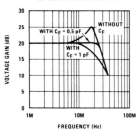

$V_{o(DC)} = 5.1V$
Differential phase error<1° for 3.58 MHz f_{IN}
Differential gain error<0.5% for 3.58 MHz f_{IN}
$f_{-3\,dB}$ low = 2.5 Hz

A NON-INVERTING VIDEO AMPLIFIER

For this case several design considerations must be dealt with.

- The output voltage (AC and DC) is strictly a function of the size of the feedback resistor and the sum of AC and DC "mirror current" flowing into the (+) input.
- The amplifier always has 100% current feedback so external compensation is required. Add a small (1 pF–5 pF) feedback capacitance to leave the amplifier's open loop response and slew rate unaffected.
- To prevent saturating the mirror stage the total AC and DC current flowing into the amplifier's (+) input should be less than 2 mA.
- The output's maximum negative swing is one diode above ground due to the V_{BE} diode clamp at the (−) input.

3-234

Reprinted with Permission of National Semiconductor Corp.

Application Hints (Continued)

DESIGN EXAMPLE:

$e_{IN} = 50$ mV (MAX), $f_{IN} = 10$ MHz (MAX), desired circuit BW = 20 MHz, $A_V = 20$ dB, driving source impedance = 75Ω, $V^+ = 12V$.

1. Basic circuit configuration:

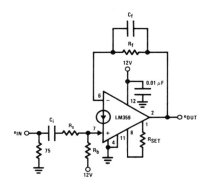

2. Select I_{SET} to provide adequate amplifier bandwidth so that the closed loop bandwidth will be determined by R_f and C_f. To do this, the set current should program an amplifier open loop gain of at least 20 dB at the desired closed loop bandwidth of the circuit. For this example, an I_{SET} of 0.5 mA will provide 26 dB of open loop gain at 20 MHz which will be sufficient. Using single resistor programming for I_{SET}:

$$R_{SET} = \frac{V^+ - 2V_{BE}}{I_{SET}} - 1 \text{ k}\Omega = 20.6 \text{ k}\Omega$$

3. Since the closed loop bandwidth will be determined by R_f and C_f $\left(f_{-3 \text{ dB}} = \frac{1}{2\pi R_f C_f} \right)$ to obtain a 20 MHz

bandwidth, both R_f and C_f should be kept small. It can be assumed that C_f can be in the range of 1 pF to 5 pF for carefully constructed circuit boards to insure stability and allow a flat frequency response. This will limit the value of R_f to be within the range of:

$$\frac{1}{2\pi \text{ 5 pF 20 MHz}} \leqslant R_f \leqslant \frac{1}{2\pi \text{ 1 pF 20 MHz}}$$

or 1.6 kΩ ⩽ R_f ⩽ 7.96 kΩ

Also, for a closed loop gain of +10, R_f must be 10 times $R_s + r_e$ where r_e is the mirror diode resistance.

4. So as not to appreciably load the 75Ω input termination resistance the value of $(R_s + r_e)$ is set to 750Ω.

5. For $A_V = 10$; R_f is set to 7.5 kΩ.

6. The optimum output DC level for symmetrical AC swing is:

$$V_{oDC(opt)} = \frac{V_{o(MAX)} - V_{o(MIN)}}{2} + V_{o(MIN)}$$

$$= \frac{(12 - 1.8)V - 0.6V}{2} + 0.6V = 5.4V_{DC}$$

7. The DC feedback current must be:

$$I_{FB} = \frac{V_{oDC(opt)} - V_{BE}(-)}{R_f} = \frac{5.4V - 0.6V}{7.5k}$$

$$= 640 \ \mu A = I_{IN}(+)$$

DC biasing predictability will be insured because 640 μA is greater than the minimum of $I_{SET}/5$ or 100 μA.

For gain accuracy the total AC and DC mirror current should be less than 2 mA. For this example the maximum AC mirror current will be;

$$\frac{\pm e_{in \ peak}}{R_s + r_e} = \frac{\pm 50 \text{ mV}}{750\Omega} = \pm 66 \ \mu A$$

therefore the total mirror current range will be 574 μA to 706 μA which will insure gain accuracy.

8. P_b can now be found:

$$R_b = \frac{V^+ - V_{BE}(+)}{I_{IN}(+)} = \frac{12 - 0.6}{640 \ \mu A} = 17.8 \text{ k}\Omega$$

9. Since $R_s + r_e$ will be 750Ω and r_e is fixed by the DC mirror current to be:

$$r_e = \frac{KT}{q \ I_{IN}(+)} = \frac{26 \text{ mV}}{640 \ \mu A} \cong 40\Omega \text{ at } 25\,°C$$

R_s must be 750Ω-40Ω or 710Ω which can be a 680Ω resistor in series with a 30Ω resistor which are standard 5% tolerance resistor values.

10. As a final design step, C_i must be selected to pass the lower passband frequency corner of 8 Hz for this example.

$$C_i = \frac{1}{2\pi \ (R_s + r_e) \ f_{low}} = \frac{1}{2\pi \ (750\Omega) \ (8 \text{ Hz})} = 26.5 \ \mu F$$

A larger value may be used and a 0.01 μF ceramic capacitor in parallel with C_i will maintain high frequency gain accuracy.

Reprinted with Permission of National Semiconductor Corp.

Application Hints (Continued)

Final Circuit Using Standard 5% Tolerance Resistor Values:

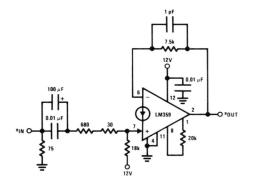

Circuit Performance:

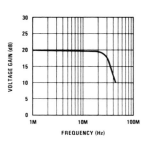

$V_{O(DC)} = 5.4V$
Differential phase error $<0.5°$
Differential gain error $<2\%$
$f_{-3\,dB}$ low $= 2.5$ Hz

GENERAL PRECAUTIONS

The LM359 is designed primarily for single supply operation but split supplies may be used if the negative supply voltage is well regulated as the amplifiers have no negative supply rejection.

The total device power dissipation must always be kept in mind when selecting an operating supply voltage, the programming current, I_{SET}, and the load resistance, particularly when DC coupling the output to a succeeding stage. To prevent damaging the current mirror input diode, the mirror current should always be limited to 10

mA, or less, which is important if the input is susceptible to high voltage transients. The voltage at any of the inputs must not be forced more negative than $-0.7V$ without limiting the current to 10 mA.

The supply voltage must never be reversed to the device; however, plugging the device into a socket backwards would then connect the positive supply voltage to the pin that has no internal connection (pin 5) which may prevent inadvertent device failure!

Typical Applications

DC Coupled Inputs

Inverting

$$V_{O(DC)} = \left[\frac{V + - V_{BE(+)}}{R_b} - \frac{V_{IN(DC)} - V_{BE(-)}}{R_s}\right] R_f + V_{BE(-)}$$

$$A_{V(AC)} = -\frac{R_f}{R_s}$$

Non-Inverting

$$V_{O(DC)} = V_{BE(-)} + \frac{(V_{IN(DC)} - V_{BE(+)})R_f}{R_s}$$

$$A_{V(AC)} = +\frac{R_f}{R_s + r_e(+)}$$

- Eliminates the need for an input coupling capacitor
- Input DC level must be stable and can exceed the supply voltage of the LM359 provided that maximum input currents are not exceeded.

Reprinted with Permission of National Semiconductor Corp.

Application Hints (Continued)

Noise Reduction using nV$_{BE}$ Biasing

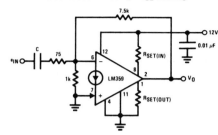

Typical Input Referred Noise Performance

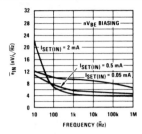

nV$_{BE}$ Biasing with a Negative Supply

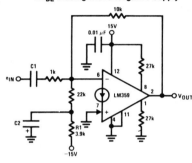

- R1 and C2 provide additional filtering of the negative biasing supply

Adding a JFET Input Stage

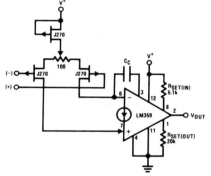

- FET input voltage mode op amp
- For $A_V = +1$; BW = 40 MHz, S$_r$ = 60 V/μs; C$_C$ = 51 pF
- For $A_V = +11$; BW = 24 MHz, S$_r$ = 130 V/μs; C$_C$ = 5 pF
- For $A_V = +100$; BW = 4.5 MHz, S$_r$ = 150 V/μs; C$_C$ = 2 pF
- V$_{OS}$ is typically <25 mV; 100Ω potentiometer allows a V$_{OS}$ adjust range of ≈ ± 200 mV
- Inputs must be DC biased for single supply operation

Photo Diode Amplifier

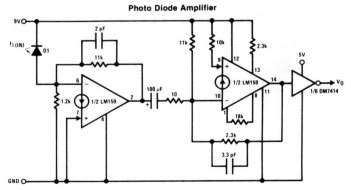

D1∼RCA N-Type Silicon P-I-N Photodiode
- Frequency response of greater than 10 MHz
- If slow rise and fall times can be tolerated the gate on the output can be removed. In this case the rise and the fall time of the LM359 is 40 ns.
- T$_{PDL}$ = 45 ns, T$_{PDH}$ = 50 ns—T^{2}L output

Reprinted with Permission of National Semiconductor Corp.

LM159/LM359

Typical Applications (Continued)

Balanced Line Driver

For $V_O1 = V_O2 = \dfrac{V^+}{2}$, $\dfrac{R3}{R2} = \dfrac{V^+ - 2\phi}{2(V^+ - \phi)}$, $\dfrac{R6}{R5} = \dfrac{V^+ - 2\phi}{\phi}$ where $\phi \approx 0.6V$

$$A_V = \frac{R3}{R1}\left(\frac{R6}{R4} + 1\right)$$

- 1 MHz—3 dB bandwidth with gain of 10 and 0 dbm into 600Ω
- 0.3% distortion at full bandwidth; reduced to 0.05% with bandwidth of 10 kHz
- Will drive $C_L = 1500$ pF with no additional compensation, ± 0.01 μF with $C_{comp} = 180$ pF
- 70 dB signal to noise ratio at 0 dbm into 600Ω, 10 kHz bandwidth

Difference Amplifier

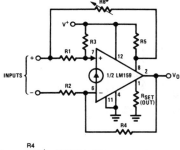

$$V_{O(DC)} = \frac{R4}{R3}(V^+ - \phi) \text{ where } \phi = 0.6V$$

$$A_V = \frac{R4}{R1} \quad \text{for } R1 = R2$$

*CMRR is adjusted for max at expected CM input signal

$R6 \approx \dfrac{R5}{5}$, for $R5 = 100$ kΩ

- Wide bandwidth
- 70 dB CMRR typ
- Wide CM input voltage range

Voltage Controlled Oscillator

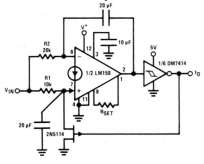

$$f_O = \frac{V_{IN} - \phi}{4C\Delta V \, R1}$$

where: $R2 = 2R1$

ϕ = amplifier input voltage = 0.6V

ΔV = DM7414 hysteresis, typ 1V

- 5 MHz operation
- T^2L ouput

3-238

Reprinted with Permission of National Semiconductor Corp.

LM159/LM359

Typical Applications

High Performance 2 Amplifier Biquad Filter(s)

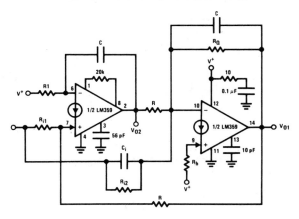

- The high speed of the LM359 allows the center frequency Q_0 product of the filter to be : $f_0 \times Q_0 \leq 5$ MHz
- The above filter(s) maintains performance over wide temperature range
- One half of LM359 acts as a true non-inverting integrator so only 2 amplifiers (instead of 3 or 4) are needed for the biquad filter structure

DC BIASING EQUATIONS FOR $V_{O1(DC)} \cong V_{O2(DC)} \cong V^+/2$

Type I	$\dfrac{2 V_{IN(DC)}}{V^+ (R_{i2})} + \dfrac{1}{R} - \dfrac{1}{R_Q} + \dfrac{2}{R_b} = \dfrac{2}{R}$; $R1 = 2R$
Type II	$\dfrac{1}{R} + \dfrac{1}{R_Q} = \dfrac{2}{R_b}$; $R1 = 2R$
Type III	$\dfrac{1}{R} + \dfrac{1}{R_Q} = \dfrac{2}{R_b}$; $\dfrac{1}{R1} = \dfrac{V_{IN(DC)}}{V^+ (R_{i1})} + \dfrac{1}{2R}$

ANALYSIS AND DESIGN EQUATIONS

Type	V_{O1}	V_{O2}	C_i	R_{i2}	R_{i1}	f_o	Q_o	f_Z (notch)	$H_{o(LP)}$	$H_{o(BP)}$	$H_{o(HP)}$	$H_{o(BR)}$
I	BP	LP	O	R_{i2}	∞	$\frac{1}{2}\pi RC$	R_Q/R	—	R/R_{i2}	R_Q/R_{i2}	—	—
II	HP	BP	C_i	∞	∞	$\frac{1}{2}\pi RC$	R_Q/R	—	—	$R_Q C_i/RC$	C_i/C	—
III	Notch/ BR	—	C_i	∞	R_{i1}	$\frac{1}{2}\pi RC$	R_Q/R	$\frac{1}{2}\pi\sqrt{RR_iCC_i}$	—	—	—	$H_o\big|_{f\to\infty} = C_i/C$ $H_o\big|_{f\to o} = R/R_i$

Reprinted with Permission of National Semiconductor Corp.

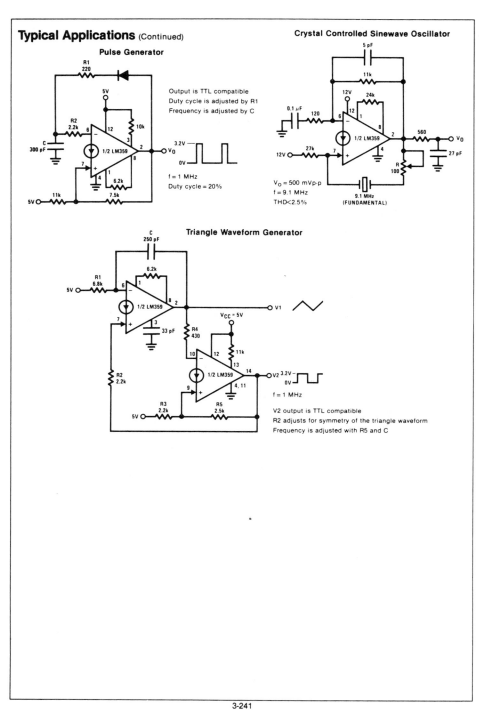

LM2900/LM3900, LM3301, LM3401

Operational Amplifiers/Buffers

LM2900/LM3900, LM3301, LM3401 Quad Amplifiers

General Description

The LM2900 series consists of four independent, dual input, internally compensated amplifiers which were designed specifically to operate off of a single power supply voltage and to provide a large output voltage swing. These amplifiers make use of a current mirror to achieve the non-inverting input function. Application areas include: ac amplifiers, RC active filters, low frequency triangle, squarewave and pulse waveform generation circuits, tachometers and low speed, high voltage digital logic gates.

Features

- Wide single supply voltage range or dual supplies   4 V_{DC} to 36 V_{DC} ±2 V_{DC} to ±18 V_{DC}
- Supply current drain independent of supply voltage
- Low input biasing current   30 nA
- High open-loop gain   70 dB
- Wide bandwidth   2.5 MHz (Unity Gain)
- Large output voltage swing   (V^+ −1) Vp-p
- Internally frequency compensated for unity gain
- Output short-circuit protection

Schematic and Connection Diagrams

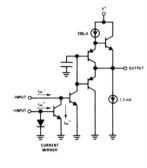

Order Number LM2900J
See NS Package J14A
Order Number LM2900N,
LM3900N, LM3301N
or LM3401N
See NS Package N14A

Dual-In-Line and Flat Package

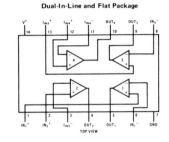

Typical Applications   (V^+ = 15 V_{DC})

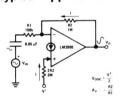

Inverting Amplifier

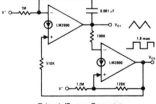

Triangle/Square Generator

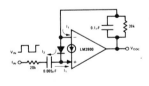

Frequency-Doubling Tachometer

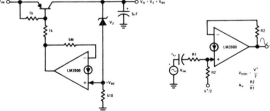

Low V_{IN} – V_{OUT} Voltage Regulator   **Non-Inverting Amplifier**

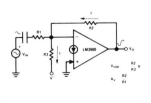

Negative Supply Biasing

Absolute Maximum Ratings

	LM2900/LM3900	LM3301	LM3401
Supply Voltage	32 V$_{DC}$	28 V$_{DC}$	18 V$_{DC}$
	±16 V$_{DC}$	±14 V$_{DC}$	±9 V$_{DC}$
Power Dissipation (T$_A$ = 25°C) (Note 1)			
Cavity DIP	900 mW		
Flat Pack	800 mW		
Molded DIP	570 mW	570 mW	570 mW
Input Currents, I$_{IN}$$^+$ or I$_{IN}$$^-$	20 mADC	20 mADC	20 mADC
Output Short-Circuit Duration — One Amplifier T$_A$ = 25°C (See Application Hints)	Continuous	Continuous	Continuous
Operating Temperature Range			
LM2900	−40°C to +85°C	−40°C to +85°C	0°C to +75°C
LM3900	0°C to +70°C		
Storage Temperature Range	−65°C to +150°C	−65°C to +150°C	−65°C to +150°C
Lead Temperature (Soldering, 10 seconds)	300°C	300°C	300°C

Electrical Characteristics (Note 6)

PARAMETER	CONDITIONS	LM2900 MIN	TYP	MAX	LM3900 MIN	TYP	MAX	LM3301 MIN	TYP	MAX	LM3401 MIN	TYP	MAX	UNITS
Open Loop														
Voltage Gain	T$_A$ = 25°C, f = 100 Hz										800			V/mV
Voltage Gain	T$_A$ = 25°C, Inverting Input	1.2	2.8		1.2	2.8		1.2	2.8		1.2	2.8		V/mV
Input Resistance			1			1			1		0.1	1		MΩ
Output Resistance			8			8			8			8		kΩ
Unity Gain Bandwidth	T$_A$ = 25°C, Inverting Input		2.5			2.5			2.5			2.5		MHz
Input Bias Current	T$_A$ = 25°C, Inverting Input		30	200		30	200		30	300		30	300	nA
Inverting Input													500	nA
Slew Rate	T$_A$ = 25°C, Positive Output Swing		0.5			0.5			0.5			0.5		V/µs
	T$_A$ = 25°C, Negative Output Swing		20			20			20			20		V/µs
Supply Current	T$_A$ = 25°C, R$_L$ = ∞ On All Amplifiers		6.2	10		6.2	10		6.2	10		6.2	10	mADC
Output Voltage Swing	T$_A$ = 25°C, R$_L$ = 2k, V$_{CC}$ = 15.0 V$_{DC}$													
V$_{OUT}$ High	I$_{IN}$$^-$ = 0, I$_{IN}$$^+$ = 0	13.5			13.5			13.5			13.5			VDC
V$_{OUT}$ Low	I$_{IN}$$^-$ = 10µA, I$_{IN}$$^+$ = 0		0.09	0.2		0.09	0.2		0.09	0.2		0.09	0.2	VDC
V$_{OUT}$ High	I$_{IN}$$^-$ = 0, I$_{IN}$$^+$ = 0 R$_L$ = ∞, V$_{CC}$ = Absolute Maximum Ratings		29.5			29.5			25.5			15.5		VDC
Output Current Capability	T$_A$ = 25°C													
Source		6	18		6	10		5	18		5	10		mADC
Sink	(Note 2)	0.5	1.3		0.5	1.3		0.5	1.3		0.5	1.3		mADC
I$_{SINK}$	V$_{OL}$ = 1V, I$_{IN}$ = 5µA		5			5			5			5		mADC

LM2900/LM3900, LM3301, LM3401 3

3-271

Reprinted with Permission of National Semiconductor Corp.

Electrical Characteristics (Continued) (Note 6)

LM2900/LM3900, LM3301, LM3401

Electrical Characteristics (Continued) (Note 6)

PARAMETER	CONDITIONS	LM2900			LM3900			LM3301			LM3401			UNITS
		MIN	TYP	MAX	MIN	TYP	MAX	MIN	TYP	MAX	MIN	TYP	MAX	
Power Supply Rejection	$T_A = 25°C$, f = 100 Hz		70			70			70			70		dB
Mirror Gain	@ 20µA (Note 3)	0.90	1.0	1.1	0.90	1.0	1.1	0.90	1	1.10	0.90	1	1.10	µA/µA
	@ 200µA (Note 3)	0.90	1.0	1.1	0.90	1.0	1.1	0.90	1	1.10	0.90	1	1.10	µA/µA
ΔMirror Gain	@ 20µA To 200µA (Note 3)		2	5		2	5		2	5		2	5	%
Mirror Current	(Note 4)		10	500		10	500		10	500		10	500	µADC
Negative Input Current	$T_A = 25°C$ (Note 5)		1.0			1.0			1.0			1.0		mADC
Input Bias Current	Inverting Input		300			300								nA

Note 1: For operating at high temperatures, the device must be derated based on a 125°C maximum junction temperature and a thermal resistance of 175°C/W which applies for the device soldered in a printed circuit board, operating in a still air ambient.

Note 2: The output current sink capability can be increased for large signal conditions by overdriving the inverting input. This is shown in the section on Typical Characteristics.

Note 3: This spec indicates the current gain of the current mirror which is used as the non-inverting input.

Note 4: Input V_{BE} match between the non-inverting and the inverting inputs occurs for a mirror current (non-inverting input current) of approximately 10µA. This is therefore a typical design center for many of the application circuits.

Note 5: Clamp transistors are included on the IC to prevent the input voltages from swinging below ground more than approximately -0.3 V_{DS}. The negative input currents which may result from large signal overdrive with capacitance input coupling need to be externally limited to values of approximately 1 mA. Negative input currents in excess of 4 mA will cause the output voltage to drop to a low voltage. This maximum current applies to any one of the input terminals. If more than one of the input terminals are simultaneously driven negative smaller maximum currents are allowed. Common-mode current biasing can be used to prevent negative input voltages; see for example, the "Differentiator Circuit" in the applications section.

Note 6: These specs apply for $-55°C \leq T_A \leq +125°C$, unless otherwise stated.

3-272

Reprinted with Permission of National Semiconductor Corp.

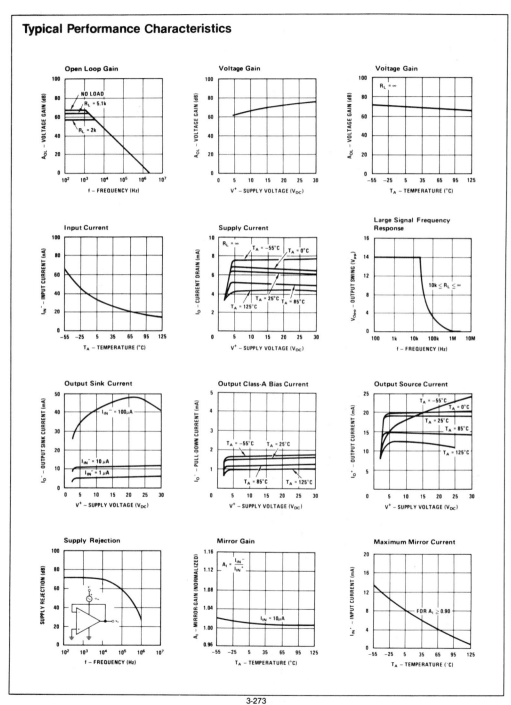

Typical Performance Characteristics

LM2900/LM3900, LM3301, LM3401

3

3-273

Reprinted with Permission of National Semiconductor Corp.

LM2900/LM3900, LM3301, LM3401

Application Hints

When driving either input from a low-impedance source, a limiting resistor should be placed in series with the input lead to limit the peak input current. Currents as large as 20 mA will not damage the device, but the current mirror on the non-inverting input will saturate and cause a loss of mirror gain at mA current levels—especially at high operating temperatures.

Precautions should be taken to insure that the power supply for the integrated circuit never becomes reversed in polarity or that the unit is not inadvertently installed backwards in a test socket as an unlimited current surge through the resulting forward diode within the IC could cause fuzing of the internal conductors and result in a destroyed unit.

Output short circuits either to ground or to the positive power supply should be of short time duration. Units can be destroyed, not as a result of the short circuit current causing metal fuzing, but rather due to the large increase in IC chip dissipation which will cause eventual failure due to excessive junction temperatures. For example, when operating from a well-regulated +5 V_{DC} power supply at T_A = 25°C with a 100 kΩ shunt-feedback resistor (from the output to the inverting input) a short directly to the power supply will not cause catastrophic failure but the current magnitude will be approximately 50 mA and the junction temperature will be above T_J max. Larger feedback resistors will reduce the current, 11 MΩ provides approximately 30 mA, an open circuit provides 1.3 mA, and a direct connection from the output to the non-inverting input will result in catastrophic failure when the output is shorted to V^+ as this then places the base-emitter junction of the input transistor directly across the power supply. Short-circuits to ground will have magnitudes of approximately 30 mA and will not cause catastrophic failure at T_A = 25°C.

Unintentional signal coupling from the output to the non-inverting input can cause oscillations. This is likely only in breadboard hook-ups with long component leads and can be prevented by a more careful lead dress or by locating the non-inverting input biasing resistor close to the IC. A quick check of this condition is to bypass the non-inverting input to ground with a capacitor. High impedance biasing resistors used in the non-inverting input circuit make this input lead highly susceptible to unintentional ac signal pickup.

Operation of this amplifier can be best understood by noticing that input currents are differenced at the inverting-input terminal and this difference current then flows through the external feedback resistor to produce the output voltage. Common-mode current biasing is generally useful to allow operating with signal levels near ground or even negative as this maintains the inputs biased at +V_{BE}. Internal clamp transistors (see note 5) catch negative input voltages at approximately −0.3 V_{DC} but the magnitude of current flow has to be limited by the external input network. For operation at high temperature, this limit should be approximately 100μA.

This new "Norton" current-differencing amplifier can be used in most of the applications of a standard IC op amp. Performance as a dc amplifier using only a single supply is not as precise as a standard IC op amp operating with split supplies but is adequate in many less critical applications. New functions are made possible with this amplifier which are useful in single power supply systems. For example, biasing can be designed separately from the ac gain as was shown in the "inverting amplifier," the "difference integrator" allows controlling the charging and the discharging of the integrating capacitor both with positive voltages, and the "frequency doubling tachometer" provides a simple circuit which reduces the ripple voltage on a tachometer output dc voltage.

Typical Applications (Continued)

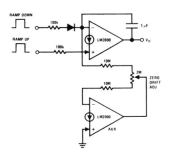

Low-Drift Ramp and Hold Circuit

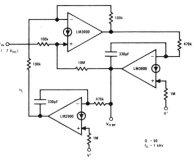

Bi-Quad Active Filter
(2nd Degree State-Variable Network)

Reprinted with Permission of National Semiconductor Corp.

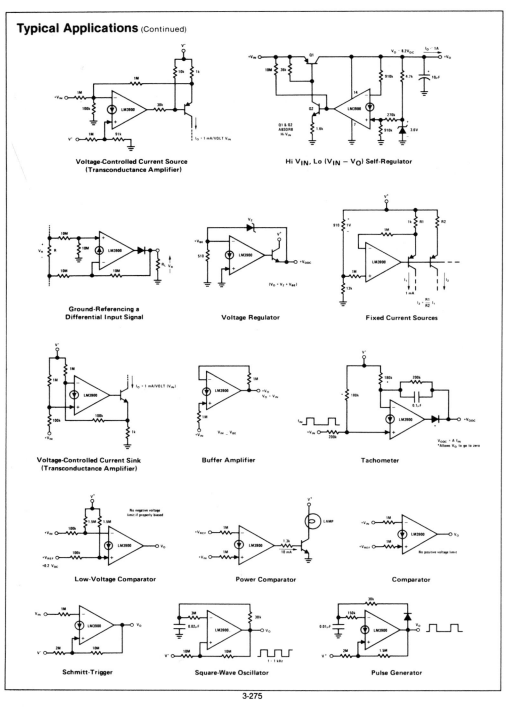

Typical Applications (Continued)

Voltage-Controlled Current Source
(Transconductance Amplifier)

Hi V_{IN}, Lo (V_{IN} − V_O) Self-Regulator

Ground-Referencing a
Differential Input Signal

Voltage Regulator

Fixed Current Sources

Voltage-Controlled Current Sink
(Transconductance Amplifier)

Buffer Amplifier

Tachometer

Low-Voltage Comparator

Power Comparator

Comparator

Schmitt-Trigger

Square-Wave Oscillator

Pulse Generator

Typical Applications (Continued)

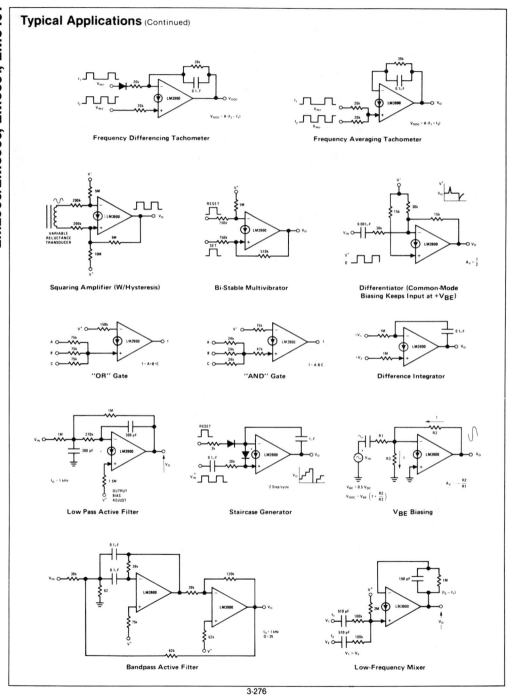

Frequency Differencing Tachometer

Frequency Averaging Tachometer

Squaring Amplifier (W/Hysteresis)

Bi-Stable Multivibrator

Differentiator (Common-Mode Biasing Keeps Input at +V_{BE})

"OR" Gate

"AND" Gate

Difference Integrator

Low Pass Active Filter

Staircase Generator

V_{BE} Biasing

Bandpass Active Filter

Low-Frequency Mixer

Reprinted with Permission of National Semiconductor Corp.

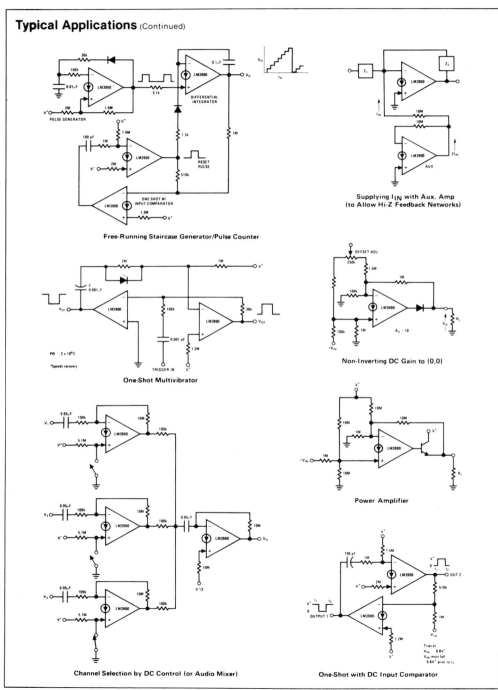

Typical Applications (Continued)

Free-Running Staircase Generator/Pulse Counter

Supplying I_{IN} with Aux. Amp
(to Allow Hi-Z Feedback Networks)

One-Shot Multivibrator

Non-Inverting DC Gain to (0,0)

Channel Selection by DC Control (or Audio Mixer)

Power Amplifier

One-Shot with DC Input Comparator

LM2900/LM3900, LM3301, LM3401

Reprinted with Permission of National Semiconductor Corp.

LM2900/LM3900, LM3301, LM3401

Typical Applications (Continued)

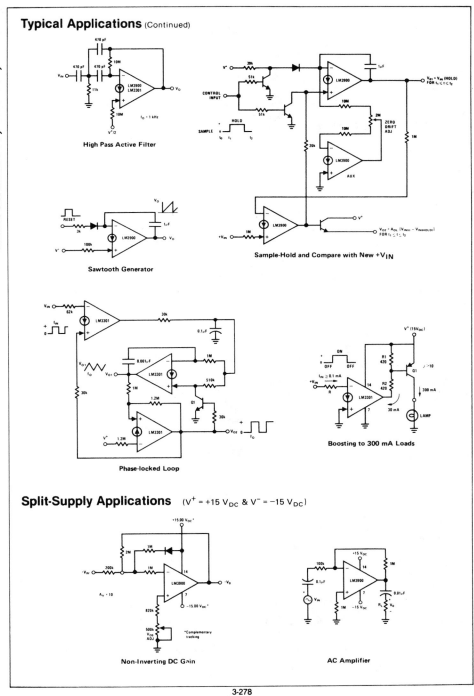

High Pass Active Filter

Sawtooth Generator

Sample-Hold and Compare with New +V$_{IN}$

Phase-locked Loop

Boosting to 300 mA Loads

Split-Supply Applications (V$^+$ = +15 V$_{DC}$ & V$^-$ = −15 V$_{DC}$)

Non-Inverting DC Gain

AC Amplifier

3-278

Reprinted with Permission of National Semiconductor Corp.

appendix d

Answers to Selected Problems

CHAPTER 1

2. Monolithic: whole circuit made of one slab of silicon.
   Hybrid: individual components mounted on a ceramic substrate.

4. More linear because nonlinearity caused by r'_e is cancelled, extremely stable DC-wise because Q_1 and Q_2 must share a fixed amount of current.

6. Input resistance much greater than standard bipolar, and greater even than Darlington.

8. Ratio of (resistor connected to negative source)/(resistor connected to emitter) $= 1/0.626$.

10. Many solutions are possible.

12. $A_{I_{cl}} = I_{OUT}/I_{IN} = (A_{ol}I_i)/(I_i + I_f) = (A_{ol}I_i)/(I_i + \beta I_i) = A_{ol}/(1 + \beta A_{ol})$
    $Z_{IN} = V_i/I_s = V_i/(I_i + I_f) = I_iR_i/(I_i + \beta A_{ol}I_i)$
    $= R_i/(1 + \beta A_{ol})$
    For Z_{OUT}, we proceed as in deriving equation 1.20, except that we open the signal source. Then:
    $I_s = 0$
    $I_i = I_f = \beta I_{OUT}$
    $I_{OUT} = V/R_{OUT} + A_{ol}I_i = V/R_{OUT} + A_{ol}\beta I_{OUT}$
    $V/R_{OUT} = A_{ol}\beta I_{OUT} + I_{OUT}$
    $V = I_{OUT}R_{OUT}(A_{ol}\beta - 1)$
    $Z_{OUT} = V/I_{OUT} = (I_{OUT}R_{OUT}(A_{ol}\beta + 1))/I_{OUT} = R_{OUT}(A_{ol}\beta + 1)$

14. a. 1.01 MΩ; b. 99 Ω; c. 1.01 MΩ; d. 99Ω

16. a. 0.99 Ω; b. 0.99 Ω; c. 10.1 kΩ; d. 10.1 kΩ

CHAPTER 2

2. See the discussion on pages 37–40 in the text.
   a. 741 or 411; b. 147 or 411; c. 147 or 411; d. 411; e. 147 or 411;
   f. 147 or 411; g. 147

4. Supply voltage must be ± 6 V. Use 5-kΩ input resistors and apply 4 V to negative input. Use protection diodes across input.

6. Many solutions are possible.

8. Use 3-input inverting summer. All R_i's are 1 kΩ. $R_f = 2.475$ kΩ. Apply +20

mV to one input; sensors connect to other inputs. Many other solutions are possible.

10. Frequency

Frequency	X_C	Z_f	A_V
10	318 kΩ	9.995 kΩ	9.99
100	31.8 kΩ	9.54 kΩ	9.54
1,000	3.18 kΩ	3 kΩ	3
10,000	318 Ω	317 Ω	0.317

12. The time constant must be much less than $1.5 \cdot 10^{-8}$. A diode in series with the output will clip off negative spikes. Use an op amp having a GBW of 20 MHz or greater.

CHAPTER 3

2. a. 500 nA; b. 60 nA
4. Inverting: $R_i = 100$ kΩ, $R_f = 10$ MΩ, $R_{comp} = 99.09$ kΩ
   Noninverting: $R_g = 1$ kΩ, $R_f = 99$ kΩ, $R_{comp} = 990$ Ω
6. a. Both inverting and noninverting would require R_f of about 100 MΩ, which is not available. Even if it were available, R_{comp} would have to be accurate within about 30 kΩ (3%) to keep output offset voltage less than 1.5 V, with matched bias currents. Even with a perfect R_{comp}, an input offset current of 15 nA would give an output offset voltage of 1 V. This design is therefore impractical from at least two standpoints.
   b. Noninverting would require $R_{comp} = 1$ MΩ, which would still give offset problems. Inverting can use $R_i = 1$ MΩ. Then $R_t = 100$ kΩ and $R_s = 99.8$ Ω would give the required gain. Resistance to ground would be approximately 100 kΩ, as would R_{comp}. This would allow 150 nA offset current before the output offset voltage reached 1.5V.
   c. Since R_{comp} will still have to be 1 MΩ, this would offer no advantage over the standard circuit for this application. The tee-feedback circuit is the only one practical.
8. a. The −3 dB frequency must be at least 103 kHz. Therefore, 3 stages are required, with a gain of 4.64 per stage.
   b. can be done with one stage if op amp has a GBW of 10.33 MHz or greater.
10. Rise times are as follows:
    a. 2.5 μs; b. 4.3 μs; c. 22.3 μs; d. 2.5 μs; e. 4.3 μs; f. 22.3 μs
12. See pages 124–126 in the text.
14. $M_G = -50$ dB; $M_P = 50°$.
16. See pages 129 to 130 in the text.
18. See page 130 in the text.

CHAPTER 4

2. The 10 V common-mode signals will be rejected by 90 dB, giving a resulting equivalent differential voltage input of 0.3 mV. The desired output is 30 dB greater than this. This performance would only add a 0.4% error in an in-

strumentation application, but would be unsatisfactorily noisy for an audio system, in which the S/N ratio should be 50–60 dB if possible.

4. At 80°C, slew rate is about 1.05 times the typical value. Thus f = 434.5 kHz.

6. See Fig. 4–2B. Minimum transistor ratings: $BV_{CEO} = 30$ V; $I_{Cmax} = 100$ mA; $P_{DISS} = 3$ W.

8. Pin 3 (noninverting input) has a higher voltage than pin 2 (inverting input), so output at pin 6 should be positive. Therefore IC is defective.

10. Open coupling capacitor.

12. a. Poor ground and/or power-supply connections
    b. Lack of bypass or decoupling capacitors
    c. Output leads too near input leads

CHAPTER 5

2. Size, thermal conductivity

4. 0.25°C/W

6. 4.03 W

8. a. 16 A; b. 8 A

10. a. 0.3 W; b. 0.85 W; c. 1.25 W

12. Use the bridge circuit shown in the data sheet, but driving a motor instead of a speaker. Omit gain control. Reversing polarity of input voltage will reverse motor. 8 W total dissipation means 4 W per device. Use Staver V7 heat sink clip.

14. Ground inverting input of 741. Drive triac directly from output, since 741 will limit output current to a safe value. Triac must be rated at the peak value of 120 V_{rms} as a minimum, preferably, the triac should be rated at five times this voltage. Triac should have a forward-current rating ≥ 5 A, minimum.

CHAPTER 6

2. See pages 225–228 in text

4. Many solutions are possible.

6. Open rectifier diode.

8. Many solutions are possible, depending upon minimum and maximum V_{IN} chosen. V_{INmin} must be at least 16 V

10. Depends upon the solution to #8.

12. Many solutions are possible, depending upon minimum and maximum V_{IN} chosen. V_{INmin} must be at least 19 V.

14. a. shorted transistor, open Zener, defective op amp
    b. shorted Zener, open transistor, defective op amp
    c. Zener voltage is temperature-sensitive.

16. a. greater efficiency, smaller transformer, smaller filter capacitor
    b. greater efficiency, smaller filter capacitor

18. Need for filter capacitor having low ESR at high frequencies, need for powdered-iron or ferrite-core choke, need to avoid radiating RFI.

20. a. See Fig. 6–18. $I_{OUT,max} = \pm 1$ A, Reg. = 1% at each output, $V_{mismatch}$ can be 1.8 V.
    b. See Fig. 6–21. $I_{OUT,max} = \pm 1.5$ A, Reg. = ± 0.1% at each output, $V_{mismatch}$ adjustable to zero.

CHAPTER 7

2. 482 Hz
4. 0.01 µF would require a 1.6-kΩ resistor, which is reasonable both from R_{IN} and bias-current standpoints. Other solutions are possible.
6. GBW at least 78.2 kHz. Many solutions are possible.
8. $f_b = 1$ kHz. If $C = 0.1$ µF and $A_0 = 1$, $R_1 = 1783$ Ω. $R_2 = 1181$ Ω, $R_3 = 3565$ Ω. Many other solutions are possible.
10. Many solutions are possible, depending upon the gain.

CHAPTER 8

2. 71.2 kHz
4. See page 348 in the text.
6. Many solutions are possible.
8. Many solutions are possible. Would use two 5-V Zeners.
10. Many solutions are possible.
12. R and C
14. Power-supply voltage and the threshold-setting resistors of the comparator.
16. See Fig. 8–14.
18. Many solutions are possible. See Fig. 8–18A.
20. Many solutions are possible. See pages 380–381.

CHAPTER 9

2. a. 300 µA; b. 0.4 V/µs; c. 50 nA
4. 5 mV · 5000 µs = 25 µA
   25 µA · 30 kΩ = 0.75 V
   We assume that the β of the buffer transistors is great enough so that their input resistance can be ignored.
6. K = less than 0.156. R_L, R_X, R_Y, R_3.
8. $C_1 = 1$ nF, $R = 6.67$ kΩ, $C_2 = 1$ nF. $V_{CC} = \pm 10$ V. Many other solutions are possible.
10. Use Figs. 9–17B and 9–21B. Since R_m (the meter resistance) = R_L, $R_s = 10$ mV/I_m, where I_m = full-scale meter current. V_{CC} must be at least 10 mV + $I_m R_m$ + 1 V.
12. A clipper prevents instantaneous voltage from going above (or below) a certain level. A clamper adds a DC value to an AC wave.

Index